Postvention in Action

About the Editors

Karl Andriessen, MSuicidology, BSW, has been working in suicide prevention and postvention for three decades and is currently pursuing a PhD at the School of Psychiatry, University of New South Wales, Sydney, Australia, supported by a research grant of the Anika Foundation for Adolescent Depression and Suicide. He has published many peer-reviewed articles, book chapters, and co-edited volumes. He is also an affiliated researcher with the Faculty of Psychology and Educational Sciences, KU Leuven–University of Leuven, Belgium. He has been Co-Chair of the Special Interest Group on Suicide Bereavement of the International Association for Suicide Prevention (IASP) for almost 15 years and received the 2005 IASP Farberow Award for outstanding contributions in the field of bereavement and survivors after suicide.

Karolina Krysinska, PhD, is a research fellow at the School of Psychiatry, University of New South Wales, Sydney, Australia, and is affiliated as a research fellow at the Faculty of Psychology and Educational Sciences, KU Leuven–University of Leuven, Belgium. Her research interests include risk and protective factors of suicide, suicide prevention, thanatology, psychology of trauma and bereavement, and psychology of religion. She is author and coauthor of peer-reviewed articles and book chapters on various aspects of suicide, trauma, and bereavement.

Onja T. Grad, PhD, is a clinical psychologist working as a psychotherapist and supervisor in the outpatient clinic at the University Psychiatric Hospital in Ljubljana, Slovenia, mainly with patients who have lost somebody close by suicide or other traumatic death. As a professor at the University of Ljubljana she has a long-standing interest in bereavement research. She has published in national and international journals and contributed to international textbooks on suicide and suicide bereavement. In 1997, she was the first recipient of the Farberow Award, given biannually by the IASP for outstanding contributions in the field of postvention.

Postvention in Action

The International Handbook of Suicide Bereavement Support

Edited by
Karl Andriessen
Karolina Krysinska
Onja T. Grad

Library of Congress Cataloging in Publication information for the print version of this book is available via the Library of Congress Marc Database under the LC Control Number 2016956065

Library and Archives Canada Cataloguing in Publication

Postvention in action : the international handbook of suicide bereavement support / edited by Karl Andriessen, Karolina Krysinska, Onja T. Grad.

Includes bibliographical references and index.
Issued in print and electronic formats.
ISBN 978-0-88937-493-5 (hardback).--ISBN 978-1-61676-493-7 (pdf).--
ISBN 978-1-61334-493-4 (epub)

    1. Bereavement. 2. Bereavement--Psychological aspects. 3. Grief. 4. Grief therapy. 5. Suicide. 6. Suicide victims--Family relationships. I. Andriessen, Karl, 1964-, editor II. Krysinska, Karolina, 1969-, editor III. Tekavčič Grad, Onja, editor

BF575.G7P678 2017   155.9'37   C2016-906719-X
                                       C2016-906720-3

The authors and publisher have made every effort to ensure that the information contained in this text is in accord with the current state of scientific knowledge, recommendations, and practice at the time of publication. In spite of this diligence, errors cannot be completely excluded. Also, due to changing regulations and continuing research, information may become outdated at any point. The authors and publisher disclaim any responsibility for any consequences which may follow from the use of information presented in this book.

Registered trademarks are not noted specifically in this publication. The omission of any such notice by no means implies that any trade names mentioned are free and unregistered.

PUBLISHING OFFICES

USA: Hogrefe Publishing Corporation, 7 Bulfinch Place, Suite 202, Boston, MA 02114
              Phone (866) 823–4726, Fax (617) 354–6875; E-mail customerservice@hogrefe.com
EUROPE: Hogrefe Publishing GmbH, Merkelstr. 3, 37085 Göttingen, Germany
              Phone +49 551 99950–0, Fax +49 551 99950–111; E-mail publishing@hogrefe.com

SALES & DISTRIBUTION

USA: Hogrefe Publishing, Customer Services Department,
              30 Amberwood Parkway, Ashland, OH 44805
              Phone (800) 228–3749, Fax (419) 281–6883; E-mail customerservice@hogrefe.com
UK: Hogrefe Publishing, c/o Marston Book Services Ltd., 160 Eastern Ave., Milton Park,
              Abingdon, OX14 4SB, UK
              Phone +44 1235 465577, Fax +44 1235 465556; E-mail direct.orders@marston.co.uk
EUROPE: Hogrefe Publishing, Merkelstr. 3, 37085 Göttingen, Germany
              Phone +49 551 99950–0, Fax +49 551 99950–111; E-mail publishing@hogrefe.com

OTHER OFFICES

CANADA: Hogrefe Publishing, 660 Eglinton Ave. East, Suite 119–514, Toronto, Ontario, M4G 2K2
SWITZERLAND: Hogrefe Publishing, Länggass-Strasse 76, CH-3000 Bern 9

Hogrefe Publishing
Incorporated and registered in the Commonwealth of Massachusetts, USA, and in Göttingen, Lower Saxony, Germany

Cover image: © gldburger – istockphoto.com

Printed and bound in the USA

ISBN 978-0-88937-493-5 (print) • ISBN 978-1-61676-493-7 (PDF) • ISBN 978-1-61334-493-4 (EPUB)
http://doi.org/10.1027/00493-000

Contents

Overview of Tables, Figures, and Boxes

Dedication

This book is dedicated to Dr. Norman L. Farberow (1918–2015).

Foreword

It is an honor and a pleasure to have been invited by such a distinguished group of researchers and clinicians to contribute a Foreword to this important publication.

In the mid-20th century, there were usually only veiled references to suicide, let alone any suggestion that those who were bereaved through suicide should be considered worthy of study or indeed support. Furthermore, any references were usually in stigmatizing terms, as in many countries, suicide was considered not only a legal offence, but a sin against one's religion.

How this has changed has been quite remarkable, something that is comprehensively documented in this timely overview. It is timely in at least two ways: It's publication is on the 50th anniversary of Edwin Shneidman's having coined the term *postvention* in 1967; and there is now a considerable body of research that has been undertaken in the ensuing years, research which has benefitted from the introspective scrutiny which characterizes this volume.

The editors of this volume have each been leading figures in this research for several decades, and have gathered together all of the contemporary significant contributors to the field. There is no doubt that the early influential pioneers in this field, who are no longer with us, would be delighted with the result. This would particularly be the case with Norman Farberow, to whom this book is dedicated.

I have been privileged to have had a working life that has encompassed these changes. As a new graduate in the late 1960s, I was unprepared for the realities of the emergency room, where suicide attempts were increasingly prevalent, and where those who had died by suicide were brought for certification of death. These were also usually accompanied by distraught relatives or friends in both scenarios.

Pursuing the literature at that time was easy, notwithstanding the absence of computer retrieval assistance, as there had been so little written. It quickly became evident that Norman Farberow and Edwin Shneidman of the Los Angeles Suicide Prevention Center were leaders in the nascent field of suicide prevention, and they were not ignoring those who were bereaved by suicide.

I am delighted to say that I was one of a steady stream of young researchers, not the least of whom was Onja Grad, one of the editors of this work, who travelled to Los Angeles and sat at the feet of those early pioneers. Furthermore, because of the longevity of both Norman Farberow and Edwin Shneidman, both Karl Andriessen and Karolina Krysinska have also had the privilege of contact with them, thereby providing a unique editorial experience in being able to document this important area of clinical practice.

The book is divided into four logical sections: current knowledge and implications for support, suicide bereavement support in different settings, suicide bereavement support in different populations, and help for the bereaved by suicide in different countries.

In the first part, a useful introduction, which clarifies the concepts and definitions to be used and which sets the scene for the book, is followed by chapters delineating current demographic and clinical issues which are to be pursued.

The second part offers a succinct historical overview of survivor support, and then a range of different settings is described. These include family practitioner and peer counseling, and the role of religion and spirituality is not forgotten, as commonly occurs. As one would anticipate in the 21st century, the place of online suicide bereavement supports is also explored. More traditionally, but until relatively recently often overlooked, the importance of supporting families through the forensic and coronial process is addressed, a process which is almost always a harrowing experience for all involved.

The third part contains fewer chapters than the others, but each is of critical importance. The impact of cluster suicides and murder–suicide should not be underestimated; the lack of trust in the health care system is of major concern; the effect on health professionals can be a determinant of whether or not one continues in clinical work; and a description of healing practices in First Nation peoples in Canada is a good illustration of a challenge facing many other countries as well.

The final part provides a synopsis of the services for those bereaved by suicide in over 20 different countries. Not unexpectedly, most are situated in the United States and Europe. It could be argued that the number may not reflect the work that is undoubtedly being conducted in a number of other countries, as organizations such as the International Association for Suicide Prevention have many more member countries whose representatives would be familiar with the need for such services, even if they have not been formalized.

This book will be valuable as a reference for researchers and as a practical guide for clinicians who practice in this challenging but rewarding area. Much has changed in the last 50 years, and we are indebted to the editors for collating such a comprehensive overview of this previously ignored area.

Robert D. Goldney, AO, MD, FRCPsych, FRANZCP
Emeritus Professor of Psychiatry, University of Adelaide, Australia
Past-President of the International Association for Suicide Prevention

Preface

Postvention

Every year, more than 800,000 people die by suicide; that is one suicide every 40 seconds (World Health Organization [WHO], 2014). Though suicide is an individual act, it happens within a sociocultural environment and a relational context. Hence, feelings of abandonment, rejection, and being a part of the "decision" for suicide are frequent among the bereaved by suicide. The bereaved may face a long and painful process of acknowledging and expressing their feelings of shock, guilt, shame, anger, and/or relief. They often struggle with thoughts, doubts, and agonizing questions related to "why this has happened," and "if I had done – or not done – this or that, *it* would not have happened." The bereaved cope with the loss, sometimes on their own, sometimes with the help of family or friends. Some turn to support groups or seek advice or therapy from professionals. Given that suicide bereavement is a risk factor for adverse mental health outcomes and suicidal behavior, there is a need for adequate suicide bereavement support.

Fifty years ago Edwin Shneidman coined the term *postvention,* referring to the support for those left behind after a suicide (Shneidman, 1969). At that time, suicidology was a young discipline, and there was neither support for the bereaved nor postvention research. Currently, postvention integrates a dual aim of facilitating recovery after suicide, and preventing adverse health outcomes among the bereaved (Andriessen, 2009). Suicide bereavement support has become available in many countries and has been recognized by the WHO (2014) as an important strategy for suicide prevention. The WHO stipulates that communities can provide support to those bereaved by suicide (WHO, 2014, p. 9), that interventions should be offered to grieving individuals (WHO, 2014, p. 37), and national suicide prevention objectives should include support for the bereaved by suicide (WHO, 2014, p. 54). It suffices to say that the evolutions of the past few decades have been truly impressive. Importantly, in many countries, survivor support has been initiated by the bereaved themselves, and clinicians and researchers have followed. In many countries, still, those bereaved by suicide are actively involved in suicide bereavement support, as well as in suicide prevention activities and research. Indeed, the days are over when postvention was looked upon as the poor counterpart of prevention: This handbook evidences the global research and clinical interest in survivor support. Postvention has become an integral and indispensable part of any comprehensive suicide prevention program. Suicidology and suicide prevention without the active involvement of survivors would be poor suicidology. Postvention is prevention. Postvention is action.

Postvention in Action

Experiences with suicide loss, working with people bereaved by suicide, involvement in postvention research and development of support programs have inspired the three editors of this handbook. It has been written for clinicians and researchers, as well as for support group facilitators and survivors involved in community activities. 94 experts from all over the world have contributed to this book. The authors have generously shared their knowledge, experience, and insights into implications for the practice of suicide survivor support. The editors of the handbook and many contributing authors are members of the International Association for Suicide

Prevention (IASP), and specifically of the IASP Special Interest Group (SIG) on Suicide Bereavement and Postvention, which has become a major platform for the exchange of research and clinical expertise related to suicide bereavement support. Interestingly, the awareness of suicide bereavement support within the IASP has been raised due to the advocacy of dedicated survivors–researchers and survivors–clinicians, especially in the 1990s, which resulted in the first plenary presentations on postvention at IASP world congresses, and the establishment by Professor Norman L. Farberow of a Taskforce on Postvention in 1999, the taskforce being the forerunner of the current SIG.

This handbook aims to present a comprehensive overview of the state of the art of postvention, and demonstrates the evidence and practice base of suicide survivor support. All chapters are based on thorough reviews of the literature and/or original research of the authors. The book is organized into four parts. Part I is an in-depth and comprehensive presentation of current knowledge of suicide bereavement. This includes a discussion of concepts and definitions, and the age- and gender-related effects of suicide loss, especially in adults and adolescents. The following chapters focus on the grief process and on how the bereaved deal with the loss. These chapters, illustrated with vignettes, will be highly informative for clinicians, and present novel insights regarding posttraumatic growth after suicide loss, trajectories of dealing with feelings of responsibility and guilt, challenges regarding meaning making, and the process of reintegration after experiencing a suicide.

Starting with a scholarly overview of the history of survivor support, Part II of the handbook discusses suicide bereavement support in a variety of settings, including underresearched areas that may be more challenging or may require special attention regarding provision of services and support. Chapters in this part have been written by clinicians and/or researchers with ample practical experience. These chapters present a review of the effectiveness of support groups (the best-known format of survivor support), and differences in priorities of support groups between countries (Japan and the United States). Other chapters explore the suitability and pitfalls of peer counseling, and provide insights regarding the roles that general practitioners may have in survivor support. Other chapters address how bereaved families can be supported through the forensic and coronial services, discuss how workplaces may provide survivor support, and examine the roles of religion and spirituality in suicide bereavement support. Part II concludes with an overview of the fast-growing field of online suicide bereavement support, and a presentation of how personal experiences and artistic expressions can be used for the benefit of those bereaved by suicide.

Part III focuses on suicide bereavement support in specific populations. While cluster-suicide and murder–suicide events may be rare, their traumatic aftermath warrants dedicated aftercare. Suicide-bereaved parents may be in need of survivor support; however, they may have lost trust in the health care system. Health professionals who have lost a client by suicide also have to deal with the impact of the loss, and may do so in a variety of ways. Little is known about the Indigenous peoples' experience with a suicide loss, and the elders of Ojibway First Nation have shared their knowledge of healing practices involving family and the community, and the important roles of rituals and spirituality.

Part IV presents an overview of postvention practice and research in no less than 23 countries. Besides chapters covering the "usual suspects" such as the United States and western European countries, this part includes chapters presenting postvention in South America, the Asia-Pacific, and Africa. Obviously a wide variety of suicide survivor support has been developed and implemented across the world. Many countries included in this part of the handbook report on the availability of support groups; however, it is also clear that support groups may have a variety of formats and goals. For example, authors from Uruguay and Thailand report on the availability of therapeutic, professionally led groups, whereas in other countries peer-led groups are also available. Other countries, such as Denmark and France, report wide availability of individual psychotherapy. Most of the survivor organizations are volunteer-based or involve a collaboration of professionals and peers (e.g., Canada and Italy). Typically, these organizations provide one point of access, such as a helpline, involve counselors, who may provide assessment, and offer individual or group support. Sometimes the face-to-face support is extended to online support (e.g., in Brazil), or to community awareness-raising activities, such as a national survivor day or a "walk out of darkness. Alternatively, survivor support may also be professionally based – for example, through a forensic department or coroner's office (e.g., in Australia and Hong Kong).

Support may be targeted at specific groups in society. Several countries report activities specifically for children and adolescents through support groups (Belgium), youth camps (Norway and Slovenia), or interventions at schools (Portugal). Postvention support in workplaces has become available through community organizations (Canada and the United States) or occupational health services (France), as well as support for health care professionals (e.g., from peers, supervisors, or through training; in Austria, Portugal, Slovenia, Thailand, and the United States). Some countries have developed specific support for the aftermath of suicides on the railways (e.g., Austria, The Netherlands, and the United Kingdom), and several countries offer postvention training and resources, such as websites (Australia, Slovenia, etc). Importantly, a number of countries (Ireland, the United States) have integrated postvention in national suicide postvention standards, which certainly is one way to go.

Action

It is the first time that such a vast overview of country reports has been compiled, demonstrating how postvention has become a worldwide strategy for suicide prevention. Nevertheless, this attempt at an overview also reveals serious gaps in the knowledge and practice of postvention. While there is a reasonable representation of the North American and European region, far fewer chapters could be solicited from Asia-Pacific and South American countries, and especially from Africa. Given that the majority of suicides occur outside the Westernized world, this poses challenges to the global understanding of suicide grief and mourning.

The book is dedicated to the ones we have lost through suicide, and their friends, families, and clinicians. More, the handbook is dedicated to the memory of Professor Norman L. Farberow (1918–2015), a founding father of the International Association for Suicide Prevention, who died on September 10, 2015, the World Suicide Prevention Day. Professor Farberow was a pioneer of postvention, a mentor, and a friend, and he will be remembered for his inspiring lifelong commitment to suicide prevention and postvention. It is hoped that this handbook will be a landmark resource for researchers, clinicians, and all those involved in survivor support. It is a testimony of how far and strongly the field has evolved, and it is hoped that the book may inspire further discussions and exchanges of expertise, which is essential to ensure the ongoing progress of postvention.

Postvention in action!

Karl Andriessen
Karolina Krysinska
Onja T. Grad
March 2017

References

Andriessen, K. (2009). Can postvention be prevention? *Crisis, 30*(1), 43–47. http://doi.org/10.1027/0227-5910.30.1.43

Shneidman, E. (1969). Prologue: Fifty-eight years. In E. Shneidman (Ed.), *On the nature of suicide* (pp. 1–30). San Francisco, CA: Jossey-Bass.

World Health Organization. (2014). *Preventing suicide: A global imperative*. Geneva, Switzerland: Author.

Part I

Current Knowledge and Implications for Support

Chapter 1

Current Understandings of Suicide Bereavement

Karl Andriessen[1], Karolina Krysinska[1], and Onja T. Grad[2]

[1]School of Psychiatry, University of New South Wales, Sydney, Australia
[2]University Psychiatric Hospital, Ljubljana, Slovenia

Abstract: Suicide may have a lasting impact on those bereaved by the death – that is, the survivors. They may embark on a long journey of acknowledging and expressing their grief, either alone or with the help of family, friends, support groups, and clinicians. Over the years, suicide survivor support and research – in other words, postvention – has been increasing, and the World Health Organization has identified postvention as an important suicide prevention strategy. However, major challenges remain to be solved. To further develop the field and to facilitate communication, there is a need for clarity regarding (1) concepts and definitions, (2) how many people are bereaved through suicide, and (3) whether bereavement after suicide is different and/or similar compared with bereavement after other causes of death. In addition, over the decades, several grief models have been formulated, and this chapter highlights the major models that may help to understand the grief process after loss by suicide.

Introduction

Suicide ends the pain of one but brings new pain to those left behind. For centuries, the impact of suicide on bereaved individuals and families has been ignored. The act of suicide was condemned, and often the bereaved were blamed for having a family member die by suicide (Farberow, 2003). Shneidman (1972, p. xi) referred to the tragedies that continue after the self-destructive act as "the illegacy of suicide." Only lately, since the 1960s, have the bereaved through suicide – that is, the survivors – received clinical and research attention. Contrary to past beliefs, it is now clear that those affected by suicide may face a long and painful process of acknowledging and expressing their emotions, thoughts, and behaviors to be able to move on with their lives (Grad & Andriessen, 2016). Those bereaved by suicide are at increased risk of suicidal behavior, either as a result of a bio-psycho-social vulnerability or because of identification with the person who has died by suicide (see Chapter 2 in this volume). Kinship, gender (see Chapter 4), psychological closeness, time since loss, personal and family history of mental health problems, and preloss life events, such as interpersonal loss and separations, may affect the impact of the suicide death among adults (see Chapter 2), as well as bereaved adolescents (see Chapter 3).

Over the last 50 years, the postvention field has evolved enormously (see Chapter 9 in this volume). Firstly peer, and subsequently clinical support and research activity emerged, and national survivor organizations were created. The International Association for Suicide Prevention (IASP) stressed the importance of survivor support by the establishment in 2011 of the Special Interest Group (SIG) on Suicide Bereavement and Postvention, the SIG being the formal continuation of the IASP Taskforce on Postvention initiated by Norman Farberow in 1999 (https://www.iasp.info/postvention.php). Currently, support for people bereaved through suicide is recognized as an important strategy for suicide prevention (World Health Organization [WHO], 2014). According to the WHO (2014), "intervention efforts for individuals bereaved or affected by suicide are implemented in order to support the grieving process and reduce the possibility of imitative suicidal behaviour" (p. 37), and "to be effective, national suicide prevention objectives could be designed to: ... support individuals bereaved by suicide" (p. 54). As such, any discussion of suicide, a serious public health problem claiming globally more than 800,000 deaths per year, will be incomplete without taking into consideration the perspective of the bereaved.

Although the availability of, and research into, survivor support have increased, this chapter will discuss ongoing challenges in relation to postvention research, clinical practice, and the development of bereavement programs and policies. There is an increasing awareness that to further develop postvention and to facilitate communication from the local to the global level, certain issues have to be clarified (Andriessen & Krysinska, 2012; Jordan & McIntosh, 2011). There are challenges related to terminology and definitions, the number of people bereaved through suicide, and the question of if and how bereavement after suicide is different and/or similar compared with bereavement after other causes of death. In addition, over the decades, several general grief models, which also help to understand the grief process after loss by suicide, have been formulated, and these will be presented in this chapter.

Concepts and Definitions

A discussion about terminology and definitions may seem very technical, academic, and distant from the daily practice of supporting the bereaved. However, the primary aim of clarity in the usage of words and definitions is to facilitate communication between people involved in the field. The development of consensus definitions would require an international project in itself, and is beyond the scope of this chapter. However, it seems useful to start with a brief presentation of concepts and definitions related to postvention.

In general, the lack of consensus about terminology related to suicide survivor support can be understood in the context of its origin and history. The first suicide survivor support groups were created in the 1970s in the United States, followed by support initiatives in other countries and continents (see Chapter 9). These initiatives were often driven by the bereaved themselves, and building on the experiences of these local initiatives, national organizations were established. However, due to the grassroots (i.e., local) origins and bottom-up evolution of suicide bereavement support, consensus definitions of routinely used key concepts have never been developed.

Although the need to formulate consensus terminologies and definitions in the field of suicide bereavement has been noted before (Jordan & McIntosh, 2011), the previous attempts to formulate consensus definitions and nomenclature in suicidology have overlooked postvention (Silverman, 2016). There is a rising awareness of the necessity of dialogue and consensus finding, and a shared nomenclature – that is, a comprehensive set of mutually exclusive terms could improve communication within the field of suicidology and in the general community (Silverman, 2016). By addressing the definitions of the major concepts related to suicide bereavement, this chapter aims to contribute to a shared nomenclature in postvention, and invites researchers, clinicians, and bereaved people worldwide to join this endeavor.

Postvention

The term *postvention* was coined and originally broadly defined by Shneidman (1969, pp. 19 & 22) as "the helpful activities which occur … after a stressful or dangerous situation … after a suicidal event." Shneidman specified that "postvention aims primarily at mollifying the psychological sequelae of a suicidal death in the survivor-victim" (Shneidman, 1969). Currently, *postvention* refers to dealing with the aftermath of suicide, with a dual focus on bereavement support and suicide prevention among the bereaved. Postvention consists of "the activities developed by, with, or for suicide survivors, in order to facilitate recovery after suicide, and to prevent adverse outcomes including suicidal behavior" (Andriessen, 2009, p. 43). Postvention involves peer and social support, clinical work, advocacy, community action, research, and policy development related to suicide bereavement.

Survivor

There are many different words for describing a person who has lost someone through suicide, such as *survivor, suicide survivor, survivor of suicide, survivor after suicide, suicide loss survivor, survivor of suicide loss, bereaved by suicide,* and *bereaved through suicide.* Words such as *survivor* have different meanings in different countries and contexts. For example, a survey among 293 people who receive the newsletter *Surviving Suicide* of the American Association of Suicidology showed that among 19 options mentioned by the respondents, more than half (58 %) endorsed *suicide survivor* as their preferred term (Honeycutt & Praetorius, 2016). However, in the equally Anglo-Saxon environment of Australia, the term *suicide survivor* is hardly used because of the confusion with suicide attempts, and the term *bereaved by suicide* is better understood (see, e.g., the *Information and Support Pack for Those Bereaved by Suicide or Other Sudden Death,* developed under the national Living Is for Everyone framework: http://livingisforeveryone.com.au/Information--Support-pack-for-those-bereaved-by-suicide-or-other-sudden-death.html).

While the term *survivor* commonly refers to those bereaved by suicide, it can mean both "to continue to live after the death of another" and "to remain alive, live on" [after an event] (Simpson & Weiner, 1989, Vol. 17, p. 313). Rather than surviving a suicide attempt, in postvention, *survivor* refers to the behavior of someone else, the subsequent death and absence of that person, and the impact on the remaining persons (Farberow, personal communication, 2007). The term *suicide attempt survivor,* recently introduced by the American Association of Suicidology in 2014, acknowledges those who have engaged in nonfatal suicidal behavior, while at the same time, makes a distinction with *suicide loss survivors* or *survivors of suicide loss* (http://www.suicidology.org).

Taking into account Farberow's principles, Andriessen (2009, p. 43) defined a survivor as "a person who has lost a significant other (or a loved one) by suicide, and whose life is changed because of the loss." Jordan and McIntosh (2011, p. 7) defined a survivor as "someone who experiences a high level of self-perceived psychological, physical, and/or social distress for a considerable length of time after exposure to the suicide of another person." While acknowledging efforts to formulate these definitions, Berman (2011) noted inherent difficulties with the inclusion of the life-changing aspect in the first definition, and the high level of distress over a length of time in the second definition.

As implied by these definitions, being exposed to a suicide is not a sufficient condition to become a survivor. However, bystanders, witnesses, or acquaintances can be deeply affected by a suicide, with survivorship being predominantly a self-identified status (Andriessen, 2009). Psychological closeness appears to be a key concept in the identification as a survivor (Cerel,

McIntosh, Neimeyer, Maple, & Marshall, 2014). The formulation of a continuum of survivorship according to the magnitude of the impact of the loss (Cerel et al., 2014) may be an important approach to include the variations in survivor status inherent in the definitions. The model of Cerel et al. (2014) distinguishes four subgroups based on the level of impact: (1) those exposed to suicide without being personally affected; (2) those affected by a suicide; and those closest to the deceased who may experience grief reactions either on (3) a short-term or (4) a long-term basis. Research is needed to further specify how the different levels can be delineated and what risk or protective factors are involved.

Bereavement, Grief, Mourning

The terms *bereavement, grief,* and *mourning* are sometimes used interchangeably, whereas they do have different meanings. The word *bereaved* is defined as "deprived or robbed," and especially as "deprived by death of a near relative, or of one connected by some endearing tie" (Simpson & Weiner, 1989, Vol. 2, p. 123). Thus, *bereavement* refers to "the fact of the loss" (Zisook & Shear, 2009) and is understood, in both the dictionary and the clinical literature, as the objective status of having lost someone significant (Stroebe, Hansson, Schut, & Stroebe, 2008; Stroebe, Hansson, Stroebe, & Schut, 2001).

Grief is defined as "hardship, suffering," "mental pain, distress, or sorrow" (Simpson & Weiner, 1989, Vol. 6, pp. 834–835). In the clinical and research literature, this is understood as the "primarily emotional (affective) reaction to the loss of a loved one through death. It is a normal, natural reaction to loss" (Stroebe et al., 2008, p. 5). It incorporates diverse psychological (emotional, cognitive), physical, and behavioral responses to the death (Stroebe et al., 2001; Zisook & Shear, 2009).

Mourning is defined as "the action of mourn" and "the feeling or the expression of sorrow for the death of a person." It is "the conventional or ceremonial manifestation of sorrow for the death of a person" (Simpson & Weiner, 1989, Vol. 10, pp. 19–20). Consequently, in the clinical and research literature, mourning is understood as the public display of grief, the social expressions of grief that are shaped by the (often) religious beliefs and practices of a given society or cultural group (Stroebe et al., 2008, 2001; Zisook & Shear, 2009). Stroebe et al. (2008, 2001) emphasized the sociocultural nature of mourning. Grief expressions – for example, crying in public – that are acceptable or expected in one society may be unacceptable in other societies. Understanding grief reactions necessitates understanding the context in which the loss occurred. Given the fact that suicide bereavement has been studied almost exclusively in Western and Anglo-Saxon countries (Andriessen, 2014), while the majority of suicides occur in other parts of the world (WHO, 2014), the global understanding of suicide grief and mourning might still be in its infancy.

Complicated Grief

Whereas grief is understood as a normal, purposeful reaction to a loss, many words are currently in use to refer to an "abnormal" grief, such as *traumatic, pathological, chronic, prolonged,* or *persistent complex grief.* Most of these words are routinely used without definition, but they refer to a grief that is different from the clinical or sociocultural norm with regards to the time course, intensity, or symptoms of the grief (Stroebe, Schut, & van den Bout, 2013; Stroebe et al., 2008). They entail a state of chronic debilitating mourning, with persistent and disruptive yearning, pining, and longing for the deceased – with, for example, expressions of separation anxiety and trauma (Stroebe et al., 2013; Zisook & Shear, 2009). Suicide loss can be a risk factor for complicated or prolonged grief, and it is estimated that 7–10% of grievers fall into this category (Kersting, Brähler, Glaesmer, & Wagner, 2011).

Most of these concepts have been developed by researchers, and are based on diagnostic criteria (Prigerson et al., 2009; Stroebe et al., 2013). However, the diagnostic criteria for these concepts often overlap. In addition, there is an overlap with diagnostic criteria for mental disorders, such as anxiety disorders, depression, posttraumatic stress disorder, and substance abuse (Stroebe et al., 2013).

Two issues warrant attention when trying to define complicated grief. Firstly, as mentioned above, cultural variation in grief expressions might challenge the understanding of "deviant" mourning. Secondly, there is a discussion in the literature over whether medicalization of grief and providing a label to a subgroup of grievers would either facilitate treatment for those in need, or increase stigmatization and treatment thresholds (Stroebe et al., 2013). A cultural and/ or economic perspective might help to shed light on this discussion: A diagnosis might facilitate treatment in one country – for example, through health insurance reimbursement – but might deter people from seeking help in other countries.

Lived Experience

The expression *lived experience*[1] is used in a variety of fields related to social and health issues, mostly without a definition. In mental health, it refers to people living with mental illness (i.e., consumers or users) and their family and friends (i.e., carers) (South Australia Health, 2016). Definitions related to suicidology are almost nonexistent. Suicide Prevention Australia has described lived experience as "having experienced suicidal thoughts, survived a suicide attempt, cared for someone who has attempted suicide, been bereaved by suicide, or been touched by suicide in another way" (Suicide Prevention Australia, 2016). As such, it appears to be an umbrella term for all suicide-related experiences, including suicidal ideation, nonfatal and fatal suicidal behavior, either from one's own experience, or as a relative or carer. While this description has the potential of appealing to as many people as possible, its inherent broad character limits its usability for research purposes, and for application in postvention. In fact, the double meaning of *survivor* (referring to a suicide loss vs. a suicide attempt) may further obfuscate the understanding of lived experience, and highlights the need for conceptual clarity.

While *lived experience* is popular, it may not differ from well-established concepts such as *experiential knowledge* and *experiential expertise* (Borkman, 1976). The former term means "truth learned from personal experience with a phenomenon rather than truth acquired by discursive reasoning, observation, or reflection on information provided by others" (Borkman, 1976, p. 446), whereas the latter is defined as "competence or skill in handling or resolving a problem through the use of one's own experience" (Borkman, 1976, p. 447).

How Many People Are Bereaved Through Suicide?

The question of how many people are bereaved by suicide, and potentially in need of support, is particularly important for service planning and delivery. Shneidman (1969, p. 22) originally estimated that on average a "half-dozen" survivors are left behind after a suicide. While this educated guess of six survivors per suicide has been perpetuated in the literature, other authors have

---

1   The concept of *lived experience* is derived from the German *Erlebnis*, which includes the word *Leben*, life or *to live*. The verb *erleben* literally means *living through something*; the English term *experience* does not include the meaning of *lived* (van Manen, 2004). The current broad and undefined usage of *lived experience* risks considering everyone with a certain experience as an "expert," whereas the active and intentional process of appropriating meaning and transforming a given (passive) experience into an expertise that transcends the particular experience (Husserl, 1970; van Manen, 2004) is neglected.

estimated higher numbers: for example, Wrobleski (2002) mentions 10 survivors per suicide. A survey by Berman (2011) among members of the Survivor Division of the American Association of Suicidology found that the estimated numbers of survivors varied depending on kinship and age: Parents bereaved by child suicide estimated that there were 80 survivors ("deeply affected"; Berman, 2011, p. 111), partners and spouses estimated the number of survivors as 60, and siblings and friends indicated between 45 and 50 survivors. For all respondents, Berman (2011) estimated an average of five immediate family members bereaved by a single suicide. Also, studies based on population registers have calculated the number of survivors per suicide for selected types of relationship. Kuramoto et al. (2010) and Wilcox et al. (2010) found that on average two children are bereaved after the suicide of a parent. Botha et al. (2009) and Chen et al. (2009) estimated an average of four to five relatives bereaved by a suicide in the family.

Findings regarding the variety of relationships of people being exposed to a suicide have fueled the ambiguity regarding the numbers of survivors. Campbell (1997) described 28 different types of relationship among individuals seeking suicide bereavement support from the Crisis Intervention Center in Baton Rouge, Louisiana, USA. The majority consisted of nuclear family members (80%); other relatives, friends, and acquaintances accounted for the remaining 20%. A telephone survey in the United States found 27 different relationships among individuals who knew someone who had died by suicide (Cerel, Maple, Aldrich, & van de Venne, 2013). In this study, friends were the largest relationship category (35%), and nuclear family members accounted for 7.5% of the group. In addition, while the reported exposure to suicide is higher among certain populations, such as clinicians, prisoners, and military veterans, it has been noted that the social networks of those dying by suicide are smaller than those of people with natural deaths (Stack, 2007). Those dying by suicide are more likely to be divorced, living alone, less frequent churchgoers, and more socially isolated. On the other hand, younger suicides may have more living relatives (Stack, 2007).

To better comprehend the diversity of numbers cited in the literature, Andriessen, Rahman, Draper, Dudley, and Mitchell (2017), conducted a meta-analysis of 18 population-based studies, which reported rates of past-year and lifetime prevalence of people who had experienced a suicide among family or friends, or had personally known someone who had died through suicide. The meta-analysis found that pooled lifetime prevalence of exposure to suicide was higher than past-year prevalence (21.8% and 4.3%, respectively). Past-year prevalence of suicide in the family (1.1%) was significantly lower than exposure to suicide among friends and peers (5.6%), and in all relationships (6.3%). There were no statistically significant differences regarding past-year prevalence of exposure to suicide by age group – that is, adolescents versus adults.

Similar to the past-year prevalence, lifetime prevalence of suicide in the family (3.9%) was significantly lower than exposure to suicide in friends and peers (14.5%), and in all relationships (29.4%). Life-time exposure to suicide by age group and type of relationship revealed a mixed picture. Among adults exposure to suicide in the family (3.9%) was lower than exposure to suicide in all relationships (36%) while there were no differences among adolescents.

Further analysis found that both past-year and lifetime prevalence of exposure to suicide in the family was approximately 8 to 5 times lower respectively, than prevalence of exposure in all relationships after controlling for country and age group of exposure. Given that the impact of suicide might be stronger when experienced at a younger age (see Chapter 3 in this volume), studies are needed to further investigate suicide exposure, impact of the loss, and support needs among adolescents, with regard to types of relationship and psychological closeness to the deceased.

Is Suicide Bereavement Different From Other Bereavement?

There appear to be contradictions in the answers to the question of whether suicide bereavement is different from bereavement experienced after other causes of death, usually depending on who is answering the question. Personal accounts of the bereaved, including published autobiographies (e.g., Fine, 1999), and narratives of clinicians seem to stress the uniqueness of the experience of suicide survivors. The recurrent themes in the narratives of survivors include guilt, shame, social stigma, search for meaning, and suicidal ideation. Research findings, especially from controlled studies, indicate that there are more similarities than differences between different groups of the bereaved, regarding major grief themes, the grief process, its duration and outcomes (Bolton et al., 2013; Sveen & Walby, 2008).

The model developed by Jordan and McIntosh (2011, p. 34) might be helpful to accommodate the contradictory perspectives of survivors, clinicians, and researchers (**Figure 1.1**). The model consists of four concentric circles. The outside circle represents features of bereavement that may be found independent of the cause of death: sorrow, pain, missing, and yearning to be reunited with the deceased. The second circle includes features typical for bereavement after unexpected deaths, such as shock and a sense of unreality. The third circle includes features of bereavement after violent deaths, such as the experience of trauma, and the shattered illusion

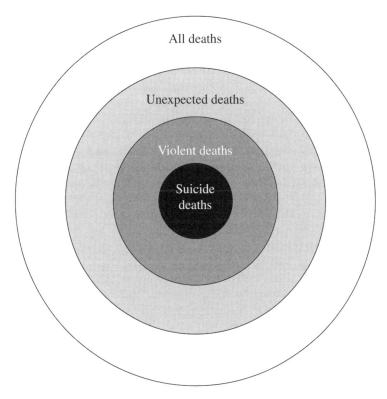

Figure 1.1 Aspects of bereavement related to the mode of death. Republished with permission of Routledge, from Jordan & McIntosh, 2011, p. 34; permission conveyed through Copyright Clearance Center, Inc.

of personal invulnerability. Finally, the fourth and inner circle includes features typically associated with bereavement after suicide. These include anger at the deceased, aggression, and feelings of abandonment and rejection (Jordan & McIntosh, 2011).

Some grief features seem to be more pronounced, though not unique, in suicide bereavement. The feeling of *guilt* is one of the most common feelings experienced by suicide survivors (see also Chapter 6). The reasons for this feeling may differ for each individual, but they include the feeling of not having been able to recognize the possible suicide warning signs or not having been able to prevent the death. Guilt may be fueled by the feeling that not enough attention was given to earlier suicide attempts, depressive behavior, or the effects of mental disorders on the deceased. Special circumstances, such as not living together (e.g., parents of adult children), may also trigger guilt. Guilt may stem from the feeling of relief – for example, when the suicide ended suffering associated with a chronic mental or physical illness, or when family members or caregivers became fatigued and hoped that the suffering would stop. Overestimating one's own responsibility and ability to stop the suicidal process, and thoughts and fears of having directly contributed to the death – for example, because of marital separation, a threat to leave, or a quarrel prior to the suicide – may also result in feelings of guilt (Grad & Andriessen, 2016). Sometimes the bereaved start to worry that another family member may become suicidal. Additional care and attention may be directed toward a family member who retains the same lifestyle as before the suicide, which seems dangerous, such as engaging in life-threatening sports or substance/alcohol abuse (Grad, 2011).

Another common theme is *searching for reasons* for the person's decision to end their life. This process may happen even if the suicidal person had more or less clearly talked about the suicide. It may be difficult to accept that someone close has not communicated their thoughts and problems, has neither asked for help nor shown any recognizable signs of risk. Many bereaved meticulously investigate their own behavior and the behavior of the deceased to find internal (psychological or biological) and/or external explanations for the suicide. It is important for the suicide survivors to know whether the suicide was a personal, willful decision or an act that was driven by particular problems, mental illness or other difficult circumstances (Grad, 2011).

This process of searching for reasons may result in *blaming and anger* toward oneself and/or others. Blame and anger are very difficult and painful to admit, and even more difficult to express openly (Grad, 2011; Tekavčič Grad & Zavasnik, 1992). The most painful is self-blame fueled by guilt. Blaming others can be directed at members of the close and extended family, colleagues, friends, schoolmates, teachers, and superiors at work. Professionals who took care of the person who died, such as doctors, therapists, and nurses, are also often blamed for the suicide. Moreover, blame and anger can be directed at the deceased for letting the survivor down or leaving them alone with their problems.

Many survivors report changed behavior within their social network. They may feel that they are being looked down upon or overlooked by others, and they may interpret this in the context of the taboo associated with suicide. It is unclear to what extend these feelings result from the survivors' projection of feelings of guilt and shame onto others, and to what extent these are real reactions of others (Feigelman, Gorman, & Jordan, 2009; Grad, 2011). Lower self-esteem, embedded in the social stigma of suicide, brings particular challenges to caregivers as they attempt to help suicide survivors. The self-stigmatizing process of survivors often makes it difficult to accept social support even though it is offered. Furthermore, suicide survivors often report that people in their social network do not know how to react *(social ineptitude)* (Dyregrov, 2003). As a result, some people prefer to ignore the fact of suicide or to withdraw from the survivor's social circle. Conversely, the bereaved may feel that they are "being silenced" by others, or they might silence themselves, and refrain from talking about their bereavement (Maple, Edwards, Plummer, & Minichiello, 2010).

Grief Models and Suicide Bereavement

Though no grief models have been developed specifically or solely to describe grief after suicide (let aside if that would be desirable), general grief models may provide useful frameworks and concepts to understand suicide bereavement. This section presents a snapshot overview of models relevant to grief after suicide. A comprehensive overview of the development of theories of grief in general can be found elsewhere (e.g., Stroebe, Hansson, Schut, & Stroebe, 2008).

While the literature on grief and mourning can be traced back over centuries (Burton, 1621/2001; Darwin, 1872/2009), the works of Freud (1917/1957) and Lindemann (1944) have been instrumental in shaping contemporary Western views on grief. Freud (1917/1957) distinguished grief (which he called "mourning") from melancholia, and based on clinical observations, he found that grief may lead to depression. Freud introduced the notion of *grief work (Trauerarbeit)* emphasizing the intrapersonal nature of the grief process, which should result in detachment of the lost object. Lindemann (1944) shaped the notion of "acute" grief, and the characteristics of what he considered to be "normal" grief reactions, such as preoccupation with the deceased and feelings of guilt, versus unhealthy, for example, delayed grief or absence of grief reactions. As such, the literature of the first half of the 20th century laid a foundation for current views that grief is a normal reaction to a major loss. However, those early views already acknowledged that grief may result in adverse health outcomes, including psychiatric problems.

The course of grief was first initially studied and described as a series of stages (e.g., Bowlby, 1980). According to the stage models, the grief process starts with an initial stage of shock, denial, and numbness, followed by intermediate stages of yearning and protest, and disorganization and despair, and results in adjustment and acceptance of the loss. Revisiting Freud's (1917) notion of grief work, Worden (1991) shifted the focus from the consecutive grief stages to the *how* of grieving. Worden postulated that a grieving person faces four tasks: accepting the reality of the loss, experiencing the pain of the loss, adjustment to an environment without the deceased person, and relocating the deceased emotionally to embark on a new life. The stage models tend to view the grief process as a temporary phase in life, which usually ends in acceptance of the loss (detachment from the deceased), and recovery after having worked through (or having resolved) the loss (Rothaupt & Becker, 2007; Wortman & Silver, 2001). According to the literature on complicated or *prolonged grief disorder,* prolonged grief should be diagnosed after 6 months (Prigerson et al., 2009). Yet, no research has found a common endpoint in terms of resolution, detachment, or recovery of normal grief, which varies in duration from short-lived grief reactions to longer-term or delayed reactions, which may occur even a few years after the loss (Bonanno, Boerner, & Wortman, 2008; Wortman & Silver, 2001). Obviously, the stage models are not helpful for understanding the bereaved person if they are interpreted in a rigid, prescriptive way regarding how people should process their loss, rather than as a description of what might occur.

Research of recent decades has broadened the perspective and helped to overcome some of the limitations inherent to (interpretations of) the earlier models (Rothaupt & Becker, 2007). The perspective on grief has shifted from stage thinking to a more humanistic approach to how individuals deal with the loss, taking into consideration the sociocultural aspects of grieving, and possible positive outcomes of the grief process. For example, in line with the task of emotional relocation of Worden (1991), Klass, Silverman, and Nickman (1996) found that the majority of bereaved individuals stay connected with the deceased. Contrary to being a pathological factor, as postulated by stage models, the continuing bond, sometimes expressed through rituals, may be a potential source of support for the bereaved.

Stroebe and Schut (2010) transformed the grief work model by complementing its loss-oriented approach with a dynamic interaction: The bereaved individual oscillates between loss-oriented (e.g., dealing with rumination) and restoration-oriented stressors (e.g., taking up a new role). Because of the interplay between past, present, and future, this dual process model helps to better understand how the bereaved can make meaning of the loss, and provides insight into the occurrence of delayed grief reactions and anniversary reactions (Stroebe & Schut, 2001). Balk (2004) noted that recovery in terms of restoring the lost world is impossible; however, the bereaved person may redefine or reintegrate their life (see also Chapter 8 in this volume).

According to a social constructionist perspective, people understand their grief not merely by intrapsychic grief work, but primarily through interactions taking place within their social and cultural environment (Neimeyer, Klass, & Dennis, 2014). Following the loss of the assumptive world and the challenges posed to cognitive coping (Grad, 2005), the bereaved person engages in a process of narrating and interpreting the life and death of the deceased person and the loss experience, and ascribes meaning to what has happened. The grief experience is not limited to the factual situation, but consists of its interpretation and the meaning it has for the bereaved person. There seems to be an association between the inability to make sense of the loss and the impact of violent bereavement after a death through suicide, homicide, or accident on symptoms of complicated grief among the bereaved (Currier, Holland, & Neimeyer, 2006).

Suicide bereavement research and support may well benefit from recent insights of research into general grief concepts. Holland and Neimeyer (2010) conducted a study of stage theory of grief among adults bereaved by natural and violent causes of death, including suicide. They found that characteristics of grief related to specific stages waxed and waned. Meaning making appeared to be a much stronger predictor of grief characteristics than time since loss, except for those bereaved by violent deaths, where both time since loss and meaning making appeared to be important. Neimeyer and Sands (Chapter 7 in this volume) present an account of how meaning reconstruction may be achieved after loss by suicide; and Genest, Moore, and Nowicke (Chapter 5 in this volume) investigated posttraumatic growth among those bereaved by suicide, resulting in positive outcomes regarding self-perception, interpersonal relationships, and life philosophy.

Implications for Practice

A considerable number of people in the general community are exposed to suicide (Andriessen et al., 2016). For example, in a school with 500 students, or in a company with 500 employees, there are on average 20 individuals who have experienced a suicide of a family member or a friend during the last year. Given the fact that suicide loss is a risk factor for adverse health outcomes, including mental health and suicidal behavior (Chapter 2 in this volume), it is of utmost importance to provide for service planning and to secure resources for suicide bereavement support.

Despite the common feelings and reactions experienced by many bereaved irrespective of the cause of death, the individual grief process after a suicide is as unique as a fingerprint (Clark & Goldney, 2000, p. 470). This may pose challenges to clinicians and support group facilitators who work with survivors after suicide. As Bonanno et al. (2008) pointed out, views on grief trajectories are often inspired by assumptions; however, postvention training may improve the caregivers' knowledge and skills in providing survivor support.

Several grief models have been developed and studied. Holland and Neimeyer (2010) concluded that stage models should not be discarded as long as they are not used in a prescriptive way, and research should continue addressing gaps in our knowledge, including our knowledge of individual grief trajectories. Based on training and traditions, clinicians and researchers may be prone to adhere to selected grief models. Also the bereaved person may recognize their experience more in one model than in another. As such, it would be beneficial for clinicians and support group leaders to familiarize themselves with various grief models to facilitate the grief processes of the bereaved individuals. The bereaved may benefit from a wide-ranging understanding, in a safe and accepting atmosphere, of everything they bring into therapy.

Obviously different models and grief research are needed to improve the understanding of the complex experience of suicide loss and the grief processes, and many chapters in this book present examples of how postvention programs and approaches can be inspired by models of grief, clinical practice, and research.

Corresponding author

Karl Andriessen
School of Psychiatry
University of New South Wales
Black Dog Institute – Hospital Road
Randwick 2031 NSW
Australia
k.andriessen@unsw.edu.au

References

Andriessen, K. (2009). Can postvention be prevention? *Crisis, 30*(1), 43–47. http://doi.org/10.1027/0227-5910.30.1.43

Andriessen, K. (2014). Suicide bereavement and postvention in major suicidology journals: Lessons learned for the future of postvention. *Crisis, 35*(5), 338–348. http://doi.org/10.1027/0227-5910/a000269

Andriessen, K., & Krysinska, K. (2012). Essential questions on suicide bereavement and postvention. *International Journal of Environmental Research and Public Health, 9*(1), 24–32. http://doi.org/10.3390/ijerph9010024

Andriessen, K., Rahman, B., Draper, B., Dudley, M., & Mitchell, B. (2017). Prevalence of exposure to suicide: A meta-analysis of population-based studies. *Journal of Psychiatric Research, 88*, 113–120. http://doi.org/10.1016/j.jpsychires.2017.01.017

Balk, D. E. (2004). Recovery following bereavement: An examination of the concept. *Death Studies, 28*(4), 361–374. http://doi.org/10.1080/07481180490432351

Berman, A. L. (2011). Estimating the population of survivors of suicide: Seeking an evidence base. *Suicide and Life-Threatening Behavior, 41*(1), 110–116. http://doi.org/10.1111/j.1943-278X.2010.00009.x

Bolton, J. M., Wendy, A. U., Leslie, W. D., Martens, P. J., Enns, M. W., Roos, L. L., … Sareen, J. (2013). Parents bereaved by offspring suicide. A population-based longitudinal case-control study. *JAMA Psychiatry, 70*, 158–167. http://doi.org/10.1001/jamapsychiatry.2013.275

Bonanno, G. A., Boerner, K., & Wortman, C. B. (2008). Trajectories of grieving. In M. Stroebe, R. Hansson, H. Schut, & W. Stroebe (Eds.), *Handbook of bereavement research and practice: Advances in theory and intervention* (pp. 287–307). Washington, DC: American Psychological Press.

Borkman, T. (1976). Experiential knowledge: A new concept for the analysis of self-help groups. *Social Service Review, 50*(3), 445–456. http://doi.org/10.1086/643401

Botha, K. J., Guilfoyle, A., & Botha, D. (2009). Beyond normal grief: A critical reflection on immediate post-death experiences of survivors of suicide. *Australian e-Journal for the Advancement of Mental Health, 8*(1), 37–47.

Bowlby, J. (1980). *Loss: Sadness and depression*. New York, NY: Basic Books.

Burton, R. (1621/2001). *The anatomy of melancholy*. New York, NY: The New York Review of Books, Inc.

Campbell, F.R. (1997). Changing the legacy of suicide. *Suicide and Life-Threatening Behavior, 27*(4), 329–338.

Cerel, J., Maple, M., Aldrich, R., & van de Venne, J. (2013). Exposure to suicide and identification as survivor: Results from a random-digit dial survey. *Crisis, 34*(6), 413–419. http://doi.org/10.1027/0227-5910/a000220

Cerel, J., McIntosh, J.L., Neimeyer, R.A., Maple, M., & Marshall, D. (2014). The continuum of "survivorship": Definitional issues in the aftermath of suicide. *Suicide and Life-Threatening Behavior, 44*(6), 591–600. http://doi.org/10.1111/sltb.12093

Chen, J., Choi, Y.J., Mori, K., Sawada, Y., & Sugano, S. (2009). Those who are left behind: an estimate of the number of family members of suicide victims in Japan. *Social Indicators Research, 94*(3), 535–544. http://doi.org/10.1007/s11205-009-9448-3

Clark, S.E., & Goldney, R.D. (2000). Impact of suicide on relatives and friends. In K. Hawton & K. van Heeringen (Eds.), *The international handbook of suicide and suicide prevention* (pp. 467–484). Chichester, UK: Wiley.

Currier, J., Holland, J., & Neimeyer, R.A. (2006). Sense making, grief and the experience of violent loss: Toward a mediational model. *Death Studies, 30*(5), 403–428. http://doi.org/10.1080/07481180600614351

Darwin, C.R. (1872/2009). *The expression of the emotions in man and animals*. New York, NY: Penguin Group USA. http://doi.org/10.1037/10001-000

Dyregrov, K. (2003). Micro-sociological analysis of social support following traumatic bereavement: Unhelpful and avoidant responses from the community. *Omega: Journal of Death and Dying, 48*(1), 23–44. http://doi.org/10.2190/T3NM-VFBK-68R0-UJ60

Farberow, N.L. (2003). Introduction: The history of suicide. In G. Evans, N. Farberow, & Evans Associates (Eds.), *The encyclopedia of suicide* (2nd ed., pp. xv–xxxiii). New York, NY: Facts on File.

Feigelman, W., Gorman, B.S., & Jordan, J.R. (2009). Stigmatization and suicide bereavement. *Death Studies, 33*(7), 591–608. http://doi.org/10.1080/07481180902979973

Fine, C. (1999). *No time to say goodbye: Surviving the suicide of a loved one*. New York, NY: Broadway Books/Doubleday.

Freud, S. (1917/1957). Mourning and melancholia. In J. Strachey (Ed.), *The standard edition of the complete psychological works of Sigmund Freud* (pp. 237–260). New York, NY: Basic Books.

Grad, O. (2005). Suicide survivorship: an unknown journey from loss to gain – from individual to global perspective. In K. Hawton (Ed.), *Prevention and treatment of suicidal behaviour: From science to practice* (pp. 351–369). Oxford, UK: Oxford University Press.

Grad, O. (2011). The sequelae of suicide. In R.C. O'Connor, S. Platt, & J. Gordon (Eds.), *International handbook of suicide prevention: Research, policy and practice* (pp. 561–577). Chichester, UK: Wiley Blackwell.

Grad, O. & Andriessen, K. (2016). Surviving the legacy of suicide. In R.C. O'Connor & J. Pirkis (Eds.), *International handbook of suicide prevention: Research, policy and practice* (2nd ed., pp. 663–680). Chichester, UK: Wiley Blackwell.

Holland, J., & Neimeyer, R. (2010). An examination of stage theory of grief among individuals bereaved by natural and violent causes: A meaning-oriented contribution. *Omega: Journal of Death and Dying, 61*(2), 103–120. http://doi.org/10.2190/OM.61.2.b

Honeycutt, A., & Praetorius, R.T. (2016). Survivors of suicide: Who they are and how do they heal? *Illness, Crisis & Loss, 24*(2), 103–118. http://doi.org/10.1177/1054137315587646

Husserl, E. (1970). *Logical investigations* (Vols. 1–2). London, UK: Routledge & Kegan Paul.

Jordan, J.R., & McIntosh, J.L. (Eds). (2011). *Grief after suicide: Understanding the consequences and caring for the survivors*. New York, NY: Routledge.

Kersting, A., Brähler, E., Glaesmer, H., & Wagner, B. (2011). Prevalence of complicated grief in a representative population-based sample. *Journal of Affective Disorders, 131*(1), 339–343.

Klass, D., Silverman, P.R., & Nickman, S.L. (1996). *Continuing bonds: New understandings of grief*. Philadelphia, PA: Taylor & Francis.

Kuramoto, S.J., Stuart, E.A., Runeson, B., Lichtenstein, P., Långström, N., & Wilcox, H.C. (2010). Maternal or paternal suicide and offspring's psychiatric and suicide-attempt hospitalization risk. *Pediatrics, 126*(5), e1026–e1032. http://doi.org/10.1542/peds.2010-0974

Lindemann, E. (1944). Symptomatology and management of acute grief. *American Journal of Psychiatry, 101*(2), 141–148. http://doi.org/10.1176/ajp.101.2.141

Maple, M., Edwards, H., Plummer, D., & Minichiello, V. (2010). Silenced voices: Hearing the stories of parents bereaved through the suicide death of a young adult child. *Health and Social Care, 18*(3), 241–248.

Neimeyer, R.A., Klass, D., & Dennis, M.R. (2014). A social constructionist account of grief: Loss and the narration of meaning. *Death Studies, 38*(8), 485–498. http://doi.org/10.1080/07481187.2014.913454

Prigerson, H.G., Horowitz, M.J., Jacobs, S.C., Parkes, C.M., Aslan, M., Goodkin, K., ... Maciejewski, P.K. (2009). Prolonged grief disorder: Psychometric validation of criteria proposed for DSM-V and ICD-11. *PLoS Med, 6*(8), e1000121. http://doi.org/10.1371/journal.pmed.1000121

Rothaupt, J.W., & Becker, K. (2007). A literature review of Western bereavement theory: From decathecting to continuing bonds. *The Family Journal, 15*(1), 6–15. http://doi.org/10.1177/1066480706294031

Shneidman, E. (1969). Prologue: Fifty-eight years. In E. Shneidman (Ed.), *On the nature of suicide* (pp. 1–30). San Francisco, CA: Jossey-Bass.

Shneidman, E.S. (1972). Foreword. In A.C. Cain (Ed.), *Survivors of suicide* (pp. ix–xi). Springfield, IL: Charles C. Thomas.

Silverman, M.M. (2016). Challenges to defining and classifying suicide and suicidal behaviors. In R.C. O'Connor & J. Pirkis (Eds.), *International handbook of suicide prevention: Research, policy and practice* (2nd ed., pp. 11–35). Chichester, UK: Wiley Blackwell.

Simpson, J.A., & Weiner, E.S.C. (Eds.). (1989). *Oxford English dictionary* (2nd ed.). Oxford, UK: Clarendon Press.

South Australia Health. (2016). *Mental health lived experience register*. Retrieved from http://www.sahealth.sa.gov.au/

Stack, S. (2007). Societal economic costs and benefits from death: Another look. *Death Studies, 31*(4), 363–372. http://doi.org/10.1080/07481180601187217

Stroebe, M., Hansson, R., Schut, H., & Stroebe, W. (Eds.). (2008). *Handbook of bereavement research and practice: Advances in theory and intervention.* Washington, DC: American Psychological Press. http://doi.org/10.1037/14498-000

Stroebe, M., Hansson, R., Stroebe, W., & Schut, H. (2001). Introduction: Concepts and issues in contemporary research on bereavement. In M. Stroebe, R. Hansson, W. Stroebe, & H. Schut (Eds.), *Handbook of bereavement research: Consequences, coping, and care* (pp. 3–22). Washington, DC: American Psychological Press.

Stroebe, M., & Schut, H. (2001). Meaning making in the Dual Process Model of coping with bereavement. In R.A. Neimeyer (Ed.), *Meaning reconstruction and the experience of loss* (pp. 55–73). Washington, DC: American Psychological Press.

Stroebe, M., & Schut, H. (2010). The Dual Process Model of coping with bereavement: A decade on. *Omega: Journal of Death and Dying, 61*(4), 273–289. http://doi.org/10.2190/OM.61.4.b

Stroebe, M., Schut, H., & van den Bout, J. (Eds.). (2013). *Complicated grief: Scientific foundations for health care professionals.* New York, NY: Routledge.

Suicide Prevention Australia. (2016). *What is lived experience?* Retrieved from https://www.suicidepreventionaust.org/projects/learning-lived-experience/what-lived-experience

Sveen, C.A., & Walby, F.A. (2008). Suicide survivors' mental health and grief reactions: A systematic review of controlled studies. *Suicide and Life-Threatening Behavior, 38*(1), 13–29. http://doi.org/10.1521/suli.2008.38.1.13

Tekavčič Grad, O., & Zavasnik, A. (1992). Aggression as a natural part of suicide bereavement. *Crisis, 13*(2), 65–69.

van Manen, M. (2004). Lived experience. In M.S. Lewis Beck, A. Bryman, & T.F. Liao, *The SAGE encyclopedia of social science research methods* (pp. 579–580). Thousand Oaks, CA: Sage.

Wilcox, H.C., Kuramoto, S.J., Lichtenstein, P., Långström, N., Brent, D.A., & Runeson, B. (2010). Psychiatric morbidity, violent crime, and suicide among children and adolescents exposed to parental death. *Journal of the American Academy of Child & Adolescent Psychiatry, 49*(5), 514–523. http://doi.org/10.1016/j.jaac.2010.01.020

Worden, W.J. (1991). *Grief counseling and grief therapy: A handbook for the mental health practitioner* (2nd ed.). New York, NY: Springer.

World Health Organization. (2014). *Preventing suicide: A global imperative.* Geneva, Switzerland: Author.

Wortman, C. B., & Silver, R. C. (2001). The myths of coping with loss revisited. In M. Stroebe, R. Hansson, W. Stroebe, & H. Schut (Eds.), *Handbook of bereavement research: Consequences, coping, and care* (pp. 405–429). Washington, DC: American Psychological Press.

Wrobleski, A. (2002). *Suicide survivors: A guide for those left behind.* Minneapolis, MN: SAVE.

Zisook, S., & Shear, K. (2009). Grief and bereavement: What psychiatrists need to know. *World Psychiatry, 8*(2), 67–74. http://doi.org/10.1002/j.2051-5545.2009.tb00217.x

Chapter 2

Effects of Suicide Bereavement on Mental and Physical Health

Annette Erlangsen[1] and Alexandra Pitman[2]

[1]Danish Research Institute for Suicide Prevention, Mental Health Centre Copenhagen, Denmark
[2]UCL Division of Psychiatry, University College London, London, UK

Abstract: The suicide of a significant other can be a devastating experience for those left behind. Relatives, partners, and friends bereaved by suicide may be deeply affected by the loss, with the experience of suicide bereavement constituting a major psychosocial stressor. Recent research findings indicate that people bereaved by suicide have higher risks of developing both mental and physical health problems than people bereaved by other causes of death, although the mechanisms for these associations have yet to be fully understood.

The support for people bereaved by suicide is limited. Thus, documenting adverse effects related to bereavement will help emphasize the need for support. The aim of this chapter is to review the evidence describing the association between bereavement by suicide and subsequent mental disorders, suicidal behavior, and physical disorders, with respect to the kinship relationship between the bereaved and the deceased. The mental health problems associated with suicide bereavement include depression, anxiety, and posttraumatic stress disorder. The chapter discusses methodological considerations for future research and concludes with implications for policy, practice, and research. Despite the increased risks of mental health problems in those bereaved by suicide, it is important to recognize that the absolute risk is low. Rigorous research is needed to evaluate the interplay of risk and protective factors, such as effective coping, in suicide bereavement.

Introduction

Recent research findings confirm long-held hypotheses that family members and others bereaved by suicide may be deeply affected by the loss, and have higher probabilities of developing both mental and physical diseases, which in turn also affect their personal as well as productive lives (Stroebe, Schut, & Stroebe, 2007). The death of a loved one is often accompanied by feelings of loss, shock, denial, and anger (Dunne-Maxim, 1986). In addition, for persons bereaved by suicide, feelings of guilt, shame, and relief are common (Dunne-Maxim, 1986; McIntosh, 1993). As a consequence, chronic prolonged phases of grief – that is, complicated grief – may arise (Shear & Shair, 2005).

Bereavement by suicide is devastating and may affect psychosocial functioning and increase the risk of developing a range of adverse outcomes. Next of kin have a higher risk of developing psychiatric disorders, such as depression, anxiety, and posttraumatic stress disorders (PTSD) (Brent, Moritz, Bridge, Perper, & Canobbio, 1996; Cerel, Fristad, Weller, & Weller, 1999; Dyregrov & Dyregrov, 2005). An increased risk of suicidal behavior has been found in partners, parents, and children, as well as in those who are unrelated to the deceased (Agerbo, 2005; Pitman, Osborn, Rantell, & King, 2016; Wilcox et al., 2010). Also, more physical illnesses and health care service usage have been observed following parental bereavement by the suicide of an adult son (Séguin, Lesage, & Kiely, 1995). This chapter reviews the evidence describing possible links to mental and physical disorders as outcomes of bereavement by suicide. It highlights the clinical importance of considering a range of negative outcomes after suicide bereavement, and screening for wider health impacts in addition to attending to the potential for intense grief. It also identifies a need for clinicians to be alert to need for support, and the range of local and national resources for people bereaved by suicide. The focus on diagnoses reflects the approach of published studies describing the epidemiology of mental and physical health problems after suicide bereavement, and the predominance of quantitative studies. Qualitative research may be better able to capture other dimensions of the painful experience of grief after bereavement. The chapter highlights the burden of mental and physical impairments that may occur after the loss, and the need for adequate support for the bereaved.

Pathways of Psychological Stress

Stress has been defined as a condition where external factors exceed what can be coped with by an organism, thus causing psychological and biological changes that could potentially lead to disorders (Cohen, Kessler, & Gordon, 1997). While physical stressors, such as a toxin, affect the organisms directly, psychological stressors affect the individual through their perception or appraisal (Reiche, Nunes, & Morimoto, 2004; Cohen et al., 1997), and have been linked to elevated risks of mental disorders, such as depression, anxiety, and PTSD, as well as self-harm and death by suicide (Brent et al., 1996; Cerel et al., 1999; Dyregrov & Dyregrov, 2005; Wilcox et al., 2010).

Having been bereaved by suicide is considered a psychological stressor. Scientific studies have found that being exposed to stress not only impacts on one's mental well-being, but also on one's physical health. Physiological responses to psychological stress can arise through autonomic, neuroendocrine, and immune responses and may result in diseases such as cardiovascular diseases, cancers, type 2 diabetes, osteoporosis, rheumatoid arthritis, sleep disorders, and alcohol abuse disorders (Fang et al., 2012; Hammen, 2005; Irwin & Pike, 1993; Irwin et al., 1990; Reiche et al., 2004; Stroebe et al., 2007). Spousal bereavement has, for example, been linked to ischemic heart disease and lung cancer (Martikainen & Valkonen, 1996a; Martikainen & Valkonen, 1996b; Reiche et al., 2004). A large body of literature has, furthermore, suggested an increased risk of suicidal behavior among people bereaved by suicide (Agerbo, 2005; Pitman et al., 2016; Qin, Agerbo, & Mortensen, 2003; Wilcox et al., 2010). At least two potential causal mechanisms must be considered: The suicide may act as a stressor, and/or the significant other may serve as a role model (De Leo & Heller, 2008).

Previous studies of the impact of bereavement by suicide have compared its impact with that of bereavement by all other causes – that is, to investigate whether bereavement by suicide is a more distressing exposure than bereavement by any other cause of death (Sveen & Walby, 2008). A recent systematic review found that when compared with bereavement by all other causes, bereavement by suicide is associated with an increased risk of suicide in partners and mothers (Pitman, Osborn, King, & Erlangsen, 2014). When investigating the effect of bereavement by suicide, it is important to use defined comparison groups and to allow testing of a specific hypothesis. Large-scale studies in this area indicate that when compared with nonbereaved population samples, bereavement by suicide is more distressing in terms of mental disorders and risks of suicidal behavior (Bolton et al., 2013).

Review of Evidence

The chapter provides an update of a previous systematic review (Pitman et al., 2014). The original search, conducted in October 2013, identified 57 peer-reviewed publications that fulfilled the inclusion criteria. On rerunning the search in July 2015, five additional relevant studies were identified. The inclusion criteria were studies (a) that examined persons who had been bereaved by suicide; (b) with a sufficiently large study sample, operationally defined as more than 100 participants exposed to bereavement by suicide; (c) including a comparison group that would be considered as representative for the general population either as matched controls or from an entire population; (d) with outcomes that were directly indicative of mental or physical disorders – that is, diseases that had required treatment, not just reports of symptoms.

Findings related to mental and physical disorders, as well as suicidal behavior, were summarized using the terms from the original studies. Several high-quality studies have been conducted, such as register-based studies and studies involving an appropriate control group; these types of studies were prioritized in this review. The majority of identified studies focused on people bereaved by the suicide of a family member. The following sections summarize the main findings with respect to type of outcome observed among the people bereaved by suicide – that is, mental disorders, suicidal behavior, physical disorders, and relationships and social functioning.

Mental Disorders

Various studies have evaluated whether bereavement by suicide is linked to an elevated risk of mental disorders. Two large-scale and adjusted studies found that being bereaved by the suicide of a relative was associated with a 1.7- to 2.0-fold higher risk of mental disorders (Bolton et al., 2013; Erlangsen et al., 2016). Both parents bereaved by suicide of a child, and partners bereaved by a spousal suicide, had higher risks of developing mental disorders than peers who were not bereaved. In terms of specific disorders, people bereaved by suicide were more likely to develop depressive disorders, than the general population. The loss of a child to suicide was linked to threefold higher risk of depression among parents (Bolton et al., 2013). However, children whose parents died by suicide also had a twofold risk of depression (Wilcox et al., 2010). The same was the case for men and women bereaved by spousal suicide (Erlangsen et al., 2016).

Alcohol use disorders, identified through contacts with hospital and general practitioner, were linked to a 1.7-fold increase in bereaved children and a 3.6-fold increase in bereaved parents, while slightly lower but also significant values were found for bereaved spouses (Bolton et al., 2013; Erlangsen et al., 2016; Wilcox et al., 2010). A higher risk of being diagnosed with drug abuse disorders has been documented for children and spouses, but not parents, bereaved by suicide (Bolton et al., 2013; Erlangsen et al.,2016; Wilcox et al., 2010); the highest risk (2.3-fold) was noted among children (Wilcox et al., 2010).

Bereavement by suicide has also been linked to other mental disorders. Parents bereaved by a child's suicide have a 1.7-fold increased risk of anxiety disorder (Bolton et al., 2013). Spousal suicide was linked to a twofold risk of neuroses among bereaved partners, and a six-fold risk of PTSD, with risks being slightly higher among men than women (Erlangsen et al.,

2016). Children who were bereaved by a parent's suicide before the age of 13 had a 2.5-fold increased risk of being diagnosed with a personality disorder later in their lives and a 2.8-fold risk of psychotic disorders than those who were not exposed (Wilcox et al., 2010). No elevated risk to develop dementia has been observed among bereaved when compared with nonbereaved controls (Bolton et al., 2013).

It should be noted that the statistical analyses in the majority of the cited studies take account of preexisting conditions, such as mental disorders, preceding the bereavement. This is important, because of evidence to suggest that people bereaved by suicide are a vulnerable group even before the bereavement, by dint of their tobacco use, physical inactivity, and adverse childhood experiences (Pitman et al., 2014). For this reason, the more rigorous epidemiological studies of suicide bereavement take into account the potential contribution of factors such as psychopathology and suicidal behavior with an onset prior to the loss, poor social functioning, family history of suicide, and sociodemographic variables, in explaining poor health outcomes after the loss. In summary, substantial evidence points to an elevated risk of mental disorders – specifically, depressive disorders, substance abuse disorder, PTSD, and anxiety disorders – when comparing persons bereaved by suicide, with the general population.

Suicidal Behavior

The majority of the reviewed studies found an increased risk of self-harm among persons bereaved by suicide. Children bereaved by a parent's suicide, before the age of 13, had a 1.9-fold higher risk of self-harm later in life than peers with no exposure (Wilcox et al., 2010). Across the age spectrum, studies least affected by selection bias found risk of self-harm to range from 1.7- to 2.5-fold higher among those bereaved by suicide, when compared with the general population. Although length of follow-up varied greatly between studies, there was no clear point at which risk of self-harm appeared to be highest. However, as self-harm is a relatively rare event, the studies may have lacked the statistical power to demonstrate any risk patterns over time. Studies involving large sample sizes are needed to detect a significant risk difference.

Interestingly, the highest risk was observed for a sample of young adolescents: A 9.4-fold higher risk of self-harm was found among youngsters bereaved by the suicide of a friend, compared with peers with no such experience (Cerel, Roberts, & Nilsen, 2005). This analysis was adjusted for a series of other potential explanatory factors, such as exposure to self-harm in peers, but not for prebereavement mental disorders. Given the possibility of assortative relating between peers prone to suicidality, it cannot be excluded that preexisting conditions, such as a mental disorder, might have caused the self-harm episode rather than the exposure to the suicide bereavement.

Large-scale population-based studies have shown a 22-fold increased risk of suicide among spouses by suicide during the first 2 years after bereavement; a comparable increase in risk was found for cohabiting partners (Agerbo, 2005). The high risk estimates in this study might be related to the focus on the time immediately after bereavement. Long-term follow-up of partners, that is, married or cohabiting, found comparable lower increases in risk of suicide in the bereaved partner – specifically, a 3.7-fold increase in men and a 4.7-fold increase in women – when compared with the unexposed (Erlangsen et al., 2016).

Another kinship group that has been studied in relation to suicidal behavior after suicide bereavement is siblings, and in particular twins. Siblings who were bereaved by suicide were found to have a 2.6-fold higher risk of dying themselves by suicide (Qin et al., 2003). A Swedish study, found a 3.1-fold higher risk of suicide among bereaved by sibling's suicide than in those not bereaved, but this study did not control for other factors, such as psychiatric diagnoses prior to the bereavement, which also might contribute to an elevated risk (Tidemalm et al.,

2011). Higher risk estimates were found for monozygotic twins, dizygotic twins of opposite sex, and dizygotic twins of same sex who lost their co-twin to suicide; however, the differences between the types of twins were not statistically significant (Tidemalm et al., 2011). Elevated suicide risks among other bereaved family members, such as cousins and grandchildren, have also been suggested (Tidemalm et al., 2011).

Physical Disorders

A substantial body of literature indicates that psychological stressors, such as sudden bereavement, might be linked to various physical disorders. However, there is limited evidence suggesting an increased risk of physical disorders specifically after exposure to bereavement by suicide (Séguin et al., 1995). Based on diagnoses made by general practitioners, a 1.1-fold elevated risk of any physical disorder was found among parents bereaved by child's suicide compared with nonbereaved parents (Bolton et al., 2013). In terms of specific disorders, there is a 1.5-fold increased risk of chronic obstructive pulmonary disease and diabetes mellitus among parents bereaved by suicide compared with unexposed controls (Bolton et al., 2013). These disorders could be considered as lifestyle-related disorders, possibly indicative of changed smoking habits or a less healthy diet after bereavement by suicide.

Relationships and Social Functioning

It is thought that the degree of psychological closeness to the deceased, frequency of contact, kinship relationship, and level of emotional dependence on the deceased are likely to modify physical and mental health outcomes following bereavement by suicide (Cerel, McIntosh, Neimeyer, Maple, & Marshall, 2014). However these mechanisms have yet to be explored empirically in much detail. Qualitative research suggests that the nature of the kinship relationship between deceased and bereaved influences the nature or degree of the impact of a suicide bereavement (Demi & Howell, 1991). However quantitative studies indicate that a greater probability of poor social and occupational functioning is likely in people bereaved by suicide irrespective of kinship when compared with bereaved by other causes (Pitman et al., 2016). Previous studies have found a greater impact of adolescent suicide on mothers rather than fathers, and a greater impact of maternal rather than paternal suicide on the children (Agerbo, Nordentoft, & Mortensen, 2002; Brent et al., 1996; Tsuchiya, Agerbo, & Mortensen, 2005). Bereavement by suicide seems to have a stronger impact on younger siblings than older siblings, based on the time of the exposure (Brent et al., 1996). Based on the reviewed studies, there is no clear evidence for distinct differences in risk of adverse disorders by kinship group following bereavement by suicide: Differences in risk between different kinship groups were too small to be interpreted as significant, and only a minority of studies specified distinct kinship comparison groups. There are reasons to assume that the experience of grief after bereavement might differ substantially depending on kinship, but this may be less important than the quality of the relationship.

The age at which the bereavement is experienced influences outcomes; children and adolescents experiencing bereavement have been found to react more severely and over a longer term than young adults, following parental suicide (Kuramoto, Runeson, Stuart, Lichtenstein, & Wilcox, 2013; Wilcox et al., 2010). In the same respect, kinship might be indicative of cognitive differences in the processing of grief; an adolescent sibling in contrast to a grandparent, for example. Still, this may not represent the intensity of the stress caused by the bereavement. Little is known about the impact by the suicide of a grandchild (of any age) on grandparents (Andriessen, 2014; Cerel, Jordan, & Duberstein, 2008), and this requires specific study.

Methodological Considerations

Decades ago McIntosh (1993) identified a number of key methodological obstacles to providing reliable estimates of the impact of bereavement by suicide: small sample sizes, nonstandardized instruments, selection bias, and lack of suitable comparison groups (bereaved and nonbereaved). In addition, the problem of response bias, where studies rely on the subjective memory of interviewed participants, and the need for longer-term follow-up have been underlined by numerous studies (Brent et al., 1996; Cerel et al., 2008; Cerel, Fristad, Weller, & Weller, 2000; Demi & Howell, 1991; Jordan & McMenamy, 2004; Murphy, Tapper, Johnson, & Lohan, 2003; Ness & Pfeffer, 1990). Many of these challenges have been overcome through studies analyzing population register data. Register data offer the advantages of large sample sizes, representative samples, and no loss to follow-up. However, these come at the cost of a lack of detailed information regarding personal circumstances. Typically, register data will not provide information on social networks, coping strategies, subjective impact of grief, or other relevant psychological measures. Some surveys have attempted to assess the influence on bereavement outcomes of the closeness of the relationship, but there are problems with the validity of this measure. In this respect, population-based studies will be limited to using a household variable as a proxy for closeness.

Implications for Policy, Practice, and Research

It is important to point out that although severe distress is common in people bereaved by suicide, adverse health outcomes are rare. Although higher risks of mental disorders have been found among those bereaved by suicide when compared with those who are not, the actual risk is still relatively low. For instance, in the general population, approximately two to three persons out of 100 will develop depression in a given year. If the risk of depression among those bereaved by suicide is twofold higher than in the general population, this implies that among 100 people bereaved by suicide, approximately four to six people will develop a depressive illness. As such, support group leaders and counsellors should be aware of emergent signs of mental health problems, and be trained to screen and provide treatment or refer the bereaved for professional help when needed.

While the understanding of the negative health effects of bereavement by suicide is increasing, there are few insights into what might help the bereaved navigate through the grieving phase. Very few randomized controlled trials have been conducted to assess the effectiveness of interventions for people bereaved by suicide. Among the few published evaluations, beneficial effects have been found from a cognitive behavior family intervention delivered by a psychiatric nurse, a psychologist-led bereavement group intervention for children, and group therapy for adults delivered by a mental health professional and a suicide-bereaved volunteer (McDaid, Trowman, Golder, Hawton, & Sowden, 2008). In the absence of evidence-based guidelines, it has been suggested that people bereaved by suicide might benefit from being monitored proactively for mental health problems, including for suicidal behavior (Jordan, 2001). Studies eliciting the views of people bereaved by suicide indicate that they express a need for proactive outreach from peers and professionals immediately after the death (Dyregrov, 2011; Provini, Everett, & Pfeffer, 2000). US-based research has shown that this outreach may shorten the time between the loss and receiving help (Cerel & Campbell, 2008). However, there is yet no evidence that these bereaved are better off than those who do not receive active outreach support.

The individual country reports in this volume (see Part IV) describe contemporary developments in the design of interventions delivered at various stages after suicide bereavement.

Those that address the specific physical and mental health problems described in this chapter, including suicidality, might contribute to reducing the health and mortality burden of suicide bereavement. At this stage, it is not clear whether it is more beneficial to target interventions following suicide bereavement toward preventing or treating adverse mental and physical health outcomes. Preventive work could aim to enhance potential protective factors, such as social support, coping styles, and help-seeking behavior.

Significant investment in the design of rigorous trials is required to evaluate this range of interventions. The input of people bereaved by suicide is required to prioritize the interventions to be evaluated, and to identify meaningful outcome measures. In this context, promising work has been conducted into support for persons with traumatic grief – that is, when grieving has become a chronic and static stage (Prigerson et al., 1997). Given cultural dimensions of grief, and differing needs for support by developmental stage and kinship, tailored interventions – for example, for specific ethnic, age, or kinship groups – are needed. Qualitative studies involving the bereaved could provide insights into the acceptability of support provided – for example, interventions delivered by police officers attending the scene of a suicide – and improve the understanding of *why* interventions work or do not. The cost of each suicide includes not only the loss to society of that person, but also the cost of the health impacts on those left behind. This increase in health care expenses and lost productivity is likely to be high and underlines the need for effective interventions for people bereaved by suicide.

Conclusion

This chapter has summarized research evidence describing the impact that bereavement by suicide has on relatives, partners, or friends. Studies investigating mental health sequelae show increased risks of depression, alcohol abuse disorders, drug abuse disorders, anxiety disorders, PTSD, personality disorders, psychotic disorders, self-harm, and completed suicide, but not dementia, among those bereaved by suicide when compared with people who are not bereaved. Studies describing the physical health outcomes demonstrate an increased risk of chronic obstructive pulmonary disease and diabetes mellitus among parents who have lost a child to suicide. Although increased risks were found, the studied events are relatively rare among those bereaved by suicide. Differences in risk between different kinship groups remain unclear, and only a minority of studies have specified distinct kinship comparison groups. Given the scant evidence base for interventions to address poor psychosocial functioning as well as adverse health outcomes in people bereaved by suicide, rigorous quantitative trials alongside qualitative studies are needed.

Corresponding author

Annette Erlangsen
Danish Research Institute for Suicide Prevention
Mental Health Centre Copenhagen
Denmark
annette.erlangsen@regionh.dk

References

Agerbo, E. (2005). Midlife suicide risk, partner's psychiatric illness, spouse and child bereavement by suicide or other modes of death: A gender specific study. *Journal of Epidemiology and Community Health, 59*(5), 407–412. http://doi.org/10.1136/jech.2004.024950

Agerbo, E., Nordentoft, M., & Mortensen, P. B. (2002). Familial, psychiatric, and socioeconomic risk factors for suicide in young people: Nested case-control study. *BMJ, 325*(7355), 74. http://doi.org/10.1136/bmj.325.7355.74

Andriessen, K. (2014). Suicide bereavement and postvention in major suicidology journals. *Crisis. 35*(5), 338–348. http://doi.org/10.1027/0227-5910/a000269

Bolton, J. M., Au, W., Leslie, W. D., Martens, P. J., Enns, M. W., Roos, L. L., ... Walld, R. (2013). Parents bereaved by offspring suicide: A population-based longitudinal case-control study. *JAMA Psychiatry, 70*(2), 158–167. http://doi.org/10.1001/jamapsychiatry.2013.275

Brent, D. A., Moritz, G., Bridge, J., Perper, J., & Canobbio, R. (1996). The impact of adolescent suicide on siblings and parents: A longitudinal follow-up. *Suicide and Life-Threatening Behavior, 26*(3), 253–259.

Cerel, J., & Campbell, F. R. (2008). Suicide survivors seeking mental health services: A preliminary examination of the role of an active postvention model. *Suicide and Life-Threatening Behavior, 38*(1), 30–34. http://doi.org/10.1521/suli.2008.38.1.30

Cerel, J., Fristad, M. A., Weller, E. B., & Weller, R. A. (1999). Suicide-bereaved children and adolescents: A controlled longitudinal examination. *Journal of the American Academy of Child & Adolescent Psychiatry, 38*(6), 672–679. http://doi.org/10.1097/00004583-199906000-00013

Cerel, J., Fristad, M. A., Weller, E. B., & Weller, R. A. (2000). Suicide-bereaved children and adolescents: II. Parental and family functioning. *Journal of the American Academy of Child & Adolescent Psychiatry, 39*(4), 437–444. http://doi.org/10.1097/00004583-200004000-00012

Cerel, J., Jordan, J. R., & Duberstein, P. R. (2008). The impact of suicide on the family. *Crisis, 29*(1), 38–44. http://doi.org/10.1027/0227-5910.29.1.38

Cerel, J., McIntosh, J. L., Neimeyer, R. A., Maple, M., & Marshall, D. (2014). The continuum of "survivorship": Definitional issues in the aftermath of suicide. *Suicide and Life-Threatening Behavior, 44*(6), 591–600. http://doi.org/10.1111/sltb.12093

Cerel, J., Roberts, T. A., & Nilsen, W. J. (2005). Peer suicidal behavior and adolescent risk behavior. *The Journal of Nervous and Mental Disease, 193*(4), 237–243. http://doi.org/10.1097/01.nmd.0000158377.45920.0a

Cohen, S., Kessler, R. C., & Gordon, L. (1997). Strategies for measuring stress in studies of psychiatric and physical disorders. In S. Cohen, R. C. Kessler, & L. Gordon (Eds.), *Measuring stress* (pp. 3–28). New York, NY: Oxford University Press.

De Leo, D., & Heller, T. (2008). Social modeling in the transmission of suicidality. *Crisis, 29*(1), 11–19. http://doi.org/10.1027/0227-5910.29.1.11

Demi, A. S., & Howell, C. (1991). Hiding and healing: Resolving the suicide of a parent or sibling. *Archives of Psychiatric Nursing, 5*(6), 350–356. http://doi.org/10.1016/0883-9417(91)90036-5

Dunne-Maxim, K. (1986). Survivors of suicide. *Journal of Psychosocial Nursing and Mental Health Services, 24*(12), 31–35.

Dyregrov, K. (2011). What do we know about needs for help after suicide in different parts of the world? *Crisis, 32*(6), 310–318. http://doi.org/10.1027/0227-5910/a000098

Dyregrov, K., & Dyregrov, A. (2005). Siblings after suicide: "The forgotten bereaved". *Suicide and Life-Threatening Behavior, 35*(6), 714–724. http://doi.org/10.1521/suli.2005.35.6.714

Erlangsen, A., Runeson, B., Bolton, J., Wilcox, H. C., Forman, J., Krogh, J., ... Conwell, Y. (2016). *Mental and physical illness after spousal suicide*. [Manuscript submitted for publication]

Fang, F., Fall, K., Mittleman, M. A., Sparén, P., Ye, W., Adami, H. O., & Valdimarsdóttir, U. (2012). Suicide and cardiovascular death after a cancer diagnosis. *New England Journal of Medicine, 366*(14), 1310–1318. http://doi.org/10.1056/NEJMoa1110307

Hammen, C. (2005). Stress and depression. *Annual Review of Clinical Psychology, 1*, 293–319. http://doi.org/10.1146/annurev.clinpsy.1.102803.143938

Irwin, M., Patterson, T., Smith, T. L., Caldwell, C., Brown, S. a., Gillin, J. C., & Grant, I. (1990). Reduction of immune function in life stress and depression. *Biological Psychiatry, 27*(1), 22–30. http://doi.org/10.1016/0006-3223(90)90016-U

Irwin, M., & Pike, J. (1993). Bereavement, depressive symptoms, and immune function. In M. S. Stroebe, W. Stroebe, & R. O. Hansson (Eds.), *Handbook of bereavement: Theory, research, and intervention* (pp. 160–171). Cambridge, UK: Cambridge University Press.

Jordan, J. R. (2001). Is suicide bereavement different? A reassessment of the literature. *Suicide and Life-Threatening Behavior, 31*(1), 91–102. http://doi.org/10.1521/suli.31.1.91.21310

Jordan, J. R., & McMenamy, J. (2004). Interventions for suicide survivors: A review of the literature. *Suicide and Life-Threatening Behavior, 34*(4), 337–349. http://doi.org/10.1521/suli.34.4.337.53742

Kuramoto, S. J., Runeson, B., Stuart, E. A., Lichtenstein, P., & Wilcox, H. C. (2013). Time to hospitalization for suicide attempt by the timing of parental suicide during offspring early development. *JAMA Psychiatry, 70*(2), 149–157. http://doi.org/10.1001/jamapsychiatry.2013.274

Martikainen, P., & Valkonen, T. (1996a). Mortality after death of spouse in relation to duration of bereavement in Finland. *Journal of Epidemiology and Community Health, 50*(3), 264–268. http://doi.org/10.1136/jech.50.3.264

Martikainen, P., & Valkonen, T. (1996b). Mortality after the death of a spouse: Rates and causes of death in a large Finnish cohort. *American Journal of Public Health, 86*(8), 1087–1093. http://doi.org/10.2105/AJPH.86.8_Pt_1.1087

McDaid, C., Trowman, R., Golder, S., Hawton, K., & Sowden, A. (2008). Interventions for people bereaved through suicide: Systematic review. *British Journal of Psychiatry, 193*(6), 438–443. http://doi.org/10.1192/bjp.bp.107.040824

McIntosh, J. L. (1993). Control group studies of suicide survivors: A review and critique. *Suicide and Life-Threatening Behavior, 23*(2), 146–161.

Murphy, S. a., Tapper, V. J., Johnson, L. C., & Lohan, J. (2003). Suicide ideation among parents bereaved by the violent deaths of their children. *Issues in Mental Health Nursing, 24*(1), 5–25. http://doi.org/10.1080/01612840305307

Ness, D. E., & Pfeffer, C. R. (1990). Sequelae of bereavement resulting from suicide. *American Journal of Psychiatry, 147*(3), 279–285. http://doi.org/10.1176/ajp.147.3.279

Pitman, A., Osborn, D., King, M., & Erlangsen, A. (2014). Effects of suicide bereavement on mental health and suicide risk. *Lancet Psychiatry, 1*(1), 86–94. http://doi.org/10.1016/S2215-0366(14)70224-X

Pitman, A., Osborn, D. P. J., Rantell, K., & King, M. B. (2016). Bereavement by suicide as a risk factor for suicide attempt: a cross-sectional national UK-wide study of 3432 young bereaved adults. *BMJ Open, 6*(1), e009948. http://doi.org/10.1136/bmjopen-2015-009948

Prigerson, H. G., Bierhals, A. J., Kasl, S. V., Reynolds, C., Shear, M. K., Day, N., ... Jacobs, S. (1997). Traumatic grief as a risk factor for mental and physical morbidity. *American Journal of Psychiatry, 154*(5), 616–623. http://doi.org/10.1176/ajp.154.5.616

Provini, C., Everett, J. R., & Pfeffer, C. R. (2000). Adults mourning suicide: Self-reported concerns about bereavement, needs for assistance, and help-seeking behavior. *Death Studies, 24*(1), 1–19. http://doi.org/10.1080/074811800200667

Qin, P., Agerbo, E., & Mortensen, P. B. (2003). Suicide risk in relation to socioeconomic, demographic, psychiatric and familial factors: A national register-based study of all suicides in Denmark, 1981–1997. *American Journal of Psychiatry, 160*(4), 765–772. http://doi.org/10.1176/appi.ajp.160.4.765

Reiche, E. M., Nunes, S. O., & Morimoto, H. K. (2004). Stress, depression, the immune system, and cancer. *Lancet Oncolology, 5*(10), 617–625. http://doi.org/10.1016/S1470-2045(04)01597-9

Séguin, M., Lesage, A., & Kiely, M. C. (1995). Parental bereavement after suicide and accident: A comparative study. *Suicide and Life-Threatening Behavior, 25*(4), 489–492.

Shear, K., & Shair, H. (2005). Attachment, loss, and complicated grief. *Developmental Psychobiology, 47*(3), 253–267. http://doi.org/10.1002/dev.20091

Stroebe, M., Schut, H., & Stroebe, W. (2007). Health outcomes of bereavement. *The Lancet, 370*(9603), 1960–1973. http://doi.org/10.1016/S0140-6736(07)61816-9

Sveen, C. A., & Walby, F. A. (2008). Suicide survivors' mental health and grief reactions: A systematic review of controlled studies. *Suicide and Life-Threatening Behavior, 38*(1), 13–29. http://doi.org/10.1521/suli.2008.38.1.13

Tidemalm, D., Runeson, B., Waern, M., Frisell, T., Carlström, E., Lichtenstein, P., & Långström, N. (2011). Familial clustering of suicide risk: A total population study of 11.4 million individuals. *Psychological Medicine, 41*(12), 2527–2534. http://doi.org/10.1017/S0033291711000833

Tsuchiya, K. J., Agerbo, E., & Mortensen, P. B. (2005). Parental death and bipolar disorder: A robust association was found in early maternal suicide. *Journal of Affective Disorders, 86*(2), 151–159. http://doi.org/10.1016/j.jad.2005.01.006

Wilcox, H. C., Kuramoto, S. J., Lichtenstein, P., Langstrom, N., Brent, D. A., & Runeson, B. (2010). Psychiatric morbidity, violent crime, and suicide among children and adolescents exposed to parental death. *Journal of the American Academy of Child & Adolescent Psychiatry, 49*(5), 514–523. http://doi.org/10.1016/j.jaac.2010.01.020

Chapter 3

Suicide Bereavement and Postvention Among Adolescents

Karl Andriessen, Michael Dudley, Brian Draper, and Philip B. Mitchell

School of Psychiatry, University of New South Wales, Sydney, NSW, Australia

Abstract: Adolescents are frequently among those bereaved by a suicide. However, the impact of suicide on adolescents is poorly understood, and little is known about the effectiveness of the delivery of supportive interventions. Based on a systematic review of the literature, this chapter presents the characteristics of suicide bereavement of adolescents. It takes into consideration all kinship relationships with the deceased, and reports on the impact of the loss as expressed in grief experiences, mental health, and risk and suicidal behaviors. Preloss and postloss characteristics, such as psychological closeness and quality of remaining relationships, which affect the grief level and outcomes among adolescents, are addressed. Major postvention strategies for adolescents are counseling, support group interventions, and concerted postvention in the school community. The chapter posits that any support needs to take into consideration the broad relational and mental health context of suicide bereavement, the experience of bereaved adolescents regarding help seeking, and age-specific issues. Future research should focus on social, and professional support, and postvention training.

Introduction

There is a peculiar contradiction concerning adolescents in the field of suicidology. Over the decades, adolescents have been among the priority target groups for suicide prevention and research (World Health Organization [WHO], 2014). In contrast, only a few studies have examined the aftermath of suicide in this population (Andriessen, Draper, Dudley, & Mitchell, 2015; Cerel & Aldrich, 2011). A recent analysis of the postvention articles published in the four core suicidology journals over the last 40 years found only five articles on characteristics of suicide bereavement, and seven articles on support programs focused on adolescents or students (Andriessen, 2014). However, there are a number of important reasons for justifying that greater attention should be paid to suicide bereavement of adolescents. Not only may a large number of adolescents be affected by suicide, concerns have been raised regarding the transmission of vulnerability to suicide, and psychosocial morbidity among bereaved adolescents (Cerel & Aldrich, 2011).

Similar to the varying estimated numbers of people bereaved through suicide in the total population, the estimates for young people also vary considerably. According to Pfeffer, Jiang, Kakuma, Hwang, and Metsch (2002), in the United States, children are bereaved by the suicide of a relative in one third of all suicides. In a survey of a representative sample ($N=5{,}918$) of US adolescents, Cerel and Roberts (2005) found that 1.2% had been exposed to the suicide of a close relative in the prior year, while 3.2% had been exposed to the suicide of a peer in that time (Cerel, Roberts, & Nilsen, 2005). A meta-analysis of population-based studies calculated the past-year prevalence of exposure to suicide among adolescents at 4%, and the lifetime prevalence at 16.5% (Andriessen, Rahman, Draper, Dudley, & Mitchell, 2017). This means that, for example, in a school of 500 students, annually there are 20 students exposed to a suicide in their personal environment – for example, among family and friends.

Exposure to fatal and nonfatal suicidal behavior in the family or peer environment can be a risk factor for adolescent suicidal behavior (Qin, Agerbo, & Mortensen, 2002). Several mechanisms may play a role in the transmission: for example, environmental mechanisms through social learning, modeling, or imitation (De Leo & Heller, 2008), and/or biological mechanisms through a vulnerability for impulsivity, aggression, and suicidal feelings (Brent & Melhem, 2008).

The limited number of review studies on adolescent suicide bereavement have focused on specific aspects (morbidity or suicidality) of selected kinship relationships, mainly parental suicide (Geulayov, Gunnell, Holmen, & Metcalfe, 2012; Hung & Rabin, 2009; Kuramoto, Brent, & Wilcox, 2009) and, to a lesser extent, peer suicidal behavior (Crepeau-Hobson & Leech, 2014). This chapter aims to present a comprehensive overview of research findings regarding the impact of suicide loss on adolescents including all kinship relationships with the deceased, either family or peer.

Characteristics of Suicide Bereavement Among Adolescents

This section summarizes and updates the first published systematic review of the literature on the characteristics of suicide bereavement of adolescents (Andriessen, Draper, Dudley, & Mitchell, 2016). This review was comprehensive as it included all kinship relationships with the deceased; focused on the impact of the loss as expressed in grief experiences, mental health, risk behavior, and suicidal behavior; and disentangled preloss and postloss features that affect the grief level and outcomes among adolescents. For this review, adolescents were defined as young people aged 12 to 18 years (high school age range). Studies on exposure to suicide via the media were excluded, as this would not entail a personal relationship, as were review papers. Fifty-eight original studies (qualitative, quantitative, and mixed-methods studies) were included. More than half of the studies ($n=33$, 57%) were US based; 32 articles studied the impact of suicide in the family environment, predominantly parental suicide and sibling suicide; 22 studies focused on suicide in the peer environment – for example, suicide of friends, acquaintances, and school mates; and four studies reported on both peer and family suicide. A re-run in April 2016 of the original search of September 2014 identified one new study; however, the results of that study did not affect the findings of the published systematic review (a full list of the references is available from the authors of the review).

Grief Experience

Studies have reported a variety of thoughts and feelings experienced by bereaved adolescents, and the effect of grief on their behavior and relationships (Abbott & Zakriski, 2014; Bartik, Maple, Edwards, & Kiernan, 2013; Cerel, Fristad, Weller, & Weller, 1999; Dyregrov & Dyregrov, 2005). Reported feelings included guilt, blaming, and anger (toward others and self), shame, rejection, perceived stigma, and sometimes also relief and gratitude. Adolescents engaged in risky coping behaviors such as increased alcohol consumption (Bartik et al., 2013), and the experience of a suicide changed their perspective on relationships, life, and their level of maturity (Bartik et al., 2013; Dyregrov & Dyregrov, 2005). The young survivors expressed a need to make meaning of the suicide, and to be able to talk about their experience. Their positioning in their social circle oscillated between active and passive, between help seeking and isolation (Bartik et al., 2013). The reported grief experiences have been studied mostly through qualitative studies. While these studies provide valuable insights and increase the understanding of the grief experience, it is not possible, due to lack of control groups, to determine whether these grief themes were unique or similar to other types of adolescent bereavement.

Mental Health

There is evidence of increased new onset of psychiatric problems, especially depression, anxiety, posttraumatic stress disorder (PTSD), and substance abuse, shortly after bereavement and irrespective of kinship relationship with the deceased (Brent, Moritz, Bridge, Perper, & Canobbio, 1996b; Bridge, Day, Richardson, Birmaher, & Brent, 2003; Cerel, Fristad, Weller, & Weller, 1999). In addition, long-term mental health risks in peer (Brent et al., 1996b; Melhem et al., 2004) and parentally bereaved adolescents have been reported (Brent, Melhem, Masten, Porta, & Payne, 2012; Melhem, Porta, Shamseddeen, Payne, & Brent, 2011), as opposed to sibling-bereaved adolescents, though few studies have investigated adolescent sibling suicide bereavement (Brent, Moritz, Bridge, Perper, & Canobbio, 1996a; Dyregrov & Dyregrov, 2005).

At-Risk Behaviors

Studies of at-risk behaviors among suicide-bereaved adolescents have focused on smoking, marijuana use, binge drinking, fighting, and inflicting serious injuries to others. There were mixed findings regarding these at-risk behaviors on a short-term basis (Cerel & Roberts, 2005; Cerel et al., 2005; Feigelman & Gorman, 2008). In contrast, a long-term increased risk of at-risk behaviors after parental death, irrespective of cause of death, has been reported (Shepherd & Barraclough, 1976; Wilcox, Kuramoto, Lichtenstein, Långström, Brent, & Runeson, 2010). Increased social adjustment problems – for example, difficulties with school, leisure, peers, and siblings, and more internalizing behavior – have been found in suicide-bereaved children and adolescents, though no differences were found in overall psychosocial and school functioning as rated by teachers (Cerel et al., 1999).

Suicidal Behavior

Studies of suicidal behavior of adolescents exposed to peer suicide have presented mixed findings, with some mostly cross-sectional studies reporting increased risks, but other mostly controlled and longitudinal studies have not (Brent et al., 1996b). However, there is robust evidence from large population-based (Agerbo, Nordentoft, & Mortensen, 2002; Wilcox et al., 2010; Qin et al., 2002) and case-control studies (Cheng et al., 2014) of increased suicide risk in adolescents related to aggregation of suicide in families, specifically parental suicide. Studies have found a twofold to threefold (Qin et al., 2002; Wilcox et al., 2010) risk of suicide among exposed children and adolescents, independent of family history of psychopathology. Maternal suicide may have a stronger impact than paternal suicide (Agerbo et al., 2002; Cheng et al, 2014). Cheng et al. (2014) also found a sex-decedent effect, and a small-scale case-control study found evidence of transmission of suicide method in adolescent–parent suicide dyads (Lu, Chang, Lin, & Li, 2011). In addition to increased suicide risk, exposure to parental suicide is related to a twofold risk of attempted suicide (Cerel & Roberts, 2005; Mittendorfer-Rutz, Rasmussen, & Wasserman, 2008).

Several studies have found an age effect, with impact of suicide being stronger when experienced at younger age (e.g., before ages 10 or 12), with regard to suicide (Agerbo et al., 2002; Wilcox et al., 2010), attempted suicide, and early onset and long-term risk of attempted suicide hospitalization among exposed children/adolescents (Kuramoto, Runeson, Stuart, Lichtenstein, & Wilcox, 2013; Wilcox et al., 2010).

Preloss and Postloss Characteristics

A review of the literature reveals a mixed picture with regard to the grief experience and impact of the suicide loss among adolescents. However, several preloss and postloss characteristics may affect the process of adaptation after the loss. Half a century ago, Hilgard, Newman, and Fisk (1960), while investigating the impact of the death of a parent during childhood among adults, found that features of relationships before and after the death affected the development of the child after the loss, either as risk or protective factors, irrespective of the type of death of the parent – for example, suicide or illness.

Psychological Closeness Before the Loss

Studies refer to the quality of the family context and emotional closeness of a relationship as factors that affect the bereavement process. Abbott and Zakriski (2014) found that the level of grief was highest in peers closest to suicides, and that closeness of relationship and level of grief were linked to a weaker belief in the preventability of the suicide. Closeness of relationships, visual exposure to suicide, and related postloss feelings of accountability were risk factors for new-onset psychiatric problems (Bridge et al., 2003). The mean duration of new-onset depression after peer suicide was 9 months, and rates of new-onset psychiatric problems became nonsignificant after 6 months in exposed compared with unexposed adolescents (Brent et al., 1996b). Closeness of relationship in the group of suicide peers was also associated with increased risk of suicidal communication and suicidal plans.

Contrary to these findings, studies have not found increased risks of attempted suicide or suicide among friends versus acquaintances exposed to a suicide (Brent et al., 1996b; Feigelman & Gorman, 2008), despite increased onset of psychopathology shortly after bereavement. This finding led Brent et al. (1996b) to suggest that exposure to suicide of a friend might serve as a protective factor against one's own suicidal behavior.

Mental Health History

Whereas personal history of depression and family history of psychopathology are related to new-onset psychiatric problems after the loss, either by suicide or other cause of death (Brent et al., 1996b; Melhem et al., 2011), a longitudinal controlled follow-up of parentally bereaved adolescents found that preloss depression, PTSD at 9 months, and loss of mother predicted depression 2 years after the loss (Melhem et al., 2011). At 3-year follow-up, Melhem et al. (2011) distinguished three grief trajectories which emerged irrespective of cause of death: (1) a low grief group (58.8 % of the total sample), (2) an initially high-grief group steadily declining over time (30.8 % of sample), and (3) a high-grief group which continued over time (10.4 %).

Prior personal history of depression and functional impairment were related to prolonged grief (Melhem et al., 2011).

Follow-up of the same study group at 5 years postloss revealed that bereavement and mental health may affect developmental outcomes (Brent et al., 2012). Parentally bereaved youth compared with nonbereaved controls had lower competence regarding work performance, career planning, peer attachment, and future educational aspirations, and higher levels of new onset of alcohol and substance abuse and dependence, the latter especially in adolescent boys. Predeath parental and child psychiatric disorder had a negative impact on parent and child functioning, and was related to the developmental outcomes mentioned. Strikingly, neither age at time of the death, sex of deceased parent, nor cause of death affected the developmental outcomes (Brent et al, 2012).

Social Support After the Loss

With regard to adolescents bereaved by suicide, social support among peers seems to have beneficial effects on more helpful attitudes toward suicide, such as the belief that suicide is preventable, but it is also related to more negative or stigmatizing attitudes, such as the belief that suicide is normal or selfish (Abbott & Zakriski, 2014). Moreover, social support of friends might prolong grief through mechanisms of *corumination,* defined as an extremely negative form of self-disclosure involving discussion focused on problems and emotions to the exclusion of other activities or discourse. Levels of corumination are found to predict the onset of depression, as well as its severity and duration (Stone, Hankin, Gibb, & Abela, 2011).

Quality of Remaining Relationships

Longitudinal controlled follow-up of bereaved adolescents showed that a higher level of functioning of the remaining parent after the death (any cause), and self-esteem of the surviving adolescent, were protective factors for bereaved adolescents. Conversely, at 3-year follow-up, complicated grief in the remaining parent, feeling that others were accountable for the death, and life events subsequent to the death were related to new-onset depression. The cause of death was not significant (Melhem et al., 2011). Indeed, it has been noted that while children mostly impacted by the loss might have experienced the most preloss problems, children who have been separated from the suicidal parent might cope well with the loss, without serious effects, even despite possible major changes in living circumstances. They appear to be helped by "the fact that the ill parent died and the well one survived" (Shepherd & Barraclough, 1976, p. 272).

Dose-Response Effect

There is evidence of a cumulative or a dose–response effect due to an aggregation of preloss and postloss features. Jakobsen and Christiansen (2011) found that the death of both parents, compared with loss of one parent, more than doubled the risk of adolescent attempted suicide (relative risk [RR] = 4.66 vs. 1.71). Also, the adolescent's attempted suicide risk seems to increase with the number of exposed risk factors. Mittendorfer-Rutz et al. (2008) found that 47% of the suicide attempts in the study group could be attributed to the cumulative effects of familial psychopathology, family suicide attempt, familial suicide, and the person's own psychopathology. Similar findings were reported by Christiansen, Goldney, Beautrais, and Agerbo

(2011); however, high paternal but not maternal income, appeared to mitigate risk of attempted suicide after maternal death (Jakobsen & Christiansen, 2011). According to the authors, income of father is an indicator of socioeconomic status, which would correlate with levels of social support. This indicates that social support in families following a suicide would mitigate impact of suicide, whereas social support among friends could be a risk factor for increased corumination.

Suicide Bereavement Support

The review of the research literature revealed that neither cause of death nor mental health or risk behavior determines the level of grief. Preloss and postloss features appear to be related to the grief level, mental health, and behavioral outcomes. Research and provision of support to suicide-bereaved adolescents should therefore consider this broad relational and mental health context. In addition, it has been argued that development of support for adolescents should be based on research and theoretical models, and appropriate training should be provided to those supporting the bereaved (Mitchell et al., 2007). A meta-analysis of interventions (counseling, support groups, music and play therapy, and trauma-based and other psychotherapy) for bereaved children and adolescents after any type of death, found a small to moderate overall treatment effect, though further research is needed to scrutinize the effective ingredients of these interventions (Rosner, Kruse, & Hagl, 2010). The effect of interventions among those bereaved is stronger in those with a greater number of symptoms. Preventive interventions do not aim to reduce symptoms and therefore need specific evaluation measurements not focused upon symptomatology (Rosner et al., 2010). The following section of this chapter reviews findings regarding supportive interventions specifically after loss through suicide.

Counseling

A study by Dyregrov (2009a) provides insights into the experience of adolescents, and their preferences for counseling. A majority of the adolescents bereaved by suicide indicated that they would need help from beyond the family – that is, professional help – and they identified factors within themselves, the counselors, and the way the help is organized, that play a role in achieving that help. In their experience, there appeared to be a wide variety of the types of help that they received, and they perceived service provision as "random." Some would prefer to be contacted through active outreach by services.

Barriers to establishing contact with professionals, which were identified by bereaved adolescents, included lack of knowledge of what exists or where to go for help, lack of energy to contact services, and previous disappointing experiences. Also lack of encouragement by parents, and mismatch in timing between when the young person is ready to accept help and its availability (pointing to the need for a long-term offer), further contributed to not receiving professional help.

Some adolescents discontinued seeing their counselor or psychologist because of dissatisfaction with the relation or the support, whereas others reported having received major support from their psychologist (Dyregrov, 2009a). Adolescents felt that counselors not addressing their problem, professional uncertainty, passivity, and lack of empathy and compassion were related to their dissatisfaction, contrary to flexibility of support delivery, being able to speak freely, and receiving psychoeducation and reassurance of strengths. Knowledge of the counselor about suicide and community resources such as support groups were deemed to be important for the adolescents.

Although these findings arose from one study only (Dyregrov, 2009a), they provide valuable clues for clinicians offering help to adolescents bereaved through suicide. Irrespective of the theoretical or psychotherapeutic school to which a therapist adheres, an engaged, involved, humanistic, compassionate approach would be preferred to overly directive or passive approaches (Andriessen & Krysinska, 2016; Dunne, 1992).

Support Group Interventions

The strongest evidence of effectiveness for a support group intervention for children and adolescents bereaved by suicide stems from the controlled study by Pfeffer et al. (2002) (see Chapter 10 for a comprehensive overview of the characteristics and effectiveness of suicide survivor support groups irrespective of the age of the bereaved). The intervention consisted of ten 90-min weekly group sessions delivered by a trained clinician. Groups were limited to a maximum of five participants, and arranged according to age (with the total group ranging in age from 6 to 15 years). The intervention was based on theoretical models of attachment and cognitive coping, and facilitators used a manual regarding the facilitation of group activities and psychoeducational aspects. The program focused on reactions to death and suicide, and aimed to allow children to express their grief, to promote positive identification with the deceased, and to foster hope. Participants were empowered with problem-solving, social, and self-care skills. Simultaneously, parents received psychoeducational and support sessions to enhance their understanding of childhood bereavement and their capability to support them.

Comparison of pretests and posttests found greater reduction in anxiety and depression symptoms in the intervention group compared with controls, with symptoms dropping from above to below clinically significant levels in the intervention group. As posttraumatic stress symptoms and social maladjustment were not reduced over the course of the intervention, the authors concluded that this would require a longer follow-up period. The parents' psychoeducational component was perceived as contributing to the success of the intervention.

The model of Pfeffer et al. (2002) has become a point of reference for others (e.g., see the support groups for adolescents presented in Chapter 31 in this volume), and in their review, Hung and Rabin (2009) found that suicide support groups for young people may help their members, through the provision of empathy and sharing of experiences, which may balance feelings of stigma and isolation. In addition, groups offer psychoeducation, learning of coping skills, promotion of positive outcomes, and instilling of hope, and the group work should include age-appropriate methods involving play and music (Mitchell et al., 2007; Hung & Rabin, 2009). Also, the concept of offering support to parents simultaneously with the children has been adopted by others (e.g., see Chapter 38 in this volume).

Sandler, Tein, Wolchik, and Ayers (2016) evaluated the Family Bereavement Program which offered a series of both group and individual sessions to families and children (8 to 16 years old) bereaved by all causes of death including suicide. At follow-up after 6 years, the intervention group had improved levels of parenting, coping, grief, and mental health compared with controls. Follow-up after 15 years also found reduced levels of suicide ideation and suicide attempts. Hung and Rabin (2009) had commented that it would be possible to modify the program for application among families bereaved by suicide. However, as far as is known, such a suicide-specific adaptation of the program has never been developed. In fact, Brown, Sandler, Tein, Liu, and Haine (2007) reported that after the first year of intervention, the cause of death (suicide or other) had not affected outcomes for the bereaved children.

There is debate in the literature whether it is useful to organize separate groups for suicide-bereaved youngsters versus general-bereavement groups (Hung & Rabin, 2009). Indeed, the research indicates that the grief process, and risk and protective factors for suicide bereavement outcomes, are similar to those for other types of bereavement. However, people bereaved by suicide may feel differently because of feelings of shame or rejection, which may be more typical after suicide loss. Also, an increased risk of psychopathology (especially in the first months after the loss) and suicidal behavior may warrant the organization of specific suicide survivor support groups. In the same vein, the increased risk of morbidity necessitates specialized training of support group facilitators.

School Communities

A school community, including students, teachers, other staff, and parents, may be deeply affected by the suicide of a student or staff member. There is consensus in the literature and among experts that an a priori well-planned whole-school approach is preferred to an ad hoc crisis intervention response (Cox et al., 2016; Dunne-Maxim, Godin, Lamb, Sutton, & Underwood, 1992; Dyregrov, 2009b), which may, particularly if ill-prepared and ill-delivered, trigger adverse effects such as an increase of suicidal communications and behavior (Callahan, 1996; Goldney & Berman, 1996). A timely, appropriate, and coordinated response may help the bereaved adolescents, and may prevent suicidal behavior of vulnerable students. However, because each suicide and each school community is unique, implementation of guidelines for school-based postvention requires tailoring to the school context, and framing within the existing school health and well-being policy (e.g., see the *+Contigo* program, implemented in secondary schools in Portugal, presented in Chapter 39 in this volume).

Due to a lack of research regarding the effectiveness of postvention in schools, Cox et al. (2016) developed a set of guidelines titled *Responding to Suicide in Secondary Schools: A Delphi Study* (http://headspace.org.au/assets/School-Support/hSS-Delphi-Study-web.pdf), following the Delphi method. The authors developed a questionnaire, based on a review of the literature, which was sent in three rounds to 40 experts from English-speaking countries to find maximum consensus. Actions endorsed by 80 % of the experts were included in the guidelines, and grouped into 20 sections. Sections include the establishment of a response team, and working with the students, the family, the school staff, and the wider community including the media. Specific attention is given to attending the funeral, dealing with the student's belongings, ensuring long-term support for high-risk students, and self-care and support for the response team (the consensus guidelines do not discuss dealing with social media such as Facebook, for a deceased student or staff member. Chapter 17 addresses dealing with the online legacy). It is emphasized that formulation of the response plan has to be as specific as possible in terms of who is doing what and when for whom, and it needs formal approval by the principal or school board. School staff involved as caregivers, gatekeepers, or referrers may benefit from designated training (Grossman et al., 1995; Mackesy-Amiti, Fendrich, Libby, Goldenberg, & Grossman, 1996). All actions must be documented, and the response plan needs yearly review.

Though not mentioned by the authors (Cox et al., 2016), the newly developed set of guidelines may be suitable for adaptation, or may serve as a starting point for other relevant organizations, such as youth homes, youth community organizations, or adolescent clinics.

Implications for Research and Practice

The suicide of a friend or a family member can have a profound, debilitating, and potentially lasting impact on adolescents. However, across kinship relationships with the deceased, aspects of the impact (grief experience, mental health, at-risk behaviors, and suicidal behavior) may be expressed differently over time. Future studies, especially studies involving different types of death and nonbereaved controls, and longitudinal studies might further improve our understanding of the impact of suicide, grief trajectories, and long-term effects regarding mental health, at-risk behaviors, and suicidal behavior among affected adolescents. Future studies should also broaden the perspective, by focusing not only on risk factors for adverse outcomes or maladaptive coping, but also on protective factors to better understand adaptive processes after a significant loss through death. For example, little is known regarding attitudes toward life, death, and suicide, and resilience and help seeking among adolescents bereaved through suicide.

Suicide should not be considered as an isolated event, and its impact should be placed within a broader relational and mental health context, including (1) preloss features related to personal and family history of mental health, family life and stressors, suicidal behavior, type of kinship, and psychological closeness of relationship; and (2) postloss features such as quality of remaining relationships. Sociocultural and communal understandings of suicide bereavement also require further exploration.

The overall picture that emerges is that preloss and postloss characteristics are more important regarding the impact of bereavement than the type of death per se. This observation does not minimize the grief or the pain of the loss that is suffered by the bereaved through suicide. On the contrary, it acknowledges the loss and establishes a perspective of hope. The perspective that suicide bereavement does not have to be more severe than other bereavement, and that adolescents bereaved through suicide are not predisposed to pathological outcomes, may help to destigmatize suicide bereavement.

Despite the availability (albeit still limited in amount) of support for adolescents bereaved by suicide, research into its effectiveness is scant, and there is a clear need for research of implementation and evaluation of supportive interventions taking into account the level of distress of the bereaved adolescent, and the timing of the interventions. Based on the literature, professionally led support groups providing age-appropriate activities, and interventions that include psychoeducation and a parent component appear to be the most promising. Postvention training should be offered to clinicians, support group facilitators, and family caregivers.

Acknowledgments

This study was supported by the Anika Foundation for Adolescent Depression and Suicide.

Corresponding author

Karl Andriessen
School of Psychiatry
University of New South Wales
Black Dog Institute – Hospital Road
Randwick 2031 NSW
Australia
k.andriessen@unsw.edu.au

References

Abbott, C. H., & Zakriski, A. L. (2014). Grief and attitudes toward suicide in peers affected by a cluster of suicides as adolescents. *Suicide and Life-Threatening Behavior, 44*(6), 668–681. http://doi.org/10.1111/sltb.12100

Agerbo, E., Nordentoft, M., & Mortensen, P. B. (2002). Familial, psychiatric, and socioeconomic risk factors for suicide in young people: nested case-control study. *BMJ, 325*(7355), 74–77. http://doi.org/10.1136/bmj.325.7355.74

Andriessen, K. (2014). Suicide bereavement and postvention in major suicidology journals: Lessons learned for the future of postvention. *Crisis, 35*(5), 338–348. http://doi.org/10.1027/0227-5910/a000269

Andriessen, K., Draper, B., Dudley, M., & Mitchell, P. B. (2015). Bereavement after suicide. *Crisis, 36*(5), 299–303. http://doi.org/10.1027/0227-5910/a000339

Andriessen, K., Draper, B., Dudley, M., & Mitchell, P. B. (2016). Pre-and postloss features of adolescent suicide bereavement: A systematic review. *Death Studies, 40*(4), 229–246. http://doi.org/10.1080/074 81187.2015.1128497

Andriessen, K., & Krysinska, K. (2016). A psycho-educational perspective on family involvement in suicide prevention and postvention. In D. Wasserman (Ed.), *Suicide: An unnecessary death* (2nd ed., pp. 333–344). Oxford, UK: Oxford University Press.

Andriessen, K., Rahman, B., Draper, B., Dudley, M., & Mitchell, B. (2017). Prevalence of exposure to suicide: A meta-analysis of population-based studies. *Journal of Psychiatric Research, 88*, 113–120. http://doi. org/10.1016/j.jpsychires.2017.01.017

Bartik, W., Maple, M., Edwards, H., & Kiernan, M. (2013). Adolescent survivors after suicide. *Crisis, 34*(3), 211–217. http://doi.org/10.1027/0227-5910/a000185

Brent, D. A., & Melhem, N. (2008). Familial transmission of suicidal behavior. *Psychiatric Clinics of North America, 31*(2), 157–177. http://doi.org/10.1016/j.psc.2008.02.001

Brent, D. A., Melhem, N. M., Masten, A. S., Porta, G., & Payne, M. W. (2012). Longitudinal effects of parental bereavement on adolescent developmental competence. *Journal of Clinical Child & Adolescent Psychology, 41*(6), 778–791. http://doi.org/10.1080/15374416.2012.717871

Brent, D. A., Moritz, G., Bridge, J., Perper, J., & Canobbio, R. (1996a). The impact of adolescent suicide on siblings and parents: A longitudinal follow-up. *Suicide and Life-Threatening Behavior, 26*(3), 253–259.

Brent, D. A., Moritz, G., Bridge, J., Perper, J., & Canobbio, R. (1996b). Long-term impact of exposure to suicide: A three-year controlled follow-up. *Journal of the American Academy of Child & Adolescent Psychiatry, 35*(5), 646–653. http://doi.org/10.1097/00004583-199605000-00020

Bridge, J. A., Day, N. L., Richardson, G. A., Birmaher, B., & Brent, D. A. (2003). Major depressive disorder in adolescents exposed to a friend's suicide. *Journal of the American Academy of Child & Adolescent Psychiatry, 42*(11), 1294–1300. http://doi.org/10.1097/01.chi.0000084830.67701.9

Brown, A. C., Sandler, I. N., Tein, J. Y., Liu, X., & Haine, R. A. (2007). Implications of parental suicide and violent death for promotion of resilience of parentally-bereaved children. *Death studies, 31*(4), 301–335. http://doi.org/10.1080/07481180601187092

Callahan, J. (1996). Negative effects of a school suicide postvention program: A case example. *Crisis, 17*(3), 108–115. http://doi.org/10.1027/0227-5910.17.3.108

Cerel, J., & Aldrich, R. S. (2011). The impact of suicide on children and adolescents. In J. R. Jordan & J. L. McIntosh (Eds.), *Grief after suicide: Understanding the consequences and caring for the survivors* (pp. 81–92). New York, NY: Routledge.

Cerel, J., Fristad, M. A., Weller, E. B., & Weller, R. A. (1999). Suicide-bereaved children and adolescents: A controlled longitudinal examination. *Journal of the American Academy of Child & Adolescent Psychiatry, 38*(6), 672–679. http://doi.org/10.1097/00004583-199906000-00013

Cerel, J., & Roberts, T. A. (2005). Suicidal behavior in the family and adolescent risk behavior. *Journal of Adolescent Health, 36*(4), 352-e8. http://doi.org/10.1016/j.jadohealth.2004.08.010

Cerel, J., Roberts, T. A., & Nilsen, W. J. (2005). Peer suicidal behavior and adolescent risk behavior. *Journal of Nervous and Mental Disease, 193*(4), 237–243. http://doi.org/10.1097/01.nmd.0000158377. 45920.0a

Cheng, C. C., Yen, W. J., Chang, W. T., Wu, K. C., Ko, M. C., & Li, C. Y. (2014). Risk of adolescent offspring's completed suicide increases with prior history of their same-sex parents' death by suicide. *Psychological Medicine, 44*(9), 1845–1854. http://doi.org/10.1017/S0033291713002298

Christiansen, E., Goldney, R. D., Beautrais, A. L., & Agerbo, E. (2011). Youth suicide attempts and the dose–response relationship to parental risk factors: a population-based study. *Psychological Medicine, 41*(2), 313–319. http://doi.org/10.1017/S0033291710000747

Cox, G. R., Bailey, E., Jorm, A. F., Reavley, N. J., Templer, K., Parker, A., ... Robinson, J. (2016). Development of suicide postvention guidelines for secondary schools: A Delphi study. *BMC Public Health, 16*(1), 1–11.

Crepeau-Hobson, M. F., & Leech, N. L. (2014). The impact of exposure to peer suicidal self-directed violence on youth suicidal behavior: A critical review of the literature. *Suicide and Life-Threatening Behavior, 44*(1), 58–77. http://doi.org/10.1111/sltb.12055

De Leo, D., & Heller, T. (2008). Social modeling in the transmission of suicidality. *Crisis, 29*(1), 11–19. http://doi.org/10.1027/0227-5910.29.1.11

Dunne, E.J. (1992). Psychoeducational intervention strategies for survivors of suicide. *Crisis, 13*(1), 35–40.

Dunne-Maxim, K., Godin, S., Lamb, F., Sutton, C., & Underwood, M. (1992). The aftermath of youth suicide: Providing postvention services for the school and community. *Crisis, 13*(1), 16–22.

Dyregrov, K. (2009a). How do the young suicide survivors wish to be met by psychologists? A user study. *Omega: Journal of Death and Dying, 59*(3), 221–238. http://doi.org/10.2190/OM.59.3.c

Dyregrov, K. (2009b). The important role of the school following suicide in Norway. What support do young people wish that school could provide? *Omega: Journal of Death and Dying, 59*(2), 147–161. http://doi.org/10.2190/OM.59.2.d

Dyregrov, K., & Dyregrov, A. (2005). Siblings after suicide, "The forgotten bereaved". *Suicide and Life-Threatening Behavior, 35*(6), 714–724. http://doi.org/10.1521/suli.2005.35.6.714

Feigelman, W., & Gorman, B.S. (2008). Assessing the effects of peer suicide on youth suicide. *Suicide and Life-Threatening Behavior, 38*(2), 181–194. http://doi.org/10.1521/suli.2008.38.2.181

Geulayov, G., Gunnell, D., Holmen, T.L., & Metcalfe, C. (2012). The association of parental fatal and non-fatal suicidal behaviour with offspring suicidal behaviour and depression: a systematic review and meta-analysis. *Psychological Medicine, 42*(8), 1567–1580. http://doi.org/10.1017/S0033291711002753

Goldney, R.D., & Berman, L. (1996). Postvention in schools: Affective or effective? *Crisis, 17*(3), 98–99. http://doi.org/10.1027/0227-5910.17.3.98

Grossman, J., Hirsch, J., Goldenberg, D., Libby, S., Fendrich, M., Mackesy-Amiti, M.E., … Chance, G.H. (1995). Strategies for school-based response to loss: Proactive training and postvention consultation. *Crisis, 16*(1), 18–26. http://doi.org/10.1027/0227-5910.16.1.18

Hilgard, J., Newman, M., & Fisk, F. (1960). Strength of adult ego following childhood bereavement. *American Journal of Orthopsychiatry, 30*(4), 788–798. http://doi.org/10.1111/j.1939-0025.1960.tb02094.x

Hung, N.C., & Rabin, L.A. (2009). Comprehending childhood bereavement by parental suicide: A critical review of research on outcomes, grief processes, and interventions. *Death Studies, 33*(9), 781–814. http://doi.org/10.1080/07481180903142357

Jakobsen, I.S., & Christiansen, E. (2011). Young people's risk of suicide attempts in relation to parental death: A population-based register study. *Journal of Child Psychology and Psychiatry, 52*(2), 176–183. http://doi.org/10.1111/j.1469-7610.2010.02298.x

Kuramoto, S.J., Brent, D.A., & Wilcox, H.C. (2009). The impact of parental suicide on child and adolescent offspring. *Suicide and Life-Threatening Behavior, 39*(2), 137–151.

Kuramoto, S.J., Runeson, B., Stuart, E.A., Lichtenstein, P., & Wilcox, H.C. (2013). Time to hospitalization for suicide attempt by the timing of parental suicide during offspring early development. *JAMA Psychiatry, 70*(2), 149–157. http://doi.org/10.1001/jamapsychiatry.2013.274

Lu, T.H., Chang, W.T., Lin, J.J., & Li, C.Y. (2011). Suicide method runs in families: A birth certificate cohort study of adolescent suicide in Taiwan. *Suicide and Life-Threatening Behavior, 41*(6), 685–690. http://doi.org/10.1111/j.1943-278X.2011.00064.x

Mackesy-Amiti, M.A., Fendrich, M., Libby, S., Goldenberg, D., & Grossman, J. (1996). Assessment of knowledge gains in proactive training for postvention. *Suicide and Life-Threatening Behavior, 26*(2), 161–174.

Melhem, N.M., Day, N., Shear, M.K., Day, R., Reynolds, C.F., & Brent, D. (2004). Traumatic grief among adolescents exposed to a peer's suicide. *American Journal of Psychiatry, 161*(8), 1411–1416. http://doi.org/10.1176/appi.ajp.161.8.1411

Melhem, N.M., Porta, G., Shamseddeen, W., Payne, M.W., & Brent, D.A. (2011). Grief in children and adolescents bereaved by sudden parental death. *Archives of General Psychiatry, 68*(9), 911–919. http://doi.org/10.1001/archgenpsychiatry.2011.101

Mitchell, A.M., Wesner, S., Garand, L., Gale, D.D., Havill, A., & Brownson, L. (2007). A support group intervention for children bereaved by parental suicide. *Journal of Child and Adolescent Psychiatric Nursing, 20*(1), 3–13. http://doi.org/10.1111/j.1744-6171.2007.00073.x

Mittendorfer-Rutz, E., Rasmussen, F., & Wasserman, D. (2008). Familial clustering of suicidal behaviour and psychopathology in young suicide attempters: A register-based nested case control study. *Social Psychiatry and Psychiatric Epidemiology, 43*(1), 28–36. http://doi.org/10.1007/s00127-007-0266-0

Pfeffer, C.R., Jiang, H., Kakuma, T., Hwang, J., & Metsch, M. (2002). Group intervention for children bereaved by the suicide of a relative. *Journal of the American Academy of Child & Adolescent Psychiatry, 41*(5), 505–513. http://doi.org/10.1097/00004583-200205000-00007

Qin, P., Agerbo, E., & Mortensen, P. B. (2002). Suicide risk in relation to family history of completed suicide and psychiatric disorders: A nested case-control study based on longitudinal registers. *The Lancet, 360*(9340), 1126–1130. http://doi.org/10.1016/S0140-6736(02)11197-4

Rosner, R., Kruse, J., & Hagl, M. (2010). A meta-analysis of interventions for bereaved children and adolescents. *Death Studies, 34*(2), 99–136. http://doi.org/10.1080/07481180903492422

Sandler, I., Tein, J. Y., Wolchik, S., & Ayers, T. S. (2016). The effects of the Family Bereavement Program to reduce suicide ideation and/or attempts of parentally bereaved children six and fifteen years later. *Suicide and Life-Threatening Behavior, 46*(Suppl 1), S3 2-S3 8. http://doi.org/10.1111/sltb.12256

Shepherd, D. M., & Barraclough, B. M. (1976). The aftermath of parental suicide for children. *British Journal of Psychiatry, 129*(3), 267–276. http://doi.org/10.1192/bjp.129.3.267

Stone, L. B., Hankin, B. L., Gibb, B. E., & Abela, J. R. (2011). Co-rumination predicts the onset of depressive disorders during adolescence. *Journal of Abnormal Psychology, 120*(3), 752–757. http://doi.org/10.1037/a0023384

Wilcox, H. C., Kuramoto, S. J., Lichtenstein, P., Långström, N., Brent, D. A., & Runeson, B. (2010). Psychiatric morbidity, violent crime, and suicide among children and adolescents exposed to parental death. *Journal of the American Academy of Child & Adolescent Psychiatry, 49*(5), 514–523. http://doi.org/10.1016/j.jaac.2010.01.020

World Health Organization. (2014). *Preventing suicide: A global imperative.* Geneva, Switzerland: Author. Retrieved from http://www.who.int/mental_health/suicide-prevention/world_report_2014/en/

Chapter 4

Suicide Bereavement and Gender

Onja T. Grad[1], Marta Treven[2], and Karolina Krysinska[3]

[1]University Psychiatric Hospital, Ljubljana, Slovenia
[2]Slovenian Association for Suicide Prevention, Ljubljana, Slovenia
[3]School of Psychiatry, University of New South Wales, Sydney, Australia

Abstract: Gender is an important determinant of how the bereaved, including suicide survivors, will respond to the loss. Men are usually difficult to include in bereavement research, and there is a paucity of methodologically sound studies on men's bereavement in general, and even less on men's bereavement after suicide. The common stereotype is that men and women respond differently, and men are expected to show less emotion and to be the major support for their family. This chapter seeks to determine the gender differences and commonalities in bereavement, especially bereavement after suicide, and what kind of support and help men and women may need and accept as useful.

Introduction

Contrary to gender differences in suicide bereavement, differences between men and women are frequently studied and reported in the epidemiology of fatal and nonfatal suicidal behavior, suicide means, and risk factors. (A detailed analysis of the issues of gender and sex in the context of grief and suicidal behavior is outside the scope of the chapter. Interested readers can find more information in Canetto and Lester [1995]; Lester, Gunn, and Quinnett [2014]; and Martin and Doka [2000]). In almost all countries, male suicide rates exceed female rates, although the gender ratios of suicide differ between countries, while being female is a strong risk factor for suicidal ideation and attempts. Differences in the use of suicide methods can be related to different prevalence of fatal and nonfatal suicidal behavior in men and women (Samaritans, 2012). Also, a number of risk factors may be gender specific, including depressive and anxiety disorder in women and alcohol abuse disorder in men, work-related and financial problems for men, and problems with children for women (Shiner, Scourfield, Fincham, & Langer, 2009).

When researchers and clinicians try to better understand and to explain grief and bereavement after death in general, and specifically after suicide, two important facts can be pointed out. First, most studies mention gender as a confounding factor in the grief process, and second, most pioneering studies on grief have predominantly been based on women's data because the participation of men in research has been (and still is) very difficult to obtain (McGoldrick, 2004; Stroebe, Hansson, Schut, & Stroebe, 2008). The same problem is encountered in clinical practice, where only a small proportion of bereaved patients, especially after suicide, are men. Data collected from female participants has often been generalized to both genders, and male and female respondents have been treated as a single sample (Gibson, Gallagher, & Jenkins,

2010; Ogata, Ishikawa, Michiue, Nishi, & Maeda, 2011). Already in 1989, this fact was recognized as a problem by Stroebe and Stroebe: "If gender is an issue in the bereavement—how reliable are the values of studies where parents are taken as one piece instead of two different individuals?" (1989, cited in Bolton et al., 2013). More recent studies on bereavement have addressed this limitation and balanced the data by including male participants only (e.g., Cacciatore, Erlandsson, & Rådestad, 2013; Creighton, Oliffe, Butterwick, & Saewyc, 2013; Walton, Coyle, & Lyons, 2004; Wood & Milo, 2001) or by including as many men as possible in mixed-gender samples (Callahan, 2000; Rostila, Saarela, & Kawachi, 2014; Säflund & Wredling, 2006; Schwab, 1996).

Moreover, most studies of bereavement rely on participants who are self-selected and found through clinical services, online recruitment procedures, or other announcements made to attract participants. This may bias the study sample, as those who respond to surveys tend to be healthier and recover differently from nonresponders. As Stroebe and Stroebe (1989) have pointed out, "Whether a bereaved person agrees to participate in research or not is undoubtedly influenced by his or her mental and/or physical state, which are precisely the variables that such studies are attempting to measure" (p. 2). The number of male participants is usually (too) small (McDaid, Trowman, Golder, Hawton, & Sowden, 2008), and men who are willing to participate tend to be more verbally skilled and more prone to talk about their feelings than other men (Ozbič, 2015). There may also be differences in grief reactions between male participants and male nonparticipants. These may all be reasons for the literature on men's bereavement to be scant, controversial, and often unreliable (McDaid et al., 2008); and the effect of the gender of the survivor remains a controversial issue (Callahan, 2000, p. 105).

Although anecdotal clinical evidence has often been quoted in the literature, even in this domain, one encounters the problem of insufficient information on men's bereavement. Men seek help less often than women do, and according to Baum (2004), this reluctance on the part of men to seek professional help could be understood in light of socialization and social expectations. A man who seeks help does not fit the stereotype of a "strong man" and can be perceived by himself and others as weak, vulnerable, and incompetent. As McGoldrick (2004) rather extremely stated: "The general failure of the literature on death to discuss gender is remarkable, given that the ways how men and women handle death are so profoundly different and that society's rules for mourning show no overlap whatsoever regarding expectations for how men and women are supposed to mourn" (p. 99).

Although grief in general has been widely studied in psychiatric and psychological research, not much is known about men's specific modes of coping with grief and how these may differ from the women's experience of bereavement (Cacciatore et al., 2013). This chapter presents an overview of the literature, along with clinical vignettes, showing how gender may influence the process of bereavement and seeking help and support, focusing on similarities and differences between bereaved women and men. It is noted that most literature concerns bereavement in general. Where possible, the chapter addresses findings specific to suicide bereavement.

The Impact of Death on Men and Women

In the history of humankind, social expectations for men and women regarding bereavement have varied. In some cultures and religions, women were forbidden to attend funerals, to see and to wash the dead body; in others they were expected to lament and keep wake with the corpse, whereas men were expected to be stoic and undisturbed by the event (McGoldrick, 2004). Some women were even not supposed to continue living after the death of their husbands. An extreme example would be the practice of *sati* in India when a widow throws herself into the fire at the funeral along with the husband's dead body. There is the question of nurture or nature. Were the responses of men and women after loss and death different in the first place, and was it only afterwards that society responded with sex-specific demands for how to respond? Or did society first prescribe the reactions for bereaved women and men, and then over the generations, did the sociocultural demands receive a "proper" echo in sex-specific behaviors?

There are variations and fluidity in grief experiences, which differ considerably in intensity and length among cultural groups and from person to person. The idiosyncratic ways in which bereaved individuals cope with loss, the fact that they experience varying degrees and types of distress at different times, and the differences in how or when they adjust to life without their loved one, give no clear answers to what the average "gender-specific" bereavement may look like (Zisook & Shear, 2009).

Studies on bereavement in men and women have usually used participants' self-reported narratives about the bereavement process (qualitative studies), questionnaires measuring the responder's own assessment of various dimensions of their bereavement (quantitative studies), and/or objective measures of bereavement, such as mortality rates, length and frequency of a sick leave, depression, and/or anxiety score. Many studies have been carried out into the grief responses after different kinds of death, especially a natural death, and fewer studies have looked at bereavement by suicide; most of which did not look especially at gender. It has been estimated that men represent less than 25 % of the samples when studying bereavement, especially in the older population of widows and widowers (Daggett, 2002). Stroebe and Stroebe (1993) have also argued that direct comparisons between men and women are inappropriate because the baseline rates of depression, anxiety, substance dependence, and other measures are not equal. When researchers have compared bereaved men with nonbereaved men and bereaved women with nonbereaved women, the results have shown that men have poorer outcomes than women (Callahan, 2000). In contrast, using the same methodology of comparing bereaved and nonbereaved by gender, Murphy et al. (1999) found poorer outcomes for bereaved women than for bereaved men.

According to the popular explanations of men's and women's bereavement, based on social constructs and knowledge about gender-specific socialization in the Western culture, women are more vulnerable, show emotions more often and more easily, and have emotional reactions that are more intense and long-lasting. Some popular explanations have been confirmed in different studies. Women ask for help and talk about their problems more often than men (Martin & Doka, 2000; McGoldrick, 2004; Lund, 2001). Men are less prone to talk about themselves and their feelings; they express their sadness through anger and tend to self-medicate with alcohol or other substances. Men also use work as a preferred way of coping, as it helps them to forget and to keep themselves occupied (Berman, 2005). Western men do not share their pain, do not grieve openly, and avoid strong, dependent, and warm feelings (Jansz, 2000). They may also avoid grief through silence, secrecy, action, anger, and addiction (Aho, Tarkka, Åstedt-Kurki, & Kaunonen, 2006; Cacciatore et al., 2013; Golden & Miller, 1998; Walton et al., 2004). Nonetheless, a study of coping strategies following a child's violent death from accident, suicide, or homicide, showed that grieving mothers and fathers use a wide range of coping methods (Murphy, Johnson, & Weber, 2002). The authors observed that neither parents reported exclusive use of coping strategies prescribed by gender stereotypes – that is, problem-focused coping in men and emotion-focused coping in women; instead they used more gender-neutral strategies, such as active coping, planning, positive reinterpretation and growth, and religion.

Rather than using stereotypes and clichés, it is important to observe that bereaved men and women face different problems and different social roles after the traumatic event. Gender differences also exist in patterns of communication, in the way men and women express emotions, and in their resources for coping with loss. Psychological and biological factors and cultural conditioning influence the development of gender-specific grieving (Daggett, 2002). Nonetheless, similarities can be found between the genders regarding bereavement outcomes. Bereaved men and women, including suicide survivors, have an increased risk of physical and psychiatric disease and increased mortality rates (Bolton et al., 2013; Brent, Moritz, Bridge, Perper, & Canobbio, 1996; Huang, Valdimarsdóttir, Fall, Ye, & Fang, 2013; Pitman, Osborn, King, & Erlangsen, 2014). In a general population study, Wilcox and colleagues (2015) found that fathers and mothers of children who died through suicide (or in accidents) had an equally high risk (over tenfold greater compared with nonbereaved participants) of taking parental sick leave related to psychiatric diagnoses, most commonly stress-related disorders, unipolar depression, and anxiety. Rostila, Saarela, and Kawachi (2014) found an elevated mortality rate from all causes, including suicide, among men and women who had experienced a sibling's suicide, although women's risk of suicide was somewhat higher than men's. Agerbo (2005) reported an elevated risk of suicide both for men and women after the suicide of a child or a partner. Of note, the suicide rates associated with losing a child differed little by gender, whereas the suicide rate for widowers was significantly higher than the suicide rate for widows. In any case, the loss of a spouse or child through suicide increased the suicide risk in both genders more than other cause of death of a spouse or a child (Agerbo, 2005).

Although in quantitative research, mothers score higher on the majority of bereavement scales (Murphy et al., 1999; Schwab, 1996), in a qualitative study by Wood and Milo (2001), fathers who lost a disabled child adamantly rejected the belief that they grieve less than mothers. In a study by Aho et al. (2006), fathers who had lost a child due to natural death described emotions, such as shock, denial, numbness, despair, sorrow, pain, fear, emptiness, anger, bitterness, and guilt, which were in all likelihood indistinguishable from mothers' emotional reactions. Levi-Belz (2014) found that social interactions, and positive coping strategies, especially planning for the future, were important factors in stress-related growth in suicide survivors, but there were no differences between male and female suicide survivors regarding personal transformation after the loss. In a study by Schwab (1996), which included a mixed sample of bereaved, including suicide survivors, both bereaved parents appeared to feel equally cut off socially and distant from others, and equally conscious of their personal loss. Also, a study of fathers' stories and poems about their grief did not conclude that men were less affected than women, only that they expressed their grief differently (Dilts, 2001; Lund, 2001).

Expressing Grief: The Influence of Gender

The bereaved person's expression of grief is their individual way of showing the inner distress and feelings following the loss. Expression of grief is deeply influenced by gender (Creighton et al., 2013) and also by expectations of the society and culture. In the Western culture, it is expected that grieving women will talk, confide, and show emotions. Knowledge about grieving men and expectations regarding expression of emotions (despite stereotypes) are less homogenous and are not all that well known. Emotions and emotional expressions in men have been constructed as dependent on the object, source, or context; and men generally strive to control the expression of emotional distress in social contexts, to the point of concealment (Creighton et al., 2013).

Men tend toward action as the primary mode of dealing with grief and, contrary to women, use relating with others as a secondary strategy (Golden, 1996). Men have been found to use four primary coping strategies in response to loss: setting aside the grief response, instrumental coping, expressive coping, and searching for meaning (Starek, 2000). It could be said that "to experience emotions is human, to control their expression is masculine" (Walton et al., 2004, p. 413). Martin and Doka (2000) labeled patterns of masculine grief as *instrumental* or *problem solving* and feminine grief as *intuitive* or *emotional,* and stated that "patterns [of grieving] are influenced by gender, but not determined by it" (Martin & Doka, 2000, p. 4). According to Martin and Doka (2000), grief responses can be viewed on a continuum between *masculine* or *action-oriented* versus *feminine* or *affective* patterns of mourning.

Men tend to bottle up their grief, to deny it; they may grieve alone or in secret, try to minimize or mask their feelings (Aho et al., 2006), and may underreport their feelings and reactions in studies. When men feel obliged to engage in public expressions of mourning, they report an uncomfortable and suffocating experience. The social dictate is to "man up" (Creighton et al., 2013). In a longitudinal study of couples who suffered a loss due to miscarriage, men were found to grieve less intensely and over a shorter period of time than their female partners (Beutel, Willner, Deckardt, Von Rad, & Weiner, 1996). They cried less, and did not feel much need to talk about their experiences, although they felt burdened by their wives' grief and depressive reactions. Similarly, Valizadeh et al. (2013) found that men do not express their feelings (or suppress them), because they have to be supportive of, and protective toward, their bereaved wives. Still, some fathers who had lost a child to stillbirth, felt ignored and not acknowledged as a legitimately grieving parent (Cacciatore et al., 2013).

Similar to the fact mentioned above that men are reluctant to participate in studies, it is also true that many male clients are unwilling to express and share their grief reactions after traumatic loss, even with professionals to receive support or help. Results of studies on the gender differences in the bereavement process, mostly including bereaved parents, vary depending on the type of death, on whether the death was anticipated, on personality traits of the responders, their lifecycle, and the age of the bereaved (Reed, 1993; Murphy et al, 2010).

The major gender difference reported in studies with parents after the death of a child to cancer (Alam, Barrera, D'Agostino, Nicholas, & Schneiderman, 2012) or violent death, including suicide (Murphy et al., 1999), is the intensity of expressed emotions and the timeline of bereavement. Mothers tend to express more intense pain in the initial year after death, which decreases in the following year, whereas fathers tend to express their grief later. Emotional reactions of fathers may be delayed due to external demands, such as a need to protect the spouse (and not burden her with his own distress), funeral arrangements, responsibility to bring in income, and caring for surviving children (Cacciatore et al., 2013).

Work, in addition to being a source of income for the family, may be a helpful way for men to withdraw and to forget, and to regain a sense of control through activity (Aho et al., 2006; Chapter 15 discusses the role of workplaces in the aftermath of suicide). Bereaved men may work more hours, but their attitude may change over time, as work outside the family becomes less meaningful (Alam et al., 2012). Some bereaved fathers report inducing pain and suffering through hard physical work after the death of a child (Aho et al., 2006). Too much work may add to a greater risk of somatic leave among fathers after the suicide of a child (Wilcox et al., 2015), especially given that the predominant causes of absence include back pain and musculoskeletal disorders.

Bereaved mothers may express their feelings through talking about their deceased child(ren) and maintaining continuing bonds with the deceased, and they may be ambivalent about their own mortality and express suicidal thoughts (Harper, O'Connor, Dickson, & O'Carroll, 2011). Bereaved fathers may react differently: They use an action-oriented style of coping to prevent being overwhelmed by painful feelings; they feel isolated and find it difficult to see their wife's pain (Wood & Milo, 2001). In contrast to their wives, who report many changes, men stay unchanged and consistent in their self-identity and worldview. Lannen and colleagues (2008) found that fathers with unresolved grief after a child's death to cancer, suffered from poorer physical and mental health and reported more difficulties falling asleep and more often waking up with emotional distress than fathers who reported resolved grief. Baum (2004) found that bereaved men engage in self-medication with alcohol and drugs more often than women.

Vignette 1 shows that reversal of gender roles in bereavement responses is possible, gender roles can change over time, and a new context may trigger new reactions in a bereaved person, be it a man or a woman. Although generally women are more open and expressive in their emotional reactions and behaviors (Jordan & McIntosh, 2011), one should be aware of gender stereotypes and related expectations. Some male suicide survivors may have (or show) no problems and may need no professional help. Men in this group never seek support, but may accompany a family member who is seeking professional help. Other men notice that they need to talk about their grief and seek professional support. These men come to mental health professionals or look for peer support (approximately 25 % from both sources; Daggett, 2002). There are also suicide-bereaved men who do not acknowledge, recognize, or talk about psychological or emotional difficulties. Their problems are expressed through somatization or psychosomatic problems, such as arrhythmia, migraine or tiredness (Aho et al., 2006), ulcer, feelings of pressure, or breathing difficulties. Men in this group may go to their general practitioner and, if not asked otherwise, complain about somatic problems. Bereaved men have problems with their physical health: They have more medical examinations but less conversation with their doctor (Berman, 2005). **Vignette 2** illustrates how mourning can be expressed through a phobic somatization, which would remain hidden without professional help.

Vignette 1

After losing their 16-year-old only son by suicide, the mother shows no emotional reactions. Against her husband's wishes she gives away all of the deceased son's belongings, goes back to work, and very soon gets pregnant. When the child she is pregnant with, dies prenatally for no obvious reason, she collapses, cannot get out of bed, and starts to cry for the first time since the son's suicide. She cannot stop crying. The husband brings her to therapy. He says he feels fine and will wait outside. After a few sessions, he decides to see the therapist. He says how difficult, almost unbearable, the situation is for him. He and the extended family take care of his wife, whereas he is left out and is only expected to support her.

Vignette 2

After losing a 17-year-old son through a self-inflicted gunshot, both parents come to therapy. The mother has been struggling with severe posttraumatic stress disorder symptoms since finding the son's body. She is crying and has lost her motivation to live. The father has developed a somatic reaction: He feels a tumor growing in his throat, has serious problems with swallowing food, and has lost 20 kg in a few months. Briefly before the suicide of his son, he was the main caregiver for his brother, who had a terminal illness and died of throat cancer.

Bereaved Women and Bereaved Men: Implications for Practice

People who have to deal with loss and pain in isolation (McGoldrick, 2004), or are in denial, can become overwhelmed by pain, and their grief may become a complicated grief disorder (Zisook & Shear, 2009). Women usually find it easier to openly share the subtleties of their grief, and receive more help from family, friends, and professionals. Less support is offered to men in distress. Men may refuse help or not search for it. Mental health professionals often perceive men as benefiting less from professional help, but they are often unable to look beyond men's rage, and fail to recognize the full extent of men's losses (Baum, 2004). Some men have difficulties talking about themselves and their feelings, but when they do come to a mental health professional, they feel obliged to talk. There may be an undercurrent of concern that the mental health professional will judge them as not really grieving, if they choose not to talk (Wood & Milo, 2001).

Social support offered to bereaved fathers can be effective and related to fewer atypical grief reactions (Kreicbergs, Lannen, Onelov, & Wolfe, 2007). If therapy helps grieving men to find and maintain a sense of meaning in their lives, less negative adaptation may follow (Floyd, Mailick Seltzer, Greenberg, & Song, 2013). Social networks do not always understand men's grief and do not provide adequate support. This can contribute to a feeling of loneliness and isolation, and lead to social withdrawal (Aho et al., 2006). It is very important that professional and peer support is offered to bereaved men. Professionals can provide much needed informational support, and peers can be a valuable source of emotional support; both potentially very helpful.

Targeted support and treatment services can be effective in helping parents bereaved by the sudden death of children. Studies show a tenfold higher risk of taking sick leave exceeding 30 days due to psychiatric problems, in both mothers and fathers of children who have died through suicide or a traffic accident, and fathers bereaved by a child suicide may have an elevated risk of absence due to somatic illness (Wilcox et al., 2015). These studies, as well as **Vignette 3**, illustrate that bereaved men may react with somatization rather than sadness, apathy, or anger. Professionals may not recognize these reactions as connected to the loss, and treat them as purely somatic complaints. It is important that medical professionals in the primary health care system, such as GPs, are trained to recognize the psychosomatic nature of these health problems and treat them accordingly (see Chapter 13).

Vignette 3

A successful owner of a large IT company seeks psychotherapy after the suicide of his teenage daughter. He says that his wife wanted him to come, because he had stopped talking to her and their two younger children. He reports sleep problems and headaches, but denies any other problems or difficulties. He works a lot, plays golf, and is too tired in the evening to talk to his family. He becomes very angry when the therapist asks him about his deceased daughter, and says that such "rubbish" questions do not help. He strongly believes that suicide is for weak people and talking about it does not help. Eventually, he is willing to talk about his deceased daughter. He becomes very agitated, gesticulates a lot, and has problems finding the words to tell his story. After a few sessions, he starts talking more fluently, the sleep problems diminish, the headache is gone. Still, he announces that he will go to an alternative healer, who will prescribe him a special diet to calm him down. He stops with the talking therapy and, in spite of the obvious good results, denies any influence of psychotherapy on his improved well-being.

In the past and even still today, the most widespread professional and lay help for the bereaved has been based on verbal expression of grief and feelings. Some people, predominantly men, but some women as well, have difficulty accepting this mode of help. As Jordan and McMenamy (2004) observed, "the typical structure of support interventions (e.g., self-disclosure and sharing of feelings) may be less effective or even deleterious, for people with an instrumental or more avoidant orientation to coping which is generally more characteristic of men" (p. 341). This is why alternative means of support using nonverbal resources that bereaved people might possess and use, such as artistic expression (Lund, 2001), are being developed. For example, Creighton et al. (2013) used a photo-elicitation method along with in-depth interviews for men who had lost somebody due to a sudden death. The male study participants were able to express their feelings more easily through photo descriptions, and the study provided novel insights into men's grief and counseling practice. Other projects have aimed to support men through engagement in activities connected to the deceased, such as establishing a foundation to promote research, other work dedicated to the memory of the deceased, and organizing professional or peer meetings (Lund, 2001). Interventions with a practical emphasis, including problem solving, with a focus on social benefits of help seeking and framing help receiving as cognitively (vs. emotionally) focused, may be effective for men (Johal, Shelupanov, & Norman, 2012).

Conclusions

In earlier studies on bereavement, including bereavement after suicide, the differences and similarities between men and women were rarely studied. Later, the issue of gender was recognized as an important confounder in bereavement, but male participants were few and rarely willing to take part in research or therapy. Recently more knowledge regarding gender and bereavement has been gathered from various sources, such as self-reports, a combination of qualitative and quantitative research studies, indirect objective measures, and evidence from the clinical field. The stereotypical schism of gender-specific bereavement still seems to be alive, but similarities in reactions and support-seeking behavior between bereaved men and women have been demonstrated. Bereaved men try to retain a sense of control, take care of their family members first, and then possibly seek help for themselves. Their expressions of grief can be very diverse: from sadness, depression, and sleep problems to difficulties at work, substance abuse, and (psycho)somatic reactions. Although these reactions may also occur in bereaved women, they can be found more often in men.

Bereaved women may have more opportunities to find a supportive social network than men, and the model of professional help based on the disclosure of inner feelings and working through the twists and turns of grief, seems well fitted to their needs. The traditional male role is often in conflict with socially prescribed mourning and grief reactions, at least in the Western world. It is extremely important that clinicians and bereaved families are aware that men and women may grieve differently. An important finding and major implication for practice is that not everyone likes talk therapy and that alternative methods of support and therapy need to be further studied and applied.

Corresponding author

Onja T. Grad
University Psychiatric Hospital
Center for Mental Health
Grablovičeva 44a
1000 Ljubljana
Slovenia
onja.grad@guest.arnes.si

References

Agerbo, E. (2005). Midlife suicide risk, partner's psychiatric illness, spouse and child bereavement by suicide or other modes of death: A gender specific study. *Journal of Epidemiology and Community Health, 59*(5), 407–412. http://doi.org/10.1136/jech.2004.024950

Aho, A. L., Tarkka, M. T., Åstedt-Kurki, P., & Kaunonen, M. (2006). Fathers' grief after the death of a child. *Issues in Mental Health Nursing, 27*(6), 647–663. http://doi.org/10.1080/01612840600643008

Alam, R., Barrera, M., D'Agostino, N., Nicholas, D. B., & Schneiderman, G. (2012). Bereavement experiences of mothers and fathers over time after the death of a child due to cancer. *Death Studies, 36*(1), 1–22. http://doi.org/10.1080/07481187.2011.553312

Baum, N. (2004). On helping divorced men to mourn their losses. *American Journal of Psychotherapy, 58*(2), 174–185.

Berman, L. (2005). Help-seeking among men: Implications for suicide prevention. *Pogled/The View, 3*(1–2), 36–52.

Beutel, M., Willner, H., Deckardt, R., Von Rad, M., & Weiner, H. (1996). Similarities and differences in couples' grief reactions following a miscarriage: Results from a longitudinal study. *Journal of Psychosomatic Research, 40*(3), 245–53. http://doi.org/10.1016/0022-3999(95)00520-X

Bolton, J. M., Au, W., Leslie, W. D., Martens, P. J., Enns, M. W., Roos, L. L., … Walld, R. (2013). Parents bereaved by offspring suicide: A population-based longitudinal case-control study. *JAMA Psychiatry, 70*(2), 158–167. http://doi.org/10.1001/jamapsychiatry.2013.275

Brent, D. A., Moritz, G., Bridge, J., Perper, J., & Canobbio, R. (1996). The impact of adolescent suicide on siblings and parents: A longitudinal follow-up. *Suicide and Life-Threatening Behavior, 26*(3), 253–259.

Cacciatore, J., Erlandsson, K., & Rådestad, I. (2013). Fatherhood and suffering: A qualitative exploration of Swedish men's experiences of care after the death of a baby. *International Journal of Nursing Studies, 50*(5), 664–670. http://doi.org/10.1016/j.ijnurstu.2012.10.014

Callahan, J. (2000). Predictors and correlates of bereavement in suicide support group participants. *Suicide and Life-Threatening Behavior, 30*(2), 104–124.

Canetto, S. S., & Lester, D. (1995). *Women and suicidal behavior.* New York, NY: Springer.

Creighton, G., Oliffe, J. L., Butterwick, S., & Saewyc, E. (2013). After the death of a friend: Young men's grief and masculine identities. *Social Science & Medicine, 84,* 35–43. http://doi.org/10.1016/j.socscimed.2013.02.022

Daggett, L. M. (2002). Living with loss: Middle-aged men face spousal bereavement. *Qualitative Health Research, 12*(5), 625–639. http://doi.org/10.1177/104973202129120142

Dilts, M. (2001). The eloquence of pain: Poetry of bereaved fathers following a perinatal loss. In D. A. Lund (Ed.), *Men coping with grief (Death, value and meaning)* (pp. 349–363). Amityville, NY: Baywood.

Floyd, F. J., Mailick Seltzer, M., Greenberg, J. S., & Song, J. (2013). Parental bereavement during mid-to-later life: Pre- to postbereavement functioning and intrapersonal resources for coping. *Psychology and Aging, 28*(2), 402–413. http://doi.org/10.1037/a0029986

Gibson, J., Gallagher, M., & Jenkins, M. (2010). The experiences of parents readjusting to the workplace following the death of a child by suicide. *Death Studies, 34*(6), 500–528. http://doi.org/10.1080/07481187.2010.482879

Golden, T. (1996). *Swallowed by a snake: The gift of the masculine side of healing.* Kensington, MD: Golden Healing.

Golden, T. R., & Miller, J. E. (1998). *When a man faces grief: 12 practical ideas to help you heal from loss.* Fort Wayne, IN: Willowgreen.

Harper, M., O'Connor, R., Dickson, A., & O'Carroll, R. (2011). Mothers continuing bonds and ambivalence to personal mortality after the death of their child: An interpretative phenomenological analysis. *Psychology, Health & Medicine, 16*(2), 203–214. http://doi.org/10.1080/13548506.2010.532558

Huang, J., Valdimarsdóttir, U., Fall, K., Ye, W., & Fang, F. (2013). Pancreatic cancer risk after loss of a child: A register-based study in Sweden during 1991–2009. *American Journal of Epidemiology, 178*(4), 582–589. http://doi.org/10.1093/aje/kwt045

Jansz, J. (2000). Masculine identity and restrictive emotionality. In A. H. Fischer (Ed.), *Gender and emotion: Social psychological perspectives* (pp. 166–186). Cambridge, UK: Cambridge University Press.

Johal, A., Shelupanov, A., & Norman, W. (2012). *Invisible men: Engaging more men in social projects.* Big Lottery Fund. Retrieved from http://www.biglotteryfund.org.uk/er_invisible_men.pdf

Jordan, J. R., & McIntosh, J. L. (2011). Is suicide bereavement different? A framework for rethinking the question. In J. R. Jordan & J. L. McIntosh (Eds.), *Grief after suicide: Understanding the consequences and caring for the survivors* (pp. 19–43). New York, NY: Routledge.

Jordan, J. R., & McMenamy, J. (2004). Interventions for suicide survivors: A review of the literature. *Suicide and Life-Threatening Behavior, 34*(4), 337–349. http://doi.org/10.1521/suli.34.4.337.53742

Kreicbergs, U. C., Lannen, P., Onelov, E., & Wolfe, J. (2007). Parental grief after losing a child to cancer: Impact of professional and social support on long-term outcomes. *Journal of Clinical Oncology, 25*(22), 3307–3312. http://doi.org/10.1200/JCO.2006.10.0743

Lannen, P. K., Wolfe, J., Prigerson, H. G., Onelov, E., & Kreicbergs, U. C. (2008). Unresolved grief in a national sample of bereaved parents: Impaired mental and physical health 4 to 9 years later. *Journal of Clinical Oncology, 26*(36), 5870–5876. http://doi.org/10.1200/JCO.2007.14.6738

Lester, D., Gunn, J. F., & Quinnett, P. (2014). *Suicide in men.* Springfield, IL: Charles C. Thomas.

Levi-Belz, Y. (2014). Stress-related growth among suicide survivors: The role of interpersonal and cognitive factors. *Archives of Suicide Research, 19*(3), 305–320. http://doi.org/10.1080/13811118.2014.957452

Lund, D. A. (Ed.). (2001). *Men coping with grief.* Amityville, NY: Baywood.

Martin, T., & Doka, K. J. (2000). *Men don't cry, women do: Transcending gender stereotypes of grief.* Philadelphia, PA: Brunner Mazel.

McDaid, C., Trowman, R., Golder, S., Hawton, K., & Sowden, A. (2008). Interventions for people bereaved through suicide: Systematic review. *British Journal of Psychiatry, 193*(6), 438–443. http://doi.org/10.1192/bjp.bp.107.040824

McGoldrick, M. (2004). Gender and mourning. In F. Walsh & M. McGoldrick (Eds.), *Living beyond loss: Death in the family* (2nd ed., pp. 99–118). New York, NY: Norton.

Murphy, S. A. (2010). Women's and children's exposure to mass disaster and terrorist attacks. *Issues in Mental Health Nursing, 31*(1), 45–53.

Murphy, S. A., Das Gupta, A., Cain, K. C., Johnson, L. C., Lohan, J., Wu, L., & Mekwa, J. (1999). Changes in parents' mental distress after the violent death of an adolescent or young adult child: A longitudinal prospective analysis. *Death Studies, 23*(2), 129–159. http://doi.org/10.1080/074811899201118

Murphy, S. A., Johnson, L. C., & Weber, N. A. (2002). Coping strategies following a child's violent death: How parents differ in their responses. *Omega: Journal of Death and Dying, 45*(2), 99–118. http://doi.org/10.2190/D9NT-WC8V-KMJN-3P8T

Ogata, K., Ishikawa, T., Michiue, T., Nishi, Y., & Maeda, H. (2011). Posttraumatic symptoms in Japanese bereaved family members with special regard to suicide and homicide cases. *Death Studies, 35*(6), 525–535. http://doi.org/10.1080/07481187.2011.553327

Ozbič, P. (2015). Medsebojna podpora partnerjev v procesu žalovanja po otrokovi smrti. [Mutual partners-support in the process of the bereavement after the death of the child]. *Psihološka obzorja, 24,* 44–56. Retrieved from http://psy.ff.uni-lj.si/psiholoska_obzorja/arhiv_clanki/2015/ozbic.pdf http://doi.org/10.20419/2015.24.425

Pitman, A., Osborn, D., King, M., & Erlangsen, A. (2014). Effects of suicide bereavement on mental health and suicide risk. *The Lancet Psychiatry, 1*(1), 86–94. http://doi.org/10.1016/S2215-0366(14)70224-X

Reed, M. D.(1993). Sudden death and bereavement outcomes: The impact of resources on grief symptomatology and detachment. *Suicide and Life-Threatening Behavior, 23*(3), 204–220.

Rostila, M., Saarela, J., & Kawachi, I. (2014). "The psychological skeleton in the closet": Mortality after a sibling's suicide. *Social Psychiatry and Psychiatric Epidemiology, 49*(6), 919–927. http://doi.org/10.1007/s00127-013-0780-1

Säflund, K., & Wredling, R. (2006). Differences within couples' experience of their hospital care and well-being three months after experiencing a stillbirth. *Acta Obstetricia et Gynecologica Scandinavica, 85*(10), 1193–1199. http://doi.org/10.1080/00016340600804605

Samaritans. (2012). *Men, suicide and society.* Retrieved from http://www.samaritans.org/sites/default/files/kcfinder/files/Men%20and%20Suicide%20Research%20Report%20210912.pdf

Schwab, R. (1996). Gender differences in parental grief. *Death Studies, 20*(2), 103–113. http://doi.org/10.1080/07481189608252744

Shiner, M., Scourfield, J., Fincham, B., & Langer, S. (2009). When things fall apart: Gender and suicide across the life-course. *Social Science & Medicine, 69*(5), 738–746. http://doi.org/10.1016/j.socscimed.2009.06.014

Starek, J. E. (2000). *Men, masculinity and bereavement: A qualitative investigation* (Unpublished doctoral dissertation). Fort Collins, CO: Colorado State University.

Stroebe, M. S., Hansson, R. O., Schut, H., & Stroebe, W. (2008). Bereavement research: 21st century prospects. In M. S. Stroebe, R. O. Hansson, H. Schut, & W. Stroebe (Eds.), *Handbook of bereavement research and practice* (pp. 577–605). Washington, DC: American Psychological Association.

Stroebe, M. S., & Stroebe, W. (1989). Who participates in bereavement research? An empirical study of the impact of health on attrition. *Omega: Journal of Death and Dying, 20*(1), *20,* 1–29. http://doi.org/10.2190/C3JE-C9L1-5R91-DWDU

Stroebe, M. S., & Stroebe, W. (1993). Mortality of bereavement: A review. In M. S. Stroebe, W. Stroebe, & R. O. Hansson (Eds.), *Handbook of bereavement* (pp. 175–196). New York, NY: Cambridge University Press.

Valizadeh, L., Zamanzadeh, V., & Rahiminia, E. (2013). Comparison of anticipatory grief reaction between fathers and mothers of premature infants in neonatal intensive care unit. *Scandinavian Journal of Caring Sciences, 27*(4), 921–926. http://doi.org/10.1111/scs.12005

Walton, C., Coyle, A., & Lyons, E. (2004). Death and football: An analysis of men's talk about emotions. *British Journal of Social Psychology, 43*(3), 401–416. http://doi.org/10.1348/0144666042038024

Wilcox, H. C., Mittendorfer-Rutz, E., Kjeldgård, L., Alexanderson, K., & Runeson, B. (2015). Functional impairment due to bereavement after the death of adolescent or young adult offspring in a national population study of 1,051,515 parents. *Social Psychiatry and Psychiatric Epidemiology, 50*(8), 1249–1256. http://doi.org/10.1007/s00127-014-0997-7

Wood, J. D., & Milo, E. (2001). Fathers' grief when a disabled child dies. *Death Studies, 25*(8), 635–661. http://doi.org/10.1080/713769895

Zisook, S., & Shear, K. (2009). Grief and bereavement: What psychiatrists need to know. *World Psychiatry, 8*(2), 67–74. http://doi.org/10.1002/j.2051-5545.2009.tb00217.x

Chapter 5

Posttraumatic Growth After Suicide

Christine Genest[1], Melinda Moore[2], and Clinton M. Nowicke[2]

[1]CRISE – Centre for Research and Intervention on Suicide and Euthanasia, Faculté des sciences infirmières, Université de Montréal, QC, Canada
[2]Department of Psychology, Eastern Kentucky University, Richmond, KY, USA

Abstract: While most research on suicide bereavement has focused on adverse outcomes, the concept of posttraumatic growth stems from the field of positive psychology. It refers to positive transformations regarding self-perception, interpersonal relationships, and life philosophy that occur as the result of one's struggles with a traumatic event. This chapter presents two studies of this underresearched concept in the context of suicide bereavement: a Canadian-based study of families that had lost an adolescent through suicide, and a US-based study of parents bereaved by the suicide of a child of any age. These studies showed that there are different pathways to posttraumatic growth, and several psychological factors and resources within and outside the family play a role in its process. The chapter concludes that posttraumatic growth offers a window of hope for the bereaved through suicide. Although further research is needed to better understand its dynamics, it may offer clues for clinical and psychoeducational practices.

Introduction

Bereavement after suicide is frequently associated with feelings of guilt (Bell, Stanley, Mallon, & Manthrope, 2012), stigma (Cvinar, 2005), shame (Sveen & Walby, 2008), anger (Jordan & McIntosh, 2011), rejection (Elder & Knowles, 2002), and denial of the suicide itself (Clark & Goldney, 1995; Lester, 2004). Suicide survivors may be more at risk of depression, posttraumatic stress disorder (PTSD), and suicidal ideation and behavior (Jordan & McIntosh, 2011; also see Chapter 2 in this volume). While the research on suicide bereavement has focused mostly on the psychopathology associated with this experience of loss, recent studies in positive psychology have offered another perspective by investigating the possibilities for personal growth within the context of this distressing and potentially traumatic event.

Posttraumatic growth (PTG) is a concept developed by Tedeschi and Calhoun in the mid-1990s (Calhoun & Tedeschi, 2000; Tedeschi & Calhoun, 1996, 2004). It refers to positive transformation following internal changes that occur as the result of one's struggle with a traumatic event. Such changes can happen in different dimensions, such as self-perception, interpersonal relations, and life philosophy (Calhoun & Tedeschi, 2000; Tedeschi & Calhoun, 1996, 2004). When changes occur in self-perception, the person has greater self-confidence and a sense of being stronger. The changes in interpersonal relations refer to an increase of sensitivity toward others, becoming closer to others, and a greater appreciation of relationships. Finally, the changes in life philosophy refer to finding meaning from traumatic experiences and seeing new possibilities.

PTG has been studied in diverse populations, such as the military (Smyth, Hockemeyer, & Tulloch, 2008), patients with cancer (Antoni et al., 2006; Cruess et al., 2001; Kállay & Baban, 2008; Heinrichs et al., 2012), survivors of motor vehicle accidents (Zoellner, Rabe, Karl, & Maercker, 2011), and people experiencing grief (Black & Wright, 2012). PTG has been understudied in the context of suicide bereavement. As this concept can provide significant hope for the bereaved, it is important to forward research that explores PTG among suicide bereaved in various populations. This chapter presents the findings of two studies. The first study explored PTG in Canadian families after the suicide of an adolescent (Genest, 2014). The second, a US-based study focused on parents who had lost a child (of any age) to suicide (Moore, Cerel, & Jobes, 2015).

Study 1: Posttraumatic Growth Among Families Following an Adolescent Suicide

Suicide is the second leading cause of death in adolescents in Canada (Statistic Canada, 2012). Death of an adolescent falls outside the normal order of life and can create a crisis within the family (Walsh & McGoldrick, 1991). Even though a suicide can have a negative impact on family, clinical practice and the literature show that most families survive this traumatic event and continue to engage in everyday activities, such as work, child care, and family development (de Montigny & Beaudet, 1997). This raises a question about the positive transformation and growth process in a family following suicide of an adolescent.

To explore this question, a qualitative study, based on a grounded theory approach, was undertaken to give voice to the families bereaved by suicide (Genest, 2014). For the families to have been part of this study, the suicide must have occurred at least 1 year ago, the family members must have been French speaking (the study was carried out in the French-speaking part of Canada), and the siblings who were part of the study must have been aware that suicide was the cause of death. The sample ($N = 17$) came from seven families living in Quebec, Canada, who were grieving the death of one or two adolescents due to suicide. The participants were parents ($n = 10$), siblings ($n = 4$), stepparents, or stepsisters ($n = 3$). The time since the suicide ranged from 4 to 10 years at the time of the interview. The deceased adolescents (four boys and four girls) were between 13 and 19 years of age at the time of suicide, and three of them had received a psychiatric diagnosis during their lifetime.

Data were collected through nonstructured in-depth interviews, from written documents provided by participants, such as diaries, previous interviews, farewell letters, a sermon, and field notes. A sociodemographic questionnaire was used to describe the participants. Depending on participants' preference, the interviews were conducted either individually or in group. The interviews were recorded and transcribed, and the triple codification method was used to analyze the data (Strauss & Corbin, 1998). This method is a constant comparative analysis that consists of open, axial, and selective coding. Open coding is the coding of every line of the text verbatim. Axial coding is when relations are established between previous categories. The paradigm model developed by Strauss and Corbin (1998) was used at that time. Finally, selective coding is identifying and using the core concept that best represents the phenomenon.

The main results of the study showed that the family process of positive transformation and growth after a suicide can be understood as *emerging despite the indelible wound*. In this process, the family faces a cataclysm, which is caused by the suicide, and which is influenced by the family background, social context, and emotions experienced by the bereaved. This cataclysm is followed by a sinking period which is important given the life buoys – that is, resources present within and around the family. Life buoys outside the family can include grief counselors, support groups, and (other) survivor-led organizations. Examples of buoys inside the family include family members supporting one another, maintaining sports and hobbies, and honoring positive memories of the loved one. The presence of these intrafamilial and extra-familial buoys allows a more or less rapid rebound of the family. Subsequently, various actions within and outside the family enable the family members to grow – in other words, a positive transformation and learning that can be associated with PTG.

The Cataclysm Period

The cataclysm period is created by the suicide of an adolescent. As a mother participating in the study stated, the suicide was *"like a bomb for me."* Different elements, such as the family background, the social context and circumstances of the suicide, and the emotions associated with the suicide contribute to the impact of the cataclysm within the family.

The family background refers to the adolescent's relation with their family, their behavior prior to the suicide, and the presence of other events around the time of death. For some families, the suicide was predictable since the adolescent was talking about it or had made previous attempts (*"Even though his death is painful for us, we had seen it coming,"* a father remarked). In other families, the suicide was a complete surprise (*"It cannot be happening, she had a beautiful life,"* stated a mother). The adolescent's behavior also refers to the adolescent being antagonistic toward parents and family members, which may have overwhelmed family members. The breadth of the cataclysm can also be influenced by the social context surrounding the suicide. Even though suicide occurs relatively frequently in society, it may still be a taboo for some persons or communities, rendering it more difficult to communicate with others and to seek, receive, or give support.

The circumstances of the suicide can also influence the cataclysm: the location of the suicide (at home or elsewhere), its timing, the method used, and the discovery of the body. In almost every family interviewed in the study, one of the family members had discovered the deceased adolescent, and these family members were more impacted by the suicide than the others. The contact with the first responders, such as firefighters, police officers, and paramedics, can also influence the experience of the cataclysm by the family. In some cases, the contact was warm, imbued with empathy, and helpful for the bereaved. In other families, the contact with first responders was tenser and less helpful, and this negative experience caused anger and frustration in the family, and made it difficult to seek help afterwards.

Families participating in the study spoke of a range of emotions influencing the transformation process: surprise associated with the suicide, followed by sadness created by the loss, and guilt over not having seen the depth of the suffering or not having been able to prevent the suicide. Also anger was reported: anger toward the adolescent for causing pain to the family, anger toward other family members for not having been there to support the adolescent, or toward professionals who were not able to help the adolescent while they were alive. Some families mentioned fear, usually a fear of experiencing another loss or developing new relationships and being hurt again.

The Wreck Period

The study found that the cataclysm created by the suicide of an adolescent led to the wreck period, described by one family as a *"descent into hell."* The wreck period is mediated by the presence of life buoys – that is, resources within and outside the family. The life buoys within the family include previous experiences, family cohesiveness, presence of facilitating beliefs, and individual strength. Previous experiences with professional help may shape how the family will deal with the suicide bereavement process. Family cohesion is characterized by the mutual respect and support of family members. According to one of the mothers, the key element of the positive transformation in the family was the fact that they were there for each other after the loss of a loved one. The presence of a facilitating belief, such as a belief that death is not the end of a relationship and that the family is strong enough to cope with the loss, can also influence how the family members experience the bereavement process. It is important for clinicians working with the bereaved families to be aware of and support such beliefs. For example, a mother participating in the study mentioned that her family lost everything to a fire when she was young, and this experience made her realize that she could overcome anything. Although the study looked at the family process of positive transformation, in some cases it was an individual strength of one of the family members, such as leadership, flexibility, optimism, and motivation to live, that has helped the entire family to cope with the loss.

Other life buoys are located outside the family and include availability of support and the passage of time. Support refers to the informal and formal support available to the family, and professional help some families received prior to the suicide. Regarding the passage of time, all families stated that with time the pain became less intense. The memories and the longing for the deceased are still present but they are less overwhelming (a father shared: *"I still cry sometimes alone in my car, but now it is maybe once or twice a week, instead of every day"*).

The Emergence Period

The emergence period begins with the rebound of the family. Actions within and outside the family enable its members to learn and to grow through the painful experience. Some of these actions take place within the family, such as keeping the memory of the deceased alive, regaining family homeostasis, and making sense of the suicide. For most of the families, it was important to keep the memories of the deceased alive – for instance, through rituals. Such rituals can be structured by cultural norms – for example, in a family where every step of the grieving process is prescribed by culture. This ensures that social support is always available, and the deceased adolescent can be remembered at certain times. Rituals can also be developed by the family or by an individual family member to keep the memory of the deceased alive and to structure the experience of grieving. For example, some families created a special place for the deceased, such as a memory box, which included all of their important memories. The family members did not feel the need to look at the mementos every day, but it was important for them to know that the box existed.

The suicide of an adolescent usually shook the homeostasis of the family system. Regaining homeostasis, or at least reaching a new form of homeostasis, is essential for the family to achieve positive transformation. To achieve this aim, family members need to open up to discussion or find a shared goal, which will help them direct their energy toward a positive outcome. Another way can be revisiting relationships within the family and with friends.

Making sense of the suicide can take place within or outside the family. Some family members looked for answers in books or in the farewell letter of the adolescent. Others talked to the friends of the deceased person, to professionals, or to other suicide survivors. In the end, some of the bereaved realized that *"we have to stop asking questions and looking for answers. When you are able to do so, you are able to move forward"* (a mother). Even though the family may not be able to find answers to all of the questions, the process of making sense of the suicide and of the experience of loss can alleviate the suffering of the bereaved.

Sharing experiences is a way for the family to break isolation and to help other bereaved. This can help the family feel that their struggle has some value (*"We are able to help others in need"*; a father). Family members also needed to accept that life goes on, and that they can be happy even though the adolescent is no longer there. Sometimes this can be difficult, as it may trigger a feeling of guilt, but it is an important part of the process of positive transformation.

The actions presented here allow the transformation of the family, which can be understood as a process of learning and growth. Through the experience of loss, family members can get to know each other better, can learn about the family, and about life in general. One of the fathers participating in the study stated that *"through this experience we have learned a lot; we have learned that we had capacities, big capacities."* This experience can also help to recognize the importance of the family and of life itself. Families can learn about the fragility of life and the importance of living it fully (*"I have realized that life is fragile and that it hangs by a thread"*), and this learning experience can change the family life philosophy (*"We have returned to the basics of life"*; a mother). Moreover, this painful experience can bring growth within individuals. In the words of a stepmother: *"It is not because of the suicide itself that we change, but because of the journey we go through after the suicide."* Individual family members can develop new ways of communicating with others, gain a new sensitivity to the grief and suffering of others, and recognize that through the grief experience their relationships can strengthen. Talking about her relationship with her husband, a bereaved mother said: *"We became inseparable; he* [my husband] *is the only person on earth that can fully understand me and what I've been through."*

Pathways to Growth

The analysis of the qualitative data revealed four types of positive transformation following suicide of an adolescent, characterized by the timing of rebound (fast vs. late) and the type of emergence (continuous vs. discontinuous). An *energic family* refers to a family where the rebound happens rapidly, and the emergence is continuous. These families usually have numerous life buoys within or outside the family and begin the growth process sooner than the other three types of families. An energic family is infrequently seen in clinical practice, because the growth process is rapidly put into motion, but it can still be relevant to inform these families of available services, as they may need support at some point in the future.

A *combative family* is a family where the rebound is fast, but the emergence is discontinuous. These families have enough life buoys to allow the rebound, but afterwards, when the actions that lead to growth are implemented, new negative events may cause a crisis. As these families are always struggling to recover after every crisis, it is important for the counselor or clinician to offer long-term support. It may be helpful to draw up an inventory of all of the support available within the family network to prevent exhaustion of the social support.

In the case of a *stunned family,* the rebound occurs later, but the emergence is continuous. There is usually a lack of life buoys, or the life buoys that are present are insufficient. These families can get stuck in their grief, and they may need professional help to support them and to provide the lacking resources. It is important for a clinician to identify the right timing to intervene and help a stunned family to get out of the helplessness.

Finally, a *tenacious family* refers to a family where the rebound happens later and the emergence is discontinuous. These families might lack life buoys and are confronted with consecutive crises. Hence, professionals should offer long-term support and collaborate with the family during the late rebound and the discontinuous emergence as long as is needed.

In conclusion, depending on the time of the rebound and the continuity of the emergence, the process of positive transformation in a family can vary. It is important to acknowledge these differences, as they have implications for clinical practice and how professionals can effectively provide support to the bereaved after suicide. Shortly after the suicide, it can be difficult to ascertain the type of process the family will go through, and therefore, it is important to adapt interventions to the needs of each individual family. (It should be noted that not all families will achieve this positive transformation since PTG is not universal.)

Study 2: Posttraumatic Growth Among Suicide-Bereaved Parents

Moore and colleagues (2015) investigated PTG among suicide–bereaved parents in the United States. This study specifically looked at suicide–bereaved parents because of the ubiquity of parents bereaved by suicide in the suicidology community and their willingness to participate in research. Participants were recruited through suicide bereavement groups, and online through the Suicidology Listserv – that is, the e-mail discussion list of the American Association of Suicidology. To be eligible to participate, an individual had to be a parent or step-parent of a person, of any age, who had died by suicide within 2 years prior to entering the study. Because PTG pioneers Calhoun and Tedeschi (2006) argued that growth occurs closer to the seismic, or "cataclysmic," event rather than farther away from it, this study investigated growth occurring closer in time to the suicide death, with 2 years as the cutoff mark. The sample consisted of 154 parents (10% men, 65% married).

The suicide–bereaved parents' overall PTGI score, as measured by the Posttraumatic Growth Inventory (PTGI; Tedeschi & Calhoun, 1996), was 46.3 out of a potential 105. Calhoun and Tedeschi have not developed cutoff scores to describe low, medium, and high growth (Calhoun & Tedeschi, 2006), but according to Feder and colleagues (2008), total scores exceeding 60 represent "moderate positive life change," and scores equal to 80 or above indicate "great or a very great degree of positive life change." Thus, the overall mean PTGI score achieved by this sample signaled a lower level of growth. Twenty–six percent of the participants registered a score equal to or great than 60, and 12% of the scores were equal to or above 80. Of the study participants who signalled lower PTG, 31% of the participants indicated a PTGI score between 20 to 40, and 27% of the participants scored between 40 and 60.

Individuals taking the PTGI receive both an overall score and factor or domain scores in areas of growth under the overall umbrella of PTG. These areas of growth include: Relating to Others, New Possibilities, Personal Strength, Spiritual Change, and Appreciation of Life. To gain some understanding of the domains where growth was achieved in the current study, the factor scores were analyzed. Factor scores equal to or above 3 on a scale of 0 to 6 represented "at least moderate growth" (Feder et al., 2008, p. 363). For the group as a whole, the items endorsed most strongly on the PTGI corresponded to the first factor, Relating to Others (40%), followed by the fourth factor, Spiritual Change (34%), and the fifth factor, Appreciation of Life (33%). Much lower percentages of factor scores demonstrating at least moderate growth were attributed to the second factor, New Possibilities (18%), and the third factor, Personal Strength (19%).

Given the lower mean PTGI score of this sample and the lower percentages of moderate growth scores on the individual PTG factors, when compared with other studies, one must wonder about the temporality of these responses and the proximity to the death of the child as being a disadvantage in signalling PTG in this sample of suicide–bereaved parents rather than an advantage. Marilyn Koenig, founder of Friends for Survival Inc. (http://www.friendsforsur vival.org), a California-based suicide bereavement nonprofit organization that helped recruit participants for this study, has pondered the relationship between length of time from the suicide, the internal processes that this manner of death spurs, and potential growth as a result. As Koenig noted,

Due to the sheer trauma of this experience, the terrible shock and, sometimes, the PTSD experienced by family and friends, it takes months and years for suicide survivors to gain perspective on this experience. It takes a long time for survivors to appreciate how this death has affected their lives, in both positive and negative ways. (Marilyn Koenig, personal communication, June 9, 2011)

Role of Cognitive Engagement in Posttraumatic Growth

According to Calhoun and Tedeschi (2006), cognitive engagement with a traumatic event in its aftermath makes PTG more likely. Their theory posits that it is necessary for the bereaved to "ruminate" over elements of the event to repair and restructure their understanding of their "shattered" world view. This rumination includes two types or phases: a sense-making "brooding" rumination phase (which occurs earlier and is more intrusive), and a meaning–making "reflective" rumination phase (which occurs later and is more deliberate). These two types are typically thought of as being linearly connected, where brooding rumination in the immediate aftermath of a traumatic event leads to reflective rumination (Treynor, Gonzalez, & Nolen-Hoeksema, 2003). Types of rumination in this study were analyzed using the Ruminative Response Scale (RSS; Treynor et al., 2003). It is through reflective rumination that new meanings can be construed, plans developed, and personal narratives rewritten, which leads to PTG (Tedeschi & Calhoun, 2004).

Significant close relationships were identified between brooding and reflective rumination in this study, suggesting that the ruminative process among this particular population of suicide–bereaved individuals is not linear but co-occurring. Additionally, moderate positive relationships between both the brooding and reflective processes of rumination, on the one hand, and prolonged grief, on the other, may indicate an ongoing experience of cognitive sense making and meaning making in the bereavement trajectory. In the context of PTG, *sense making* refers to understanding and accepting that the suicide occurred, while *meaning making* refers to finding a positive response to the suicide that initiates personal growth. The study also investigated whether either type of rumination predicted PTG. The finding that neither brooding rumination nor reflective rumination was predictive of PTG is inconsistent with what is found in the literature (Tedeschi & Calhoun, 2004). It is possible that these parent survivors were engaging in brooding and reflective rumination concurrently, or that their emotional trauma interfered with these cognitive processes.

Resilience and Posttraumatic Growth

Individual PTG domains and other variables of interest, such as resilience, dispositional optimism, PTSD, prolonged grief, personality constructs of Openness to Experience, Neuroticism, and Extraversion, and positive and negative affect were examined for their ability to predict PTG. Resilience, as measured by the Resilience Scale (RS-14; Wagnild & Young, 2009), was the only variable to predict lower levels of PTG. This inverse relationship between PTG and resilience supported the theory that highly resilient individuals, who have stronger coping skills and who may not struggle with the psychological consequences of trauma, do not, as a result, experience positive life changes (Tedeschi & McNally, 2011).

Because resilience was the only variable that significantly predicted PTG, it was determined that resilience needed further investigation. The finding that extraversion, positive affect, reflective rumination, and neuroticism predicted resilience resulted in data that were consistent with some literature reports and in conflict with others (Calhoun & Tedeschi, 2006; Linley &

Joseph, 2004). The finding that extraversion predicted resilience was not surprising. Extraverts are more adept at social relations and are stimulated by being with others – hence, their need to be surrounded by others in moments of crisis. The resilience literature demonstrates a strong relationship between resilient outcomes and social support (Bonanno, Galea, Bucciarelli, & Vlahov, 2007). Therefore, it makes sense that extraverts would likely be able to marshal the social support resources necessary for more resilient outcomes. Along the same lines, individuals who are higher in positive affect, a hallmark of well-being, or people who appear "happier," have been demonstrated through multiple studies to have better outcomes on multiple domains (Lyubomirsky, King, & Diener, 2005). It is likely that those individuals who demonstrate more happiness may also be able to amass more internal and external resources to support themselves in a moment of crisis, and be able to maintain those critical resources and support on an ongoing basis. On the other hand, neuroticism or the tendency to experience negative emotional states, entails an emotional state that undermines a more resilient outcome. Therefore, the finding of neuroticism in an inverse relationship with resilience is consistent with the logic of the interaction between this personality construct and the elements necessary for resilient outcomes.

Future Directions and Implications for Practice

Both studies described here have contributed to and support the body of literature that indicates that bereaved individuals can and do grow from their traumatic loss experiences. These studies demonstrate that positive transformations are possible following a stressful event, such as the suicide of a child. The PTG concept offers hope to those who may be experiencing hopelessness as the result of their experience. It encourages professionals to look beyond the morbidity, and can broaden the scope of what is possible in the aftermath of a traumatic event. Clinicians interested in helping to facilitate PTG with their clients should become familiar with how to help shape a narrative in therapy with PTG domains (Tedeschi & Calhoun, 2012). Clients benefit from expert companionship in narrative reconstruction because it is hard to appreciate oneself from an internal point of view. Expert companions notice things that the client overlooks, and may facilitate the identification of growth by helping to label experiences. Professionals should build on the strengths and the resources of the bereaved, but be assertive in labeling growth when it has been approached by the client. The different pathways to growth presented in this chapter may help professionals to identify the types of individuals and families and how they could work with them to enhance their life buoys, and guide them in their actions to foster growth.

Much can be uncovered about the relationship between PTG and the experience of losing a loved one to suicide. Future research should consider different types of relationships, such as various family members, work colleagues, and intimate partner relationships, as well as the quality and psychological closeness of the relationship between the loved one and the bereaved. This may be accompanied by an investigation of the suddenness or (un)expectedness of the death, whether or not the death occurred after previous suicide attempts and/or struggles with long-term mental and/or physical illness. Another consideration is adding measures or approaches that capture the pretrauma state of the bereaved more adequately to gauge whether actual growth has occurred. Lastly, conducting studies in other cultures or with international samples may help to better appreciate the potential of PTG within diverse contexts.

Corresponding author

Christine Genest
CRISE – Centre for Research and Intervention on Suicide and Euthanasia
Faculté des sciences infirmières, Université de Montréal
Canada
christine.genest@umontreal.ca

References

Antoni, M. H., Lechner, S. C., Kazi, A., Wimberly, S. R., Sifre, T., Urcuyo, K. R., ... Carver, C. S. (2006). How stress management improves quality of life after treatment for breast cancer. *Journal of Consulting and Clinical Psychology, 74*(6), 1143–1152. http://doi.org/10.1037/0022-006X.74.6.1143

Bell, J., Stanley, N., Mallon, S., & Manthrope, J. (2012). Life will never be the same again: Examining grief in survivors bereaved by young suicide. *Illness, Crisis & Loss, 20*(1), 49–68. http://doi.org/10.2190/IL.20.1.e

Black, B. P., & Wright, P. (2012). Posttraumatic growth and transformation as outcomes of perinatal loss. *Illness, Crisis & Loss, 20*(3), 225–237. http://doi.org/10.2190/IL.20.3.b

Bonanno, G. A., Galea, S., Bucciarelli, A., & Vlahov, D. (2007). What predicts psychological resilience after disaster? The role of demographics, resources, and life stress. *Journal of Counseling and Clinical Psychology, 75*(5), 671–682. http://doi.org/10.1037/0022-006X.75.5.671

Calhoun, L. G.,& Tedeschi, R. G. (2000). *Posttraumatic stress intervention: Challenges, issues, and perspectives.* Springfield, IL: Charles C. Thomas.

Calhoun, L. G. & Tedeschi, R. G. (2006). *Handbook of posttraumatic growth: Research and practice.* New York, NY: Erlbaum.

Clark, S. E., & Goldney, R. D. (1995). Grief reactions and recovery in a support group for people bereaved by suicide. *Crisis, 16*(1), 27–33. http://doi.org/10.1027/0227-5910.16.1.27

Cruess, D. G., Antoni, M. H., Kumar, M., McGregor, B., Alferi, S., Boyers, A. E., ... Kilbourn, K. (2001). Effects of stress management on testosterone levels in women with early-stage breast cancer. *International Journal of Behavioral Medicine, 8*(3), 194–207. http://doi.org/10.1207/S15327558IJBM0803_2

Cvinar, J. G. (2005). Do suicide survivors suffer social stigma: A review of the literature. *Perspective in Psychiatric Care, 41*(1), 14–21. http://doi.org/10.1111/j.0031-5990.2005.00004.x

de Montigny, F., & Beaudet, L. (1997). *Lorsque la vie éclate: l'impact de la mort d'un enfant sur la famille* [When life shatters: The impact of the death of a child on the family]. Saint-Laurent, QC, Canada: ERPI.

Elder, S. L., & Knowles, D. (2002). Suicide in the family. In N. B. Webb (Ed.), *Helping bereaved children: A handbook for practitioners* (pp. 128–148). New York, NY: Guilford Press.

Feder, A., Southwick, S. M., Goetz, R. R., Wang, Y., Alonso, A., Smith, B. W., & Vythilingam, M. (2008). Posttraumatic growth in former Vietnam prisoners of war. *Psychiatry, 71*(4), 359–370. http://doi.org/10.1521/psyc.2008.71.4.359

Genest, C. (2014). *La résilience des familles endeuillées par le suicide d'un adolescent: Émerger malgré la blessure indélébile* [Family resilience after adolescent suicide: To emerge despite the indelible wound]. Saarbrücken, Germany: Presses Académiques Francophones.

Heinrichs, N., Zimmermann, T., Huber, B., Herschbach, P., Russell, D. W., & Baucom, D. h. (2012). Cancer distress reduction with a couple-based skills training: A randomized controlled trial. *Annals of Behavioral Medicine, 43*(2), 239–252. http://doi.org/10.1007/s12160-011-9314-9

Jordan, J. R., & McIntosh, J. L. (Eds.). (2011). *Grief after suicide: Understanding the consequences and the caring for the survivors.* New York, NY: Routledge.

Kállay, É., & Baban, A. (2008). Emotional benefits of expressive writing in a sample of Romanian female cancer patients. *Cognition, Brain, and Behavior, 12*(1), 115–129.

Lester, D. (2004). Denial in suicide survivors. *Crisis, 25*(2), 78–79. http://doi.org/10.1027/0227-5910.25.2.78

Linley, P. A., & Joseph, S. (2004). Positive change following trauma and adversity: A review. *Journal of Traumatic Stress, 17*(1), 11–21. http://doi.org/10.1023/B:JOTS.0000014671.27856.7e

Lyubomirsky, S., King, L., & Diener, E. (2005). The benefits of frequent positive affect: Does happiness lead to success? *Psychological Bulletin, 131*(6), 803–855. http://doi.org/10.1037/0033-2909.131.6.803

Moore, M., Cerel, J., & Jobes, D. (2015). Fruits or trauma? Posttraumatic growth among suicide-bereaved parents. *Crisis, 36*(4), 241–248. http://doi.org/10.1027/0227-5910/a000318

Smyth, J. M., Hockemeyer, J. R., &Tulloch, H. (2008). Expressive writing and post-traumatic stress disorder: Effects on trauma symptoms, mood states, and cortisol reactivity. *British Journal of Health Psychology, 13*(1), 85–93. http://doi.org/10.1348/135910707X250866

Statistic Canada. (2012). *Table 102–0561.* Retrieved from http://www.statcan.gc.ca/

Strauss, A. L., & Corbin, J. (1998). *Basics of qualitative research: Techniques and procedures for developing grounded theory.* Thousand Oaks, CA: Sage.

Sveen, C.-A., & Walby, F. (2008). Suicide survivors' mental health and grief reactions: A systematic review of controlled studies. *Suicide and Life-Threatening Behavior, 38*(1), 13–29. http://doi.org/10.1521/suli.2008.38.1.13

Tedeschi, R. G., & Calhoun, L. D. (2012). *Posttraumatic growth in clinical practice.* New York , NY: Routledge.

Tedeschi, R. G., & Calhoun, L. G. (1996). The Post-Traumatic Growth Inventory: Measuring the positive legacy of trauma. *Journal of Traumatic Stress, 9*(3), 455–471. http://doi.org/10.1002/jts.2490090305

Tedeschi, R. G., & Calhoun, L. G. (2004). Posttraumatic growth: A new perspective on psychotraumatology. *Psychiatric Times, 21*(4), 58–60.

Tedeschi, R. G., & McNally, R. J. (2011). Can we facilitate posttraumatic growth in combat veterans? *American Psychologist, 66*(1), 19–24. http://doi.org/10.1037/a0021896

Treynor, W., Gonzalez, R., & Nolen-Hoeksema, S. (2003). Rumination reconsidered: A psychometric analysis. *Cognitive Therapy and Research, 27*(3), 247–259. http://doi.org/10.1023/A:1023910315561

Wagnild, G. M., & Young, H. M. (2009). *The 14-Item Resilience Scale (RS-14).* Retrieved from http://www.resiliencescale.com/

Walsh, F., & McGoldrick, M. (1991). Loss and the family: A systemic perspective. In F. Walsh & M. McGoldrick (Eds.), *Living beyond loss: Death in the family* (pp. 1–29). New York, NY: Norton.

Zoellner, T., Rabe, S., Karl, A., & Maercker, A. (2011). Post-traumatic growth as outcome of a cognitive-behavioural therapy trial for motor vehicle accident survivors with PTSD. *Psychology and Psychotherapy: Theory, Research and Practice, 84*(2), 201–213. http://doi.org/10.1348/147608310X520157

Chapter 6

Feeling Responsible

Pathways From Guilt Toward Inner Peace

Dolores Angela Castelli Dransart

School of Social Work Fribourg, University of Applied Sciences and Arts
Western Switzerland, Givisiez, Switzerland

Abstract: According to the literature, feelings of responsibility and haunting questions related to the possible role and involvement (if any) in the suicidal act, are major challenges experienced by the bereaved after the suicide of a loved one. Based on 50 interviews with people bereaved by suicide in Switzerland, this chapter presents findings on how the bereaved dealt with the issue of responsibility both with themselves – for example, feeling of guilt and self-accusation – and in social relations – for example, others' attribution of responsibility and societal reactions following the suicide. The chapter concludes with implications for postvention practice.

Introduction

Suicide usually triggers, among other things, significant emotional reactions and questions regarding meaning – the *why* question and responsibility with regard to a possible personal involvement in the suicidal act (Castelli Dransart, 2005, 2013; Dyregrov, Grad, De Leo, & Cimitan, 2014). This chapter focuses on the latter, addressing the issue both from an individual point of view (guilt, shame) and a social point of view (social uneasiness, possible disrupted social relations, and the assignment of responsibility).

According to Grad (2005) the feeling of being somewhat involved in the deceased's decision is distinctive of suicide bereavement (see also Chapter 1 in this volume). Research of the last 30 years (Bartik, Maple, Edwards, & Kiernan, 2013; Begley & Quayle, 2007; Botha, Guilfoyle, & Botha, 2009; Gaffney & Hannigan, 2010; Levi-Belz, 2015; Maple, Plummer, Edwards, & Minichiello, 2007; McMenamy, Jordan, & Mitchell, 2008; Ratnarajah & Schofield, 2008) has shown that guilt and shame are experienced by most of those bereaved by suicide, sometimes in a more frequent or intense way than after other causes of death (Bailley, Kral, & Dunham, 1999; Jordan, 2001; McMenamy et al., 2008; Miles & Demi, 1991; Sveen & Walby, 2008). Guilt and shame, as well as feelings of rejection, self-, and social stigma (Dyregrov, Plyhn, & Dieserud, 2011; Feigelman, Gorman, & Jordan, 2009; Harwood, Hawton, Hope & Jacoby, 2002) can lead to social uneasiness (Dyregrov, 2003–2004), greater social discomfort (Demi, 1984), difficulties in the social arena (McMenamy et al., 2008) or stigmatization of the bereaved (Grad, Clark, Dyregrov, & Andriessen, 2004; Ratnarajah & Schofield, 2008; Dyregrov et al., 2014).

Throughout history, most societies and cultures have condemned the act of suicide, which has been viewed as an escape from societal and community obligations or the result of madness. Despite social evolution and the fact that more knowledge about the suicidal process and its contributing factors has become available, stigma still seems to be linked to a suicide death (Cvinar, 2005; Grad et al., 2004; Maple, Edwards, Plummer, & Minichiello, 2010). The bereaved persons have to deal with this legacy, and are often perceived more negatively than other bereaved (Jordan, 2001). To avoid social disapproval, survivors may silence their voices (Maple et al., 2010) and retreat (Smith, Joseph, & Das Nair, 2011).

Self-blame, self-recrimination, or blaming others for the suicide are also frequent reactions (Lindqvist, Johansson, & Karlsson, 2008; Wilson & Marshall, 2010). These reactions can disturb social interactions and hinder the receiving or offering of support (Dyregrov, 2009; Sugrue, McGilloway, & Keegan, 2013), which may in turn complicates the grief process. Whereas guilt, shame, and feelings of responsibility are often mentioned in the literature, little is known about the ways in which survivors deal with them, and possibly come to terms with them. This chapter addresses these issues by presenting findings from a qualitative study carried out in Switzerland.

Method

Fifty in-depth interviews (2–4.5 hr) were conducted with 11 male and 39 female survivors of suicide (23 parents, 13 siblings, 7 partners/spouses, 4 children, 3 others) over 18 years old (age range at first interview: 20–79 years). The interviewees were related to 35 suicide decedents (age range at death: 17–77 years), of which five were females. Data were analyzed using ATLAS-ti (2000) software. Principles of grounded theory were applied to generate a theoretical framework by constant comparison of data, and by a three-step coding strategy: open coding (descriptive and thematic), axial coding (categories and their dimensions), and selective coding (core categories and their articulation, modeling) (Strauss & Corbin, 1997).

Facing Feelings of Guilt and Dealing With Stigma and Social Relations

The confrontation with the survivors' potential involvement or feelings of responsibility in the process that led to the suicide was at the heart of the process by which the bereaved reshaped and reconstructed their life. Survivors who heartbreakingly scrutinized their own actions asked themselves questions such as *"Did I play a part in the other's suicidal act?"* and *"Could I have avoided it?"* Similarly, family, friends, and acquaintances asked themselves, *"Why did he/she take their own life?"*, *"Who is responsible?"*, *"Did anyone tried to help?"* On the one hand, survivors must face their own feelings of guilt, powerlessness, or shame, as they believed they might have misestimated the situation. On the other hand, they were expected to answer questions from other people and to be able to give an account of what happened and to position themselves in relation to potential social judgments (Gall, Henneberry, & Eyre, 2014; Maple et al., 2010).

Facing and Dealing With One's Own Feelings of Responsibility

Survivors talked about guilt and shame following a suicide as something gnawing at them from the inside. Their mind was plagued by the idea that they could have, or should have, done something to avoid the tragedy. It was not uncommon for suicide to be interpreted by the bereaved as a well-deserved punishment for having been unable to deal with the situation or having failed the relationship.

> You know, after the suicide, feelings of guilt come into play. What was wrong in our family? Did I not hold you in my arms enough? Is it me? Did I fail to give you enough self-esteem? (Mother)

Oscillation Between Victim and Guilty Party

Guilt led survivors to oscillate between two different positions: victim and guilty party. This dynamic reflects all of the doubts that survivors face. Feelings of guilt following a suicide tended to induce accusations against the self and self-inflicted punishments. The feeling of being a victim was dual. On the one hand, survivors were victims of the other's act, against which there is nothing they can do anymore, and which made them felt powerless. They felt that since they could not prevent it, all that was left for them was to endure their suffering forever. On the other hand, survivors were also victims of their own negative self-judgment, dictated by guilt. That judgment was often much harsher than any other possible accusation from others. By contrast, in the position of guilty party, survivors assigned themselves the role of actors in the drama, as they believed that through their actions or omissions, they sometimes had taken a more or less active role in a play with a tragic outcome.

> I was blaming myself, I should have seen, I should have sensed that he was in danger. Would he have completed suicide if I had told him to come to my place during our last phone call? (Friend)

In the guilty party position, survivors not only felt guilty, but they also proclaimed themselves as such. If the victims went through never-ending suffering to redeem themselves, the guilty parties self-punished by way of social isolation – for example, they felt that they were not entitled to, or were unworthy of, sympathy or support from others.

Both the victim and the guilty party position may have a significant impact in the long-term on survivors' identity and life trajectory. Most of them realized after a certain amount of time (sometimes months, mostly years), that constantly oscillating between these two extremes, or settling into one, not only prevented them from carrying on with their life but may also threaten it in the long term.

> Only now, after eight years, do I want to [live], like a rage, a rebellion, because I could see myself ending up badly. I had become a wreck, I was all 'undone' and I said to myself: 'no.' It took eight years to feel like living again, eight years. (Mother)

Clarification of Feelings of Personal Involvement

Survivors hence engaged in a long process which allowed most of them to find some kind of inner peace. Over time, they modified an important part of their perception of the situation or the relationship with the deceased person. They also built up a more nuanced interpretation of the realities they faced and their own part in them. All of this was possible after going through complex processes divided into several steps which presupposed an assessment of their actions and the context of the suicide, together with an assessment of the relationship they had with the deceased person.

The first step of this process entailed ruthlessly seeking clues of their own guilt – that is, any kind of shortcomings – by dissecting facts, gestures, and words that had been said, and potential omissions during the weeks, days or hours preceding the suicide.

> I've always tried to give him courage but after that [the suicide attempt], I know now that we should have talked about it a lot more at the time. We tried to avoid it. We didn't ask too many questions, as he seemed to not want to talk about it, we didn't and then, we went on with our little lives. (Mother)

The relationship with the deceased person was also scrutinized. At first, the suicide was often interpreted as an implicit assessment of the value of the relationship that they had with them ("If I had loved him/her enough or if he/she had loved me enough, he/she would not have done it"). From that moment on, it became crucial for survivors to understand in which way this relationship, during the days or hours preceding the death, may have contributed to the tragic end.

The second step of the process consisted of a similarly ruthless evaluation of the influence that potential shortcomings may have had on the suicidal process. To measure this influence, survivors relied on their knowledge of suicidal behavior (role of family functioning, mental health issues, life circumstances) or on appreciations and indications from their family and friends (blaming or offering forgiveness to the family).

During a third step, survivors strived to find ways toward inner peace. With time and the assistance of others who helped them to consider other perspectives and elements, most survivors (35/50) gradually managed to take into account the role that the context and environment may have had in the suicidal process of their loved one.

> I told myself: "it is useless, you were missing pieces of the puzzle," and I convinced myself that in the end, I could not have done much more because I was not aware of the situation, I didn't understand it due to lack of maturity and because some things had been hidden from me [disease of the brother]. (Sister)

They could then place their role in a context and distinguish between being at fault, and having been careless or made an error. Being at fault presupposed the intention to harm or adversely affect the suicide victim's well-being, whereas carelessness or making an error stems from an involuntary involvement or action, which, while it might have been inappropriate, was not meant to hurt. Moreover, the assessment of the relationship with regard to their involvement and impact on the life of the other, at a second stage, took into consideration the entire life shared with the suicidal person rather than the last moments of the relationship. This amounted to putting into perspective or weighing up actions and their consequences in a different way by constructing a holistic view of oneself, the deceased person, and the relationship with the deceased.

> I started to understand the mechanisms, I started to understand that there was something in him, a source of fragility which had expanded. It was inside him, I could not do anything about it. … me, [sic] I was anyhow outside and I could not do much: when I started to understand the situation a little better, my brother's personality and the things around him, I found some kind of explanation, not the whole story… And to have put together the pieces of the puzzle and to have accepted the situation, I think that with time, we formulate things better, we take a step back. Then there is some easing up which gradually comes over the tension, and which makes you see things more clearly. (Sister)

Taking those aspects into account, together with the contextualization of the situation and the final act of the deceased person, gradually allowed survivors to neutralize the particularly negative self-judgment which prevailed at the beginning of the process. Then, the feeling of guilt could evolve toward facing one's own responsibility. The exit from the victim–guilty party's dynamic occured when people managed to recognize, without destroying themselves, that having been involved in some situations did not mean having to take responsibility for the final suicidal act. A distinction was made between what they were co-responsible for (the terms and contents of the relationships with the other) and what they were not directly responsible for.

> I gave both my children everything that I possibly could, I was there for them, but I think that if one son ends his life by suicide at age 25, we cannot put the blame on someone, I think this person is a grown up, responsible man. I am not responsible anymore when my children are this old. (Mother)

Cognitively, survivors acknowledged the limits of their involvement and responsibilities, while emotionally they came to terms with, and let go of, the ideal image of themselves and the need to find a culprit or the need for self-punishment. This allowed some people to find some inner peace, or to forgive themselves, as well as to make peace with the deceased person or other parties potentially involved in the situation. Survivors gradually reached the conclusion that while this situation (death) cannot be changed, it was possible to approach the issue of responsibility in a broader sense by not focusing only on the period preceding the suicide. This allowed them to reconsider the responsibility that they were willing to take toward their own life following the suicide (responsibility to reconstruct oneself, to carry on) and for some, to think about social responsibility. The residual feeling of guilt was transformed by almost half of the survivors into a commitment toward oneself and others so that what happened was not in vain and might help others. The notion of involvement became more nuanced and multifaceted: It encompassed not only the involvement in the life of the deceased person but also involvement and investment in one's own life and the life of others. Suicide became not only a destructive event which questions the person, but the starting point of a renewed vision of oneself, one's own life, and relationships to others.

Dealing With Responsibilities Assigned by Others

Suicide remains a particular type of death, with a strong social connotation. The suicide of the loved one imposed a social deviance by proxy and a symbolic inheritance that must be dealt with. While only a few bereaved interviewees had openly been subjected to disapproval or rejection from others, most mentioned reactions of unease, discomfort, or avoidance.

> A couple of days after his death, I met a girlfriend downtown who used to know him too, and she looked the other way. It is weird to see people turn away. (Sister)

Inappropriate reactions and judgments expressed by others were sometimes reported:

> An ex-colleague also told me: but listen, he chose. He made his own decision and we must accept it. He chose to end his days, why can't you accept it? (Mother)

Survivors therefore faced many challenges linked to the consequences of the death by suicide within their social circles, among which, for example, were the management of information and being assigned an identity as a victim or guilty party.

Management of Information

Upon receiving the news of the death, survivors must decide what they wanted or may tell others, and how. Talking about suicide may indeed mean receiving support or sympathy, but it may also generate suspicious looks, curiosity (*"What may have happened?"*) or unease (*"What do I have to say?"*). It may entail the risk of being judged or rejected. Survivors selected the environments and situations where, and people with whom, they shared this information, according to their state of mind and the potential consequences.

The bereaved managed the announcement and the information sharing in various ways. Transparency was generally used with loved ones, allowing survivors to obtain support and not having to strive to keep it a secret. In defined public spaces (funerals or workplaces), survivors distilled information in a targeted manner. The cause of death was mentioned, but it was placed into the whole context and life trajectory, which allowed them to prevent potential social or moral judgment from others. However, relatively high levels of discretion and *social coding* of the event were used in the wider public sphere, generally to preserve the memory of the deceased person and to avoid stigmatization or the disruption of social interactions. Younger survivors often chose to hide the suicide, especially in trivial social gatherings.

> There are occasions where, if someone asks: "How many brothers and sisters do you have?" and there is no real relationship with this person, only occasional meetings, then we don't feel like telling it, because they would be very surprised and would think: "Why did I ask this question ?" Whereas usually, when someone asks, "How many brothers and sisters do you have?" they want to make contact and connect with you, so if this kind of event comes in between ... (Brother)

The ways survivors managed the information may also change over time. Some people chose to talk about the suicide openly from the beginning, as they thought that it will help them in their grieving process and allowed them to receive support or dispel potential suspicions regarding their involvement in the suicidal act. Among those, some would continue to talk about it openly, even after many years, while others stopped doing it after a while. Others, however, were only able to talk about it after some time.

> It took me years to manage to talk about it, to say the word suicide, to be able to say, "He jumped," simple words but words that take time, of course we think about it, but telling others "my brother completed suicide," this is not simple to say it ... because people react madly, they are even more embarrassed than us, they don't know how to approach us, we are some kind of monsters, to have been around this type of event. (Brother)

Social Assignment of the Victim or Guilty Party Identity

Based on the information that they had (or had not) and on the reactions of the bereaved, others constructed a meaning, a story, or even a picture of the deceased person and their relationships with their loved ones. Generally, survivors could not escape being assigned an identity: the poor mother, devastated by pain; the unworthy wife, who could not prevent the suicide; the fickle sister, who goes out to party instead of mourning her brother. These assignments of identities placed a great burden on the bereaved. They forced them to position themselves, failing which they may become strongly constrained in their social interactions, or even cast aside. To do so, they learned to identify signs, words, and nonverbal behaviors implying that others were in the process of assessing or judging them.

> I did not receive explicit comments, but sometimes little innuendos, indirect things, sometimes I would even ask myself if I had interpreted them correctly, I was sensitive. (Sister)

Survivors learned to evaluate relationship issues within situations, to anticipate other people's reactions, to avoid them.

> Some harsh words were said so I avoided them [the persons], I protected myself. (Mother)

Sometimes, they chose to face others. For example, a mother decided to talk about her son's mental illness in public, also explaining all the steps taken to help him. In this way, she partly prevented being assigned a guilty party identity or, at least, being accused of negligence as some people may have indicated to her. Most survivors declared that beyond the initial surprise or shock, most people, either close or distant, perceived them as victims. As such, they benefited from other people's support and sympathy, at least initially. Sometimes, they received pity, which they generally disliked. However, in time, the identity as a victim may become very restrictive, as others reduced the survivor to a person defined by the tragedy they have been through.

> I still have this wish to not make myself, to not be a victim. Being seen as a victim makes me feel uncomfortable, and then, when my mother's death came on top of my brother's death, even more so "oh, it is surprising that you are still alive." This disturbs me, a lot, terribly. (Sister)

If the persistence of being assigned a victim identity may constitute a problem, its sudden disappearance may also be difficult, as it may coincide with a withdrawal of social support. Indeed, according to the interviewees, the social time frame of bereavement only seldom matched the pace of personal bereavement. After a certain amount of time, support and sympathy from others decreased. Survivors were then invited, sometimes pressed, to "start living normally again."

> And then, there are these labels that they put on you…. At first, it is terrible, everybody is around you with a sad face, and then they watch you evolve, then, after a while, it is them who decide, if you are still not, if you don't get a grip, they say, "It is time to start living again." So once again, others decide who you are. (Wife)

From then on, in other people's eyes, the victim who deserved sympathy became a victim lacking good will, if the victim did not comply with social expectations and did not try hard enough to come back to "normality." If most survivors were initially considered as victims, some were nevertheless held responsible or blamed by others, on the basis of clues sought in the life of the suicide decedent, but also by assessing the relationship between the deceased and the survivor.

> He was always functioning well professionally, he used to manage, and his colleagues held his wife responsible, they made her feel guilty. "He was such a good person, what kind of woman is she, to make him want to kill himself, to make him suffer so much as to lead him to suicide…." It was very difficult for her, people could not stand it, she lost many acquaintances and friends, not many people could keep up and accompany her. (Friend)

The assignment of an identity as a guilty party was also based on an assessment of public expressions of grief (especially emotional ones) following the suicide. This assessment may also lead to guilt-inducing judgments. Whereas public expression of extreme emotions (anger, distress) are unwelcome in Switzerland (as well as in many other Western countries), too much self-control may be considered as indifference or lack of love for the deceased, which could be interpreted as a possible cause for the suicide. Hence, survivors reacted in a cautious way.

> I was always careful of my behaviour in public, I knew that others were watching me, I must not embarrass them or be too cold. (Mother).

Survivors mostly mitigated the potential risk of being misjudged by presenting a social and public story in which they explained some of the elements that, in their eyes, had been crucial in the suicidal act. This social version of the story was aimed both at preserving the memory of the deceased by describing the qualities but also the difficulties they had, and at avoiding being blamed and marginalized by showing, for instance, how they tried to help.

Supporting the Bereaved in Clarifying Responsibility Issues

Suicide as a peculiar cause of death is likely to call into question the responsibility of those left behind who have to deal with this issue (Grad, 2005; Dyregrov et al., 2014). To find some form of release and relief as well as to pursue positive interactions in social settings, those bereaved through suicide had to deal with their own feelings of guilt, on the one hand, and on the other hand, with attributions of responsibility from others.

About two third of survivors came to terms with their own feelings of guilt and shame in several steps: by taking stock of the circumstances of the death and the relationship with the deceased, by evaluating their own role, by giving up the need to punish themselves or others, and sometimes by forgiving themselves or giving back the ultimate responsibility of the suicidal act to their loved one. For some, responsibility for the loved one became responsibility for, and increased awareness of, their own self, whereas others committed themselves to suicide prevention: Responsibility toward the decedent changed into responsibility for others in distress.

About one third of the bereaved, however, continued to experience guilt, shame together with self-blame, and self-isolation even many years after the loss. They still perceived the suicide as an assessment, or worse, as a more or less direct condemnation of the relationship that existed between themselves and the decedent. They believed they'd failed, that they had played a part in the other's suicide, which they could have, or should have prevented.

Most of them were mothers who had devoted their life to rearing their children. Older survivors at the time of the suicide were also more likely to experience more severe and long-lasting feelings of guilt and shame. These survivors needed to be supported by their social network and by professionals. Strong feelings of inadequacy, guilt, and shame as well as the need for self-punishment can seriously complicate the grief process, contribute to adverse outcomes, and put their life in danger. Professional support could ease the severity of the emotional response (Schneider, Grebner, Schnabel, & Georgi, 2011).

Empathic professional help is crucial (McMenamy et al., 2008) when supporting vulnerable survivors, as well as offering time and space to ventilate and sort out feelings and facts. Recursive narration is a powerful tool (i.e., allowing people to tell and retell their stories) to sustain survivors' realignment of their world view. But sometimes narration alone is not enough. Survivors need to interact and confront others in a constructive way to be able to reframe their perceptions and feelings and put them into perspective, so that they can take into account the multicausality of suicide (Jordan, 2008). Compassionate professionals can help them in this process, only if they are well trained and knowledgeable about suicide matters and suicide bereavement in particular. Unfortunately, not many professionals are trained in these matters in Switzerland (Castelli Dransart, 2013), where self-help groups are rare, and professional support is very scarce.

Professionals need to actively reach out to survivors, as feelings of guilt and shame (McMenamy et al., 2008) or self-isolation (Dyregrov, 2009) may prevent them from seeking help, or receiving and accepting it, whereas there is evidence that bereaved people wish to be supported in dealing with emotional or social issues (Dyregrov & Dyregrov, 2008).

Because suicide is likely to challenge social interactions and support, the survivors in this study had to learn to manage information in various situations, so that other people could understand their situation and support them in the most appropriate manner. Sometimes, identities assigned to them (either as victim or as guilty party) or judgments concerning the deceased's act became an additional burden on their recovery process. Most of them had to take measures against these assignments, either by avoiding some situations or people or by confronting them. To preserve the reputation of the deceased person and their own, survivors presented a public story which allowed other people to comprehend what had happened, and explained their role in a socially acceptable manner.

Although only a few survivors were openly rejected and ostracized, most of them felt awkwardness and embarrassment on both sides while interacting with others. Therefore, public awareness with regard to suicide and suicide bereavement should increase so that people better understand, respect, and respond to those bereaved through suicide. Indeed, people are not always prepared or are "socially inept" to interact with survivors (Dyregrov, 2003–2004; Grad et al. 2004; Owens Lambert, Lloyd, & Donovan, 2008). Psychoeducation for relatives and colleagues, or public education by means of media coverage, would help to create a more positive social climate around survivors and relieve some of the survivors' burden by allowing them to speak more openly about their experience and not having to refrain from doing so, for fear of disapproval. This seems especially important when considering that stigmatization is associated with grieving difficulties, depression, and suicidal thoughts (Feigelman et al., 2009).

Professionals need to support survivors when dealing with social issues, if necessary by taking the role of a go-between. They can assist them by elaborating a balanced public storyline and developing communication skills to convey the story and to interact with others without getting hurt unnecessarily. Moreover, it would be beneficial for professionals to understand and take into account the various processes and dynamics taking place, as well as the various outcomes with regard to the responsibility issue. This would allow professionals to provide more specific and appropriate support for survivors in their stress-related growth.

Conclusions

Coming to terms with the responsibility issue is a major challenge following the suicide of a loved one, on both a personal and social level. On a personal level, it involves scrutinizing the relationship with the deceased and the acts performed prior to their death, as well as the circumstances that led to the suicide. Survivors who came to the conclusion that the loved ones endorsed the ultimate responsibility for their final act could find inner peace more easily.

On a social level, survivors had to adopt communication and information management strategies to avoid judgment against both the deceased and themselves. In particular, they had to face the attribution of an identity as victim or guilty party. Survivors who managed information in nuanced ways according to settings and people, and who presented a public story which gave an account of the suicidal act, were more at ease in social encounters, more likely to avoid stigmatization and obtain more support.

By reaching out to survivors who refrained from seeking help due to feelings of guilt or shame and by providing empathic support in sorting out feelings and behavior, trained professionals can help survivors dealing with responsibility issues.

Corresponding author

Dolores Angela Castelli Dransart
University of Applied Sciences and Arts Western Switzerland
School of Social Work Fribourg
Givisiez
Switzerland
angela.castelli@hefr.ch

References

ATLAS-ti. (2000). *Software for qualitative data analysis management, and model building* [Computer software]. Berlin, Germany: Scientific Software Development.

Bailley, S. E., Kral, M. J., & Dunham, K. (1999). Survivors of suicide do grieve differently: Empirical support of a common sense proposition. *Suicide and Life-Threatening Behavior, 29*(3), 256–271.

Bartik, W., Maple, M., Edwards, H., & Kiernan, M. (2013). Adolescent survivors after suicide. *Crisis, 34*(3), 211–217. http://doi.org/10.1027/0227-5910/a000185

Begley, M., & Quayle, E. (2007). The lived experience of adults bereaved by suicide. *Crisis, 28*(1), 26–34. http://doi.org/10.1027/0227-5910.28.1.26

Botha, K. J., Guilfoyle, A., & Botha, D. (2009). Beyond normal grief: A critical reflection on immediate post-death experiences of survivors of suicide. *Australian e-Journal for the Advancement of Mental Health, 8*(1), 37–47.

Castelli Dransart, D. A. (2005). Se reconstruire après le suicide d'un proche: de la culpabiliteé à l'éclaircissement de la responsabilité [Recovery after a suicide: From guilt to the clarification of responsibility]. In J. J. Chavagnat (Ed.), *Prévention du suicide* (pp. 151–160). Montrouge, France: J. Libbey.

Castelli Dransart, D. A. (2013). From sense-making to meaning-making: Understanding and supporting survivors of suicide. *British Journal of Social Work, 43*, 317–335. http://doi.org/10.1093/bjsw/bct026

Cvinar, J. G. (2005). Do suicide survivors suffer social stigma: A review of the literature. *Perspectives in Psychiatric Care, 41*(1), 14–21. http://doi.org/10.1111/j.0031-5990.2005.00004.x

Demi, A. S. (1984). Social adjustment of widows after a sudden death: Suicide and non-suicide survivors compared. *Death Education, 8*(Suppl.), 91–111. http://doi.org/10.1080/07481188408252491

Dyregrov, K. (2003–2004). Micro-sociological analysis of social support following traumatic bereavement: Unhelpful and avoidant responses from the community. *Omega: Journal of Death and Dying, 48*(1), 23–44.

Dyregrov, K. (2009). Do professionals disempower bereaved people? *Bereavement Care, 24*(1), 7–10. http://doi.org/10.1080/02682620508657622

Dyregrov, K., & Dyregrov, A. (2008). *Effective grief and bereavement support: The role of family, friends, colleagues, schools and support professionals.* Philadelphia, PA: Jessica Kingsley.

Dyregrov, K., Grad, O., De Leo, D., & Cimitan, A. (2014). Surviving suicide. In D. De Leo, A. Cimitan, K. Dyregrov, O. Grad, & K. Andriessen (Eds.), *Bereavement after traumatic death: Helping the survivors* (pp. 37–48). Boston, MA: Hogrefe.

Dyregrov, K., Plyhn, E., & Dieserud, G. (2011). *After the suicide: Helping the bereaved to find a path to recovery.* London, UK: Jessica Kingsley.

Feigelman, W., Gorman, B., & Jordan, J. (2009). Stigmatization and suicide bereavement. *Death Studies, 33*(7), 591–608. http://doi.org/10.1080/07481180902979973

Gaffney, M., & Hannigan, B. (2010). Suicide bereavement and coping: A descriptive and interpretative analysis of the coping process. *Procedia Social and Behavioral Sciences, 5*, 526–535. http://doi.org/10.1016/j.sbspro.2010.07.137

Gall, T. L., Henneberry, J., & Eyre, M. (2014). *Two perspectives on the needs of individuals bereaved by suicide, Death Studies, 38*(7), 430–437.

Grad, O. (2005). Suicide survivorship: An unknown journey from loss to gain-from individual to global perspective. In K. Hawton (Ed.), *Prevention and treatment of suicidal behavior* (pp. 351–369). Oxford, UK: Oxford University Press.

Grad, O. T., Clark, S., Dyregrov, K., & Andriessen, K. (2004). What helps and what hinders the process of surviving the suicide of somebody close? *Crisis, 25*(3), 134–139. http://doi.org/10.1027/0227-5910.25.3.134

Harwood, D., Hawton, K., Hope, T., & Jacoby, R. (2002). The grief experiences and needs of bereaved relatives and friends of older people dying through suicide: A descriptive and case-control study. *Journal of Affective Disorders, 72*(2), 185–194. http://doi.org/10.1016/S0165-0327(01)00462-1

Jordan, J. R. (2001). Is suicide bereavement different? A reassessment of the literature. *Suicide and Life-Threatening Behavior, 31*(1), 91–102. http://doi.org/10.1521/suli.31.1.91.21310

Jordan, J. R. (2008). Bereavement after suicide. *Psychiatric Annals, 38*(10), 679–685. http://doi.org/10.3928/00485713-20081001-05

Levi-Belz, Y. (2015). Stress-related growth among suicide survivors: The role of interpersonal and cognitive factors. *Archives of Suicide Research, 19*(3), 305–320. http://doi.org/10.1080/13811118.2014.957452

Lindqvist, P., Johansson, L., & Karlsson, U. (2008). In the aftermath of teenage suicide: A qualitative study of the psychosocial consequences for the surviving family members. *BMC Psychiatry, 8*, 26. http://doi.org/10.1186/1471-244X-8-26

Maple, M., Edwards, H., Plummer, D., & Minichiello, V. (2010). Silenced voices: Hearing the stories of parents bereaved through the suicide death of a young adult child. *Health & Social Care in the Community, 18*(3), 241–248.

Maple, M., Plummer, D., Edwards, H., & Minichiello, V. (2007). The effects of preparedness for suicide following the death of a young adult child. *Suicide and Life-Threatening Behavior, 37*(2), 127–134. http://doi.org/10.1521/suli.2007.37.2.127

Miles, M. S., & Demi, A. S. (1991). A comparison of guilt in bereaved parents whose children died by suicide, accident, or chronic disease. *Omega: Journal of Death and Dying, 24*(3), 203–215. http://doi.org/10.2190/G41E-RKTF-P0XD-LJLK

McMenamy, J. M., Jordan, J. R., & Mitchell, A. M. (2008). What do suicide survivors tell us they need? Results of a pilot study. *Suicide and Life-Threatening Behavior, 38*(4), 375–389. http://doi.org/10.1521/suli.2008.38.4.375

Owens, C., Lambert, H., Lloyd, K., & Donovan, J. (2008). Tales of biographical disintegration: How parents make sense of their sons' suicides. *Sociology of Health & Illness, 30*(2), 237–254. http://doi.org/10.1111/j.1467-9566.2007.01034.x

Ratnarajah, D., & Schofield, M. J. (2008). Survivors' narratives of the impact of parental suicide. *Suicide and Life-Threatening Behavior, 38*(5), 618–630. http://doi.org/10.1521/suli.2008.38.5.618

Schneider, B., Grebner, K., Schnabel, A., & Georgi, K. (2011). Do suicides' characteristics influence survivors' emotions? *Suicide and Life-Threatening Behavior, 41*(2), 117–125. http://doi.org/10.1111/j.1943-278X.2011.00024.x

Smith, A., Joseph, S., & Das Nair, R. (2011). An interpretative phenomenological analysis of posttraumatic growth in adults bereaved by suicide. *Journal of Loss and Trauma, 16*(5), 413–430. http://doi.org/10.1080/15325024.2011.572047

Strauss, A. L., & Corbin, J. (1997). *Grounded theory in practice*. Thousand Oaks, CA: Sage.

Sugrue, J. L., McGilloway, S., & Keegan, O. (2013). The experiences of mothers bereaved by suicide: An exploratory study. *Death Studies, 38*(2), 118–124. http://doi.org/10.1080/07481187.2012.738765

Sveen, C. A., & Walby, F. A. (2008). Suicide survivors' mental health and grief reactions: A systematic review of controlled studies. *Suicide and Life-Threatening Behavior, 38*(1), 13–29. http://doi.org/10.1521/suli.2008.38.1.13

Wilson, A., & Marshall, A. (2010). The support needs and experiences of suicidally bereaved family and friends. *Death Studies, 34*(7), 625–640. http://doi.org/10.1080/07481181003761567

Chapter 7

Suicide Loss and the Quest for Meaning

Robert A. Neimeyer[1] and Diana C. Sands[2]

[1]Department of Psychology, University of Memphis, TN, USA
[2]Bereaved by Suicide Centre for Intense Grief, Sydney, Australia

Abstract: In response to recent calls to bridge postvention research and practice more fully with the field of bereavement studies, this chapter reviews the possible contribution to this effort that could be made by recent work on a meaning reconstruction approach to loss and grief. Especially when the deaths of loved ones occur suddenly, violently, and in a way that raises complex issues of intentionality – as in suicide – research documents the formidable struggle of survivors to make sense of the loss and the complicated grief associated with it. Viewing adaptation through the lens of a quest for meaning in seemingly senseless loss, the chapter introduces several methods of clinical assessment and intervention that focus on the ongoing reconstruction of the survivor's assumptive world, and illustrates their application in two case studies.

Vignette 1

As a brilliant but troubled college student, Daniel had alternated between excelling in classes and succumbing to binges of drinking that challenged both his academic and social success. The decade that had followed college was similarly stormy, marked by lost jobs, a lost marriage and several rounds of treatment for substance abuse. Finally, in his early 30s, he moved back into his parents' home, stabilizing for a time before sliding back into the recurrent cycle of substance abuse.

It was in this context that Daniel arrived at his parents' home late one night, obviously inebriated, when his mother, Carol, met him. Exasperated, Carol broke off the ensuing confrontation between Daniel and his father about the son's behavior, suggesting that they all get to bed and return to the discussion in the morning. For Daniel, however, morning never came. As Carol began to worry about him as noon approached, she opened the door of his silent bedroom to a scene of horror instantly stamped in her mind: her son, tangled in the sheets, torso off the bed, the bedding awash in a swath of blood. Rushing to him as she screamed for her husband, she attempted resuscitation as he called emergency services. Arriving to the scene within 20 minutes, the first responders rushed Daniel's unresponsive body to the hospital, where his death – apparently of self-inflicted poisoning – was confirmed. Tormented by the horrific imagery of the death scene as well as her guilt for not having recognized his condition that fateful night, Carol sought therapy a few months later.

After inviting Carol to share photos of her son on her iPhone and hearing stories of her pride and concern about his turbulent life, the therapist was struck by the power of the death narrative to eclipse any sense of secure connection to her son's "spirit," as Carol put it, though she was a religious person. The therapist therefore introduced the possibility of doing a "slow motion replay," as described below, of what she had seen, sensed, and suffered the morning she discovered her son's body, with the goal of helping her give voice to the silent story of the trauma, while being supported in managing the powerful emotions it triggered and in addressing the painful questions it posed. Bravely, Carol announced her readiness for this retelling, and the therapist began by soliciting a detailed description of the events of the night before, the disturbed night of sleep for Carol that followed, and a careful unpacking in sensory detail of what unfolded as she, with increasing apprehension, opened her son's bedroom door. Braiding together the horrific images – the tangled body, the purple face, the splash of congealed red blood spilling from his mouth across the white sheets – with the associated feelings that welled up in her, Carol and her therapist gradually walked through the experience, tracing its objective and subjective contours and the struggle to make sense of his death that ensued.

Finally, as the therapist asked what Carol would have done if she had been present to his dying, but unable to prevent it, she sobbed, "Just hold him, hold him ... and tell him I loved him." Gently handing Carol a cushion, the clinician watched as she spontaneously hugged it tightly to her chest and tearfully affirmed her love for her precious if imperfect child. After a few minutes, she set the pillow aside, dried her eyes, and noted how she felt "flooded with comfort" following the retelling, and less alone in a tragic story. Together they then reflected on further healing steps that could be taken, including how she might explore the partly parallel, partly unique grief of her husband following a shared loss.

Introduction

When suicide ends the suffering of one person, it initiates or deepens the suffering of many others. A recent review of controlled studies of suicide bereavement documents its effects on those left behind, who depending on the nature of their relationship with the deceased, suffer higher incidence rates of depression and other psychiatric symptomatology, hospitalization, and heightened suicide risk in its wake (Pitman, Osborn, King, & Erlangsen, 2014). Indeed, mounting evidence underscores the impact of even less intimate suicide exposure, such as witnessing the suicide of an unknown person, or learning of that of a fellow student, coworker, or colleague (Survivors of Suicide Loss Task Force, 2015; see also Chapter 1 in this volume). It is for this reason that the broad continuum of suicide "survivorship" is being more widely recognized (Cerel, McIntosh, Neimeyer, Maple, & Marshall, 2014). In response to this accumulating evidence for the impact of suicide loss, national guidelines for responding to such exposure urge clinical researchers to "investigate factors from general bereavement research that may mediate the response to suicide (e.g., kinship relationship, psychological closeness, attachment security, coping style, meaning making, social support)" (Survivors of Suicide Loss Task Force, 2015, p. 35). The goal of the present chapter is to summarize the contributions of one major contemporary theory of bereavement adaptation, which concentrates on survivors' attempts to find meaning in loss in general, and suicide loss in particular (Neimeyer & Sands, 2011; see also Chapter 1), and to illustrate its implications for clinical practice with actual case material.

Mourning and Meaning

Viewed through a wide-angle lens, the effort after meaning displayed by survivors of sudden, tragic death is simply the focal point of a broader process of human beings' construction and reconstruction of lives that have comprehensibility and continuity across an endless series of life losses and transitions. Accordingly, recent US national guidelines for postvention, presented in Chapter 27 in this volume, urge the field to "surmount the intellectual isolationism of research on suicide loss by linking studies more clearly to contemporary theories and associated research paradigms in adjacent fields" (Neimeyer & Cerel, 2015, p. 8). This section therefore first describes the broad outlines of a meaning making approach to bereavement, then reviews what has been learned about the search for meaning in mourning more generally, and finally turns to the more germinal research on meaning reconstruction in the wake of a loved one's suicide, per se.

For the most part, the quest for meaning in life entails minimal conscious effort, as the meanings discerned in the replicative themes (Kelly, 1955, p. 54) of daily life (the rhythms of people's work, play, and life with others) are in some measure predictable and unquestioned and, if we are fortunate, coherent with our larger life goals and roles. But when this assumptive world of taken-for-granted patterns is shattered by traumatic life events (Janoff-Bulman & Berger, 2000), as it was for Carol in the opening case study (**Vignette 1**), survivors are commonly thrust into a crisis of meaning, and struggle to find sense and significance in the terrain of a landscape made alien by loss. Most vividly evident in the early days and weeks following trauma, meaning reconstruction frequently weaves subtly but no less importantly throughout life, justifying its description as a developmental process that addresses evolving needs and goals in a changing social field (Neimeyer & Cacciatore, 2015).

It is in the wake of tragic loss that the process of "relearning the world" (Attig, 1996) and the psychological and situational impediments to it are most readily observed, as survivors of tragic transitions seek to reaffirm or reconstruct a world of meaning that has been challenged by loss (Neimeyer, 2001). From a narrative constructivist perspective, mourners who are able to preserve or construct meaning in this transition experience the loss as more bearable; though they may be grieving, the loss still makes sense in secular or spiritual terms, perhaps even seeming appropriate or inevitable in the larger scheme. Conversely, when the death of a loved one occurs at a time or in a way that violates the bereaved person's assumptive world, the pain of separation is compounded by an equally profound sense of invalidation, injustice, or incomprehensibility, intensifying, prolonging, and complicating the course of grief (Neimeyer, Prigerson, & Davies, 2002). However, reparative reconstruction of one's meaning system can occur even in the face of massive disruption, as the mourner across time finds unsought benefit in the loss in terms of greater maturity, compassion, or spiritual/philosophic growth (Gillies & Neimeyer, 2006). Though most bereaved people would gladly exchange any such life lessons or personal growth to have their loved one returned, in the face of the impossibility of this wish, this newfound sense of meaning resulting from suffering provides at least partial compensation. The result is a changed, but nonetheless valued *self-narrative*, one that provides a viable frame for reestablishing a sense of continuity and coherence in a life story disrupted by loss (Neimeyer, 2004, 2006).

The Search for Meaning in Bereavement

Over the past 10 years, a great deal of evidence has been amassed that supports the broad outlines of this meaning reconstruction model. For example, Holland and Neimeyer (2010) conducted one of the few empirical tests of a stage theory of grief across the first 2 years of bereavement, examining the association between time since loss and five grief indicators focusing on disbelief, anger, yearning, depression, and acceptance, among an ethnically diverse sample of young adults who had been bereaved by natural ($n = 441$) or violent ($n = 173$) causes, the latter group including adults bereaved by suicide, homicide, or fatal accident. They also examined the potential salience of meaning making and assessed the extent to which participants had made sense of their losses. Overall, results provided only weak support for stage theory's predicted patterns of waxing and waning of particular indicators. Moreover, sense making about the loss emerged as a far more substantial predictor of each of the grief indicators than did the passage of time, a finding more supportive of a meaning reconstruction model of bereavement adaptation than of stage theory.

In another study of over 1,000 bereaved young adults, Holland and his colleagues (2006) found that the ability to make sense of a variety of death-related losses emerged as the most robust predictor of adaptation during the first 2 years of bereavement, and that benefit finding played a compensatory role in predicting fewer grief complications when participants reported finding little meaning in the loss. However, when sense making was high, the perception of a hidden compensation or benefit in the loss was actually associated with more complications, perhaps because it carried an implication of selfish gain in a loss that in the judgment of survivors otherwise made sense in its own terms (Holland, Currier, & Neimeyer, 2006).

Similar results emerged in a study of 157 bereaved parents who had lost their children to a variety of causes, both natural and violent, suicide included. Although several factors, including age of the child, time since the loss, and cause of death, accounted for significant differences in normative and complicated grief symptoms, sense making was greatly more predictive of parent grief, accounting for 5 to 15 times as much of the variance in bereavement outcome as other factors (Keesee, Currier, & Neimeyer, 2008). A follow-up study of the narrative accounts of these parents identified numerous meaning making themes they spontaneously invoked, with fewer symptoms of complicated grief being associated with sense-making themes emphasizing that the death was God's will and that the child was no longer suffering. Likewise, fewer complications were found to be associated with benefit-finding themes suggesting enhanced spirituality and changed life priorities (Lichtenthal, Currier, Neimeyer, & Keesee, 2010). Other controlled research further suggests that mourners with fragile world assumptions – weaker beliefs in the meaningfulness of the world and lower perceptions of self-worth – may be especially vulnerable to high distress when faced with significant loss, even if they function well enough when these vulnerabilities are not triggered (Currier, Holland, & Neimeyer, 2009).

Still stronger evidence for the salutary role of sense making has been provided by prospective longitudinal research on older bereaved spouses whose partners had died from a variety of causes. Tracking 250 widows and widowers across the early years of bereavement, investigators found that those who reported an anguished search for meaning (e.g., struggling to comprehend their spouse's death and its implications for their lives) at 6 and 18 months following the loss, continued to report high levels of distress as much as 4 years following the death of their partner. Conversely, higher degrees of sense making at these earlier points in bereavement predicted high levels of positive affect (e.g., pride, well-being) in the months and years that followed (Coleman & Neimeyer, 2010). Related research on young adults demonstrates that those who move toward greater meaning making regarding their loss over a period of 3 months also display significant reductions in their level of complicated grief symptomatology (Holland, Currier, Coleman, & Neimeyer, 2010).

Spiritual Struggle in the Wake of Loss

Given the great hardship caused by many experiences of the death of loved ones, it is not surprising that mourners in many cultures turn toward the resources of their religious faith and communities to seek consolation and comprehensibility in the transition. However, especially when these deaths are violent and sudden, survivors commonly confess a significant spiritual struggle, and sometimes crisis, in the aftermath (Neimeyer & Burke, 2015). Research on this process in the lives of a diverse group of religiously inclined mourners documents the complex challenges entailed in trying to make spiritual sense of difficult loss (Burke, Neimeyer, Young, & Piazza-Bonin, 2014). It also demonstrates the clear relation between this quest and the pervasive and profound grief symptomatology that accompanies it (Burke & Neimeyer,

2014). Again, in keeping with a meaning reconstruction model, both "negative religious coping" (such as protesting against God's seeming indifference or cruelty) and challenges with meaning making have been found to predict prolonged grief disorder symptoms, with meaning making partially mediating the impact of such spiritual struggles in explaining this association (Lichtenthal, Burke, & Neimeyer, 2011). Stated differently, a crisis of faith in the context of troubling bereavement can be understood in large part as a crisis of meaning.

Suicide Loss and the Quest for Meaning

Although the above studies and many others have documented the role of meaning making in losses of various kinds, only a handful of studies have been conducted to date on violent death loss and suicide bereavement in particular. Those that have, however, document the devastating impact of such deaths in terms of not only complicated grief but also the profound struggle to reconstruct meaning in their wake. For example, Currier and his colleagues (2006) investigated over 1,000 bereaved adults who had lost loved ones to violent causes (suicide, homicide, and fatal accident) as well as to natural causes (both sudden and anticipated). As predicted, they found that violent deaths were associated with both more intense and complicated grief than natural deaths, as well as less ability to make sense of the loss. Most importantly, degree of sense making statistically mediated or explained this difference, even when the former losses were compared with natural death losses that shared the feature of suddenness. No differences were observed between the severity of grief or a struggle for meaning between survivors of suicide loss and those bereaved by homicide or fatal accident, (Currier, Holland, & Neimeyer, 2006). More recent research has replicated the finding that violent death losses, including suicide, are characterized by heightened complicated grief symptoms relative to natural death losses, and added evidence that suicide, homicide, and accidental deaths also precipitate greater spiritual struggle than natural death losses, a phenomenon the authors termed *complicated spiritual grief* (Burke & Neimeyer, 2014).

Posttraumatic Growth

Finally, despite, or perhaps because of, the substantial repercussions of tragic loss for people's assumptive worlds, research has also documented the resulting growth through grief shown by a significant minority of survivors. For example, Currier and his associates (2013) compared 369 young adults divided equally into three groups: bereaved by violent death, bereaved by natural death, and stressed but nonbereaved in the last 2 years. They reported that the first group, who had lost loved ones to suicide, homicide, or fatal accident, were more psychologically distressed but also showed more posttraumatic growth than did those bereaved by natural death and nonbereaved controls, across all five domains measured: relating more compassionately to others, perceiving new possibilities, appreciating life, endorsing newfound personal strength, and reporting spiritual growth (Currier, Malott, Martinez, Sandy, & Neimeyer, 2013). A second study focusing on bereaved parents also found that those who had lost children to violent death emphasized appreciation of life in their meaning making narratives, and that those surviving a child's suicide further reported positive changes in their life priorities (Lichtenthal, Neimeyer, Currier, Roberts, & Jordan, 2013). Overall, this positive form of benefit finding has been found to be most feasible when the pain of grief is sufficiently intense to provoke new attempts at adaptation, but not so intense as to be overwhelming (Currier, Holland, & Neimeyer, 2012). Importantly, the reconstruction of the self-narrative along growth-producing lines is commonly a longer-term proposition, as the survivor revisits and makes new sense of the loss, opening to new and deepened relations to others, the self, and the world in the process.

Clinical Implications of a Meaning Reconstruction Approach

Viewed in constructivist terms, adaptive grieving entails two fundamental narrative processes: (1) processing the *event story* of the death and its implications for the survivor's ongoing life, and (2) accessing the *back story* of the deceased loved one's life, in a way that restores some measure of secure attachment (Neimeyer & Thompson, 2014). Interestingly, these distinguishable but interbraided narrative processes correspond to evidence that *traumatic distress* associated with the circumstances of the death can be distinguished from the *separation distress* associated with the nature of the relationship to the deceased, both of which are components of complicated grief (Holland & Neimeyer, 2011). In practical terms, this dual focus on two domains of meaning reconstruction – about the loss and the nature of the attachment bond with the deceased – also provides an orienting frame for bereavement support and grief therapy, as will be briefly noted in this section.

Meaning-Oriented Assessment

One contribution of a meaning reconstruction approach to bereavement research and practice has been the systematic development and validation of several reliable measures of meaning and its associated challenges in the face of bereavement and other major life stressors. These include a 30-category codebook for analyzing specific positive and negative themes expressed in mourners' spoken or written attempts to make sense of their losses (e.g., in therapy recordings or personal journals or blogs). They also include multidimensional scales for assessing the degree of meaning making regarding a loss or other life event, for measuring particular types of meaning made, and for evaluating spiritual struggle in bereavement. These instruments are described further in **Table 7.1** (Neimeyer, 2016). All are placed in the public domain to encourage their free use by interested clinicians and researchers. For practitioners, use of such measures can identify areas of both resource and vulnerability for a given client, helping direct intervention, and with repeated use, document its efficacy.

Intervening in Meaning

Beyond identifying strengths and weaknesses in clients' efforts to reconstruct meaning in the wake of loss, a further contribution of this perspective has been the invention, recruitment, and refinement of a cornucopia of clinical strategies for supporting mourners in restoring sense and significance in the wake of loss. **Table 7.2** describes a small sampling of those that may have particular relevance to suicide bereavement as a subset of the hundreds of techniques fully described and illustrated in recent clinical manuals for grief therapists (Neimeyer, 2012, 2016; Thompson & Neimeyer, 2014). Significantly, several of these methods – those conventionally associated both with verbal psychotherapy and with expressive arts interventions – have been incorporated into evidence-informed treatment research examining their efficacy in open trial or randomized controlled designs (Lichtenthal & Cruess, 2010; Neimeyer & Young-Eisendrath, 2015; Saindon et al., 2014; Shear, Frank, Houch, & Reynolds, 2005; Shear et al., 2014). Several of these interventions are also illustrated in the opening case illustration (Vignette 1), as well as in the more detailed, clinical case study that follows. With their respective focus on the relatively immediate and relatively long-term processes of revisiting and reconstructing the story of loss and its implications, the cases that bookend the chapter also underscore the relevance of meaning making following suicide loss across much of the survivor's life.

Table 7.1. Assessment instruments for evaluating meaning making in the wake of loss

Title	Reference	Structure	Purpose
Integration of Stressful Life Experiences Scale (ISLES)	Holland et al., 2010	16-item scale with 2 factors: Comprehensibility and Footing in the World	Measure degree to which meaning making has been disrupted by loss or other major life stressor
Integration of Stressful Life Experiences Scale, Short Form (ISLES-SF)	Holland, Currier, & Neimeyer, 2014	6-item condensation of ISLES that retains factor structure	Provide briefer version of ISLES to facilitate its use in practice and large-scale studies
Inventory of Complicated Spiritual Grief (ICSG)	Burke, Neimeyer, Holland, et al., 2014	18-item scale with 2 factors: Insecurity with God and Disruption in Religious Practice	Evaluate degree of spiritual struggle in bereavement in relation to the divine and the faith community
Grief and Meaning Reconstruction Inventory (GMRI)	Gillies, Neimeyer, & Milman, 2015	29-item scale with 5 factors: Continuing Bonds, Personal Growth, Sense of Peace, Emptiness & Meaninglessness, and Valuing Life	Assess content domains of meaning making to characterize significant themes that represent sources of strength or challenge for the respondent
Meaning in Loss Codebook (MLC)	Gillies, Neimeyer, & Milman, 2014	30 category coding system for analyzing thematic content of loss narratives	Code transcriptions of client sessions, interviews, blogs, or journals regarding meanings made of loss experiences

Note. Adapted from Neimeyer, 2016.

Table 7.2. Representative techniques for intervening in meaning

Processing the Event Story of the Death	
Technique	**Purpose**
Retelling Narrative of the Death	Review the loss story in slow motion to promote mastery, coherence, and emotion regulation rather than avoidance
Chapters of Our Lives	Situate the current loss in the landscape of previous experience and experiment with new meanings
Virtual Dream Stories	Creatively write about loss themes to facilitate their exploration
Playing with Playlists	Trace the trajectory of love and loss in musical memoir on iPod
Figurative Sand Tray Therapy	Construct symbolic stories of loss and transition using figurines in sand world
Analogical Listening	Focus on bodily felt sense of grief and giving it expression to discern tacit needs
The Body of Trust	Depict impact of the death story in mixed media on body image in individual or group setting
Directed Journaling	Consolidate sense making and benefit finding in diary work
Rituals of Transition	Symbolically validate life changes occasioned by loss, either privately or with selected others

Table 7.2. continued

Assessing the Back Story of the Relationship	
Technique	**Purpose**
Disentangling Multiple Loss	Comb through relational strands with several recently deceased figures to identify unique implications of each
Introducing the Deceased	Share special features of the loved one in group or individual therapy to reopen the relationship in the present
Correspondence with the Deceased	Reopen communication with the deceased through symbolic letters written "to" and "from" them
Chair Work	Perform vivid conversations with deceased to resolve unfinished business
Photography and Videography	Review family archives and construct memorials to loved one
Singing Goodbye	Ritualize leave taking in familiar or improvisational song
Poetry of Loss	Express in verse feelings for deceased that transcend literal words
Online Memorials	Honor the loved one in words and images and share with the world
The Grief Spot	Preserve cherished mementos in a place that can be visited, but also contained
Reintegrating Attachment	Revisit client's working models of attachment and visualize restoration of a secure bond with the deceased

Note. Adapted and expanded from Neimeyer, 2012, 2016; Thompson & Neimeyer, 2014.

A Lingering Loss: Long-Term Reconstruction Following Suicide Loss

The case study in **Vignette 2** offers insight into the process of revisiting and reworking the loss narrative over time, highlighting the significance of evolving reconstructed meanings for current relational issues of trust, commitment, and self-esteem.

Vignette 2

Initially the therapist met Shelley when she was 11 years old, following the death of her father to suicide. At that time, Shelley with her mother and younger brother and sister attended family counseling. Fourteen years later, Shelley contacted the same therapist to talk about relationship issues she was experiencing with her partner, Jeff. Unfortunately, her partner was unable to attend counseling at that time due to a work secondment. In the initial session Shelley explained that she and Jeff had been together for more than 2 years and were now planning "to move in together." Although she loved Jeff, planning this next step in their relationship was making Shelley extremely anxious, as she found herself doubting his love and commitment. Shelley believed her fears were irrational. However, despite profuse reassurances from Jeff, she was unable to let go of her doubts, and at times behaved in ways that she described as "hysterical." Further probing revealed that these issues had caused difficulties in previous relationships. Shelley became thoughtful when the therapist wondered if she had considered whether losing her dad to suicide might be implicated. Initial counseling explored the cyclical effect between Shelley's emotions, thoughts, and behaviors, identifying triggers and ways to avoid escalation through intervention and self-soothing techniques, such as positive self-affirmations.

Significantly, in a session close to the anniversary of her father's death, Shelley started talking about the day her father died. As Shelley reworked this material she was able to add information gathered in the intervening years, and importantly, Shelley was able to review and reconstruct meanings that she had made as a child from her understanding now as an adult. Shelley's need to revisit the death story can be understood in the context of the Walking in the Shoes model, a meaning making and relational model (Neimeyer & Sands, 2011; Sands, 2009; Sands et al., 2011). The model identifies the interaction for those bereaved by suicide between the relationship with self, the deceased, and significant others, and how these relational themes interact with dominant meaning making themes described metaphorically as trying on the shoes, walking in the shoes, and taking off the shoes.

Trying on the shoes themes focus on the struggle to make sense of issues of self-volition, preventability, guilt, and blame. The walking in the shoes themes that Shelley engaged with focus on the death story and the imagined, or known pain of the deceased prior to and at the time of the death. Taking off the shoes themes emerge as an adaptive story is developed, presaging integration, healing, and growth through grief (Neimeyer & Sands, 2011; Sands, 2009; Sands, Jordan & Neimeyer, 2011). In the context of the model, the function of Shelley revisiting the death story can be understood as an endeavor to repair her relationship with her father provoked by her current relational issues (Sands, 2009; Sands, 2014).

Shelley recalled the strange quality of her last day with her father and the long walk they had taken together in the afternoon, walking for the most part in silence. Reaching back into her 11-year-old memory, she described her father's distracted and heavy mood and how she had felt confused and frightened. In retelling the story, Shelley reexperienced her sense of helplessness and confusion and had a sick feeling in her stomach. As Shelley talked, the therapist directed Shelley's attention to her sensory experiences. The trauma evoked by a suicide death is often stored in sensory, nonverbal memory, and accessing this information through interventions like the body of trust (Table 7.2) may assist in providing a bridge from somatic memory to verbal expression to facilitate grieving (Neimeyer & Sands, 2011; Sands, 2012). That night, her father made pasta for dinner, and Shelley remembered the stilted, uncomfortable atmosphere in the kitchen. She commented, "I think my brother and sister knew something was wrong because they were unusually quiet."

Later that evening at bedtime, Shelley recalled in a shaky voice her father's words to her: "Goodnight Princess, I love you." Shelley, a tense knot in her stomach, asked him, "What's wrong, Dad? Is everything OK?" Her father did not respond and, as it eventuated, these words were his goodbye. After saying goodnight to his children he had ended his life. Shelley, with her hands gripped tightly, said, "I don't know what I could have done." The therapist intervened with reassurance that sadly, there was nothing that could have been done to prevent her father's death, as, tragically, he had not confided in anyone his suicidal intentions. Frequently those bereaved by suicide believe that the death could have been prevented by some action taken or not taken. The damaging burden of this kind of belief can be dragged around for years deeply felt but unspoken (Jordan, 2011; Sands, 2009; Sands & North, 2014).

Shelley returned to her story, describing how in the middle of the night she and her siblings had been awakened by her aunt and uncle and, without explanation, driven to their house. The following day the children were returned home, and their mother told them that their father had died. In a house full of relatives and friends they soon knew that the death was a suicide. Shelley described the terrifying and unknown world she had found herself in: "I was most scared something would happen to Mum." She had overheard her mother on the phone saying, "I wish I could just do the same thing as him." Shelley, her focus deep within, confided, "Eventually we got Mum back again." The dark brevity of her mother's words rested heavily upon Shelley's young shoulders, and the therapist acknowledged the terror they evoked.

In the months and years that followed, Shelley witnessed the consequences of her father's death in the suffering endured by her family. "It changed the family ... everything was different. There was no Dad ... and a lot of pain and turmoil. My brother and sister ... we missed out on lots of things." In the aftermath of her father's death, Shelley experienced tremors of instability within her family, and through what remained of her childhood and during her adolescent years, she had remained vigilant (Janoff-Bullman, 1992). Research has documented that those bereaved by suicide frequently hold fears for the safety of other family members (Cerel, Jordan, & Duberstein, 2008; Linn-Gust, 2004). The therapist acknowledged the terrifying nature and weight of these fears Shelley had carried and invited her to notice that despite the pain and trauma, her mother, brother, and sister had survived, and that they were now fine and getting on with their lives. Shelley was invited to lay down some of the responsibility she had carried for so long. Shelley selected heavy stones to represent the weight of her fears and worries, and cried as she said in a broken voice, "I feel so let down by Dad. ... I guess I'll never really understand. ... It's like a door closed."

At this point Shelley faltered saying, "It's more than half of my life Dad hasn't been alive and it's getting so hard to remember him." With a surge of anger, Shelley said that her memories were cloudy because of everything she and her family went through: "I feel angry on Mum and my brother and sister's behalf – because I hurt for them and for me – I loved you, Dad." In a broken voice, Shelley told her father, "It's so hard for me to completely trust. ... I didn't think you would do that to me." As her sobs lessened, the therapist asked whether Shelley could sense her dad with her. Shelley said, "Yes. He's sorry about how things spiraled out of control ending in his death." However, Shelley was not prepared to countenance her father's regrets. In a distressed voice she told him, "This is not about you. I need something from you, Dad. . . . I need more from you. . . . I need to know you loved me." This is a poignant moment of yearning for the woman, and for the child that she was when her world fell apart. Both woman and child wanted and needed reassurance of a father's love, a love Shelley has had cause to question over the years.

Having arrived at this place, Shelley was invited to gently disentangle the painful emotional threads of abandonment, broken trust, and betrayal evoked by her father's death from her feelings for her partner. Different emotional threads were represented symbolically through use of textured, colored materials that she selected from a basket. A piece of shaggy, slate gray material represented the pain of her father's betrayal, and this was twisted tightly with a shimmering piece of soft pink material representing love. As Shelley untwisted the materials her tears gradually subsided until she was soothingly smoothing out the fabrics and laying them out side by side. Often, those bereaved by suicide question their loved ones' suicidal actions and conclude that they did not love them enough to stay. The essence of this distressing dilemma is captured in the poignant words of a child bereaved by suicide: "I think he loved me. ... But I don't know" (Sands, 2010). For many, the suicide of a loved one is interpreted as an act of abandonment, a conclusion that contributes a further layer of hurt and distress to their grief (Schreiber, Sands, & Jordan, 2015).

In a subsequent session, Shelley reported feeling "lighter" and noted that she had been thinking about how her father and Jeff would have got on. The therapist asked if Shelley would like to invite Dad into the room, and a chair was placed for him. After a thoughtful pause Shelley told her father, "Jeff is very outgoing and has a lot of energy for experiences, for doing stuff ... travel and things. He makes the most of life. He's enthusiastic and positive and sees the good in other people. I really like that about him." Shelley added, "I think they would have got along – they are both sports mad." Shelley pondered about how good it would have been if Dad and Jeff could have gone to a football game together. Asked if she had a sense of what Dad would have offered regarding their plans to move in together, Shelley sighed and said, "I feel Dad would say, 'Take a leap of faith and if things don't go as planned, it's not the end of the world. ... You'll be alright.'" A conversation exploring Shelley's resilience, and the many ways that she had not only survived but thrived, caused Shelley to comment in a surprised voice, "I guess I will, you know, be alright."

Shelley mused, "In 30 years' time the percentage of Dad being here will be so small." There is a deep sadness in this knowledge. However, as she thought about her father, Shelley tentatively acknowledged that "Dad and I have a similar sense of humor and mannerisms, we saw things the same way. We laughed about the same things." The therapist noted that we get to know ourselves through our intimate relationships, and therefore, paradoxically, in her relationship with Jeff she will be learning about those parts of her that are like her father. As the session moved to a close the therapist imagined that Dad would be pleased to see Shelley happy and living her life well. "I know Dad would," Shelley agreed. "Obviously I love Dad in spite of what he did – I would do anything if it could have been different."

The case study ends at this arbitrary juncture; however, as has been illustrated by Shelly's story, as she matures, she will continue to reflect on and reconstruct her relationship with her father in ways she hopes will create possibilities for relational growth (Calhoun & Tedeschi, 2006; Sands & Tennant, 2010). These meaning-reconstruction processes may be more apparent at significant moments in her life – for example, when she becomes a mother and when she reaches the age at which her father made that fateful decision. However, throughout her life there will be a thousand other moments when she will find herself reflecting on the tragedy of her father's death and reconstructing meaning.

Conclusions

This chapter has reviewed meaning reconstruction theory, an approach to bereavement that has received increasing support in the broader literature on adaptation to life-altering loss, though its application to suicide bereavement is only beginning to be explored. Summarizing the research done to date, this brief review suggests some of the potential measures and methods associated with this perspective. It also illustrates in opening and closing case studies several of its clinical implications for assessment and intervention in the wake of suicide loss. Ultimately, the meaning making model appears well positioned to enrich postvention efforts by providing a framework for understanding not only the immediate aftermath of traumatic loss, but also the process of meaning reconstruction that can extend across the survivor's life span.

Corresponding author

Robert A. Neimeyer
Department of Psychology
University of Memphis
Memphis, TN
USA
neimeyer@memphis.edu

References

Attig, T. (1996). *How we grieve: Relearning the world.* New York, NY: Oxford University Press. http://doi.org/10.1093/acprof:oso/9780195074567.001.0001

Burke, L.A., & Neimeyer, R.A. (2014). Compicated spiritual grief. I: Relation to complicated grief symptomatology following violent death bereavement. *Death Studies, 38*(4), 259–267. http://doi.org/10.1080/07481187.2013.829372

Burke, L.A., Neimeyer, R.A., Holland, J.M., Dennard, S., Oliver, L., & Shear, M.K. (2014). Inventory of Complicated Spiritual Grief: Development and validation of a new measure. *Death Studies, 38*(4), 239–250. http://doi.org/10.1080/07481187.2013.810098

Burke, L.A., Neimeyer, R.A., Young, A.J., & Piazza-Bonin, E. (2014). Complicated spiritual grief. II: A deductive inquiry following the loss of a loved one. *Death Studies, 38*(4), 268–281. http://doi.org/10.1080/07481187.2013.829373

Calhoun, L., & Tedeschi, R.G. (Eds.). (2006). *Handbook of posttraumatic growth.* Mahwah, NJ: Lawrence Erlbaum.

Cerel, J., Jordan, J.R., & Duberstein, P.R. (2008). The impact of suicide on the family. *Crisis, 29*(1), 38–44. http://doi.org/10.1027/0227-5910.29.1.38

Cerel, J., McIntosh, J.L., Neimeyer, R.A., Maple, M., & Marshall, D. (2014). The continuum of "survivorship": Definitional issues in the aftermath of suicide. *Suicide and Life-Threatening Behavior, 44*(6), 591–600. http://doi.org/10.1111/sltb.12093

Coleman, R.A., & Neimeyer, R.A. (2010). Measuring meaning: Searching for and making sense of spousal loss in later life. *Death Studies, 34*(9), 804–834. http://doi.org/10.1080/07481181003761625

Currier, J. M., Holland, J. M., & Neimeyer, R. A. (2006). Sense making, grief and the experience of violent loss: Toward a mediational model. *Death Studies, 30*(5), 403–428. http://doi.org/10.1080/07481180600614351

Currier, J. M., Holland, J. M., & Neimeyer, R. A. (2009). Assumptive worldviews and problematic reactions to bereavement. *Journal of Loss and Trauma, 14*(3), 181–195. http://doi.org/10.1080/15325020802537153

Currier, J. M., Holland, J. M., & Neimeyer, R. A. (2012). Prolonged grief symptoms and growth in the first two years of bereavement: Evidence for a non-linear association. *Traumatology, 18*(4), 65–71. http://doi.org/10.1177/1534765612438948

Currier, J. M., Malott, J., Martinez, T. E., Sandy, C., & Neimeyer, R. A. (2013). Bereavement, religion and posttraumatic growth: A matched control group investigation. *Psychology of Religion and Spirituality, 5*(2), 69–77. http://doi.org/10.1037/a0027708

Gillies, J., & Neimeyer, R. A. (2006). Loss, grief and the search for significance: Toward a model of meaning reconstruction in bereavement. *Journal of Constructivist Psychology, 19*(1), 31–65. http://doi.org/10.1080/10720530500311182

Gillies, J., Neimeyer, R. A., & Milman, E. (2014). The Meaning of Loss Codebook: Construction of a system for analyzing meanings made in bereavement. *Death Studies, 38*(4), 207–216. http://doi.org/10.1080/07481187.2013.829367

Gillies, J., Neimeyer, R. A., & Milman, E. (2015). The Grief and Meaning Reconstruction Inventory: Initial validation of a new measure. *Death Studies, 39*(2), 61–74. http://doi.org/10.1080/07481187.2014.907089

Holland, J. M., Currier, J. M., Coleman, R. A., & Neimeyer, R. A. (2010). The Integration of Stressful Life Experiences Scale (ISLES): Development and initial validation of a new measure. *International Journal of Stress Management, 17*(4), 325–352. http://doi.org/10.1037/a0020892

Holland, J. M., Currier, J. M., & Neimeyer, R. A. (2006). Meaning reconstruction in the first two years of bereavement: The role of sense-making and benefit-finding. *Omega: Journal of Death and Dying, 53*(3), 175–191. http://doi.org/10.2190/FKM2-YJTY-F9VV-9XWY

Holland, J. M., Currier, J. M., & Neimeyer, R. A. (2014). Validation of the Integration of Stressful Life Experiences Scale – Short Form in a bereaved sample. *Death Studies, 38*(4), 234–238. http://doi.org/10.1080/07481187.2013.829369

Holland, J. M., & Neimeyer, R. A. (2010). An examination of stage theory of grief among individuals bereaved by natural and violent causes: A meaning-oriented contribution. *Omega, 61*, 103–120.

Holland, J. M., & Neimeyer, R. A. (2011). Separation and traumatic distress in prolonged grief: The role of cause of death and relationship to the deceased. *Journal of Psychopathology and Behavioral Assessment, 33*(2), 254–263. http://doi.org/10.1007/s10862-010-9214-5

Janoff-Bullman, R. (1992). *Shattered assumptions: Towards a new psychology of trauma.* New York, NY: Free Press.

Janoff-Bulman, R., & Berger, A. R. (2000). The other side of trauma. In J. H. Harvey & E. D. Miller (Eds.), *Loss and trauma: General and close relationship perspectives* (pp. 29–44). Philadelphia, PA: Brunner Mazel.

Jordan, J. R. (2011). The principles of grief counseling with adult survivors. In J. R. Jordan & J. L. McIntosh (Eds.), *Grief after suicide* (pp. 179–223). New York, NY: Routledge.

Keesee, N. J., Currier, J. M., & Neimeyer, R. A. (2008). Predictors of grief following the death of one's child: The contribution of finding meaning. *Journal of Clinical Psychology, 64*(10), 1145–1163. http://doi.org/10.1002/jclp.20502

Kelly, G. A. (1955). *The psychology of personal constructs.* New York, NY: Norton.

Lichtenthal, W. G., Burke, L. A., & Neimeyer, R. A. (2011). Religious coping and meaning-making following the loss of a loved one. *Counseling and Spirituality, 30*(2), 113–136.

Lichtenthal, W. G., & Cruess, D. G. (2010). Effects of directed written disclosure on grief and distress symptoms among bereaved individuals. *Death Studies, 34*(6), 475–499. http://doi.org/10.1080/07481187.2010.483332

Lichtenthal, W. G., Currier, J. M., Neimeyer, R. A., & Keesee, N. J. (2010). Sense and significance: A mixed methods examination of meaning-making following the loss of one's child. *Journal of Clinical Psychology, 66*(7), 791–812.

Lichtenthal, W. G., Neimeyer, R. A., Currier, J. M., Roberts, K., & Jordan, N. (2013). Cause of death and the quest for meaning after the loss of a child. *Death Studies, 37*(4), 311–342. http://doi.org/10.1080/07481187.2012.673533

Linn-Gust, M. (2004). *Do they have bad days in heaven? Surviving the suicide loss of a sibling.* Albuquerque, NM: Chellehead Works.

Neimeyer, R. A. (Ed.). (2001). *Meaning reconstruction and the experience of loss.* Washington, DC: American Psychological Association. http://doi.org/10.1037/10397-000

Neimeyer, R. A. (2004). Fostering posttraumatic growth: A narrative contribution. *Psychological Inquiry, 15*(1), 53–59.

Neimeyer, R. A. (2006). Widowhood, grief and the quest for meaning: A narrative perspective on resilience. In D. Carr, R. M. Nesse, & C. B. Wortman (Eds.), *Spousal bereavement in late life* (pp. 227–252). New York, NY: Springer.

Neimeyer, R. A. (Ed.). (2012). *Techniques of grief therapy: Creative practices for counseling the bereaved.* New York, NY: Routledge.

Neimeyer, R. A. (Ed.). (2016). *Techniques of grief therapy: Assessment and intervention.* New York, NY: Routledge.

Neimeyer, R. A., & Burke, L. A. (2015). Loss, grief and spiritual struggle: The quest for meaning in bereavement. *Religion, Brain & Behavior, 5*(2), 131–138. http://doi.org/10.1080/2153599X.2014.891253

Neimeyer, R. A., & Cacciatore, J. (2015). Toward a developmental theory of grief. In R. A. Neimeyer (Ed.), *Techniques of grief therapy: Assessment and intervention* (pp. 3–13). New York, NY: Routledge.

Neimeyer, R. A., & Cerel, J. (2015). Surviving suicide loss: Recommendations for research. *Acta Universitaria, 25*(2), 5–9.

Neimeyer, R. A., Prigerson, H., & Davies, B. (2002). Mourning and meaning. *American Behavioral Scientist, 46*(2), 235–251. http://doi.org/10.1177/000276402236676

Neimeyer, R. A., & Sands, D. C. (2011). Meaning reconstruction in bereavement: From principles to practice. In R. A. Neimeyer, D. L. Harris, H. R. Winokuer, & G. F. Thornton (Eds.), *Grief and bereavement in contemporary society: Bridging research and practice* (pp. 9–22). New York, NY: Routledge.

Neimeyer, R. A., & Thompson, B. E. (2014). Meaning making and the art of grief therapy. In B. E. Thompson & R. A. Neimeyer (Eds.), *Grief and the expressive arts: Practices for creating meaning* (pp. 3–13). New York, NY: Routledge.

Neimeyer, R. A., & Young-Eisendrath, P. (2015). Assessing a Buddhist treatment for bereavement and loss: The Mustard Seed Project. *Death Studies, 39*(5), 263–273. http://doi.org/10.1080/07481187.2014.937973

Pitman, A., Osborn, D., King, M., & Erlangsen, A. (2014). Effects of suicide bereavement on mental health and suicide risk. *The Lancet Psychiatry, 1*(1), 86–94. http://doi.org/10.1016/S2215-0366(14)70224-X

Saindon, C., Rheingold, A., Baddeley, J., Wallace, M., Brown, C., & Rynearson, E. K. (2014). Restorative retelling for violent loss: An open clinical trial. *Death Studies, 38*(4), 251–258. http://doi.org/10.1080/07481187.2013.783654

Sands, D. C. (2009). A tripartite model of suicide grief: Meaning-making and the relationship with the deceased. *Grief Matters: The Australian Journal of Grief and Bereavement, 12*(1), 10–17.

Sands, D. C. (2010). *Red chocolate elephants: For children bereaved by suicide.* Sydney, Australia: Karridale.

Sands, D. C. (2012). The body of trust. In R. A. Neimeyer (Ed.), *Grief therapy: Creative strategies for counseling the bereaved* (pp. 76–79). New York, NY: Routledge.

Sands, D. C. (2014). Restoring the heartbeat of hope following suicide. In B. R. Thompson & R. A. Neimeyer (Eds.), *Grief and the expressive arts: Practices for creating meaning* (pp. 215–221). New York, NY: Routledge.

Sands, D. C., Jordan, J. R., & Neimeyer, R. A. (2011). The meanings of suicide: A narrative approach to healing. In J. R. Jordan & J. L. McIntosh (Eds.), *Grief after suicide* (pp. 249–282). New York, NY: Routledge.

Sands, D. C., & North, J. L. (2014). Family therapy following suicide. In D. W. Kissane & F. Parnes (Eds.), *Bereavement care for families* (pp. 154–170). New York, NY: Routledge.

Sands, D., & Tennant, M. (2010). Transformative learning in the context of suicide bereavement. *Adult Education Quarterly, 60*(2), 99–121. http://doi.org/10.1177/0741713609349932

Schreiber, J., Sands, D., & Jordan, J. (2015). The perceived experience of children bereaved by parental suicide. *Omega: Journal of Death and Dying.* doi:10.1177/0030222815612297 http://doi.org/10.1177/0030222815612297

Shear, M. K., Frank, E., Houch, P. R., & Reynolds, C. F. (2005). Treatment of complicated grief: A randomized controlled trial. *Journal of the American Medical Association, 293*(1), 2601–2608. http://doi.org/10.1001/jama.293.21.2601

Shear, M. K., Wang, Y., Skriskaya, N., Duan, N., Mauro, C., & Ghesquiere, A. (2014). Treatment of complicated grief in elderly persons: A randomized clinical trial. *JAMA Psychiatry, 71*(11), 1287–1295. http://doi.org/10.1001/jamapsychiatry.2014.1242

Survivors of Suicide Loss Task Force. (2015). *Responding to grief, trauma and distress after suicide: US national guidelines*. Washington, DC: National Action Alliance for Suicide Prevention.

Thompson, B. E., & Neimeyer, R. A. (Eds.). (2014). *Grief and the expressive arts: Practices for creating meaning*. New York, NY: Routledge.

Chapter 8

The Growing Flower Model of Reintegration After Suicide

Vita Poštuvan

Slovenian Centre for Suicide Research, Andrej Marušič Institute, University of Primorska, Koper, Slovenia

Abstract: This chapter presents the growing flower model of reintegration after bereavement through suicide. Reintegration is understood as reestablishing the everyday life patterns and reengagement in daily family, work, and community life. The model is the result of a qualitative study, based on 16 semistructured in-depth interviews with suicide survivors. The model includes four levels of social relations (i.e., the bereaved person, family, social network, systems) and eight themes: (a) the event of suicide; (b) funeral and rituals; (c) expression of emotions; (d) negative reactions such as guilt, blame, condemnation, and clichés; (e) looking for explanations for the suicide; (f) bereavement support; (g) spirituality; and (h) meaning making, personal growth, and identity changes. The model can be very valuable as a psychoeducational tool in suicide bereavement support and education, and the chapter concludes with a few examples of its utility.

Introduction

After a suicide, the bereaved, also called *suicide survivors,* often face many psychological, physical, and social changes in their everyday life (Andriessen, 2009; Andriessen, Draper, Dudley, & Mitchell, 2015). Grief is an appropriate and a healthy response to the loss (Corr & Corr, 2009, Stroebe, Hanson, Schut, & Stroebe, 2011), and its common emotional responses include feelings of pain (physical and psychological), anger, regret, anxiety and fear, intrusive visual images, mental disorganization, feeling overwhelmed, relief, and loneliness. Ways of coping with emotional pain are various. They may be manifested as numbness and doubt, emotional control, changed perspective (e.g., intellectualization, rationalization, humor), avoidance or exposure, engagement in activities, passive distractions, expressions, or surrender to the pleasures of food or drink (Shuchter & Zisook, 1993). Some bereaved are preoccupied with the image of the deceased, visual memories of the circumstances around death, feelings of guilt, hostile reactions, and the tendency to become alienated from other friends and relatives (Eisma et al., 2014, Grad, 2011, Jordan, 2008, Lindemann & Greer, 1972). There may be changes in the social and professional functioning of the bereaved, including their relationships with the family and friends, as well as identity changes related to how the bereaved experience themselves and the world after the loss (Shuchter & Zisook, 1993). Many bereaved do not want to, or cannot, get involved in normal everyday life, such as work, family duties, hobbies, household activities, etc., which in some cases may be related to their active or passive avoidance of everyday social situations (Wciss, 2011, Palgi & Abramovitch, 1984).

Rituals in Bereavement

Even though the alienation and self-exclusion of bereaved from everyday life may be a normal immediate reaction to death, anthropologists emphasize the role of rituals in this process (Palgi & Abramovitch, 1984). Rituals help to overcome the alienation of the bereaved by offering engagement, giving a place to and prescribed way of expressing the intense emotions surrounding death. Rituals can be understood as a dialectic resolution of disruptive tendencies which operate in times of social crisis (Palgi & Abramovitch, 1984, p. 389); in other words, the rituals help to deal with the strong emotional reactions after the death. The emotions surrounding death are complex and contradictory: Love and attachment to the dead person are mixed with the fear of the corpse (Malinowski, 2004). Elements are intertwined and reflected in spontaneous behavior and death rituals. Development of funeral customs is a part of self-preservation, and these customs help to handle the fear of the corpse, which symbolizes the fear of annihilation. As such, rituals help to control the emotional forces triggered in contact with death and the body of the deceased, which, if enacted, could endanger the cohesion of the community. Ritualized despair, the funeral ceremony, mourning, etc., are ways to express the feelings of bereaved relatives, provide a space for the wider social network to express condolences, and help reestablish social order and community cohesion and solidarity, as well as tradition and culture (Malinowski, 2004; Palgi & Abramovitch, 1984; Petrović, 2002).

Reintegration After the Loss

The suicide of a close person can be a life-changing experience. Dealing with such a loss depends on the interaction between a number of factors, such as personality traits, coping strategies, cognitive appraisals, adaptation abilities, and physical and social environment of the bereaved, including rituals (Moos & Schaefer, 1987). A *reintegrated life* can be considered a benign outcome of the grieving process. The term *reintegration* is often used in rehabilitation studies to describe the "reorganization of physical, psychological, and social characteristics of an individual into a harmonious whole so that one can resume well-adjusted living after incapacitating illness or trauma" (Wood-Dauphinee & Williams, 1987, p. 492). It has also been used in the context of disaster or critical incident recovery, including sudden death cases (Roesler, Ward, & Short, 2009). Being well-integrated relates to being a part of family and community life, successfully taking up roles and responsibilities, and being an active and contributing member of one's social groups and society as a whole (Dijkers, 1998).

Previous studies have shown that most suicide survivors manage to cope with the death and do not experience (many) long-term negative outcomes from the loss (e.g., Dunne & Dunne-Maxim, 2009). Reestablishing life patterns of the bereaved and their engagement in daily family, work, and community life can be understood as the *reintegration process*. The focus of the study presented in this chapter was to understand the reintegration process of suicide survivors.

Method

Sample

Nineteen suicide survivors participated in the study, mostly (79 %) close family members of the deceased person, such as children, siblings, or spouses of the deceased. The average age of participants was 40.4 years, and 84 % of participants were females. Half of the participants (47 %) lived in a major city, and the rest lived in suburbs, smaller cities, or villages. More than half (58%) had a university education, and a similar proportion was in full-time employment; the others had lower education levels and were unemployed, students, or retired. Time since death, a variable that may help to understand the differences in the process of bereavement and reintegration, ranged from 3 months to 34 years. Three interviews were excluded from the analysis because the participants were not in a close relationship to a person who had died by suicide – for example, they were an acquaintance or a distant family member, and they were not personally affected by the death.

Instruments

A semistructured in-depth interview was developed for the study. It included questions related to the circumstances and experiences of suicide (e.g., how the bereaved experienced the situation around the death), the social network of the bereaved (e.g., who was supporting the bereaved person, who was involved at the time of death or later), rituals (e.g., which rituals took place and how this was done), attachment (how the bereaved perceived the relationship with the deceased before and after the death), and the reintegration process of the bereaved (e.g., how they experienced the phases of bereavement, how they coped with the loss and what helped them), and their understanding of the suicide (e.g., how they perceived the suicide).

In line with the principles of constructivist approaches to grounded theory (Charmaz, 2006), the initial set of questions was further informed and modified following each concluded interview. Additional questions on the details of suicide (e.g., which method was used and how it was perceived by the bereaved), spirituality (e.g., what role spiritual experiences or dreams played in the grief process), and the broader social network (e.g., how more distant people, such as acquaintances, responded to the bereaved) were added in this process. The average length of the interview was 113 min.

Procedure

Participants in different parts of Slovenia were recruited through social networks and organizations such as the University of Primorska newsletter, NGO DAM (an nongovernmental association of people with depression and anxiety), the Slovenian Hospice Association, the Institute of Public Health, counseling centers, and the media. Prior to each face-to-face interview, details of the study were explained in a telephone conversation, and participants signed an informed consent form before the interviews. The interviews were recorded and transcribed, paying attention to emotional responses of participants, their nonverbal signs, pauses, etc.

The analytical process was based on the principles of grounded theory. The approach helped to find detailed codes, which were very close to the raw data. The study adopted a bottom-up approach (i.e., looking at the data from a perspective less influenced by previous concepts), which helped to establish new connections between the codes. The analysis was finalized after a detailed hermeneutic process of engaging and analyzing the data (Charmaz, 2006).

ATLAS.ti software (ATLAS.ti, 2009) was used to engage in initial (very close to raw data), focused (aiming to cluster common and important themes), and axial (aiming to explain hierarchical relationships) coding (Charmaz, 2006). Additional interviews were performed to assess the validity of the study results and the final model. The protocol of the study was approved by the National Medical Ethics Committee in Slovenia.

Results

In total 2,631 quotations (meaningful units) were identified and assigned a specific name. These were clustered in 263 initial codes (each having more than three quotations), which were merged into 30 focused codes. Next, in the axial coding, 15 main concepts were identified:
1. reasons for suicide;
2. relationship between deceased and bereaved and their life before the suicide;
3. the event of the suicide;
4. funeral and bereavement rituals;
5. participants' experience of suicide;
6. participants' experiencing themselves after suicide;
7. guilt;
8. reactions of and experience of social network and society;
9. interpersonal relationships of suicide survivors;
10. reactions of and experiences with help systems;
11. understanding suicide and death;
12. attachment and relationships after death;
13. spirituality, dreams and parapsychological experiences;
14. reintegration after suicide; and
15. meaning making and impact on the future.

The 15 axial codes offered a format to understand the details of each of the eight main themes, and allowed creation of a coherent *growing flower model* presenting the process of reintegration and bereavement in a new way.

Interpretation of the Model

The growing flower model includes four levels of reintegration after suicide and eight themes (Poštuvan, 2014). The four levels refer to (1) the bereaved person; (2) their family; (3) a social network, such as acquaintances, colleagues, and neighbors, and (4) systems in the society (such as help systems, police, social care, funeral management, etc.). These levels of reintegration can be represented as concentric circles, where the bereaved person is in the innermost part (see **Figure 8.1**). There is interaction and communication between the levels, illustrated by the dotted lines in Figure 8.1.

All four levels play a role in the eight themes of the reintegration process: (a) the event of the suicide; (b) funeral and rituals; (c) expression of emotions; (d) negative reactions: guilt, condemnation, and clichés; (e) looking for explanations for the suicide; (f) bereavement support, (g) the importance of spirituality, and (h) meaning making, personal growth, and identity changes. In the *growing flower model*, these themes are represented as petals on the concentric circles, forming the figure of a flower (**Figure 8.2**).

a. The Event of Suicide

> I came home, unlocked the doors and called for my dad. Bathroom doors were opened, so I looked in – and there he was: hanging. It was horrible. He wanted to cut himself first, but did not succeed. So, there was blood everywhere. I started to scream and ran out to the neighbors. (Daughter, 49 years old)

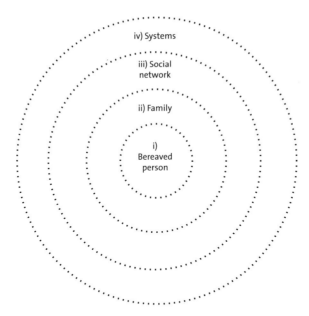

Figure 8.1.   Levels of reintegration after suicide.

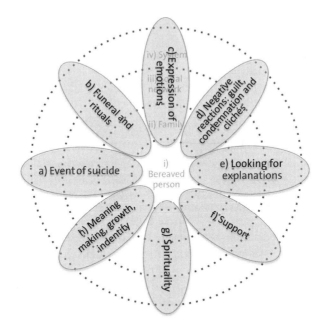

Figure 8.2.   Levels and themes of reintegration process.

The event of suicide /is a starting point for the bereaved person's journey. It touches on how suicide survivors receive the news about the death (e.g., they find the dead body, look for the missing person, or hear about the death from others), which method of suicide was used, how the body looked, and how it was treated (e.g., with respect and care, allowing contact and expressing goodbyes, a last opportunity for reconciliation). The presence of other people may influence the event. Family members may come to say goodbye or pay condolences, and others may be involved, such as neighbors, the police, health services, or strangers who found the body. This is a very emotional time for the bereaved, and they may react in many ways. First responders and services should be trained and have appropriate procedures. Some of the bereaved can remember the exact words that they heard at the scene of suicide, and these become a part of their experience.

b. Funeral and Rituals

> Preparing for the funeral, that is something. You want to make everything perfect. Somehow to please him [the deceased] and his sons, in particular. So, they [the sons] have chosen the urn, clothing.... (Sister, 45 years old)

The funeral and other rituals around death give the bereaved guidance on how to behave in these situations. The funeral is usually a very emotional and significant ritual, which provides a two-way means of communication. On the one hand, the bereaved communicate their wishes, needs, and worldviews through the nature and format of the ritual. Some people arrange a big public funeral, while others focus on close family members; sometimes influenced by the bereaved's perception of the wishes of the deceased. On the other hand, the funeral offers the broader social network an opportunity to express their condolences; this can be done through attending the ritual or through socially prescribed ways, such as giving gifts, cards, etc. In this process, the four levels of the growing flower model come into proximity and influence the process of bereavement and reintegration. Yet, more intimate rituals, such as lighting of candles and celebrating anniversaries and other important dates, have become more popular than the publicly expressed rituals, such as wearing mourning clothes. Rigid rituals or the public expectations of mourning behavior can be experienced as commitments that do not necessary fit the individual's desired way to express their emotions.

c. Emotions and Their Expression

> First came the shock. That April was a catastrophe. There was anger, a lot of it. And sadness – first three months I cried so much. But I was also angry. I mean, why did he do that to me? I did not deserve it! Not at my age – I wanted to be with him for the rest of my life. (Wife, 39 years old)

Shock, pain, sadness, anger, a sense of injustice, relief, shame, fear, helplessness, and loneliness were the most common emotions experienced by suicide survivors participating in the study. This complex system of emotions could be expressed in a way that positively affected the bereaved, such as conveying these emotions in a safe place, while interacting with family and other people, or engaging in behaviors distracting from the emotional triggers, such as being active at work, moving to a new place (for a holiday or finding a new place to live), or taking up a hobby. Other studies also found that a capacity to minimize negative emotions during bereavement can enable adaptation, problem solving, and concern for others, and can improve everyday functioning in areas of personal importance (Bonanno & Kaltman, 1999).

Sometimes participants experienced difficulties related to intrapersonal processes, such as having no desire to talk about suicide even when others were willing to listen, a decline in personal ambitions or worsening of unhealthy habits such as substance (alcohol) abuse. It can be argued that the expression of negative emotions is more difficult (or at least less desirable) on an interpersonal or society level, and therefore often takes place at an intrapersonal level.

Moreover, the bereaved need to feel that they are allowed to express their feelings in their own way, even if they feel they are violating or breaking personal or social norms. An everyday conversation, encouraging good interpersonal relationships or providing professional help, might reduce that feeling of breaking norms, and support the bereavement process. Others, included in Levels 2–4 of the growing flower model, such as relatives, friends, and people working in different organizations, may also experience emotional reactions following a suicide, and should be included in postvention interventions.

d. Negative Reactions: Guilt, Blame, Condemnation, and Clichés

> Guilt. Guilt. I mean, I think you can never erase it. Not in these matters. And it is so different here than in other types of death. There are hundred ways how you can feel it. And it is hard to live with it. (Daughter, 25 years old)

Blame and condemnation relate to the reactions of others and their speculations about the bereaved person's potential contribution to the suicide, and how the death could have been prevented. This may be particularly relevant if the deceased accused the bereaved for the act of suicide – for example, in a suicide note. Guilt might result in self-blame and even self-stigmatization, resulting in a vicious circle (the bereaved may believe that they do not deserve help) and lack of social support. Clichés, such as "it will be all right" or "everything happens for a reason," can be used to avoid direct communication with the bereaved. This may be related to feelings of guilt or uneasiness with the topic of suicide, and may result in inhibited social support (Cvinar, 2005; Dunn & Morrish-Vidners, 1987).

e. Looking for explanations

> They may accept me in the same way [even if they know about the suicide]. But, I would be ashamed if they knew. And then they would want to know why it happened. (Daughter, 37 years old)

The bereaved often try to understand why the deceased died by suicide. These attempts to understand why can be communicated to the family, society, and other support systems, especially medical professionals, or can turn into rumination about the death. Other people in the social environment of the bereaved may also seek explanations for the suicide, and this may be perceived by suicide survivors as gossiping or spreading rumors. Despite the negative connotations for the bereaved, this process of seeking explanations aims to reconfirm the social values and stability of the social order (Leming & Dickinson, 2011, Malinowski, 2004; Palgi & Abramovitch, 1984; Petrović, 2002).

f. Support

> I didn't find any support for the bereaved after suicide. It would be great if we could somehow meet. As AA [Alcoholics Anonymous] do – so, we could face our loss. (Daughter, 22 years old)

Support (and even the awareness that it is available if needed) can help boost the individual's resilience after a stressful event and can help cope with the loss. A sincere willingness to help and support the bereaved might be expressed in many direct and indirect ways, including providing everyday practical help. In the growing flower model, the available support is presented at all levels; from very close and more distant personal relationships (Levels 2 and 3) to professional help (Level 4).

g. Spirituality

> I am [a] very rational person. But after three months I had a dream. And he [the deceased] came over and … (cries) … so, he came to say goodbye. And I remember everything from that dream. It helped me to get over. (Sister, 39 years old)

Spirituality can be an important theme for the bereaved, although it can be expressed or experienced in many different ways (see Chapter 16 in this volume). For some of the bereaved, spirituality is a part of their religious views, others see it as a way of connecting with the deceased, while still others experience parapsychological phenomena, such as seeing or hearing the deceased, or report vivid dreams. Such experiences can be a part of an individual's story or support explanations about life after death. The spiritual dimension can help the bereaved to cope and give them comfort.

h. Meaning Making, Personal Growth, and Identity Changes

> Well, no story is black-and-white, they all have grey areas. I am so sure I would not be me if it wasn't for this. It was the most important story or event of my life. (Daughter, 50 years old)

Many suicide survivors lose the roles and the identity they had before the suicide, and their self-perception may change because of the loss. The process of bereavement can be a time of confusion and crisis, involving a change of identity and posttraumatic growth (Neimeyer, Baldwin, & Gillies, 2006; Padna, 2006; Smith, Joseph, & Nair, 2011). Suicide survivors may experience the suicide and the reintegration process as a push toward personal development and growth.

Personal Growth: Attachment and Relationship With the Deceased

> I have a feeling she is always here…. Right here – standing beside me. (Daughter, 25 years old)

The relationship between the bereaved and the deceased is an important component of the reintegration process after a suicide. Suicide survivors often report that they have not lost their relationship with the deceased; instead, they experience a changed relationship (Bowlby, 1980; Sands, Jordan, & Neimeyer, 2011; Worden, 2009; also see Chapter 5, Chapter 6, and Chapter 7). According to the growing flower model, the "flower" has grown based on the relationship the deceased and bereaved person had before the death. Attachment after the death is presented in the model as the stalk of the flower, and the deceased person as the soil or ground, which is connected with the petals and with all of the layers of the flower.

At the time of the death, the bereaved person feels closely attached to the deceased. Over time, they experience a distancing, but this process is not linear. The distance may seem shorter at specific moments, such as anniversaries, birthdays, holidays, important life events, or a visit to the grave. This process is depicted in the changing pattern of closeness of flower and soil in

Figure 8.3.   Growing flower model representing suicide survivors' reintegration over time.

the model (**Figure 8.3**). These changes and variations in the relationship represent the process of personal growth and reintegration after suicide. The time frame of this process is different for every bereaved person, and it can range from a few months to decades. Moreover, some bereaved may never fully reintegrate after the suicide. According to the growing flower model, reintegration is the result of a nonlinear but growing process, during which the suicide survivor may integrate the experience of suicide into their changed relationship with the deceased and their representation about themselves, others, and the world.

Implications for Practice

The growing flower model offers a holistic understanding of bereavement after suicide and the process of reintegration, based on a number of levels and themes. It provides a useful framework for designing and implementing interventions for suicide survivors, and can be used as a psychoeducational tool in supportive or psychotherapeutic interventions targeting individuals bereaved by suicide or other persons closely related to the bereaved (**Vignette 1**). The growing flower model is also a useful didactic tool in public health interventions to explain the experiences after suicide to professional gatekeepers (**Vignette 2**), and to a broader lay public (**Vignette 3**).

Vignette 1

A 22-year-old student came for counseling, a month after losing her father to suicide. She had problems controlling her anger and was not able to understand the event. The growing flower model was introduced to her at the beginning of therapy. It helped her conceptualize her experience and understand where she was in the bereavement process. The model helped her realize the importance of expressing emotions and accepting the changes she was experiencing.

At the beginning it was not easy for the client to understand the concepts related to growth, but 5 months after death she was able to color half of the petals, saying, "I feel I am half way through." Thirteen months after the suicide, she observed her anger had changed since the time of death, and she was able to see the path behind her. The visual presentation of the growing flower model helped her to express emotions at the 1-year anniversary of the death. She also found dance and arts helpful.

Vignette 2

Firefighters attended a workshop on suicide to increase their understanding of suicide, suicide bereavement, and reintegration after the loss. The growing flower model was used to explain the role and the possible impact of different social systems on the bereaved person. The firefighters saw that their behavior at the death scene might influence suicide survivors. At the same time, they were able to reflect on how suicide might impact them.

Vignette 3

*The metaphor of the flower and the growing flower model was used in a leaflet about suicide bereavement for lay public (**Figure 8.4**). The visual design (i.e., a flower) emphasized the content of the model. The leaflet helped to raise awareness within a broader campaign regarding coping with suicide bereavement among the general public.*

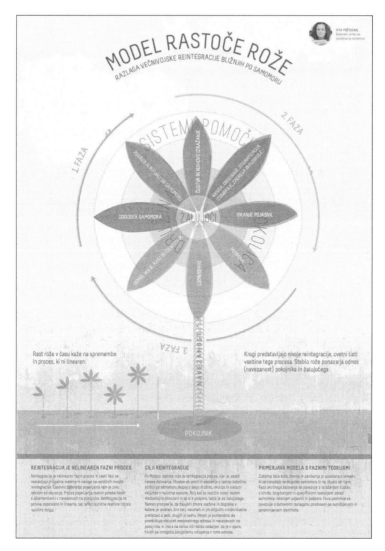

Figure 8.4.   Growing flower model in a leaflet for the lay public (in Slovene). Source: Slovene Centre for Suicide Research, Andrej Marušič Institute, University of Primorska, 2015. Reprinted by permission.

In all cases presented here, the growing flower model was a valuable visual analogy of the experiences of suicide survivors. The metaphor of a growing flower may help the lay public and professionals remember the process, levels, and themes (content) of bereavement and re-integration. Flowers are a powerful symbol used in many rituals, including those around death. Another strength of the model is the inclusion of different social levels and social groups, showing the magnitude and the range of the impact a suicide death may have.

Acknowledgments

This chapter is based on the author's PhD thesis (Poštuvan, 2014) prepared under the mentorship of Prof. Onja T. Grad.

Corresponding author

Vita Poštuvan
Slovenian Centre for Suicide Research
Andrej Marušič Institute
University of Primorska
Muzejski trg 2
6000 Koper
Slovenia
vita.postuvan@upr.si

References

Andriessen, K., Draper, B., Dudley, M., & Mitchell, P. B. (2015). Bereavement after suicide. Disentangling clues to better help bereaved adolescents. *Crisis, 36*(5), 299–303. http://doi.org/10.1027/0227-5910/a000339

Andriessen, K. (2009). Can postvention be prevention? *Crisis, 30*(1), 43–47. http://doi.org/10.1027/0227-5910.30.1.43

ATLAS.ti. (2009). *Software for qualitative data analysis management, and model building* [Computer software]. Berlin, Germany: Scientific Software Development.

Bowlby, J. (1980). *Attachment and loss: Loss – Sadness and depression* (Vol. 3). London, UK: Pimlico.

Bonanno, G. A., & Kaltman, S. (1999). Toward an integrative perspective on bereavement. *Psychological Bulletin, 125*(6), 760–776. http://doi.org/10.1037/0033-2909.125.6.760

Charmaz, K. (2006). *Constructing grounded theory: A practical guide through qualitative analysis.* London, UK: Sage.

Corr, C. A., & Corr, D. M. (2009). *Death and dying, life and living.* Pacific Grove, CA: Brooks/Cole.

Cvinar, J. G. (2005). Do suicide survivors suffer social stigma: A review of the literature. *Perspectives in Psychiatric Care, 41*(1), 14–21. http://doi.org/10.1111/j.0031-5990.2005.00004.x

Dijkers, M. (1998). Community integration: Conceptual issues and measurement approaches in rehabilitation research. *Topics in Spinal Cord Injury Rehabilitation, 1*(4), 1–15. http://doi.org/10.1310/BJJA-2018-45KL-0VTL

Dunn, R. G., & Morrish-Vidners, D. (1987). The psychological and social experience of suicide survivors. *Omega: Journal of Death and Dying, 18*(3), 175–215. http://doi.org/10.2190/6K91-GN16-0DF6-5FUE

Dunne, E. J., & Dunne-Maxim, K. (2009). Why suicide loss is different for the survivors. In D. Wasserman & C. Wasserman (Eds.), *Oxford textbook of suicidology and suicide prevention: A global perspective* (pp. 605–608). Oxford, UK: Oxford University Press.

Eisma, M. C., Schut, H. A. W., Stroebe, M. S., Boelen, P. A., Bout, J., & Stroebe, W. (2014). Adaptive and maladaptive rumination after loss: A three-wave longitudinal study. *British Journal of Clinical Psychology, 54*(2), 163–180. http://doi.org/10.1111/bjc.12067

Grad, O. (2011). Sequelae of suicide survivors. In R. O'Connor, S. Plat, & J. Gordon (Eds.), *International handbook of suicide prevention: Research, policy and practice* (pp. 561–576). Hoboken, NJ: Wiley-Blackwell.

Jordan, J. R. (2008). Bereavement after suicide. *Psychiatric Annals, 38*(10), 670–685. http://doi.org/10.3928/00485713-20081001-05

Leming, M., & Dickinson, G. (2011). *Understanding dying, death, and bereavement.* Stamford, CT: Cengage Learning.

Lindemann, E., & Greer, I. M. (1972). A study of grief: emotional responses to suicide. In A. Cain (Ed.), *Survivors of suicide* (pp. 63–69). Springfield, IL: Charles C. Thomas.

Malinowski, B. (2004). Magic, science and religion. In A. Robben (Ed.), *Death, mourning, and burial: A cross-cultural reader* (pp. 19–22). Hoboken, NJ: Blackwell.

Moos, R. H., & Schaefer, J. A. (1987). *Coping with life crises: An integrated approach*. New York, NY: Plenum Press.

Neimeyer, R. A., Baldwin, S. a., & Gillies, J. (2006). Continuing bonds and reconstructing meaning: mitigating complications in bereavement. *Death Studies, 30*(8), 715–738. http://doi.org/10.1080/07481180600848322

Padna, L. (2006). *Meaning reconstruction and identity change in successful adjustment to conjugal bereavement*. Palo Alto, CA: Pacific Graduate School of Psychology.

Palgi, P., & Abramovitch, H. (1984). Death: A cross-cultural perspective. *Annual Reviews, 13*(10), 385–417.

Petrović, M. (2002). Telo med smrtjo in življenjem [Body between death and life]. *Poligrafi, 7*(27/28), 157–180.

Poštuvan, V. (2014). *Doživljanje samomora ter varovalni dejavniki in dejavniki tveganja v procesu reintegracije bližnjih po samomoru* [Experience of suicide and protective and risk factors in the process of suicide survivors' reintegration] (Doctoral dissertation). Ljubljana, Slovenia: Filozofska Fakulteta.

Roesler, R., Ward, D., & Short, M. (2009). Supporting staff recovery and reintegration after a critical incident resulting in infant death. *Advances in Neonatal Care, 9*(4), 163–171. http://doi.org/10.1097/ANC.0b013e3181afab5b

Sands, D., Jordan, J., & Neimeyer, R. A. (2011). The meanings of suicide: A narrative approach to healing. In J. R. Jordan & J. McIntosh (Eds.), *Grief after suicide. Understanding the consequences and caring for the survivors* (pp. 249–282). New York, NY: Routledge.

Shuchter, S., & Zisook, S. (1993). The course of normal grief. In M. Stroebe, W. Stroebe, & R. Hansson (Eds.), *Handbook of bereavement: Theory, research, and intervention* (pp. 23–43). Cambridge, UK: Cambridge University Press.

Smith, A., Joseph, S., & Nair, R. D. (2011). An interpretative phenomenological analysis of posttraumatic growth in adults bereaved by suicide. *Loss and Trauma, 15*(5), 413–430. http://doi.org/10.1080/15325024.2011.572047

Stroebe, M. S., Hanson, R. O., Schut, H., & Stroebe, W. (2011). Bereavement research: contemporary perspectives. In M. S. Stroebe, R. O. Hanson, H. Schut, & W. Stroebe (Eds.), *Handbook of bereavement research and practice: Advances in theory and intervention* (pp. 3–25). Washington, DC: American Psychological Association.

Weiss, R. (2011). The nature and causes of grief. In M. S. Stroebe, R. O. Hanson, H. Schut, & W. Stroebe (Eds.), *Handbook of bereavement research and practice: Advances in theory and intervention* (pp. 29–44). Washington, DC: American Psychological Association.

Wood-Dauphinee, S., & Williams, J. I. (1987). Reintegration to normal living as a proxy to quality of life. *Journal of Chronic Diseases, 40*(6), 491–499. http://doi.org/10.1016/0021-9681(87)90005-1

Worden, J. W. (2009). *Grief counseling and grief therapy. A handbook for the mental health practitioner*. New York, NY: Springer.

Part II

Suicide Bereavement Support in Different Settings

Chapter 9

History of Survivor Support

John L. McIntosh[1], Iris Bolton[2], Karl Andriessen[3], and Frank Campbell[4]

[1]Academic Affairs, Indiana University South Bend, IN, USA
[2]Link Counseling Center, Atlanta, GA, USA
[3]School of Psychiatry, University of New South Wales, Sydney, Australia
[4]Campbell and Associates Consulting, LLC, Baton Rouge, LA, USA

Abstract: The resources and assistance available to significant others in the aftermath of suicide emerged initially in localized and individually developed approaches of support. Certainly, traditional therapeutic resources for the bereaved have been available. However, many of these support resources were often conceptually outside the traditional, professionally provided therapeutic approaches. The history of the survivor pioneers in North America and across the world is chronicled, along with the developments that have followed – resource development and dissemination, funding, research, advocacy, lessened stigmatization, professional organizations – and their impact on support for survivors. Crucial among these developments has been the substantial efforts of survivors themselves in raising awareness and bringing vital attention to the needs and issue of survivors but also to the support services for those bereaved by suicide.

Introduction

Writing a historical account of the experiences of suicide loss survivors over the centuries to contemporary times, Colt (1987, 1991/2006) related a long history for survivors – from concern based on economic and property reasons, followed by stigma and shame that led survivors to go "underground" (1987, p. 14). As he relates this defensive isolation response and the hiding of feelings such as grief and guilt, he suggests that the first recognition of the needs of survivors emerged at the birth of suicidology in North America in the late 1950s and 1960s, with research of suicides in Los Angeles, California, by Shneidman, Farberow, Litman, and others at the Los Angeles Suicide Prevention Center. This suicide prevention center was among the first to realize that survivors needed to talk about their loss. From this need sprung early survivors support groups. Additional resources and services that provide support in various other ways have also been developed. Organizations and individuals who were not themselves suicide survivors became supporters, advocates, and partners. However, the early work for recognition and support resulted primarily directly from the tremendous efforts of individuals bereaved by suicide.

Survivors and Postvention

Edwin Shneidman (1968), a psychologist and pioneer in the field of suicidology, coined the term *postvention* as early as 1967 (see Chapter 1 in this volume). Shneidman defined his terms saying,

> I would like to use the Latin root *"vention,"* using three prefixes to portray the full range of activity [action before, during, and after]. I would like to suggest *prevention, inter*vention, and *post*vention... In postvention, one deals with people after suicide attempts and with the survivor-victims of committed suicide. (Shneidman, 1968, p. 88)

Writing later, Shneidman (1975/1981) seems to focus primarily on the more traditional psychotherapy-based services approach to help the suicide bereaved, not mentioning or anticipating the grief or support group approaches that would soon proliferate. In recognition of the importance of postvention, he states that "a comprehensive suicide-prevention program should attend to the psychological needs of the stigmatized survivors" (Shneidman, 1967/1995, p. 6) and that a "benign community ought routinely to provide immediate postventive mental health care for the survivor-victims of suicidal deaths" (Shneidman, 1969, p. 22). In his foreword to Albert Cain's landmark book, *Survivors of Suicide*, Shneidman goes on to state that "of the three possible (temporal) approaches to mental health crises – prevention, intervention, and postvention – in the case of suicide at least, postvention probably represents the largest problem and thus presents the greatest area for potential aid" (Shneidman, 1972, p. x).

Postvention was established as a part of suicidology, and the provision of postventive care was on the verge of major strides toward addressing the needs of survivors. While this care would include traditional therapy approaches (see e.g., Jordan, 2015), postvention in the form of groups focusing on support in particular would emerge as a significant avenue for healing and help to the suicide bereaved.

Support Groups

While there were general grief support groups (and grief therapy) in existence, it was the efforts of individuals and small numbers of survivors that led to the development of the first mutual help and other support groups in the United States and Canada (Chapter 10 presents a review of the effectiveness of suicide survivor support groups). In the late 1970s and early 1980s, several groups were founded that led the way and often served as models for groups in other locations. Although documentation on groups or resources is minimal, one of the earliest of the programs specifically for suicide survivors was the one-on-one grief counseling offered through the Contra Costa Crisis Center in Contra Costa County, California, in 1972 (e.g., cited by E. Betsy Ross in her 1997 book describing planning efforts to begin her own support group for survivors in 1977; Ross, 1997). Working with the coroner's office, survivors were identified, contacted by letter and phone, and asked if they needed services. Appointments were made and a grief counselor visited them in their home for sessions (Doyle, 1980). In addition, the renowned suicidologist Norman Farberow (2008) relates that the then–Los Angeles Suicide Prevention Center in the "early 1970s" started a survivors program that provided a therapy (i.e., not support) approach. However, "after two or three meetings and many absences by the participants, the program was terminated" (Farberow, 2008, p. 5). Other unsuccessful starts followed, and Farberow speculated that the reason the counseling and group process approach that had been attempted did not succeed was that the approach was incorrect:

We had offered the participants *therapy,* as if they were patients, which they did not want.... [What these survivors needed was] nonjudgmental emotional support in a place where they could share their feelings with others who were experiencing the same kind of loss.... It's worth noting that the suicide survivor movement in the United States was initiated primarily by survivors who looked for help from the mental health professionals but didn't find it. (Farberow, 2008, p. 6)

Two other early locations for services and therapy/grief counseling groups for survivors of suicide were Detroit, Michigan (Danto, 1977), and Sacramento County, California (Lynd, 1976), both established in 1974.

Based on written accounts, the earliest of the mutual aid/peer support groups were started largely or entirely based on independent efforts. The majority of these groups were founded at the end of the 1970s and in the early 1980s by individuals who had lost a loved one to suicide and were seeking a way to help others who had experienced the same loss (see **Table 9.1** for some details of these groups). Thus, survivors in most cases were themselves the initiators of a major form of postvention for those bereaved by suicide. Some of these group models were utilized in other locations, such as the groups named Ray of Hope and Heartbeat (e.g., in 2011, there were 42 chapters of Heartbeat in 9 US states and 2 other countries). Many of these programs (and those they inspired elsewhere) are still serving the suicide bereaved today. The American Association of Suicidology (AAS) lists 467 entries in their *Survivors of Suicide Directory* (American Association of Suicidology, 2015, July; http://www.suicidology.org). The AAS is one of several sources that maintain national lists of support groups (see also, e.g., American Foundation for Suicide Prevention [AFSP], http://www.afsp.org; the Centre for Suicide Prevention in Canada, http://www.suicideinfo.ca; and the International Association for Suicide Prevention (IASP) for other nations, http://www.iasp.info).

Table 9.1. Early suicide support groups and services, North America

Year	Location	Group Name	Founders
1967	San Mateo County, CA	Initially survivors who called the center received telephone call-backs. Later, drop-in counseling and support services were organized as well as support groups.	San Mateo County Suicide Prevention Center, Charlotte Ross, Director
1972	Contra Costa County, San Francisco, CA	Survivors of suicide grief counseling: phone and one-on-one in-home sessions. Expanded in 1976 to include all sudden deaths.	Contra Costa Crisis Center – Polly Doyle
1974	Detroit, MI	Project Survivors of Suicide (SOS). After 2 years of crisis center work, volunteers trained in suicide grief' and grief counseling facilitated groups of suicide survivors.	Suicide Prevention and Drug Information Center
1974	Sacramento County, CA	Survivors of Sudden Death (originally called Survivors of Suicide). After initial support at the death scene, return visit usually made for continued support, and as-needed phone contacts, office therapy sessions, and/or ongoing group of survivors. Additional assistance as needed.	Suicide Prevention Service of Sacramento Co. Inc.
1977	Iowa City, IA	Ray of Hope: 1st meeting 1977, but Ray of Hope Inc. officially incorporated 1978.	Eleanora Betsy Ross (lost her husband, 1975)
1978	Albuquerque, NM	Survivors of Suicide (SOS).	Richard Schwoebel and two other men (lost their wives)
1978	Atlanta, GA	Survivors of Suicide (SOS) Support Group. Facilitator had first led a Compassionate Friends support group for parents who have lost a child to death from any cause, in 1978.	Link Counseling Center, Iris Bolton (lost her son, 1977)

Table 9.1. continued

Year	Location	Group Name	Founders
1978	Dallas, TX	Survivors of Suicide Program.	Dallas Suicide & Crisis Center. Charles Petty, Cyl Reed
1978	Minneapolis, MN	Survivors Support Grief Group.	Rev. Verlyn Smith (later, after attending Smith's group, Adina Wrobleski) (lost his wife)
1978	Somerville, MA	Safe Place.	Tom Welch & Liz Courtney. Samaritans has run SafePlace program since 1987 (L. C. lost daughter)
1979	Chicago, IL	Loving Outreach to Survivors of Suicide (LOSS).	Catholic Charities of Chicago, Fr. Charles Rubey
1979	Toronto, Canada	Survivor Support Programme.	Joy Rogers, Terri Richard, Karen Letofsky, and others
1980	Colorado Springs, CO	Heartbeat Survivors After Suicide.	LaRita Archibald (lost son, 1978)
1981	Baton Rouge, LA	Survivors of Suicide support groups.	Baton Rouge Crisis Intervention Center
1981	Los Angeles, CA	Survivors After Suicide Program.	LA Suicide Prevention Center, Janet Belland, Sam Heilig, Norman Farberow
1981	San Diego, CA	Survivors of Suicide Loss, evolved from a Traumatic Death support group.	Grief Center of Episcopal Community Services. Dorothy Godfrey, Laurel Fadke, Ron Lofgren (suicide loss in family)
1982	Aurora, IL	Survivors of Suicide (SOS).	Aurora College, Stephanie Weber-Slepicka (lost mother, 1980)
1982	Santa Clara, CA	Survivors of Suicide Program.	Meg Paris
1983	Sacramento, CA	Friends for Survival (FFS).	Marilyn Koenig, Chris Moon (lost sons)

Note. Listings gleaned from various proceedings volumes of the American Association of Suicidology since 1975, Internet information, and program descriptions, particularly appearing in the US and international sections of Jordan and McIntosh (2011a). Colt (2006/1991, p. 523) states that the first suicide survivors group was in San Diego, California, but he gives no references or details for that date and location, and no other sources were discovered that cited or discussed this group, and no online information was available to verify this statement and location and date.

Many of these groups were, and continue to be, facilitated and/or led by those who are bereaved by suicide, but groups led or facilitated by professionals as well as those cofacilitated by both survivors and professionals have been and are also common (see Chapter 10 in this volume). These support groups provide many helpful and supportive features to survivors who attend. Among the most frequent experiences are the sharing of grief and bereavement experiences, sharing and modeling coping techniques, and receiving education, as well as understanding and comfort.

Although these groups were developed initially in the United States and Canada, support groups for suicide survivors have also proliferated in other nations and continents (see **Table 9.2**). Farberow (1998) reported the results of a survey of IASP member nations (52 in 1998;

31 responses were received) that indicated that in 1998, at least 14 nations (eight in Europe) had survivor support services. At the same time, 17 members indicated they had no survivor support services (10 of these in Europe). Just 6 years later, Andriessen (2004) reported that among those 10 European countries without services, only two continued to not have them by 2004. The IASP's list of suicide bereavement services included 20 nations in July 2015. The international community has made major contributions to postvention and survivors in their own countries. While much of the knowledge gained from the early efforts in North America have been highly valuable internationally, each country has discovered and shared culturally relevant differences and universally applicable practices and principles.

Table 9.2. International suicide support groups and services

Year	Location	Group Name	Founders
1981	Ireland	Friends of the Suicide Bereaved – National Suicide Bereavement Support Network.	Theresa Millea (lost son, 1981)
1981	The Netherlands	Meeting Days, and National Platform for the bereaved by suicide.	Ans Withaar
1985	Belgium	Support group for parents who had lost a child by suicide, led by professionals.	Karel Roelants, Konstantin von Vietinghoff-Scheel, Flemish Suicide Prevention Centre
1986	Adelaide, Australia	Bereaved Through Suicide Support Group Inc.	Sheila Clark, Robert Goldney, Harold Jones, Veronica Honour
1987	Sweden	SPES (Hope), National Association for Suicide Prevention and Support for Survivors.	Maryan Fasth
1989	Slovenia	Suicide survivors program: groups of survivors after suicide, led by two therapists. Afterwards also specialized help for bereaved couples, families and individuals.	Onja Grad, Anka Zavasnik, University Psychiatric Hospital, Ljubljana
1991	Hull, UK	Survivors of Bereavement by Suicide (SOBS). Support group in 1991, National Telephone Helpline for Suicide Survivors (by survivors) in 2000.	Alice Middleton (lost brother, 1983)
1995	Germany	AGUS (Relatives of Suicides) Support groups.	
1999	Norway	LEVE, Norwegian Association for Suicide Bereaved (peer and professional help for survivors).	Kari Dyregrov
2000	Sydney, Australia	Support After Suicide Program.	
2000	Belgium	Werkgroep Verder, Flemish Working Group on Suicide Survivors.	Mental Health Centre PassAnt, Nico De fauw, Karl Andriessen
2002	Denmark	Efterladte (Survivors) National Association for the Bereaved by Suicide.	
2006	Australia	Hope for Life, Suicide Prevention, & Bereavement Support (phone & support groups).	Salvation Army, Alan Staines
2007	New Zealand	Postvention support model (in three regions).	
2013	Australia	Postvention Australia, National Association for the Bereaved by Suicide.	Alan Staines, Diego De Leo, AO

Note. Listings gleaned from various proceedings volumes of the American Association of Suicidology since 1975, Internet information, and program descriptions, particularly appearing in the US and international sections of Jordan and McIntosh (2011a). AO = Officer of the Order of Australia

Outreach Approaches

Survivors typically discover or contact support groups, general or specific-loss grief groups, and even traditional therapy approaches through referrals by first responders, emergency personnel, funeral directors, clergy, friends, and word of mouth. These forms of postvention have become essentially a standard care practice for suicide survivors. A typical traditional feature of these resources is that survivors would need to take the initiative, after finding out about or discovering the services, and travel to the site at which they are provided. However, another form of support, with some variations in approach, includes what can be referred to as outreach models of support (see **Table 9.3**). At least as early as 1972 – with the already described Contra Costa Crisis Center (California) approach, involving its cooperative working arrangement with the coroner's office and one-on-one in-home visits – some form of outreach program has existed. In addition, again in cooperation with the coroner, in 1974 the Sacramento County (also California) Suicide Prevention Service began a program that provided supportive aid at the death scene to survivors, with additional contacts and visits for ongoing assistance. In a 1977 publication (no founding date was provided), Junghardt (1977) described a San Bernardino County (California) postvention program called the Suicide Survivor Follow-up Program. In this program, a mental health nurse working for the health department contacted the family after a suicide immediately after the family received a copy of the death certificate. The mental health nurse, preferably within 24 to 48 hr (and before the funeral), with the family's agreement, visited them in their home and provided crisis intervention treatment and counseling to help them in their recovery and grieving process. Although this program was described in 1977, no current references to it can be found online or otherwise, and it is assumed that it is no longer in operation.

Later, in 1989, the Atlanta Survivors of Suicide Support Team was created by Iris Bolton, assisted by three other suicide-bereaved couples (the Weyrauchs, Glovers, and Kloosterboers). It was sponsored by The Link Counseling Center (Bolton, Black, & Bolton, 1998) and a coalition of Atlanta mental health organizations. While the roots of the team were from the late 1970s in a more informal format, the still-functioning program consists of trained team members who perform home visits, by invitation, to assist families in their immediate loss reactions as well as to start the healing process. Pairs of volunteers make the home visits, providing support, resources, information, and referrals to support groups. Currently, twice a year in a weekend workshop, The Link's National Resource Center for Suicide Prevention and Aftercare (The Link's NRC), provides the Survivors of Suicide Support Team and Group Facilitators Training, including a manual only available to attendees. A recent similar document, the *Survivor Outreach Team Training Manual,* developed by the Kern County, CA, Mental Health Department, was added to the Suicide Prevention Resource Center's Best Practice Registry (http://www.sprc.org/bpr/section-III/survivor-outreach-team-training-manual).

Established in 1998, after training of staff members and suicide survivors in late 1997 with the Atlanta-based Survivors of Suicide Support Team, the Local Outreach to Suicide Survivors (LOSS) Team was developed by Frank Campbell and presented in his 1997 AAS presidential address in Memphis, Tennessee (Campbell, 1997). It was first provided by the Baton Rouge Crisis Intervention Center. This Active Postvention Program/Model (Campbell, 2011; Campbell, Cataldie, McIntosh, & Millet, 2004) involves cooperative efforts between the coroner's office and the LOSS Team. When a suicide death occurs, multiple LOSS Team members are contacted and activated immediately to respond at the scene of the suicide and provide immediate support and resources. This approach has not only given immediate assistance to the grieving survivors but has also enhanced the sensitivity of first responders, producing a more caring and supportive experience for all involved.

Table 9.3. Suicide support and response outreach teams

Year	Location	Group Name	Founders
1974	Sacramento County, CA	Survivors of Sudden Death (originally called Survivors of Suicide). Coroner's deputies call paid professional staff members to death scene to provide supportive aid to survivors. Return visit usually made for continued support, as-needed phone contacts, office therapy sessions, and/or ongoing group of survivors. Additional assistance as needed.	Suicide Prevention Service of Sacramento Co. Inc.
1985	San Diego, CA (affiliates now serve over 250 cities)	Trauma Intervention Programs Inc. Initially within San Diego Mental Health system, in 1989 became a nonprofit. First responders and emergency personnel call trained volunteers to provide support to individuals in traumatic and crisis circumstances, including but not exclusively after suicide.	Wayne Fortin
1989	Atlanta, GA	Survivors of Suicide Support Team.	Iris Bolton, The Link Counseling Center
1998	Baton Rouge, LA	LOSS Team (Local Outreach to Suicide Survivors). The model has now been replicated in countries as diverse as Australia, Singapore, Northern Ireland, Canada and US.	Frank Campbell, Baton Rouge Crisis Intervention Center
Late 1990s, formally since 2002	Australia (national, with 17 communities listed in 2015)	StandBy Response Service Team – Crisis Response Team (also provides 24-hr crisis response number for suicide bereaved and referrals to support services).	Jill Fisher, national contact
2004	Los Angeles, CA	Suicide Response Team.	Didi Hirsch Mental Health Services
2006	Boston, MA	Survivor to Survivor Network.	Samaritans
2007	Perth, Australia	Active Response Bereavement Outreach (ARBOR). One-on-one sessions at client's home as well as counseling at various locations and support groups.	Anglicare WA

Note. Listings gleaned from various proceedings volumes of the American Association of Suicidology since 1975, Internet information, and program descriptions, particularly appearing in the US and international sections of Jordan and McIntosh (2011a).

Beyond the immediate support received is the connection to the crisis center that offers suicide support groups. The goal of *active postvention* has been to shorten the elapsed time between the death and when survivors find the assistance they feel will help them cope with this devastating loss. The active postvention model has been shown to have a positive impact on both the team members and the bereaved at the death scene. Most often the team members are bereaved individuals who themselves got help from a LOSS team when they experienced their loss, received services sooner than they likely would have without the team support, and now provide the installation of hope to the newly bereaved. Thus, the service has come full circle in many places where it has been adopted. The model has now been replicated in several countries and locations in the United States.

Campbell's original data (Campbell et al., 2004) showed that those who had been visited by the LOSS Team and then attended the support groups did in fact do so much sooner compared with what was shown by previous information on those who had sought out the group before the LOSS Team was formed (39 days vs. about 4.5 years). A follow-up study (Cerel & Campbell, 2008) comparing those who received the LOSS Team / active postvention, with survivors who had experienced a suicide in the same year, also observed that those who received the active postvention "presented sooner for treatment" than those who did not (48 days vs. 97 days).

Among programs in other the nations that have been inspired by the LOSS Team, Active Response Bereavement Outreach (ARBOR) was established in 2007 in the Perth area of Western Australia (http://www.anglicare.org.au). Its goal is also to provide early contact with survivors of suicide loss and to provide them with aid and support services. This 24-hr program utilizes trained volunteers as peer supporters. As with the LOSS Team, these supporters are suicide loss survivors. In addition to short-term immediate support and assistance, ARBOR also offers support groups for medium-term needs.

Also utilizing an approach where first responders (police, fire, hospital staff) call in individuals to assist with supporting suicide survivors is the Crisis Response Team of the Trauma Intervention Programs Inc. (TIP). This program, started in San Diego, California, in 1985 (though whether suicide survivors have been served from the beginning is not clear), sends trained volunteer team members to the scene to assist traumatized individuals in the aftermath of a large number of situations, including after deaths by suicide (but also other crises and traumatic events – e.g., other modes of death; victims of fire, rape, or assault; those involved in auto accidents). With the variety of circumstances, this assistance includes an array of services in addition to emotional support and information about community resources and general issues. There are 16 affiliates of the national TIP organization serving over 250 cities (http://www.tipnational.org).

Another major resource in Australia that includes outreach services is the StandBy Response Service, a national community-based program of suicide postvention. StandBy was formally established in 2002 (Bycroft, Fisher, & Beaton, 2011) and is funded by the Australian government. The program is offered at 17 different sites across the nation (http://www.unitedsynergies.com). This program provides a single entity that coordinates the variety of services available for survivors of suicide loss within their local communities to facilitate an immediate response following a suicide as well as services they might need over time. The service is provided by professional members of the Crisis Response Team trained in crisis intervention and responding to the bereaved. This 24-hr service, most often contacted after survivors are made aware of it by first responders, delivers individual support (via telephone, face-to-face outreach, as well as home visits) to the bereaved and information about available services and support.

Online Support Approaches

In recent years, other forms of support resources have also emerged, reflecting largely the proliferation of technology and social media worldwide (Chapter 17 in this volume). Online search engines are a logical starting point as survivors seek information and resources following their loss. Krysinska and Andriessen (2010) investigated the information from four popular search engines (Google, Yahoo!, Bing, and Ask) with respect to a variety of terms and phrases associated with suicide loss survivors and postvention. These search engines revealed a quite diverse and large number of Internet sources related to suicide bereavement. However, the quality and impact of these online support resources is unknown.

Krysinska and Andriessen (2010) observed that online and other technological support groups and resources were well represented among the online resources, including, for example, Parents of Suicides (POS, founded in 1998) and Friends & Families of Suicides (FFOS, founded in 2000), both e-mail support groups (http://www.pos-ffos.com). These groups have also established a memorial website (Faces of Suicide, at http://www.facesofsuicide.com), an electronic newsletter, a private chat room, and other activities. In addition, as Beal (2011) describes, the members of these groups have also developed other online resources and websites, and some of them lead what she refers to as partner groups, to meet specific member needs (not all related to suicide bereavement), such as groups for suicide bereaved in Australia and New Zealand, and a group for Native Americans and Canadian First Nation peoples. AFSP lists the POS and FFOS groups on their website along with others that are online resources, including Alliance of Hope (founded in 2008; http://www.allianceofhope.org), which includes a website and a public community forum for suicide survivors, as well as a blog and memorials of loved ones (see also Feigelman, Jordan, McIntosh, & Feigelman, 2012). A study by Krysinska and Andriessen (2015) of two online memorial sites (e.g., Faces of Suicide and Gone Too Soon, http://www.gonetoosoon.org – the latter not specific to suicide) identified 14 themes in the memorials posted by family survivors, but also recognized the dearth of evidence regarding the impact on the grief of survivors who become involved in posting online memorials to their loved ones.

Well before the Internet, from the beginning of the relatively recent historical stream described earlier, resources for survivors and support of survivors existed. Early in this history, individual survivors and those involved in support or other forms of postvention created brochures, newsletters, and other informational documents to assist survivors in their healing and loss. Advances in technology have greatly accelerated and advanced the dissemination and availability of such materials along with numerous websites devoted to the topic of survivors of suicide (e.g., see the various websites noted). Among these early resources was a list in "Suggestions for Survivors" (Bolton, I., Appendix C, in Dunne, McIntosh, & Dunne-Maxim, 1987) that is still widely distributed. More recently, in 2002, a Charter of Rights of Suicide Survivors was advanced in Belgium (Andriessen, De Leo, & Cimitan, 2014) and endorsed internationally that declares the rights to which survivors are entitled as they grieve (an earlier 1984 document, *Survivor's Bill of Rights,* similar in theme but of different origin and not well distributed, attributed to JoAnn Mecca of Connecticut, appeared in the books: Ross 1980, 1997).

Also included among these many materials that have been developed and made available are a variety of manuals and other documents about survivors support groups (see Chapter 10 in this volume). While organizations have been involved in the development of materials about survivor issues, many of the resources about survivors issues continue to be generated largely by those who have lost a loved one to suicide. Guides or handbooks for suicide survivors include:

- AAS, Jackson, 2004: http://www.suicidology.org/Portals/14/docs/Survivors/Loss%20Survivors/SOS_handbook.pdf;
- Calgary Health Region, 2007: http://www.health.gov.bc.ca/library/publications/year/2007/HopeandHealing.pdf;
- NASP Task Force After a Suicide Resource Directory, 2015: http://www.personalgriefcoach.net/;
- Public Health England, 2008: http://www.nhs.uk/Livewell/Suicide/Documents/Help%20is%20at%20Hand.pdf;
- WHO–IASP, 2008: http://www.who.int/mental_health/prevention/suicide/resource_survivors.pdf

Quilts

A variation on online memorials that has spread widely is the creation of memorial quilts. Communities, states, etc. have collectively produced quilts on which the squares that make up the quilt portray, honor, and remember a loved one lost to suicide. These quilts are commonly displayed at public events. Sandy Martin founded the Lifekeeper Foundation and Lifekeeper Memory Quilts in 1995 following her son's suicide (http://www.griefsupportservices.org/new-grief/griefsupportservices/organdservices_desc.php?org_id=4827; and there is also an online Digital Memory Quilt, https://afsp.org/find-support/ive-lost-someone/digital-memory-quilt/). Peters, Staines, Cunningham, and Ramjan (2015) evaluated the Lifekeeper Memory Quilt Project in Australia (established by the Salvation Army in 2008), and found evidence that it is helpful to the suicide bereaved.

Comprehensive Community Support Programs

As is apparent, the development of independent or single programs has been quite prominent in postvention efforts to support and assist survivors after their loss. A different approach is to mobilize a number of resources within a community and establish a coordinated and varied network of agencies and resources working together to help survivors of suicide. Paul (1995) describes such an effort in Fort McMurrray, Canada, with its Suicide Response Committee. This approach employs a Suicide Response Committee comprising community stakeholders employing critical incident stress intervention protocols for postvention efforts. Using similar techniques as a foundation, Mitchell and Wesner (2011) describe the Bereavement Crisis Debriefing Intervention for Survivors After a Suicide program. Forde and Devaney (2006) describe another community-based family support model reflecting family support theory and a multidisciplinary and multiagency approach. Other examples of approaches for survivors of suicide loss that are different from traditional support groups include an adaptation of the psychological autopsy method coupled with group and grief counseling techniques to permit survivors to explore the suicide death in a therapeutic process (Retrospective Profile and Facilitated Family Retreat; Schwartz, 2011).

Among the emerging national associations for the bereaved by suicide, in Belgium, the Flemish Working Group on Suicide Survivors (Andriessen, 2011) was established in 2000, and based on its efforts, Belgium observed its first annual National Suicide Survivor Day in 2002. The working group brought together survivor support groups and those working in the field as well as mental health resources and social organizations. Resources were also organized such as a directory of support groups and an interactive website with online chat and e-mail support. Andriessen (2011, p. 497) states that "the mission is to raise awareness, improve suicide-survivor support, destigmatize survivors, and increase openness in society."

Another example took place in Australia with the establishment in 2013 of Postvention Australia – National Association for the Bereaved by Suicide (http://www.postventionaustralia.org, see Chapter 43 in this volume). This association's goals include making networks and pathways for best practice information and services about postvention available to survivors. The website includes resources, lists of support groups across the nation, and how to find counselors.

Recognition of Survivors and Postvention Through Major Books

One of the important events in bringing attention to the topic of survivors and the support they have received has been the publication of professional books that have focused the field of suicidology on the needs of survivors. Among these is Cain's (1972) seminal work that began to catalog the features of suicide bereavement in particular. This was followed by the publication of professional books by Dunne et al. (1987), Lukas and Seiden (1988), Mishara (1995), Baugher and Jordan (2002), Jordan and McIntosh (2011), and De Leo, Cimitan, Dyregrov, Grad, and Andriessen (2014). In addition to these books largely for a professional audience, numerous survivors of suicide have written and published personal accounts of their loss, beginning with several of those who developed early support groups. The pioneers were Bolton (1983) and Ross (1997; originally self-published in 1990)with more recent examples such as Fine (1997), Linn-Gust (2001), Lukas (2008), Archibald (2012), and Scarr (2013). Lists of books with personal accounts by survivors may be found at the AAS, AFSP, and IASP websites and elsewhere (see also, e.g., McIntosh, 1999, for a table of personal accounts by relationship to the deceased).

Recognition of Survivors Through Major Suicidology Organizations

Organizations such as the AAS, AFSP, and IASP were and continue to be crucial in advancing and encouraging efforts and support for survivors of suicide. Presentations on survivor issues at the annual professional conferences of the AAS can be verified at least as early as 1975 (appearing in what was the first published proceedings of the association's conferences; annual conferences of the AAS began in 1968, with its founding at the first conference). Among the efforts historically for survivors were the half-day survivor workshops at the AAS annual professional conferences from 1986 to 1988. These were followed by a separate annual AAS Healing After Suicide conference starting in 1989 (held concurrently with the AAS annual professional conference starting in 1998), and the publication of a newsletter *Surviving Suicide* in that same year. AAS established a Survivors Division in 1994 (a Survivors Committee existed from 1990 to 1994) with an associated board of directors position. Later, AAS members elected survivors of suicide as presidents of the association (Dunne-Maxim for 1999–2000; Dunne for 2000–2001; Linn-Gust for 2011–2013) as well as those who brought particular emphases to survivors' issues (Campbell for 1996–1997; and Cerel who is currently president-elect for 2015–2017). Since 1995, the AAS has annually given the Survivor of the Year Award to recognize survivors' efforts. Another significant development was the establishment of a Clinician Survivor Task Force in 1997. This group, initially developed to address clinicians who had lost a patient to death by suicide, now also addresses clinicians who have lost family members to suicide. In addition to meeting and sharing at annual AAS conferences, the group initiated and continues to maintain a website that provides education, resources, and contacts; and opportunities for clinicians to share and post their experiences; as well as a bibliography of publications relevant to clinician-survivors (http://www.suicidology.org/suicide-survivors/clinician-survivors).

Starting in 2002, the AFSP has held Out of the Darkness fund-raising walks in communities, on college and high school campuses, and nationally (Out of the Darkness Overnight in the case of the last) to advocate for suicide prevention public policy and to support survivors of suicide loss (see Chapter 28 in this volume). In the United States, the AFSP and AAS have co-operated since 1999 in the annual National Survivors of Suicide Day (the Saturday before 'the US and Canada Thanksgiving Day), a congressionally designated day first proposed by Senator Harry Reid (survivor of his father's suicide). After several years of recognizing National Survivors of Suicide Day, the AFSP designated the day as International Survivors of Suicide Loss Day. Additionally, AFSP honors individuals with the Survivor of Suicide Loss Award.

The IASP reorganized a Postvention Task Force initiated by Norman Farberow in 1999 into the Special Interest Group (SIG) on Suicide Bereavement and Postvention (http://iasp.info/postvention.php) in 2011. The SIG and its task forces bring together the various IASP members across the globe with interests in survivors and postvention. Among the special efforts of the SIG are the publication of a newsletter and development of a postvention stream with symposia, workshops, and a healing and remembrance ceremony at IASP conferences. Since 2003, IASP (in cooperation with the World Health Organization) has sponsored annual World Suicide Prevention Day on September 10 (http://www.iasp.info/wspd/index.php), which occurs during, and is part of, National Suicide Prevention Week (sponsored annually by AAS in the United States). These events include recognition of survivors of suicide loss as well as other topics of suicide prevention. The IASP has presented its Farberow Award since 1997 to a person who has significantly contributed to the work with survivors of suicide.

Recognition of Survivors Through Other Organizations and Events

Many other significant events and milestones have occurred in the United States that have contributed to increased awareness of the needs of suicide survivors. These include the *Surgeon General's Call To Action to Prevent Suicide* (US Public Health Service, 1999), the *National Strategy for Suicide Prevention* (US Public Health Service, 2001) and its revision (US Department of Health and Human Services, 2012), the establishment of the National Council for Suicide Prevention (founded 1999, see below), the National Alliance for Suicide Prevention (NASP, founded 2010; http://actionallianceforsuicideprevention.org), and the recent NASP Survivors of Suicide Loss Task Force report (NASP, 2015; see Chapter 27 in this volume).

Another important contributing factor that has raised awareness and lessened stigma surrounding suicide loss has been the speaking out of celebrities (e.g., Mariette Hartley, Joan Rivers, Peter Fonda) and politicians (e.g., Senators Harry Reid and Gordon Smith) regarding their personal family suicide deaths (leading also to federal funding programs for suicide prevention efforts and research, though not specifically for postvention).

The development of suicide prevention organizations and programs by survivors of suicide has also advanced attention to the topic of survivors as well as suicide in general. Among these in the United States is the Suicide Prevention Action Network (SPAN USA), founded in 1996 by Jerry and Elsie Weyrauch after their daughter's suicide, as a public policy and lobbying organization that employed grassroots efforts by survivors of suicide. SPAN USA advocates for national suicide prevention strategy development and implementation efforts in particular. It merged with and became part of the AFSP in 2009.

The Jason Foundation focuses on youth suicide prevention (founded by Clark Flatt in 1997 after his son's suicide; http://jasonfoundation.com). The Jed Foundation endeavors to prevent suicide and promote emotional health among college students (founded in 2000 by Phil and Donna Satow after their son's suicide; http://www.jedfoundation.org). The Yellow Ribbon Suicide Prevention Program works to prevent suicide and empowers individuals to ask for help when they feel pain or despair (founded in 1994 by Dale and Dar Emme after their son's suicide;

http://yellowribbon.org). Suicide Awareness Voices of Education (SAVE; http://www.save.org) is a Minnesota organization with a goal to prevent suicide through prevention and education programs that raise public awareness and reduce stigma surrounding suicide. The group also works to assist survivors of suicide. SAVE was established in 1989 by Adina Wrobleski – who had lost a daughter to suicide – along with six other suicide survivors (including Mary and Al Kluesner). The Link Counseling Center's National Resource Center for Suicide Prevention and Aftercare (The Link's NRC) in Atlanta was established in 1996 by Iris Bolton and The Link to provide prevention, intervention, and postvention services, locally and nationally. Her son died by suicide in 1977. Suicide prevention efforts established by survivors listed here, along with several other organizations, are leaders and members of the National Council for Suicide Prevention (founded in 1999; http://www.ncsp.org), contributing to suicide prevention as well as postvention efforts nationwide.

Conclusions

As these various efforts and resources historically and currently attest, support groups and support in general have become an integral part of a more complete effort to provide postvention. Independently as well as often in cooperation with, or under the direction of, mental health professionals and organizations or agencies, survivors of suicide have developed, facilitated, and been active participants in survivor support groups. They have been sharing their personal experiences to assist others in their grieving as well as to gain understanding and often make meaning from their loss. The recognition of the impact of the loss on the survivors and their grief and bereavement process has not only led to the development of resources and services but has also lessened the social impact in the form of shame and stigma. Still, the need for more advancement remains on this front. Additional efforts to demonstrate the effectiveness of existing and new postvention efforts should continue. In each case, the experience, work, and advocacy of the bereaved by suicide themselves have been crucial components for the advancements that have taken place and will be important in new developments in the future.

Corresponding author

John L. McIntosh
Academic Affairs
Indiana University South Bend
South Bend, IN
USA
jmcintos@iusb.edu

References

American Association of Suicidology. (2015, July). *Survivors of suicide directory.* Retrieved from http://www.suicidology.org/suicide-survivors/sos-directory

Andriessen, K. (2004). Suicide survivor activities, an international perspective. *Suicidologi, 9*(2), 26–27, 31.

Andriessen, K. (2011). Survivors after suicide: A comprehensive suicide survivor program in Flanders, Belgium. In J. R. Jordan & J. L. McIntosh (Eds.), *Grief after suicide: Understanding the consequences and caring for the survivors* (pp. 495–504). New York, NY: Routledge.

Andriessen, K., De Leo, D., & Cimitan, A. (2014). Spreading awareness: The Charter of Rights of Suicide Survivors. In D. De Leo, A. Cimitan, K. Dyregrov, O. Grad, & K. Andriessen (Eds.), *Bereavement after traumatic death: Helping the survivors* (pp. 155–158). Boston, MA: Hogrefe.

Archibald, L. (2012). *Finding peace without all the pieces: After a loved one's suicide*. Colorado Springs, CO: Larch.

Baugher, B., & Jordan, J. (2002). *After suicide loss: Coping with your grief*. New Castle, WA: Authors.

Beal, K.C. (2011). Parents of Suicides-Friends & Families of Suicides internet community. In J.R. Jordan & J.L. McIntosh (Eds.), *Grief after suicide: Understanding the consequences and caring for the survivors* (pp. 381–388). New York, NY: Routledge.

Bolton, I., Black, K.M., & Bolton, J. (1998). Establishing a suicide support team in your community. In J.L. McIntosh (Ed.), *Suicide '97: Proceedings of the American Association of Suicidology 30th annual conference*. Memphis, TN, April 1997. Washington, DC: American Association of Suicidology.

Bolton, I. (with Mitchell, C.). (1983). *My son... my son...: A guide to healing after a suicide in the family*. Atlanta, GA: Bolton Press.

Bycroft, P., Fisher, J., & Beaton, S. (2011). In J.R. Jordan & J.L. McIntosh (Eds.), *Grief after suicide: Understanding the consequences and caring for the survivors* (pp. 439–465). New York, NY: Routledge.

Cain, A.C. (Ed.). (1972). *Survivors of suicide*. Springfield, IL: Charles C. Thomas.

Campbell, F.R. (1997). Changing the legacy of suicide. *Suicide & Life Threatening Behavior, 27*(4), 329–338.

Campbell, F.R. (2011). Baton Rouge Crisis Intervention Center's LOSS Team Active Postvention Model approach. In J.R. Jordan & J.L. McIntosh (Eds.), *Grief after suicide: Understanding the consequences and caring for the survivors* (pp. 327–332). New York, NY: Routledge.

Campbell, F.R., Cataldie, L., McIntosh, J., & Millet, K. (2004). An active postvention program. *Crisis, 25*(1), 30–32. http://doi.org/10.1027/0227-5910.25.1.30

Cerel, J., & Campbell, F.R. (2008). Suicide survivors seeking mental health services: A preliminary examination of the role of an Active Postvention Model. *Suicide and Life-Threatening Behavior, 38*(1), 30–34. http://doi.org/10.1521/suli.2008.38.1.30

Colt, G.H. (1987). The history of the suicide survivor: The mark of Cain. In E.J. Dunne, J.L. McIntosh, & K. Dunne-Maxim (Eds.), *Suicide and its aftermath: Understanding and counseling the survivors* (pp. 3–18). New York, NY: W.W. Norton.

Colt, G.H. (2006/1991). *November of the soul: The enigma of suicide* (New and revised edition). New York, NY: Simon & Schuster. (Original edition published with the title *The enigma of suicide*, 1991.)

Danto, B.L. (1977). Project SOS: Volunteers in action with survivors of suicide. In B.L. Danto & A.H. Kutscher (with L.G. Kutscher) (Eds.), *Suicide and bereavement* (pp. 222–239). New York, NY: Arno Press.

De Leo, D., Cimitan, A., Dyregrov, K., Grad, O., & Andriessen, K. (Eds.). (2014). *Bereavement after traumatic death: Helping the survivors*. Boston, MA: Hogrefe.

Doyle, P. (1980). *Grief counselling and sudden death: A manual and guide*. Springfield, IL: Charles C. Thomas.

Dunne, E.J., McIntosh, J.L., & Dunne-Maxim, K. (Eds.). (1987). *Suicide and its aftermath: Understanding and counseling the survivors*. New York, NY: Norton.

Farberow, N.L. (1998). Suicide survivor programs in IASP member countries. In R.J. Kosky, H.S. Eshkevari, R.D. Goldney, & R. Hassan (Eds.), *Suicide prevention: The global context* (pp. 293–297). New York, NY: Plenum Press.

Farberow, N. (2008, Fall). Norm Farberow shares his recollections of the history of the survivor movement. *Surviving Suicide, 20*(3), 5–6. (Newsletter of the American Association of Suicidology)

Feigelman, W., Jordan, J.R., McIntosh, J.L., & Feigelman, B. (2012). *Devastating losses: How parents cope with the death of a child to suicide or drugs*. New York, NY: Springer.

Fine, C. (1997). *No time to say goodbye: Surviving the suicide of a loved one*. New York, NY: Doubleday.

Forde, A., & Devaney, C. (2006). Postvention: A community-based family support initiative and model of responding to tragic events, including suicide. *Child Care in Practice, 12*(1), 53–61. http://doi.org/10.1080/13575270500526303

Jordan, J.R. (2015). Grief after suicide: The evolution of suicide postvention. In J.M. Stillion & T. Attig (Eds.), *Death, dying, and bereavement: Contemporary perspectives, institutions, and practices* (pp. 349–362). New York, NY: Springer.

Jordan, J.R., & McIntosh, J.L. (Eds.). (2011). *Grief after suicide: Understanding the consequences and caring for the survivors*. New York, NY: Routledge.

Junghardt, D.Z. (1977). A program in postvention. In C.L. Hatton, S.M. Valente, & A. Rink (Eds.), *Sui-

cide: Assessment and intervention (pp. 124–132). New York, NY: Appleton-Century-Crofts.

Krysinska, K., & Andriessen, K. (2010). On-line support and resources for people bereaved through suicide: What is available? *Suicide and Life-Threatening Behavior, 40*(6), 640–650. http://doi.org/10.1521/suli.2010.40.6.640

Krysinska, K., & Andriessen, K. (2015). Online memorialization and grief after suicide: An analysis of suicide memorials on the internet. *Omega: Journal of Death and Dying, 71*(1), 19–47. http://doi.org/10.1177/0030222814568276

Linn-Gust, M. (2001). *Do they have bad days in heaven? Surviving the suicide loss of a sibling.* Atlanta, GA: Bolton Press.

Lukas, C. (2008). *Blue genes: A memoir of loss and survival.* New York: Anchor Books.

Lukas, C., & Seiden, H. M. (1988). *Silent grief: Living in the wake of suicide.* New York, NY: Scribner.

Lynd, J. G. (1976). Helping survivors with the impact of suicide through grief counseling: With the cooperation of coroner's deputies. In B. S. Comstock & R. Maris (Eds.), *Proceedings of the eighth annual meeting American Association of Suicidology* (pp. 33–35). St. Louis, MO, April 1975. Houston, TX: American Association of Suicidology.

McIntosh, J. L. (1999). Research on survivors of suicide. In M. Stimming & M. Stimming (Eds.), *Before their time: Adult children's experiences with parental suicide* (pp. 157–180). Philadelphia, PA: Temple University Press.

Mishara, B. L. (Ed.). (1995). *The impact of suicide.* New York, NY: Springer.

Mitchell, A. M., & Wesner, S. (2011). A bereavement crisis debriefing intervention for survivors after a suicide. In J. R. Jordan & J. L. McIntosh (Eds.), *Grief after suicide: Understanding the consequences and caring for the survivors* (pp. 397–402). New York, NY: Routledge.

National Alliance for Suicide Prevention Survivors of Suicide Loss Task Force. (2015). *Responding to grief, trauma, and distress after a suicide: U. S. national guidelines.* Washington, DC: National Action Alliance for Suicide Prevention. Retrieved from http://www.actionallianceforsuicideprevention.org/sites/actionallianceforsuicideprevention.org/files/NationalGuidelines.pdf

Paul, K. (1995). The development process of a community postvention protocol. In B. L. Mishara (Ed.), *The impact of suicide* (pp. 64–72). New York, NY: Springer.

Peters, K., Staines, A., Cunningham, C., & Ramjan, L. (2015). The Lifekeeper Memory Quilt: Evaluation of a suicide postvention program. *Death Studies, 39*(6), 353–359. http://doi.org/10.1080/07481187.2014.951499

Ross, E. B. (1980). *After suicide: A unique grief process.* Iowa City, IA: Author. (Revised in 1986 as a self-published manual, *After suicide: A ray of hope*; the self-published 1990 paperback was an expanded version of the 1986 manual.)

Ross, E. B. (1997). *Life after suicide: A ray of hope for those left behind.* New York, NY: Insight Books. (Originally published as a self-published paperback in 1990, Iowa City, IA: Lynn Publications; the 1997 edition is a revised volume.)

Scarr, H. (Ed.). (2013). *Suicide grief: Personal stories of suicide loss.* New Town, Australia: Relationships Australia Tasmania. Retrieved from http://www.tas.relationships.org.au/resources/booklets-and-brochures/suicide-grief-personal-stories-of-suicide-loss

Schwartz, M. (2011). The retrospective profile and the facilitated family retreat. In J. R. Jordan & J. L. McIntosh (Eds.), *Grief after suicide: Understanding the consequences and caring for the survivors* (pp. 371–379). New York, NY: Routledge.

Shneidman, E. S. (1967, July). The NIMH Center for Studies of Suicide Prevention. *Bulletin of Suicidology, 1,* 2–7. (Reprinted in Bulletin of Suicidology (pp. 2–7). Washington, DC: American Association of Suicidology, 1995)

Shneidman, E. S. (1968). Suicide prevention: A current national view. In N. L. Farberow (Ed.), *Proceedings fourth international conference for suicide prevention of the International Association for Suicide Prevention* (pp. 83–89). Los Angeles, CA, October 1967. Los Angeles: Delmar Publishing.

Shneidman, E. S. (1969). Prologue: Fifty-eight years. In E. S. Shneidman (Ed.), *On the nature of suicide* (pp. 1–30). San Francisco, CA: Jossey-Bass.

Shneidman, E. S. (1972). Foreword. In A. C. Cain (Ed.), *Survivors of suicide* (pp. ix–xi). Springfield, IL: Charles C Thomas.

Shneidman, E. S. (1975). Postvention: The care of the bereaved. In R. O. Pasnau (Ed.), *Consultation-liaison psychiatry* (pp. 245–256). New York, NY: Grune and Stratton. (Reprinted in *Suicide and Life-Threatening Behavior, 1981, 11*(4), 349–359.)

US Department of Health and Human Services, Office of the Surgeon General and National Action Alliance for Suicide Prevention. (2012). *2012 National strategy for suicide prevention: Goals and objectives for action.* Washington, DC: Author. Retrieved from http://www.surgeongeneral.gov/library/reports/national-strategy-suicide-prevention/full-report.pdf

US Public Health Service. (1999). *The Surgeon General's call to action to prevent suicide.* Washington, DC: US Department of Health and Human Services. Retrieved from http://www.surgeongeneral.gov/library/calltoaction/index.html

US Public Health Service. (2001). *National strategy for suicide prevention: Goals and objectives for action.* Washington, DC: US Department of Health and Human Services. Retrieved from http://www.mentalhealth.samhsa.gov/publications/allpubs/SMA01–3517/

Chapter 10

Characteristics and Effectiveness of Suicide Survivor Support Groups

John L. McIntosh

Academic Affairs, Indiana University South Bend, IN, USA

Abstract: Support groups for those bereaved by suicide exist to assist the grief and healing in the aftermath of deaths by suicide. While support groups share that common goal, the manner in which they approach and achieve it is not identical. For example, groups vary in such characteristics as meeting schedules and number of meetings, type, training and background of leaders/facilitators, and open versus closed formats. Descriptions of suicide grief survivor groups and manuals on how to run support groups, along with surveys of groups and their characteristics, have been published and are reviewed here. In addition, a small number of studies that have examined the effectiveness of suicide support groups have also been conducted, and these are presented here. This body of information and evidence comprises what is currently known about support groups, what remains to be determined, and what evidence needs to be collected to demonstrate their effectiveness.

Introduction

Postvention after suicide can take several forms. Among these postvention approaches, support groups are a prevalent resource available to bereaved individuals to assist with efforts to cope with, and heal after, their loss. Support groups for survivors of suicide loss were developed by the early 1970s and have expanded to many communities in the United States and across the world (see Chapter 9 in this volume). There are common characteristics among support groups as well as differences between some models and approaches.

Characteristics of Suicide Survivor Support Groups: Definitions and Differences

Support groups are one form of postvention. That is, as defined here, they are therapeutic environments and resources that respond to and help survivors of suicide in the aftermath of their loss – emotionally and socially. This support might be sought when a survivor does not have or feel they have others in their social network from whom they can receive the support they seek. A support group might also be turned to in addition to or as a replacement for individual counseling or psychotherapy. Some support groups might be led by mental health professionals or sponsored by mental health agencies or organizations, while others are led by individuals who have also had a suicide loss. While the focus in this chapter is on groups specifically developed and intended for suicide loss survivors, the suicide bereaved may also seek support from bereavement groups that provide help to those who have experienced loss from any mode of death (general grief groups) or specific kinds or circumstances of loss (e.g., parents who have experienced the death of a child, widows, or widowers). These more general groups share many of the characteristics and goals of groups specifically for suicide loss, and some suicide bereaved benefit from that experience. More often it seems, those who have had a suicide loss seek help from groups specific to suicide loss.

Differences among suicide support groups are most fundamentally found in the leadership of the group and the format of the meeting schedule and the resulting membership (although approaches and goals can vary widely as well; see, e.g., Jordan, 2011). The backgrounds and experiences of leaders who facilitate or run the group experience differ, with three primary types of leaders and the subsequent dynamics of the group that often result. One model of leadership involves support groups in which professionals, most often mental health professionals, lead the group and establish its structure. A second type of leadership model involves the combination of a mental health professional and a trained cofacilitator who typically (but not always) is a suicide survivor (in some cases the professional might also be a survivor of suicide as well). The third type occurs when the leadership of the group sessions is performed by an individual who is, like the other group members, a survivor of suicide loss (a survivor–facilitator, often trained in facilitation and other skills). This last model, with survivor leadership, is often referred to as a peer-led, consumer-led, self-help, or mutual aid support group (e.g., Appel & Wrobleski, 1987).

It is important to note that even in groups that do not include a professional among their leadership, that often professional consultation and referrals are utilized if they are deemed appropriate for group members. At the same time, there are also peer-led groups that are not affiliated in any direct manner with professionals. In some cases, a tension exists with respect to professional involvement, as well as on the part of professionals toward survivor-led groups (see, e.g., Appel & Wrobleski, 1987, pp. 231–233; and Hall & Epp, 2001). In a survey of suicide support group leaders, Heilig (1985) noted that while most groups had a positive attitude toward professionals providing assistance, others were ambivalent, and still others expressed negative attitudes toward professionals (e.g., professionals do not understand suicide survivors, survivors are not pathological, and support groups are not therapy). Humphreys and Rappaport (1994, p. 219) noted similar issues in general mutual aid groups and professionally led support groups.

Farberow (1992, pp. 33–34) argued for groups that combined professionals as well as a coleader who was a survivor, suggesting that the two played important but different roles for group members. All leadership models are still commonly found for suicide loss survivors (see detailed survey results below), but it seems that there has been a shift in the proportions of the types of leader models over time. A recent survey (Cerel, Padgett, & Reed, 2009) has shown that compared with earlier surveys (e.g., Rubey & McIntosh, 1996), a considerably larger proportion of groups are now led by survivors rather than professionals.

The format of support groups represents another difference, such that groups are mostly either *open* or *closed* (hybrid combinations exist as well). In an open group format, meetings are scheduled regularly, but there is no fixed number of sessions. Individuals may attend group sessions any time they wish (i.e., drop-in groups) or feel they need to do so. At any meeting there may be individuals who have attended many group sessions ("veterans") as well as those who are attending for the first time (and any variation between these extremes). That is, membership in open meetings can change with virtually every meeting held, and often attendance can be quite variable as well. Open group meetings are typically less structured than closed groups, less focused on specific topics, often with no formal agenda, and more focused on attendees talking about issues they wish to address.

By contrast, closed support groups can be characterized by membership that remains the same from session to session for the duration of what is usually a fixed number of sessions (often 8–10). New cycles of sessions occur, typically with different membership, though it is often permitted for one who has completed one cycle to become a member in a later one if they feel they need to do so. Although psychoeducational goals can occur in open group formats, closed groups frequently include more structure, with informational and thematic goals from session to session and open discussion of the topic.

An open format is more typical of peer, self-help, or mutual aid groups, though the pairing is not universal. In the same way, closed formats are more often seen in groups with professionals or other nonbereaved leadership. While the open format seems to be most common in the United States, Andriessen (2004) observed that this was true also in several nations (e.g., Austria, France, Germany, Norway, the United Kingdom), but a closed format was more typical in others (e.g., The Netherlands), and similar numbers of both formats were found in still other nations (e.g., Belgium and Switzerland). Andriessen observed the same kind of national variability for leadership models (see also, e.g., Andriessen & Krysinska, 2012).

As for general bereavement groups, suicide loss survivors may seek support from groups that focus on special issues and relationships. These specialized groups can be either open or closed and led by either survivors or professionals. Generally, suicide support groups are open to all relationships, and meetings will often include individuals of quite diverse relationships to the person who died by suicide (heterogeneous membership, such as parents, spouses, children, siblings, friends). Specialized groups create support environments that enhance the identity and group cohesion as well as the empathy and modeling of coping, by focusing the membership on a specific subset of survivors who share the kind of loss on an important factor other than the mode of death alone (homogeneous membership). Examples of these groups include spouses (Constantino, Sekula, & Rubinstein, 2001), children bereaved by parental suicide (e.g., Mitchell et al., 2007), sibling survivors (e.g., Gaffney, Jones, & Dunne-Maxim, 1992) and close friends, as well as parents who have lost children (Hatton & Valente, 1981). There are also groups for therapists who have lost a client to suicide (Jones, 1987), survivors of military suicides, and gender-based suicide loss survivor groups (such as men, mothers of child suicides, widows).

Most recently, the evolution of technological changes and widespread availability have provided other options and variations of support for survivors (*thanatechnology*; Clark, 2001). The topic of the Internet and online resources will be addressed in more detail in Chapter 17 in this volume, but in the present context, it can be pointed out that online support groups (and other resources) have emerged. It has typically been assumed that group experiences involve individuals sharing the same physical space. However, there are groups for survivors of suicide loss in which the individuals interact and support one another through e-mail, online forums, and other social networks, permitting sharing of experiences and emotions, empathy and support, and sharing of advice, each similar to features seen in traditional face-to-face support groups (e.g., Chapple & Ziebland, 2011; W. Feigelman, Gorman, Beal, & Jordan, 2008; W. Feigelman, Jordan, McIntosh, & B. Feigelman, 2012; Schotanus-Dijkstra et al., 2014). Online availability of resources and information is also a valuable aspect of the contribution technology has made to survivors finding help and support following their loss (Krysinska & Andriessen, 2010).

Characteristics of Suicide Survivor Support Groups: Common Features and Objectives

Suicide loss survivors have expressed their satisfaction with their experiences in suicide survivors support groups, overwhelmingly indicating high levels of helpfulness in their healing (e.g., McMenamy, Jordan, & Mitchell, 2008). The characteristics and benefits to survivors that derive from participation in support groups represent the reason for such affirmation on the part of survivors. Survivors want and need the group environment and experience to provide particular resources and have certain organizational elements that promote healing. Although there are differences in support groups for suicide loss survivors, there are a number of common features or themes that they generally share (see **Box 10.1**).

Box 10.1. Common and beneficial elements of suicide survivor support groups

- Social and psychological/emotional support and help with the bereavement process and healing;
- Sharing grief experiences/stories in a safe (i.e., nonjudgmental, accepting) environment;
- Being able to talk to peers who understand your experience because they have had a similar loss;
- Group leaders who are skilled at facilitation;
- "Veteran" members who are models for members newer to the group, providing social learning and exchanging advice about coping and various coping strategies, as well as inspiration for hope and recovery, and normalization of grieving experiences;
- Survivors eventually may serve as a model (helper) with time, for even newer survivors (providing reciprocal support);
- Learning and education and information about suicide and resources available to assist their healing; meaning making and growth associated with their loss as well as reasons for living;
- Often the opportunity for social advocacy;
- Regaining control over one's life;
- Reducing feelings of isolation and stigma.

Based on Appel and Wrobleski, 1987; De Leo and Cimitan, 2014; Dyregrov, De Leo, and Cimitan, 2014; Dyregrov, Dyregrov, and Johnsen, 2013–2014; B. Feigelman and W. Feigelman, 2008; Jordan, 2011; Jordan, W. Feigelman, McMenamy, and Mitchell, 2011; Oulanova, Moodley, and Séguin, 2014; Sands, Jordan, and Neimeyer, 2011; Supiano, 2012.

Characteristics of Suicide Survivor Support Groups: Surveys

While some characteristics of suicide survivor support groups have been briefly noted, the specific details and evidence that established those characteristics have resulted from several surveys taken of suicide support groups and their leaders over the years. Not only do these surveys reveal the specific characteristics of suicide survivor groups, but they also permit some attention to how those characteristics have been stable as well as changing across time. The first published survey that can be found was conducted by Heilig (1985) and involved asking responses from survivor groups known about by the American Association of Suicidology

(AAS). A total of 41 groups returned the questionnaires. At that rather early time, just over half the groups ($n=21$) had been started by survivors of suicide. The other nearly half ($n=20$) had been initiated by suicide prevention, crisis intervention, or mental health programs, but from the entire set of groups, 31 were affiliated with a suicide prevention or mental health program. Groups met mostly on a monthly basis ($n=17$) or twice monthly ($n=13$), while seven met weekly. The most common format was open ended ($n=34$), and only seven groups had a set number of meetings (between 6 and 10). In 34 of the groups, mental health professionals were involved, and only in seven did the group operate without any professional. Fifteen of the groups had professional leaders (but 14 used professionals as consultants, and 5 used them for attendees who needed treatment).

A decade later, Rubey and McIntosh (1996) reported another study of AAS-listed survivors groups, with 149 groups completing surveys. As found by Heilig (1985), most groups met either monthly (46%) or twice monthly (36%), with a few meeting weekly (11%). As noted in 1985, the majority of groups were open ended (81%); only 10% had a fixed number of meetings (with almost all between 8 and 10 meetings and a mean of 9). These groups had been operating between 1 and 26 years, but only seven for more than 15 years, and most between 8 and 9 years. The average number of attendees was 10 (range 2–48). Leaders were trained facilitators in 34% of the groups, and a mental health professional was the leader in 22%. Another 28% of groups involved a combination of mental health professional and facilitator as coleaders. There were 38 groups (26%) for which it was noted that at least one person who was a survivor was part of the group leadership (this was sometimes an individual who was a mental health professional as well), and a total of 15 of the groups were described as survivor-led (peer or self-help).

In Rubey and McIntosh's (1996) survey, a large number of the groups indicated that they referred attendees for individual counseling, other forms of counseling, and/or telephone support or crisis intervention when it was deemed necessary and appropriate. The authors also asked about referrals to the survivor groups, and it was reported that the sources of referrals included most often by word of mouth (137 groups selected this item), hospitals ($n=109$), churches ($n=102$), and doctors ($n=98$), with smaller numbers for a number of other sources listed. Finally, the content or format of the meetings was also included in the questions, and most reported sharing of experiences ($n=114$), while 34 described their format as lectures as well as sharing (none of the groups indicated a lecture format alone). Groups were largely for adults, with a few serving children or teens.

Recently, Cerel and colleagues (Cerel, Padgett, & Reed, 2009) performed an update to the Rubey and McIntosh (1996) study. From among the survivor groups in the Suicide Prevention Action Network USA (SPAN USA) directory who were contacted, 100 surveys were completed and returned. In the more than a decade between the studies (and the more than 2 decades since the Heilig study), many issues about the survivor groups have remained stable in the United States. Cerel et al. found that compared with earlier studies, groups were still small (88% had fewer than 10 attendees per session), still met most often on a monthly basis (55%), and were still primarily open ended (85%). In addition, sharing remained an experience that was universal in the groups (100% reported, with this comprising 62% of the groups' time), though the issues of coping skills (91% and 16% of the time), and lectures (36% reported using lectures for 13% of group time) were also included in many cases. Referrals by other survivors to the group were also widely noted (85%), with the same proportion for mental health professionals as a referral source. Interestingly, and reflecting technological advances and pervasiveness, 78% of the groups noted online as a referral modality.

As observed earlier, most groups were still for adult survivors. Cerel et al. found, however, a larger proportion of their respondents at this time indicated that their groups now had a survivor leader (78%) than observed previously (see also Farberow, 1998, below). A larger proportion of groups who responded had been in existence for more than 15 years than in earlier surveys (27% vs. 5% for respondents in Rubey & McIntosh, 1996), and another 29% had been in operation for 6–15 years. While this reflects the now longer history and proliferation of suicide survivors groups (see Chapter 9 in this volume), there were also 44% of the groups that had existed for 5 years or less, a far higher proportion than the 16% observed by Rubey and McIntosh.

In addition to these essentially US studies of survivor groups, Farberow (1998) in 1997 conducted a survey of the membership nations of the International Association for Suicide Prevention (IASP) to determine how many and which had survivor groups in operation in their country. Of the 52 members of the IASP at the time, 31 national representatives responded, and only 14 reported that there were survivor groups in their country (17 reported that no programs existed in their country). While the number of groups in these countries varied greatly (eight were in Europe), they were relatively small outside North America (United States with 363 groups reported and 50 in Canada). There were also groups in England ($n = 16+$ groups), Sweden ($n = 10$), Ireland ($n = 5$), Denmark ($n = 5$), Norway ($n = 3$), and Australia ($n = 6+$), with no groups in the nations of Slovenia, Germany, France, Argentina, Israel, or Turkey reported by Farberow (1998).

In Farberow's (1998) survey, the entire range of leadership variations were seen in a number of the countries, with groups led by peers (survivors), professionals, and those co-led by survivors and professionals. In some separate data for the large number of US groups, it was stated that similar numbers of groups were led by professionals with a peer facilitator ($n = 135$) and by survivors alone ($n = 131$). Farberow observed that countries differed by the model of leadership they most often reported (some countries more likely to report professionals or paraprofessionals operating groups alone, while other specific countries had groups in which professionals led with a survivor, and still others indicated groups for which only professionals or only survivors were the leaders). He noted that the origin of the group seemed to be an important factor in such variation and consistency in leader preferences.

The final survey, by Andriessen (2004), is a follow-up to the study by Farberow (1998) but focuses on European countries. Andriessen asked representatives from the 31 European IASP members to report on their country's suicide survivor services and received responses from 20. In an indication of the advances that had been made in the essentially half decade since Farberow's findings, Andriessen reported that of the 10 European countries that Farberow found did not have services in 1997, only 2 still remained with none. Other countries reported that services were in preparation. One indication of the advances made in the countries of Farberow's report is the increase in the number of services within reporting countries. As examples from Andriessen's report, England (UK) had reported 16+ groups in 1997, but in the 2004 survey they indicated approximately 300, and similarly impressive growth was seen in Norway, reporting 97 services in 2004 compared with only 3 in 1997. Andriessen (2004) reported, like all other surveys, that most of the services were for adult survivors, that the open and closed formats still characterized nearly all groups, and that all group leadership models were observed. Like Farberow, he also observed that individual countries most frequently reported a preference with respect to open versus closed formats, as well as the types of group leaders (peer/survivor vs. mental health professional or both). He also noted that mental health backup by professionals was employed by many of the peer-facilitated programs.

In sum, these survey results indicate that survivor groups and services to suicide loss survivors are available across much of the world, though they are not entirely universal. Groups have common characteristics in their operation and groups served, with variability in those who provide the programs and serve as leaders. Sharing of experiences in particular is the common thread regardless of other characteristics. While there is consistency across time in many ways, some changes have taken place, it seems. In addition, while largely readily available for adult suicide survivors, services for child and adolescent survivors of suicide loss are not as common in most locations. The advances across the world in the last few decades have been significant and encouraging to make survivor groups and services available to those who grieve the loss of someone from suicide (see **Box 10.2**).

Box 10.2. Resources for developing and facilitating suicide support groups

A variety of manuals and other documents have been developed and made available related to suicide support groups, including:
- Console, Ireland, 2012, *National Quality Standards for the Provision of Suicide Bereavement Services*: http://www.hse.ie/eng/services/list/4/Mental_Health_Services/NOSP/Resources/standardsbereavement.pdf
- Flatt & SPAN USA, 2007, how to facilitate a survivors support group: http://www.sprc.org/sites/default/files/migrate/library/The_Basics_Facilitator_Guide.pdf
- Friends for Survival, 2013, starting a bereavement support group: http://www.friendsforsurvival.org/pathways.html
- Lifeline Australia, 2009, standards and guidelines for suicide bereavement support groups: https://www.lifeline.org.au
- J. Peters. (2010), Setting up a support group. In M. Linn-Gust & J. Peters (Eds.), *A winding road* (pp. 65–72). Albuquerque, NM: Chellehead Works.
- Training opportunities, such as those from the American Foundation for Suicide Prevention, for facilitating a suicide bereavement group and clinician training for suicide bereavement (https://afsp.org), the latter training jointly developed with the AAS (http://www.suicidology.org) by John R. Jordan.
- WHO–IASP, 2008, How to start a survivors support group: http://www.who.int/mental_health/prevention/suicide/resource_survivors.pdf

Research on Suicide Support Group Effectiveness

Although a number of studies have been conducted regarding effectiveness of postvention programs and interventions (McDaid, Trowman, Golder, Hawton, & Sowden, 2008; Szumilas & Kutcher, 2011), the focus here will largely be on studies of effectiveness related more directly to survivor support groups. It should be noted that there is a larger body of knowledge and findings on bereavement in general and related interventions, which may inform support group approaches specifically for suicide survivors. A careful and comprehensive review of psychotherapeutic interventions for the bereaved (including support groups) by Currier, Neimeyer, and Berman (2008) suggested a both encouraging but also disappointing conclusion: "Overall, analyses showed that interventions had a small effect at posttreatment but no statistically significant benefit at follow-up" (p. 648). More than half of the studies (63 %) included in the review were group-based interventions, and all of the studies included control groups. The authors concluded that future research should be conducted that provides clinicians (and argued here, other caregivers as well) with guidelines that will more clearly indicate which survivors will benefit from which kind of intervention.

Certainly this same goal is true with respect to interventions and particularly support group approaches for suicide survivors. Among the large number of other studies of bereavement interventions, Schwab (1995–1996) studied why some bereaved individuals participated in support groups while others did not. Schwab concluded that "it appears that bereaved parents are more likely to join a support group when they experience a particularly traumatic loss and do not find others who have suffered a similar loss in their usual social network" (Schwab, 1995–1996, p. 49). It is apparent that suicide loss, regardless of the kinship relation to the deceased, is traumatic for the survivors, and it is likely that most will not easily and obviously find others who are suicide survivors among their social groups. This may help to understand why survivor support groups have become an important resource for survivors of suicide loss..

Goldney and Berman (1996) discuss the relative dearth of studies of effectiveness and efficacy at that time as well as the numerous and serious methodological shortcomings among the existing studies of postvention in schools (issues also noted for research on postvention interventions generally by McDaid et al., 2008; Szumilas & Kutcher, 2011; see also Jordan & Neimeyer, 2003, for grief counseling in general). Goldney and Berman (1996) encourage improvements in the empirical efforts on postvention but make the important point that rather than pursuing the extremely rigorous methodologies of efficacy research, time would be better spent, and findings more beneficial to the survivors of suicide, if *effectiveness* studies were utilized – that is, studies that "evaluate real world interventions, i.e., interventions as they actually occur" (Goldney & Berman, 1996, p. 99). This crucial point is the reason to consider existing research on suicide support group interventions while encouraging stronger and expanded research of their effects on survivors.

Mixed Leadership: Professional and Peer

One of the earlier survivor support programs, established by the Los Angeles Suicide Prevention Center, was evaluated by suicidology pioneer Norman Farberow (1992). The LASPC Survivors After Suicide program was a closed format program of eight weekly support sessions co-led by a mental health professional and a trained suicide loss survivor. After completion of the eight sessions, members had the option to take part in monthly meetings any time and for as long as they wished. Program participants were compared with a control group of individuals who applied for program admission but had attended one session only or no sessions. Measures of a number of different feelings among the group members and control group were not different in a retrospective measure related to the first 4 weeks after the suicide. By the time the group was about to start the sessions, both groups had seen considerable lessening of most feelings compared with the original retrospective measure. At this time the groups were different for the three feelings of grief, shame, and guilt, with the program group members significantly higher than the controls on all three. Farberow (1992) reported that between the start of the program and the end of the 8 weeks, the program members showed significant declines in all feelings except feeling suicidal (which was low at both times of measure). By contrast, the control group showed significant changes after the 8 weeks for anxiety only (which was significantly lower). Comparing the two groups at this end-of-sessions time period showed significant differences only for depression and puzzlement, with ratings higher among the support group for both. On a direct rating of the support group experience, 92 % of the members indicated that participating in the group had helped them.

Peer Leadership

One issue regarding support groups that include survivors as peer supporters centers on whether the suicide loss survivors are helped by the support received, but also what effect it has on the peer supporter. The effectiveness of peers as supporters was more recently evaluated by Barlow et al. (2010). The Peer Support Group in Calgary, Alberta, Canada, is a suicide bereavement support program that utilizes trained volunteer survivors of suicide in support of those who have had a suicide loss. In this program, the supporter is paired with a survivor for face-to-face meetings for 4 months (with the dyad members matched on several characteristics, including gender and relationship of the loss). Both quantitative and qualitative methods were employed in the evaluation.

In this study, both survivors and peer supporters rated the support highly and indicated that the experience was helpful and contributed to their healing. Measures on grief reactions showed lessening preprogram to postprogram for all items related to mental health (e.g., despair, blame and anger, panic, detachment), and increases in personal growth not only for the survivors but also for the peer supporters. These findings of positive outcomes associated with the Peer Support Group provide evidence that peers can be effective supporters to suicide survivors and further that they also can benefit from the help and support they provide.

Trained Volunteer Leadership

Another early study of a suicide survivor support group (Rogers, Sheldon, Barwick, Letofsky, & Lancel, 1982), designed for adult family members following a suicide death, utilized trained volunteers as leaders. These volunteer leaders worked in pairs, most often with one a suicide survivor and the other not, meeting with the family members for eight 2-hr sessions. The sessions were structured discussions around topics relevant to the loss and grief feelings of the family members to promote understanding and coping with suicide loss. Following these structured sessions, family members were invited to four semistructured biweekly groups in which they could share feelings and discuss coping with issues associated with their loss. Measures of mental health were taken at multiple time periods, including 4–6 weeks after the sessions.

In this investigation, group attendees were quite pleased with the session format, and their mental health measure scores were significantly lower than those at the start of the group involvement. While improvement in mental health cannot be specifically attributed to the group experience, Rogers et al. (1982) believe that the study demonstrated the feasibility of using trained volunteers (with consultation from mental health professionals available) to provide support and aid to suicide survivors.

Professional Leadership

Support groups for suicide survivors led exclusively by professionals have also been evaluated. For example, a psychoeducational support group (part of the Australian StandBy Response Service) in Brisbane, Australia, was led by two facilitators, either two psychologists or a psychologist with either a social worker or counselor. The 6- or 8-week program, meeting once a week for 2 hr, provided group sessions based on topics consistent with recovery tasks for suicide survivors. Semistructured interviews with the survivors who attended and completed the group sessions indicated "strong positive feedback from nearly all participants about the groups existence (and further promotion), process, and facilitation" (Groos & Shakespeare-Finch, 2013, p. 16). Survivors were highly favorable about the experience of sharing and talking about their loss with those who had a similar loss. They felt also that the experience helped to normalize their bereavement and to enable them to feel hope, especially that their psychological pain would improve. The group also permitted the survivors to work on coping methods associated with their loss, such as meaning making.

A second investigation of group interventions following loss by suicide, utilizing professional leaders, was conducted with widows and studied a bereavement group psychotherapy postvention compared with a social group postvention (Constantino et al., 2001). The bereavement group postvention followed a theoretical set of factors in group psychotherapy with an emphasis on therapeutic change occurring within a setting of interactions among group members. The social group postvention fostered socialization, leisure, and recreation to promote change. Both groups followed a format of 90-min sessions for 8 weeks. A number of well-established mental health measures were completed at various times over the course of the group experiences.

Constantino et al. (2001) reported that members in both groups showed improvements in essentially all of the measures, with no significant differences observed between the groups. The authors suggested that this might mean that "the very process of interacting with a group of other survivors of suicide death, regardless of the focus of the group, may be beneficial" (Constantino et al., 2001, p. 439). Furthermore, "Entering a group where they have the interest and support of the leader and the other members may provide a level of caring and understanding that provides healing factors" (p. 439). Unfortunately, responding to the wishes of the funding agency, a no-treatment group was not included, so a number of possible issues related to improvement were not able to be determined.

Evaluation of an Outreach Approach: LOSS Team

Although not an evaluation of a support group approach for suicide survivors, evaluation data for the Active Postvention Program (APM; and specifically the Local Outreach to Suicide Survivors [LOSS] Team developed by Campbell, and first offered by the Baton Rouge Crisis Intervention Center, Louisiana), have implications for support group issues, particularly the time between the suicide death and that at which the suicide survivor seeks "active postvention" (Campbell, 1997, 2011). Although little empirical evidence can conclusively demonstrate that seeking help sooner is most beneficial to suicide survivors, this has represented the prevalent clinical and practice-based opinion from the beginning of discussions and conceptualizations of postvention. For example, Shneidman (1975/1981) suggested intervention as soon as possible after the death, but ideally within 72 hr, while Junghardt (1977) stated that their program's experience had been that initial contact was most effective if it is within 24 to 48 hr after the suicide. However, it is not uncommon for survivors to not seek help for sometimes many years after the death.

The LOSS Team (often trained survivors of suicide) visits suicide survivors at the scene of the suicide (see Chapter 9, this volume for further information), providing support as well as informing the survivors about the availability of support services at the crisis intervention center. Three separate sets of data (Aguirre & Terry, 2014; Campbell, Cataldie, McIntosh, & Millet, 2004; Cerel & Campbell, 2008) have demonstrated a substantial reduction in the time that survivors who saw LOSS Team members sought postvention services compared with both those who did not see the team and those who, in the center's previous experience with suicide survivors, had sought its assistance and its survivor support groups. These efforts are referred to as *active postvention* due not only to the experience of survivors with the team but also to the fact that they are made aware of information about support and therapeutic service availability.

Evaluation Conclusions

Based on the published findings, and similar to the conclusion by Currier et al. (2008) for bereavement groups generally, some evidence for positive effects on the part of suicide survivors is typically found following involvement in suicide support groups and postvention approaches. The evidence is tempered, however, by the weaknesses in research rigor and other methodological shortcomings, many of which are particularly challenging for the real-life circumstances involved with intervention after a death by suicide. Improvements could be made for some issues, such as by including control groups or no-treatment groups, while still working within the ethical and real-world realities of bereavement postvention. In addition to effectiveness studies, however, there are many other aspects of postvention that might be determined by future research (see, e.g., Cerel, Padgett, Conwell, & Reed, 2009; Clark, 2001; Cutcliffe & Ball, 2009; McIntosh & Jordan, 2011), including, for instance, whether the characteristics of groups, such as the background of the leadership and the format or length of the program, have different impacts on survivors' bereavement. And finally, an important point regarding postvention in general was made by Andriessen and Krysinska (2012) as well as Cerel, Padgett, Conwell, and Reed (2009) – that is, the majority of suicide loss survivors do not attend support groups or other kinds of postvention services. Much work remains to be done to determine the needs of this larger group as well as the reasons they do not seek, find, or receive help after their suicide loss.

Although support groups are often recommended as a resource for survivors of suicide loss, it must also be noted that support groups are not necessarily found to be effective or beneficial for everyone. For instance, Oulanova et al. (2014, p. 161) point out that one of the main features of support groups, the retelling of the suicide story, is not always therapeutic. Similarly, in their interviews with survivors, McKinnon and Chonody (2014) observed that some participants insisted strongly that attending a peer support group had not or would not help them in coping with their grief; some of those participants cited not wanting to listen to others retell their stories as well as expressing reluctance to relate their own stories to others. As is often found in other circumstances, the support group structure and experience might not be the best fit for all survivors. Feigelman and Feigelman (2011a, 2011b) provide data regarding not only factors influencing the joining of suicide loss support groups (e.g., positive experiences with professional bereavement counselors, frequency of religious attendance) but also those affecting withdrawing from support groups (e.g., facilitator skill issues, need for support met).

It might be suggested also that the needs of survivors vary. For instance, those who have more severe psychological or psychiatric issues might benefit more from a therapy-oriented approach, while survivors generally might benefit more (and prefer) the support orientation that support groups provide. Recognition is also needed that needs of survivors over time may also influence the fit. More understanding is required to determine what approaches are most helpful in individual cases of suicide loss survivorship as well as why many survivors do not seek any intervention in their grief but still seem to heal and cope.

Conclusions

Support groups for survivors of suicide loss are an important resource and therapeutic option in the healing process in the aftermath of suicide. Although it is recommended that a number of services be available and utilized by survivors (Jordan et al., 2011), evidence shows that survivors find support groups helpful, and effectiveness research provides evidence, though not extensive, of a positive effect. More research is needed for a large number of questions, including determining issues such as the impact of various features of support groups, the fit of support groups for various survivor subgroups, determining for which subgroups they are or may not be beneficial or necessary, and the optimal time after the death for support group attendance, as well as the varying needs of survivors from support groups over time. Suicide loss support groups continue to be a positive experience for survivors. Thus, a primary goal is providing and improving suicide support groups. Most importantly, this goal is manifested in providing an environment of support and facilitation of the healing process following survivors' devastating loss and its impact on their lives.

Corresponding author

John L. McIntosh
Academic Affairs
Indiana University South Bend
South Bend, IN
USA
jmcintos@iusb.edu

References

Aguirre, R. T. P., & Terry, L. F. (2014). The LOSS Team: An important postvention component of suicide prevention: Results of a program evaluation. In J. R. Cutliffe, J. C. Santos, P. S. Links, J. Zaheer, H. G. Harder, F. Campbell, … R. Eynan (Eds.), *Routledge international handbook of clinical suicide research* (pp. 279–288). New York, NY: Routledge.

Andriessen, K. (2004). Suicide survivor activities, an international perspective. *Suicidologi, 9*(2), 26–27, 31.

Andriessen, K., & Krysinska, K. (2012). Essential questions on suicide bereavement and postvention. *International Journal of Environmental Research and Public Health, 9*(1), 24–32. http://doi.org/10.3390/ijerph9010024

Appel, Y. H., & Wrobleski, A. (1987). Self-help and support groups: Mutual aid for survivors. In E. J. Dunne, J. L. McIntosh, & K. Dunne-Maxim (Eds.), *Suicide and its aftermath: Understanding and counseling the survivors* (pp. 215–233). New York, NY: Norton.

Barlow, C. A., Schiff, J. W., Chugh, U., Rawlinson, D., Hides, E., & Leith, J. (2010). An evaluation of a suicide bereavement peer support program. *Death Studies, 34*(10), 915–930. http://doi.org/10.1080/07481181003761435

Campbell, F. R. (1997). Changing the legacy of suicide. *Suicide and Life-Threatening Behavior, 27*(4), 329–338.

Campbell, F. R. (2011). Baton Rouge Crisis Intervention Center's LOSS Team Active Postvention Model approach. In J. R. Jordan & J. L. McIntosh (Eds.), *Grief after suicide: Understanding the consequences and caring for the survivors* (pp. 327–332). New York, NY: Routledge.

Campbell, F. R., Cataldie, L., McIntosh, J., & Millet, K. (2004). An active postvention program. *Crisis, 25*(1), 30–32. http://doi.org/10.1027/0227-5910.25.1.30

Cerel, J., & Campbell, F. R. (2008). Suicide survivors seeking mental health services: A preliminary examination of the role of an Active Postvention Model. *Suicide and Life-Threatening Behavior, 38*(1), 30–34. http://doi.org/10.1521/suli.2008.38.1.30

Cerel, J., Padgett, J. H., Conwell, Y., & Reed, G. A., Jr. (2009). A call for research: The need to better understand the impact of support groups for suicide survivors. *Suicide and Life-Threatening Behavior, 39*(3), 269–281. http://doi.org/10.1521/suli.2009.39.6.588

Cerel, J., Padgett, J. H., & Reed, G. A., Jr. (2009). Support groups for suicide survivors: Results of a survey of group leaders. *Suicide and Life-Threatening Behavior, 39*(6), 588–598. http://doi.org/10.1521/suli.2009.39.6.588

Chapple, A., & Ziebland, S. (2011). How the internet is changing the experience of bereavement by suicide: A qualitative study in the UK. *Health, 15*(2), 173–187.

Clark, S. (2001). Bereavement after suicide – How far have we come and where do we go from here? *Crisis, 22*(3), 102–108. http://doi.org/10.1027//0227-5910.22.3.102

Constantino, R. E., Sekula, L. K., & Rubinstein, E. N. (2001). Group intervention for widowed survivors of suicide. *Suicide and Life-Threatening Behavior, 31*(4), 428–441. http://doi.org/10.1521/suli.31.4.428.22044

Currier, J. M., Neimeyer, R. A., & Berman, J. S. (2008). The effectiveness of psychotherapeutic interventions for bereaved persons: A comprehensive quantitative review. *Psychological Bulletin, 134*(5), 648–661. doi:10.1037/0033–2909.134.5.648 http://doi.org/10.1037/0033-2909.134.5.648

Cutcliffe, J., & Ball, P. B. (2009). Suicide survivors and the suicidology academe: Reconciliation and reciprocity. *Crisis, 30*(4), 208–214. http://doi.org/10.1027/0227-5910.30.4.208

De Leo, D., & Cimitan, A. (2014). Support groups for the bereaved. In D. De Leo, A. Cimitan, K. Dyregrov, O. Grad, & K. Andriessen (Eds.), *Bereavement after traumatic death: Helping the survivors* (pp. 143–150). Boston, MA: Hogrefe.

Dyregrov, K., De Leo, D., & Cimitan, A. (2014). Peer support an self-help groups. In D. De Leo, A. Cimitan, K. Dyregrov, O. Grad, & K. Andriessen (Eds.), *Bereavement after traumatic death: Helping the survivors* (pp. 137–142). Boston, MA: Hogrefe.

Dyregrov, K., Dyregrov, A., & Johnsen, I. (2013–2014). Positive and negative experiences from grief group participation: A qualitative study. *Omega, 68*(1), 45–62.

Farberow, N. L. (1992). The Los Angeles Survivors-After-Suicide Program: An evaluation. *Crisis, 13*(1), 23–34.

Farberow, N. L. (1998). Suicide survivor programs in IASP member countries: A survey. In R. J. Kosky, H. S. Eshkevari, R. D. Goldney, & R. Hassan (Eds.), *Suicide prevention: The global perspective* (pp. 293–297). New York, NY: Plenum.

Feigelman, B., & Feigelman, W. (2008). Surviving after suicide loss: The healing potential of suicide survivor support groups. *Illness, Crisis & Loss, 16*(4), 285–304. http://doi.org/10.2190/IL.16.4.b

Feigelman, B., & Feigelman, W. (2011a). Suicide survivor support groups: Comings and goings, Part I. *Illness, Crisis & Loss, 19*(1), 57–71. http://doi.org/10.2190/IL.19.1.e

Feigelman, B., & Feigelman, W. (2011b). Suicide survivor support groups: Comings and goings, Part II. *Illness, Crisis & Loss, 19*(2), 165–185. http://doi.org/10.2190/IL.19.2.e

Feigelman, W., Gorman, B. S., Beal, K. C., & Jordan, J. R. (2008). Internet support groups for suicide survivors: A new mode for gaining bereavement assistance. *Omega: Journal of Death and Dying, 57*(3), 217–243. http://doi.org/10.2190/OM.57.3.a

Feigelman, W., Jordan, J. R., McIntosh, J. L., & Feigelman, B. (2012). *Devastating losses: How parents cope with the death of a child to suicide or drugs*. New York, NY: Springer.

Gaffney, D. A., Jones, E. T., & Dunne-Maxim, K. (1992). Support groups for sibling suicide survivors. *Crisis, 13*(2), 76–81.

Goldney, R. D., & Berman, L. (1996). Postvention in schools: Affective or effective? [Editorial]. *Crisis, 17*(3), 98–99. http://doi.org/10.1027/0227-5910.17.3.98

Groos, A. D., & Shakespeare-Finch, J. (2013). Positive experiences for participants in suicide bereavement groups: A Grounded Theory model. *Death Studies, 37*(1), 1–24. http://doi.org/10.1080/07481187.2012.687898

Hall, B. L., & Epp, H. L. (2001). Can professionals and nonprofessionals work together following a suicide? *Crisis, 22*(2), 74–78. http://doi.org/10.1027//0227-5910.22.2.74

Hatton, C. L., & Valente, S. M. (1981). Bereavement group for parents who suffered a suicidal loss of a child. *Suicide and Life-Threatening Behavior, 11*(3), 141–150. http://doi.org/10.1111/j.1943-278X.1981.tb00780.x

Heilig, S. M. (1985). Survey of 41 survivor groups. In R. Cohen-Sandler (Ed.), *Proceedings of the 18th annual meeting of the American Association of Suicidology* (pp. 110–113). Toronto, Canada, April 18–21, 1985. Denver, CO: American Association of Suicidology.

Humphreys, K., & Rappaport, J. (1994). Researching self-help/mutual aid groups and organizations: Many roads, one journey. *Applied & Preventive Psychology, 3*(4), 217–231. http://doi.org/10.1016/S0962-1849(05)80096-4

Jones, F. A., Jr. (1987). Therapists as survivors of client suicide. In E. J. Dunne, J. L. McIntosh, & K. Dunne-Maxim (Eds.), *Suicide and its aftermath: Understanding and counseling the survivors* (pp. 126–141). New York, NY: Norton.

Jordan, J. R. (2011). Group work with suicide survivors. In J. R. Jordan & J. L. McIntosh (Eds.), *Grief after suicide: Understanding the consequences and caring for the survivors* (pp. 283–300). New York, NY: Routledge.

Jordan, J. R., Feigelman, W., McMenamy, J., & Mitchell, A. M. (2011). Research on the needs of survivors. In J. R. Jordan & J. L. McIntosh (Eds.), *Grief after suicide: Understanding the consequences and caring for the survivors* (pp. 115–131). New York, NY: Routledge.

Jordan, J. R., McIntosh, J. L., Bolton, I. M., Campell, F. R., Harpel, J. L., & Linn-Gust, M. (2011). A call to action: Building clinical and programmatic support for suicide survivors. In J. R. Jordan & J. L. McIntosh (Eds.), *Grief after suicide: Understanding the consequences and caring for the survivors* (pp. 523–534). New York, NY: Routledge.

Jordan, J. R., & Neimeyer, R. A. (2003). Does grief counseling work? *Death Studies, 27*(9), 765–786 http://doi.org/10.1080/713842360

Junghardt, D. Z. (1977). A program in postvention. In C. L. Hatton, S. M. Valente, & A. Rink (Eds.), *Suicide: Assessment and intervention* (pp. 124–132). New York, NY: Appleton-Century-Crofts.

Krysinska, K., & Andriessen, K. (2010). On-line support and resources for people bereaved through suicide: What is available? *Suicide and Life-Threatening Behavior, 40*(6), 640–650. http://doi.org/10.1521/suli.2010.40.6.640

McDaid, C., Trowman, R., Golder, S., Hawton, K., & Sowden, A. (2008). Interventions for people bereaved through suicide: Systematic review. *British Journal of Psychiatry, 193*(6), 438–443. http://doi.org/10.1192/bjp.bp.107.040824

McIntosh, J. L., & Jordan, J. R. (2011). Going forward: A research agenda for suicide survivors. In J. R. Jordan & J. L. McIntosh (Eds.), *Grief after suicide: Understanding the consequences and caring for the survivors* (pp. 507–522). New York, NY: Routledge.

McKinnon, J. M., & Chonody, J. (2014). Exploring the formal supports used by people bereaved through suicide: A qualitative study. *Social Work in Mental Health, 12*(3), 231–248. http://doi.org/10.1080/15332985.2014.889637

McMenamy, J. M., Jordan, J. R., & Mitchell, A. M. (2008). What do survivors tell us they need? Results of a pilot study. *Suicide and Life-Threatening Behavior, 38*(4), 375–389. http://doi.org/10.1521/suli.2008.38.4.375

Mitchell, A. M., Wesner, S., Garand, L., Gale, D. D., Havill, A., & Brownson, L. (2007). A support group intervention for children bereaved by parental suicide. *Journal of Child and Adolescent Psychiatric Nursing, 20*(1), 3–13. http://doi.org/10.1111/j.1744-6171.2007.00073.x

Oulanova, O., Moodley, R., & Séguin, M. (2014). From suicide survivor to peer counselor: Breaking the silence of suicide bereavement. *Omega: Journal of Death and Dying, 69*(2), 151–168. http://doi.org/10.2190/OM.69.2.d

Peters, J. (2010). Setting up a support group. In M. Linn-Gust & J. Peters (Eds.), *A winding road: A handbook for those supporting the suicide bereaved* (pp. 65–72). Albuquerque, NM: Chellehead Works.

Rogers, J., Sheldon, A., Barwick, C., Letofsky, K., & Lancel, W. (1982). Help for families of suicide: Survivors Support Program. *Canadian Journal of Psychiatry, 27*(6), 444–449.

Rubey, C. T., & McIntosh, J. L. (1996). Suicide survivors groups: Results of a survey. *Suicide and Life-Threatening Behavior, 26*(4), 351–358.

Sands, D. C., Jordan, J. R., & Neimeyer, R. A. (2011). The meanings of suicide: A narrative approach to healing. In J. R. Jordan & J. L. McIntosh (Eds.), *Grief after suicide: Understanding the consequences and caring for the survivors* (pp. 249–282). New York, NY: Routledge.

Schotanus-Dijkstra, M., Havinga, P., van Ballegooijen, W., Delfosse, L., Mokkenstorm, J., & Boon, B. (2014). What do bereaved by suicide communicate in online support groups? A content analysis. *Crisis, 35*(1), 27–35. http://doi.org/10.1027/0227-5910/a000225

Schwab, R. (1995–1996). Bereaved parents and support group participation. *Omega, 32*(1), 49–61.

Shneidman, E. S. (1975). Postvention: The care of the bereaved. In R. O. Pasnau (Ed.), *Consultation-liaison psychiatry* (pp. 245–256). New York, NY: Grune and Stratton. (Reprinted in *Suicide and Life-Threatening Behavior*, 1981, *11*(4), 349–359.)

Supiano, K. P. (2012). Sense-making in suicide survivorship: A qualitative study of the effect of grief support group participation. *Journal of Loss and Trauma, 17*(6), 489–507. http://doi.org/10.1080/15325024.2012.665298

Szumilas, M., & Kutcher, S. (2011). Post-suicide intervention programs: A systematic review. *Canadian Journal of Public Health, 102*(1), 18–29.

Chapter 11

Priorities for Suicide Survivor Support Groups in Japan and the United States

William Feigelman[1], Beverly Feigelman[2], Daisuke Kawashima[3], Keisuke Shiraga[4], and Kenji Kawano[5]

[1]Sociology Department, Nassau Community College, Garden City, NY, USA
[2]School of Social Work, Adelphi University, Garden City, NY, USA
[3]School of Psychology, Chukyo University, Nagoya, Japan
[4]Graduate School of Education, Joetsu University of Education, Joetsu, Niigata, Japan
[5]College of Comprehensive Psychology, Ritsumeikan University, Kyoto, Japan

Abstract: Support group facilitators in different nations may prioritize their group functions differently. As a result, support groups may operate differently across countries. The present study approached this question through a survey of Japanese ($n = 56$) and US ($n = 59$) support group facilitators, based on Shulman's (2006) principles of mutual support. More similarities than differences were found. Both US and Japanese facilitators emphasized personal adaptation goals (such as helping the bereaved feel less isolated) over collective goals (such as raising monies for more research). However, differences were also noted with US facilitators evaluating helping with problem solving, sharing different ways of coping, viewing personal issues as societal problems, and advocating for promoting social change as significantly higher than the Japanese did. These contrasts suggest differences in cultural values that will play out in support group practices and suggest the need for further research to identify converging and diverging national interests for suicide bereavement groups in different countries.

Introduction

It is not well known whether suicide survivor support group facilitators in different nations prioritize their group functions differently (see also Chapter 10 in this volume). If they do, this could have broad ramifications for how support groups operate in different countries, and this would need to be better understood. This comparative research between the United States and Japan was inspired by the study by Feigelman and Feigelman (2008), influenced by Lawrence Shulman's widely read work *The Skills of Helping Individuals, Families, Groups and Communities* (Shulman, 2006). Here, Shulman offered a set of guiding principles that mutual aid groups of various kinds apply in attempting to promote their goals. The Feigelmans applied the 10 essential principles of mutual aid groups to suicide support groups to better illuminate the dynamics of these groups. The 10 principles are as follows: (1) survivors meet others and feel they are not isolated and alone ("all in the same boat" phenomenon); (2) they are able to talk about subjects openly that cannot be easily discussed within their conventional social networks (discussing tabooed areas); (3) they provide emotional support, acceptance, and hope to one another (mutual support); (4) members help each other with problem solving (individual problem solving); (5) they offer examples of successful coping to one another (sharing data); (6) they offer opinions to one another and occasionally challenge one another to change (the "dialectical process"); (7) group members offer each other help by making demands and setting expectations on personal behavior (mutual demand); (8) members use the group to rehearse how to deal with difficult situations or people (role rehearsal); (9) members begin to see their personal difficulties as a result of societal problems: prejudice, stigma, and the lack of services for the mentally ill (universal perspective); and (10) group members advocate for social change and suicide prevention (the strength-in-numbers phenomenon). Although there is obviously some overlap between some of these functions, they can be viewed as distinct from each other.

The present study aimed to compare and contrast Japanese and US support group facilitators with regard to these 10 objectives of mutual aid groups within the context of support groups for survivors of suicide.

Method

Instrument

Research participants were presented with a listing of Shulman's (2006) 10 mutual aid principles and asked to rate how frequently their groups performed each of these functions on a 3-point Likert scale, from *rarely,* to *sometimes,* to *often,* and to offer ratings on the importance of each function on a 3-point scale, from *not important,* to *somewhat important,* to *very important.*

The US survey included additional questions: whether their groups were led by peers, professionals, or a combination of both; how long their groups had been in existence; how long their current leader had held their position as facilitator; if there was a cofacilitator; whether fees were charged for participation; whether peer leaders received any specialized training; the frequency of their meetings; whether the groups were open-ended or closed-ended; and whether they applied any waiting periods before survivors could participate.

The Survey in Japan

In Japan, during the period from December 13, 2011, to January 30, 2012, a total of 34 local government offices were contacted and queried about whether their districts offered support group services for survivors of suicide, and if they did, to identify the personnel who conducted these groups. Although a national survey of suicide bereavement services has been reported before (Takeshima, 2011), a national directory of suicide bereavement services was not available. Thus, in the Japanese data collection, no records were kept of potential survey respondents. After identifying 56 interested support group facilitators, each was contacted and informed that their cooperation would be entirely voluntary, their responses would be kept completely confidential, and they were free to withdraw from the research at any point. These 56 facilitators agreed to complete surveys and 53 (94.6%) answered all questions.

The Japanese support group facilitators were not queried about their suicide bereavement experiences, so it was not possible to assess accurately how many were directly affected by the loss of a family member or a friend from a prior suicide. Almost all of the Japanese respondents (96 %) had received formal training in support group leadership on more than one occasion. Most Japanese government support group facilitators serving suicide survivors had some professional training in bereavement work and were professionally trained as psychiatric social workers. Probably, some members of this sample may have gravitated to this vocational choice because of a prior experience of suicide bereavement. There is some evidence suggesting peer counselors in suicide bereavement may be disproportionally drawn from the ranks of the suicide bereaved. (Oulanova, Moodley, & Seguin, 2014).

The Survey in the United States

The survivor of suicide (SOS) support group facilitators were drawn from listings of the available support groups offered by the American Foundation of Suicide Prevention and the American Association of Suicidology. Each organization provides listings of over 300 support groups nationwide offering support meetings of survivor of suicide groups. For example, the American Association of Suicidology website lists 481 organizations providing bereavement support to suicide survivors in the 50 US states and the District of Columbia. Some of these organizations are listed twice, with a dedicated support group for teenagers, distinct from another group earmarked for adults. Many organizations on the list are no longer functioning or have changed their contact person. Some are agencies that only provide counseling services. Some of these organizations also did not provide an e-mail address for making contact. Deciding to utilize an online survey instrument to collect the data, cover letters and surveys were sent out to 250 facilitators throughout the country. Geographic diversity was sought, selecting groups from all regions of the country – the North-East, the South, the Midwest, and the Far West – that offered e-mail addresses of their facilitators. Fifty-seven messages were returned as undeliverable. It was not known how many additional survey invitations did not reach their intended destinations because the e-mail addresses were incorrect, they were outdated, the group no longer existed, or a different person had become its contact person. Cover letters offered respondents an opportunity to participate in a confidential survey where their participation was entirely voluntary.

Fifty-nine support group facilitators returned useable surveys within the month (April, 2015) of collecting this survey data. The US support groups were predominately peer-facilitated, with 61 % reporting that one or two peers led their groups. The remaining 39 % were either run by a professional exclusively or by a peer and a professional jointly. Among the peer-supported groups, 80 % reported receiving training, usually of 1- to 3-day duration, to become capable to run their groups. Most of the support groups were long established, averaging 9.6 years in existence. Only 22 % of the groups had been functioning for 3 or fewer years. Most of the facilitators had many years of experience leading their groups. Only 13 % had been leading their group for less than a year, 33 % had led between 1 and 3 years, 28 % between 4 and 10 years, and 26 % for 11 or more years. Thus, more than half had led their groups for 4 years or longer. Most of the groups met monthly, which was true for 48 % of the groups, 39 % met twice a month and only 13 % met on a weekly basis. Most of the groups were facilitated by two or more coleaders (70 %), compared with those led by a single peer or professional leader (30 %). Virtually all of the groups were open-ended (96 %); practically all charged no fees for participation (94 %); and most had no waiting periods required for participation (93 %).

The characteristics that we found for this American sample converge closely with another larger national study of support group facilitators conducted by Cerel, Padgett, and Reed (2009), based on 100 cases. In the Cerel et al. study it was noted that most groups were led by a bereaved peer facilitator, had a coleader, were long-standing and open-ended, met on a monthly basis, and did not charge fees.

Results

Figure 11.1 and **Figure 11.2** display the mean frequency and importance ratings, respectively, for each of the 10 essential mutual aid group principles, as rated by the Japanese and US support group facilitators. One notes a close correspondence between frequency ratings and ratings of their importance, and similarities between the Japanese and US SOS group facilitators. Higher frequency ratings were invariably accompanied by higher importance ratings, and vice versa.

The most highly rated group principle, *providing the bereaved with opportunities to show they are not alone ("all in the same boat")*, had a frequency rating of 2.95 (among the US facilitators) and an importance rating of 2.6, which were the highest means over all 10 categories. For the Japanese, this item also had the highest frequency (2.89) and importance ratings (2.98). At the other end of the spectrum, the lowest rated item among the US support group facilitators was *making demands on one another to promote personal changes ("mutual demand")*, rated as 1.49 for frequency and 1.68 for importance. Japanese facilitators also reported the lowest score on *mutual demand*, rated as 1.84 for importance. However, regarding frequency, the lowest rated item among Japanese support group facilitators was *advocating for promoting social change ("strength in numbers")*, rated as 1.46. Further, Japanese participants reported the relatively lower importance score for this principle – that is, *promoting social change*, rated as 1.85.

Both groups favored goals that would enable members to make individual changes within themselves rather than to change their social environments, which was another especially striking finding. The higher overall ratings were accorded by both the Japanese and the US support group facilitators to supporting personally oriented goals, as compared with those aimed at advancing collective aims and ambitions. Only the last 2 of the 10 goals were clearly collectively oriented, and these had lower mean scores than the first eight goals, with the exception of *making demands on one another*.

Comparisons by *t* test were also run for all of the 10 frequency and importance goals between the Japanese and US facilitators. Statistically significant differences were found on four frequency and importance goals. The US facilitators showed significantly higher means for *helping survivors to solve problems, sharing different ways of coping after the loss, seeing their*

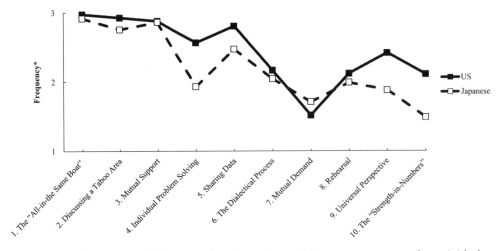

Figure 11.1. Frequency of 10 principles of mutual aid in support groups for suicide bereaved in the United States and Japan (*N* = 115 (59+56)). *Mean frequency (1 = *rarely*, 2 = *seldom*, 3 = *often*).

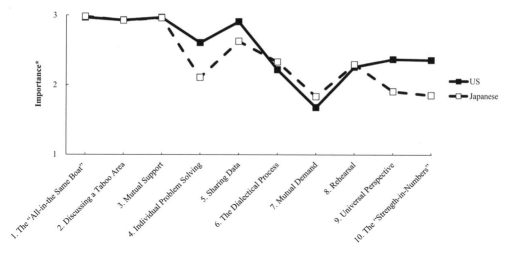

Figure 11.2. Importance of 10 principles of mutual aid in support groups for suicide bereaved in the United States and Japan (*N* = 115 (59+56)). *Mean importance
(1 = *minor importance*, 2 = *important*, 3 = *very important*).

personal issues as societal problems, and *acting to promote social change.* **Table 11.1** and **Table 11.2** below display the means, standard deviations, and *t*-test significance test differences
for each of these four criteria, both in terms of frequencies and importance ratings. There were
no statistically significant differences for the remaining 6 of the 10 comparisons. Thus, there
were more facilitator convergences than divergences between the two groups.

Table 11.1. Mean frequency ratings among Japanese and US support group facilitators

Item	*n*	Mean	*SD*	*t*	*df*	Sig.
Help each other with problem solving (Japan)	54	1.9	0.56	6.17	111	0.0001
Help each other with problem solving (US)	59	2.54	0.54			
Sharing coping strategies after a loss (Japan)	54	2.44	0.57	3.45	111	0.0008
Sharing coping strategies after a loss (US)	59	2.78	0.46			
Viewing personal issues as societal problems (Japan)	54	1.85	0.6	4.4	111	0.0001
Viewing personal issues as societal problems (US)	59	2.39	0.7			
Advocating for social change (Japan)	54	1.46	0.64	5.13	111	0.0001
Advocating for social change (US)	59	2.08	0.65			

Note. df = degrees of freedom; *SD* = standard deviation; Sig. = significance. Source: Japanese/American SOS
facilitators comparison survey, 2015.

Table 11.2. Mean importance ratings among Japanese and US support group facilitators

Item	n	Mean	SD	t	df	Sig.
Help each other with problem solving (Japan)	55	2.11	0.6	4.63	111	0.0001
Help each other with problem solving (US)	59	2.61	0.56			
Sharing coping strategies after a loss (Japan)	54	2.63	0.59	3.27	111	0.0014
Sharing coping strategies after a loss (US)	58	2.91	0.28			
Viewing personal issues as societal problems (Japan)	55	1.91	0.67	3.55	111	0.0006
Viewing personal issues as societal problems (US)	59	2.37	0.73			
Advocating for social change (Japan)	55	1.85	0.76	3.71	111	0.0001
Advocating for social change (US)	59	2.36	0.69			

Note. df = degrees of freedom; *SD* = standard deviation; Sig. = significance. Source: Japanese/American SOS facilitators comparison survey, 2015.

In the next two paragraphs, there is a discussion of diverging leadership practices. These data were not collected among the Japanese facilitators and only apply to the US support group facilitators. The study investigated whether variations in peer or professional leadership, differences in the length of time of a leader's tenure, the group's meeting frequency, and whether the group was a long-established one, or one that was recently formed, would be associated with variability in rating support group priorities. In the US groups there were only three areas where sufficient variability was noted in rating support group priorities: making demands on survivors to change, holding a universal perspective, and in advancing social goals. When these hypotheses were examined, no associations were noted between any of these group differences and whether the group made more demands on members to change or not, whether it emphasized universal perspectives, or pursued social goals.

It was expected that US professional facilitators would be disposed toward making more demands upon survivors to change after a loss than peer leaders would. This could be a possible association with a larger sample (χ^2=4.7338, 2 (*df*), *p*=.09), with 62% of professional leaders reporting sometimes making demands on survivors to change after a loss, as compared with only 33% of peer leaders.

Discussion

This first-ever cross-national comparison of Japanese and US suicide survivor support group facilitators has shown much convergence, with a majority of facilitators from both countries evaluating a majority of mutual aid principles in a similar and analogous fashion. Support group facilitators from both countries also tended to prioritize goals similarly, placing primary emphasis on promoting personal and individual goals ahead of achieving social and collective goals. Further, both the Japanese and the US support group facilitators were especially reluctant to pressure people to make changes.

The US facilitators were significantly more inclined to support helping each other with problem solving, more inclined to share different ways of coping, and more keenly aware of the need to organize and act collectively to address the problems of the suicide bereaved. These findings seem consistent with several earlier studies that have uncovered parallel trends.

Two studies (Chang, Asakawa, & Sanna, 2001; Noguchi, Gohm, Dalsky, & Sakamoto, 2007) found US respondents more likely than the Japanese to focus on positive things. Two other studies found US more than Japanese respondents inclined to assume positive attitudes toward helping others (Noguchi, Gohm, & Dalsky, 2006; Curhan, 2009). Another study found greater cynicism – that is, belief that changing people and things will be less likely to succeed – among the samples of Japanese, compared with the samples of US and British respondents, in believing that they can promote political changes (Feldman, 1997). Still another study found higher levels of trust – in other words, belief that people can work together to create desired social changes – among their samples of US and Japanese respondents (Miller & Mitamura, 2003). All of these findings appear to be convergent with the results that these support group facilitators expressed. However, it should be noted that these studies have not been drawn from the ranks of treatment professionals or from treatment populations. They were based on comparisons of Japanese and US general populations, and hence can only be viewed suggestively as relevant to understanding help giving and psychosocial support processes.

In addition, the smaller number of contrasting patterns between Japanese and the US facilitators could be partly explained by historical developments. In contrast to in the United States, social actions for suicide survivors have been drastically transformed only over the last 10 years in Japan (see Chapter 45 in this volume), and Japanese survivor support groups have greatly increased in number only during the past decade (Shirakawa et al., 2015). Until recent years, in Japan, peer-led suicide survivor support groups were virtually unknown; today they are becoming more widely known and accepted throughout the country (Kawano, 2009). Such transformations in support group developments may have affected changes in facilitators' priorities in unpredictable ways.

The results of the present study should be viewed with caution. The study was based on convenience samples from the two selected societies. Articles contrasting US and Japanese cultural values have not been altogether exhaustive, and some studies cited in the literature have not been completely consistent with the findings reported here. It should also be noted that cultural values change over time, and in the present study, it was not possible to adequately account for the temporal changes in values.

In spite of the above-mentioned limitations, the foregoing analysis does reinforce the utility of Shulman's (2006) 10 essential mutual aid functions scheme as a helpful tool to better understand survivor of suicide support groups, what they expect to accomplish for those bereaved by suicide, and how they may promote survivors' healing. This collaborative analysis of Japan and the United States suggests the presence of universal themes in support group functioning extending across national boundaries, at least in postindustrial societies. Establishing whether these themes extend to societies that are not as economically developed as the United States and Japan is an important task that remains for future research. Future cross-national surveys with Shulman's 10 mutual aid principles should help to identify how commonplace these themes may be. These questions must be examined empirically if survivors are to be helped effectively in support groups.

Acknowledgments

This chapter is a slightly edited version of the following article: Feigelman, W., Feigelman, B., Kawashima, D., Shiraga, K., & Kawano, K. (2016). Comparing facilitator priorities of suicide survivor support groups: A cross-cultural comparison between Japanese and American groups. *OMEGA–Journal of Death and Dying*. Online publication. doi: 10.1177/0030222816652799. © 2016 SAGE Publications. Reprinted by permission.

Corresponding author
William Feigelman
Emeritus Professor of Sociology
Nassau Community College
Garden City, NY
USA
william.feigelman@ncc.edu

References

Cerel, J., Padgett, J.H., & Reed, G.A. (2009). Support groups for suicide survivors: Results of a survey of group leaders. *Suicide and Life Threatening Behavior, 39*(6), 388–398. http://doi.org/10.1521/suli.2009.39.6.588

Chang, E.C. Asakawa, K., & Sanna, L.J. (2001). Cultural variations in optimistic and pessimistic bias: Do Easterners really expect the worst and westerners really expect the best when predicting future life events. *Journal of Personality and Social Psychology, 81*(3), 476–491. http://doi.org/10.1037/0022-3514.81.3.476

Curhan, K.B. (2009). Well-being strategies in Japan and the Unites States: A comparative study of the prevalence and effectiveness of strategies used to make life go well for high-schooled educated and college-educated mid-life adults (Doctoral dissertation, Harvard University). *UMI Dissertations Publishing*, #3385013.

Feigelman, B., & Feigelman, W. (2008). Surviving after suicide loss: The healing potential of suicide survivor support groups. *Illness, Crisis & Loss, 16*(4), 285–304. http://doi.org/10.2190/IL.16.4.b

Feldman, O. (1997). Culture, society and the individual: Cross-cultural political psychology in Japan. *Political Psychology, 18*(2), 327–353. http://doi.org/10.1111/0162-895X.00060

Kawano, K. (2009). Support for the bereaved family members of those who committed suicide. *Japanese Journal of Psychiatric Rehabilitation, 13*(2), 137–142.

Miller, A.S., & Mitamura, T. (2003). Are surveys on trust trustworthy? *Social Psychological Quarterly, 66*(1), 62–70. http://doi.org/10.2307/3090141

Noguchi, K., Gohm, L.C., & Dalsky, J.D. (2006). Cognitive tendencies of focusing on positive and negative information. *Journal of Research in Personality, 40*(6), 891–910. http://doi.org/10.1016/j.jrp.2005.09.008

Noguchi, K. Gohm, L.C., Dalsky, J.D., & Sakamoto, S. (2007). Cultural differences related to positive and negative valences. *Asian Journal of Social Psychology, 10*(2), 68–76. http://doi.org/10.1111/j.1467-839X.2007.00213.x

Oulanova, O., Moodley, R., & Seguin, M. (2014). From suicide survivor to peer counselor: Breaking the silence of suicide bereavement. *Omega: Journal of Death and Dying, 69*(2), 151–168. http://doi.org/10.2190/OM.69.2.d

Shirakawa, N., Tanaka, O., Fushimi, M., Ninomiya, T., Ishimoto, Y., Fukushima, N., Tanabe, H. (2015). *Jishi izoku shien guruupu no genjyo to kadai: 2015 nen zenkoku seishin hoken fukushi sentaa choukai chousa oyobi kanagawa, yokohama shi no genjyo wo fumaete* [Current situation and future challenges of support groups for suicide survivors: Based on the research for Japanese association of the directors of mental health centers and the current status in Kanagawa and Yokohama cities]. Proceedings of 39th convention of the Japanese Association for Suicide Prevention, Tokyo, Japan.

Shulman, L. (2006). *The skills of helping individuals, families groups and communities* (5th ed.). Pacific Grove, CA: Thomson Brooks/Cole.

Takeshima, T. (2011). *Research reports of efforts for suicide prevention and suicide survivor support in prefectures and ordinance-designated cities.* Tokyo, Japan: Center for Suicide Prevention, National Institute of Mental Health, National Center of Neurology and Psychiatry.

Chapter 12

Peer Counseling in Suicide Bereavement

Characteristics and Pitfalls

Olga Oulanova[1] and Monique Séguin[2]

[1]Private Practice, Toronto, ON, Canada
[2]Department of Psychology and Psychoeducation, Université du Québec en Outaouais, Gatineau, QC, Canada

Abstract: A number of individuals bereaved through suicide play an important part in postvention efforts by becoming peer counselors, and in that role, supporting other survivors. Some may do this by providing individual and group peer counseling under the umbrella of postvention organizations, while others may take a less formal approach to offering support. This chapter explores the role of peer counseling in suicide bereavement, discusses the suitability of this intervention for different populations of survivors, and suggests that in some situations it may not be recommended. Drawing on qualitative research with Canadian suicide survivors, the chapter describes the characteristics of people who become peer counselors, examines what motivated these individuals to take an active role in postvention, and addresses the rewards and the challenges of their volunteering. It also explores what this volunteering means to them and how they conceptualize their peer counseling efforts.

Introduction: Peer Counseling as a Form of Postvention

The trauma of losing a loved one to suicide, coupled with the difficult sociocultural context of suicide bereavement, result in some survivors reporting significant mental health difficulties following their loss (e.g., De Groot, De Keijser, & Neeleman, 2006; Kramer et al., 2015; Mc-Menamy, Jordan, & Mitchell, 2008; Sethi & Bhargava, 2003). Given that suicide bereavement poses considerable challenges, different types of suicide postvention programs have emerged to support survivors (see Chapter 9 in this volume). One form of suicide postvention is peer support.

Peer support in suicide bereavement takes different forms. It may include survivors of suicide providing supportive counseling in a somewhat structured fashion under the umbrella of an organization; informal community efforts wherein a survivor connects with another survivor in person or by telephone to offer a listening ear; or even web-based support forums where survivors reach out to others bereaved through suicide (Kramer et al., 2015; Krysinska & Andriessen, 2013). Historically, peer support can be traced to the work of Harry Stack Sullivan in the 1920s (for a discussion, see Rawlinson, Waegemakers Schiff, & Barlow, 2009). At that time, Sullivan advocated using former mental health patients to assist current patients in psychiatric settings. In the 1930s, the Alcoholics Anonymous (AA) movement also adopted this helping format (Rawlinson et al., 2009). Furthermore, in the bereavement context, a widow-to-widow program was conceived in the late 1960s as a means of preventing mental health problems in the newly bereaved (Silverman, 2004).

Peer counselors are nonprofessionals who share some key experiences with those they support (e.g., Rawlinson et al., 2009). In the area of suicide bereavement, a peer counselor is an individual bereaved through suicide who offers supportive counseling on a voluntary basis to other survivors after suicide.

Individuals bereaved through suicide who have obtained support from other survivors report the experience as tremendously helpful (e.g., Feigelman, Jordan, & Gorman, 2009; Jordan, Feigelman, McMenamy, & Mitchell, 2011; Kramer et al., 2015). In the view of many survivors, only other individuals bereaved through suicide can fully comprehend their experiences (e.g., van Dongen, 1993; Vandecreek & Mottram, 2009; Wagner & Calhoun, 1991–1992). Connecting with individuals who have undergone a similar form of traumatic loss may help decrease survivors' sense of isolation and stigma; normalize their difficult experiences in the aftermath of the suicide; and offer hope that they, too, will heal from their loss (Clark & Goldney, 1995; Praeger & Bernhardt, 1985). In-person support from another survivor, or peer counseling, thereby offers tremendous helping potential for survivors of suicide.

Of note, the notion of survivors of a particular affliction providing support to other individuals suffering through a similar experience is not unique to suicide bereavement. Peer counselors offer assistance in settings such as oncology (e.g., Hall, 2001), HIV/AIDS (e.g., Crook, Weir, Willms, & Egdorf, 2006), and sexual violence (e.g., Rath, 2008). While in areas other than suicide bereavement, much research has explored the experiences of peer counselors, finding that peer counselors report personal growth and psychological and spiritual healing; construct meaning through their volunteer work; and acquire new knowledge and skills (e.g., Crook et al., 2006; Hall, 2001; Rath, 2008), specific research with suicide survivors who volunteer as peer counselors has been lacking.

Peer Counseling in Suicide Postvention

Peer counselors may offer one-on-one support to suicide survivors, join support groups for survivors, or cofacilitate therapeutic survivor groups. They may provide support to individual survivors, families, groups, or to a community in which a suicide has occurred.

Research with Canadian suicide survivors who went on to become peer counselors (Oulanova, Moodley, & Séguin, 2014) revealed that individual peer counseling may take the form of informal supportive sessions either by telephone or in person wherein a suicide survivor–peer counselor connects with another survivor to share stories of loss, offer suggestions, and provide relevant resources. It may also occur under the umbrella of an organization and be more structured in nature. In those cases, peer counselors meet with either an individual survivor or a couple/family who have suffered a loss to suicide over a course of several sessions, discussing specific themes related to suicide and the grieving process.

Peer counselors also provide support in a group format. While some survivors create and subsequently run such groups, others volunteer alongside nonsurvivor professionals. Indeed, in their survey of groups for suicide survivors in the United States and Canada, Rubey and McIntosh (1996) found that suicide survivors often facilitate or cofacilitate suicide postvention groups. Another survey of groups for suicide survivors in the United States revealed that 78 % of surveyed groups had a survivor leader (Cerel, Padgett, Conwell, & Reed, 2009).

A group environment can effectively address sentiments of stigma and shame as well as offer a sense of community, thus addressing the aversive social isolation that many survivors experience (Moore & Freeman, 1995). In particular, in a support group consisting of other suicide survivors, the group environment can normalize survivors' complex reactions, such as feelings of anger, shame, abandonment, relief, and guilt (Hopmeyer & Werk, 1994; Pietilä, 2002). It is therefore not surprising that "support groups for suicide survivors are among the most widely available type of support for survivors" (Cerel et al., 2009, p. 272). Research findings provide support for the therapeutic potential of this mode of postvention in terms of alleviating symptoms of depression and feelings of isolation, improving social adjustment (Constantino, 1988), and modifying the narrative of the suicide from a victim to an agentic one (Mitchell, Dysart Gale, Garand, & Wesner, 2003).

Finally, a variation of group peer counseling is offering support to an entire community in which a suicide has occurred. For example, in Canadian Aboriginal communities, peer counselors may assist other survivors through traditional approaches to helping, such as sharing circles (Portman & Garrett, 2006). In such cases, a peer counselor may speak to a large group of bereaved individuals and share their own story of suicide loss, as well as the healing journey from that loss. In sum, connecting with another survivor after suicide and obtaining peer counseling (be it through an individual or group format) proves an inherently healing experience for individuals bereaved through suicide, as such a connection counters the loneliness and hurt that the bereaved often experience in the aftermath of their loss (Feigelman et al., 2009).

Peer Counseling for Different Groups of Survivors: Some Words of Caution

The main types of interventions for people bereaved through suicide include crisis intervention, peer counseling, and grief counseling (Andriessen, 2009; de Groot, Neeleman, van der Meer, & Burger, 2010). Traditionally, mental health programs delivering services to those bereaved through suicide have relied heavily on professionally led individual and group interventions, suggesting that survivors after suicide are at greater risk of psychological problems and complicated bereavement (Beautrais, 2004; Jordan & McMenamy, 2004). Indeed, in some cases, the process of bereavement after a suicide is experienced as more difficult by some, perhaps those with increased preexisting psychological vulnerability (Shear & Shair, 2005). In a systematic review of 57 studies focusing on the effects of suicide bereavement, Pitman and colleagues concluded that

> the body of evidence indicates that exposure to suicide bereavement is not a random event. The relatives and non-relatives of people who die by suicide differ from those not exposed to suicide bereavement in a range of sociodemographic and clinical characteristics, even before the bereavement. (Pitman, Osborn, King, & Erlangsen, 2014, p. 86)

While some bereaved individuals may require professional services in the aftermath of their loss, it is important to refrain from considering those bereaved through suicide as one homogenous group. Even though a proportion of people bereaved through suicide will have a complicated bereavement, we ought not to underestimate different pathways to resiliency (Bonanno, 2004).

Interestingly, two recent studies evaluating the effectiveness of community-based programs for those bereaved through suicide in Canada and in Australia (Barlow et al., 2010; Visser, Comans, & Scuffham, 2014) reported positive outcomes for both those providing peer support and for the bereaved participants. These results challenge the assumption that suicide survivors require services from highly skilled professionals. Rather, these research findings suggest potential benefits in developing services that consist of peer supporters and professional clinicians working in a collaborative way to offer client-centered and cost-effectiveness services.

Finally, there may be a subgroup of suicide survivors for whom neither professional nor peer services may prove necessary in the aftermath of their loss. Survivors possessing an array of healthy coping skills who are dealing with the suicide in a supportive environment of family and friends, where there is open communication about the death, may not feel the need to seek out additional support. Whereas some individuals are resilient in the face of adversity, it is indispensable to offer support to those who need this assistance in coping with their loss. It would be a mistake to assume that every suicide survivor would benefit from or welcome either professional or peer support.

Exploring Peer Counseling: Who Are These Suicide Survivors–Peer Counselors?

While peer counseling represents an important form of postvention for some individuals bereaved through suicide, little is known about the characteristics of survivors who go on to become peer counselors, and the experiences of these individuals with supporting other survivors. While scarce, the literature on this topic suggests that offering such support may hold considerable healing potential for the peer counselors themselves. Reaching out to other survivors may alleviate peer counselors' own loneliness and isolation, provide them with an opportunity to share their stories thereby keeping the memory of the loved one alive, and create a sense of community (e.g., Edmunds, 1998; Feigelman et al., 2009; Hurtig, Bullitt, & Kates, 2011; Jordan, 2011).

Research With Survivors of Suicide Who Went on to Become Peer Counselors

Given the dearth of research with peer counselors in suicide bereavement, this research aimed to explore this particular form of postvention. The purpose of the study was to gain insight into the lived experiences of a group of Canadian suicide survivors who went on to become peer counselors (Oulanova et al., 2014). The study aimed to understand what motivated these suicide survivors to become peer counselors in the first place, what kinds of challenges and rewards (if any) they encountered in this role, and how they conceptualized their volunteering in light of their own loss. The first author of this present chapter conducted semistructured interviews with 14 Canadian suicide survivors who were volunteering as peer counselors and analyzed the interview data using the interpretative phenomenology analysis (IPA) approach (Smith, Jarman, & Osborn, 1999; Smith, Flowers, & Larkin, 2009). IPA was well-suited to address the questions, as the central aim of IPA is to describe the participants' world by exploring in detail their experiences and how they make sense of those experiences (Smith, 2004).

An interview guide consisting of open-ended questions closely related to the underlying goals of the study was used. Participants were asked to describe their path to becoming peer counselors, to speak about their experience with this volunteering in terms of what they enjoy and what they find difficult, and to reflect on what being a peer counselor means to them. It was considered to be a flexible tool, and it was slightly modified during each interview to accommodate the specific experiences that the participant wished to share.

The analysis of the interview data followed the IPA guidelines provided by Smith et al. (1999). The first level of analysis consisted of preparing a written reflection immediately after each interview. This facilitated the recording of any emerging themes or preliminary interpretations of the interview data. The second level involved verbatim transcription of the interviews.

The third level of analysis entailed reading each transcript several times with the goal of becoming intimately familiar with the content of the conversation and coding in the margins any segments that directly related to the research questions, as well as those that appeared salient for the participants. This allowed for emergence of novel themes and categories which were not considered by the initial research questions. Codes close to participants' actual words were used. As additional interview transcripts became available, the emerging codes were compared with other units of text, and connections between codes began to reveal themselves. Some initial codes were condensed into more inclusive categories that united analogous concepts or instances from multiple interviews. As the goal of the study was to capture the experiences of the participants, data analysis stopped once a list of themes emerged that described participants' experiences in a coherent and comprehensive manner. These themes were shared with the participants who then reviewed the findings and offered their feedback either during a second interview, or using e-mail. This feedback was integrated, and the themes were modified accordingly.

The Study: From Suicide Survivor to Peer Counselor

Participant Characteristics

The study participants (12 women and 2 men) were recruited from across Canada, from both urban and rural settings. Most of them had lost one family member or friend to suicide, but three participants had lost two or more individuals. The time since the suicide ranged from 3 to 42 years. At the time of the study, the participants had been volunteering as peer counselors for between 2.5 and 18 years, with a mean of 7 years. While some volunteered in bereavement organizations, others provided informal peer support in their community. This was particularly common in rural areas, where in the absence of a bereavement organization, these peer counselors organized and facilitated support groups for survivors of suicide. Moreover, one participant had founded a support group for suicide survivors of a particular cultural and ethnic background as there were no services for this specific population (Oulanova et al., 2014).

Deciding to Volunteer in Suicide Postvention

As participants reflected on their journeys to becoming peer counselors, they talked about their own suicide bereavement experiences. These accounts proved important in understanding their decision to support other survivors of suicide, while contextualizing their peer counseling efforts.

Many described encountering stigma and other negative reactions as well as struggling with family silence, loneliness, and isolation in the aftermath of their loss. They had difficulty finding factual information about suicide and making sense of their emotional reactions. Interestingly, several participants received peer counseling in the aftermath of their own loss and explained that their positive experience with this form of support influenced their decision to, in time, follow the same path and thereby, "give back." One participant explained:

> As I got better, through the stages, through the journey, as I healed, I made up my mind that I wanted to give something back, somehow in some way return this. From the very beginning, I said I will give back, some way, one day.

When asked to reflect on their decision to volunteer in suicide postvention, participants described becoming a peer counselor as making an active choice about how to cope with their loss and "survive" this life experience. Indeed, they explained that part of their motivation was to help themselves cope with and heal from the suicide loss. Yet another motivation underlying participants' decision to become peer counselors stemmed from their experience of silence in the aftermath of their own loss. Some participants shared that volunteering in postvention represented a way to put an end to family silence around the suicidal death and thereby initiate dialogue about the suicide in their immediate family. Others conceptualized becoming involved in this area as breaking the silence about suicide in the community at large. As one participant put it reflecting on her motivations to become a peer counselor:

> So one would be about breaking the silence.... You know, suicide is something people don't talk about, and talking about how other people's silence to your loss has affected you. So that's one issue – the breaking the silence.

Participants also cited the desire to help others, prevent future suicides, and address what they perceived as an unmet need as motivations on their path to becoming peer counselors. As one participant explained, "I had a sense that by opening up my story, I could help prevent other people's suicides." Finally, they explained that this kind of volunteering was highly congruent with their personal qualities and their core belief in the value of helping others. Becoming a peer counselor was consistent with their other life engagements and their involvement in the community.

Describing the Experience of Providing Peer Counseling

Given that the research participants had chosen to stay on as peer counselors for several years, it is perhaps not surprising that they found many rewards in this volunteering. Specifically, they felt satisfied at being able to help other survivors and at noticing positive changes in survivors' functioning over time. Reflecting on their volunteering, they noted that supporting others further aided their own healing process from having lost a loved one to suicide. Participants explained that in the course of supporting other survivors, they engaged in an ongoing reflection on their own experience with suicide loss. Such reflection in turn allowed them to make greater sense of this event, and thereby advance in terms of their own healing. Two of the participants explained this in the following way:

> I think every time you share your experience it's different; you share pieces and different parts. Sometimes you have different "ahas!" I think healing does continue to occur as part of volunteering.

> So when you tell the story, even 10 years on, the opportunity to, it's a continual reflection. And the thing is when you are supporting other survivors, you are always reflecting on your own story. You cannot not reflect on it.... Maybe in some way, in some unrelated process through working with survivors, I've been able to reflect enough on my own experience that it puts it in place.

Finally, at the same time as participants reached out to other survivors, lending a listening ear to others, they also found a sense of voice with respect to suicide-related issues. This volunteering provided them with an opportunity to speak about their own loss, as well as to articulate their thoughts on suicide and suicide bereavement in general.

Yet alongside the rewards, participants identified a number of challenging aspects of being a peer counselor. Most of these difficult elements directly related to the traumatic nature of suicidal death and to participants' own experience with having lost a loved one in this manner. They found it difficult to hear others' painful stories, noting that other survivors' experiences touched them profoundly and that they continued to think about these stories for some time after the supportive session. While many participants found it difficult to hear survivors' stories because of the emotional pain and the violent imagery inherent in their narratives, for some, listening to such stories presented an additional challenge. A number of participants shared that they relived their own loss while hearing other survivors' bereavement experiences. This reliving seemed to be particularly salient when there were important parallels between the peer counselor's and the survivor's experiences (i.e., the circumstances surrounding the suicide, characteristics of the person who died, etc). In addition to survivors' accounts triggering participants' painful memories, another difficult element of being a peer counselor entailed telling other survivors about one's personal experiences with suicide loss. As peer counselors, participants frequently shared their own stories with losing a loved one to suicide, which represented yet another way of reliving their traumatic loss. As one participant shared:

> The challenging part is when you talk about your own experience and bring the memory back; the night the police came to notify me about my son's death, the first day that I missed him, the first year.

An additional challenging aspect of peer counseling had to do with navigating the dynamics of the interpersonal relationship with another survivor. In fact, participants reported struggling with a particular aspect of the peer counseling relationship – namely, managing boundaries. Although participants explained that they did not intend to establish a strictly "professional" relationship with those they supported, most individuals drew a distinction between being a peer counselor to another survivor and being a friend. As this was not always congruent with the survivors' understanding of the helping relationship, in some cases, setting up and maintaining adequate boundaries proved a demanding undertaking.

Learning about the rewards and, particularly, the challenges of being a peer counselor in suicide bereavement, raised the question about what facilitated or assisted participants to continue providing this important volunteer work (remember that most participants had been volunteering in this area for many years). Participants shared that maintaining close relationships with, and receiving support from, other volunteers or individuals involved in suicide postvention, as well as routinely making time for self-care were critical in allowing them to stay active as peer counselors in the long run. In one participant's words:

> I think what helps me is the bonds that I've created with some of the other [peer counselor] survivors, because we can get together and we can laugh and we cannot talk about suicide at all, we can just silently be there for each other.

With respect to self-care strategies, participants described engaging in spiritual or religious practices and ceremonies as well as taking time away from peer counseling and allowing oneself to take breaks. As one individual put it:

> Sometimes I literally have to shut down and step back from the volunteering, and I know that that is just what I need to do. To take care of me. To take a step back and to breathe and to focus on the living because you can get caught up in reliving. It's like Groundhog Day, where I seem to be just reliving the losses constantly.

The Meaning of Providing Peer Counseling

Alongside learning about the rewards, challenges, and the facilitative factors that the participants encountered, the study focused on understanding how they conceptualized their volunteering and the meaning supporting other survivors held for them. Reflecting on the meaning of being a peer counselor, participants identified offering hope to other survivors as one of the most important aspects of this volunteer work. Having found ways to cope with and heal from their own loss, peer counselors, farther along in their healing, were able to reflect back, thus assisting survivors just beginning that same healing process. Such sharing, in turn, seemed to instill hope in the recently bereaved survivors. Others explained that they fostered hope simply by being a living example of someone who, in spite of having lost a loved one to suicide, was able to go on with life, have meaningful relationships, and experience a range of emotions. Two of the participant shared their thoughts on this aspect of peer counseling:

> The big thing is there is a volunteer sitting there who has moved on with her life and can laugh at things. That's, I think, the great thing. It gives them hope. And that's great, that's worth a million bucks.

> You have no cure; you don't have anything except hope. That is a very big thing, but at first, it doesn't feel like a big thing.

Further, providing peer counseling enabled participants to maintain an ongoing connection to their loved one who had died through suicide, a connection most considered important. In the process of supporting other survivors, participants would share their own stories and speak about their loved ones who died through suicide, thus keeping their memory alive and honoring the deceased individual.

Discussion

Numerous bereaved individuals obtain professional grief counseling, get involved in support groups, or obtain peer counseling from a fellow survivor after a death by suicide. Very few studies have compared different treatment approaches (Pitman et al., 2014). Suicide support groups where a fellow survivor after suicide supports the bereaved offer an alternative to bereaved individuals who have difficulty finding support during the grief process and may not wish to access professional mental health services. Indeed, peer counseling is a significant component of suicide postvention and one that survivors report finding particularly helpful in the aftermath of their loss. Although far from all survivors seek out this form of postvention (and some may not require or even benefit from this type of intervention), for those who do obtain assistance from fellow suicide survivors, it offers them hope, normalizes their reactions, and connects them with a supportive community. As discussed in this chapter, peer counseling in suicide bereavement can take various forms, from individual informal assistance, to more structured group interventions, to community-wide efforts.

Of note, the limitations of this research must be considered. One limitation concerns the issue of the findings' generalizability to the experiences of other suicide survivors. Given the qualitative nature of this research and the interpretative phenomenological framework, the goal was not to attempt generalizations beyond the present sample, but rather to provide rich descriptions of participants' experiences and the context in which these descriptions were generated. The study surveyed a specific subgroup of suicide survivors – namely, individuals who chose to pursue peer counseling in the aftermath of their own loss. However, many survivors engage in suicide postvention through routes other than by becoming peer counselors. For example, some survivors do fund-raising, while others become active in suicide prevention and awareness raising. Others do not become involved in postvention at all. Moreover, the participating suicide survivor–peer counselors self-selected to take part in the present study, which suggests that they were actively involved and engaged with suicide-related issues. In addition, these individuals had been providing peer counseling for several years. The experiences of peer counselors who started and then quit such volunteering for various reasons were not captured. Consequently, the experiences of suicide survivor–peer counselors who took part in this research may significantly differ from those of other individuals bereaved through suicide, and even from those of other survivors who volunteer in suicide postvention.

In the recent years, clinicians, researchers, and decisions makers are acknowledging more and more the importance of understanding people's lived experiences. This research with survivors after suicide who went on to become peer counselors addressed just this issue by exploring these individuals' experiences with supporting other survivors. In-depth interviews with a group of Canadian suicide survivors who became peer counselors revealed their motivations to become active in postvention, their experiences with this supportive work (in terms of rewards, challenges, and facilitative factors they have encountered), and the meaning that being a peer counselor holds for them. Learning about their experiences elucidates this form of postvention and allows us to better understand what the experience is like for the peer counselors themselves. However, at this time, additional research is needed to answer the following important questions. What is the impact of suicide support groups, and who benefits the most from this form of postvention and in what context? For what length of time? And finally, are peer counselors more efficient and more able to instill resiliency in the aftermath of a suicide compared with professional clinicians?

Corresponding author

Olga Oulanova
Private Practice
Toronto, ON
Canada
olgaoulanova@hotmail.com

References

Andriessen, K. (2009). Can postvention be prevention? *Crisis, 30*(1), 43–47. http://doi.org/10.1027/0227-5910.30.1.43

Barlow, C., Waegemakers, J., Chugh, U., Rawlinson, D., Hides, E., & Leith, J. (2010). An evaluation of suicide bereavement peer support program. *Death Studies, 34*(10), 915–930. http://doi.org/10.1080/07481181003761435

Beautrais, A., (2004). *Suicide postvention support for families, Whanau and significant others after a suicide: A literature review and synthesis of evidence.* Christchurch, New Zealand: Christchurch School of Medicine and Health Services, Christchurch Suicide Project.

Bonanno, G. (2004). Loss, trauma and human resilience. *American Psychologist, 59*(1), 20–28. http://doi.org/10.1037/0003-066X.59.1.20

Cerel, J., Padgett, J. H., Conwell, Y., & Reed, G. A., Jr. (2009). A call for research: The need to better understand the impact of support groups for suicide survivors. *Suicide and Life-Threatening Behavior, 39*(3), 269–282. http://doi.org/10.1521/suli.2009.39.6.588

Clark, S. E., & Goldney, R. D. (1995). Grief reactions and recovery in a support group for people bereaved by suicide. *Crisis, 16*(1), 27–33. http://doi.org/10.1027/0227-5910.16.1.27

Constantino, R. E. (1988). Comparison of two group interventions for the bereaved. *Image, 20*(2), 83–87.

Crook, J., Weir, R., Willms, D., & Egdorf, T. (2006). Experiences and benefits of volunteering in a community AIDS organization. *Journal of the Association of Nurses in AIDS Care, 17*(4), 39–45. http://doi.org/10.1016/j.jana.2006.05.002

De Groot, M. H., De Keijser, J., & Neeleman, J. (2006). Grief shortly after suicide and natural death: A comparative study among spouses and first-degree relatives. *Suicide and Life-Threatening Behavior, 36*(4), 418–431. http://doi.org/10.1521/suli.2006.36.4.418

De Groot, M., Neeleman, J., van der Meer, K., & Burger, H. (2010). The effectiveness of family-based cognitive-behavior grief therapy to prevent complicated grief in relatives of suicide victims. *Suicide and Life-Threatening Behavior, 40*(5), 425–437. http://doi.org/10.1521/suli.2010.40.5.425

Edmunds, A. (1998). My story: Thoughts of a survivor. In A.A. Leenaars, S. Wenckstern, I. Sakinofsky, R.J. Dyck, M.J. Kral, & R.C. Bland (Eds.), *Suicide in Canada* (pp. 369–375). Toronto, Canada: University of Toronto Press.

Feigelman, W., Jordan, J.R., & Gorman, B.S. (2009). Personal growth after a suicide loss: cross-sectional findings suggest growth after loss may be associated with better mental health among survivors. *Omega: Journal of Death and Dying, 59*(3), 181–203. http://doi.org/10.2190/OM.59.3.a

Hall, V.P. (2001). Bearing witness to suffering in AIDS: Constructing meaning from loss. *Journal of the Association of Nurses in AIDS Care, 12*(2), 44–55. http://doi.org/10.1016/S1055-3290(06)60133-7

Hopmeyer, E., & Werk, A. (1994). A comparative study of family bereavement groups. *Death Studies, 18*(3), 243–256. http://doi.org/10.1080/07481189408252657

Hurtig, R., Bullitt, E., & Kates, K. (2011). Samaritans Grief Support Services. In J.R. Jordan & J.L. McIntosh (Eds.), *Grief after suicide: Understanding the consequences and caring for the survivors* (pp. 341–348). New York, NY: Routledge.

Jordan, J.R. (2011). Principles of grief counselling with adult survivors. In J.R. Jordan & J.L. McIntosh (Eds.), *Grief after suicide: Understanding the consequences and caring for the survivors* (pp. 179–224). New York, NY: Routledge.

Jordan, J., & McMenamy, J., (2004). Interventions for suicide survivors: A review of the literature. *Suicide and Life-Threatening Behavior, 34*(4), 337–349. http://doi.org/10.1521/suli.34.4.337.53742

Jordan, J.R., Feigelman, W., McMenamy, J., & Mitchell, A.M. (2011). Research on the needs of survivors. In J.R. Jordan & J.L. McIntosh (Eds.), *Grief after suicide: Understanding the consequences and caring for the survivors* (pp. 115–132). New York, NY: Routledge.

Kramer, J., Boon, B., Schotanus-Dijkstra, M., van Ballegooijen, W., Kerkhof, A., & van der Poel, A. (2015). The mental health of visitors of web-based support forums for bereaved by suicide. *Crisis, 36*(1), 38–45. http://doi.org/10.1027/0227-5910/a000281

Krysinska, K., & Andriessen, K. (2013). Suicide bereavement online. Sharing memories, seeking support, and exchanging hope. In B. Mishara & A. Kerkhof (Eds.), *Suicide prevention and new technologies: Evidence based practice* (pp. 150–165). New York, NY: Palgrave-Macmillan.

McMenamy, J.M., Jordan, J.R., & Mitchell, A.M. (2008). What do suicide survivors tell us they need? Results of a pilot study. *Suicide and Life-Threatening Behavior, 38*(4), 375–389. http://doi.org/10.1521/suli.2008.38.4.375

Mitchell, A.M., Dysart Gale, D., Garand, L., & Wesner, S. (2003). The use of narrative data to inform the psychotherapeutic group process with suicide survivors. *Issues in Mental Health Nursing, 24*(1), 91–106. http://doi.org/10.1080/01612840305308

Moore, M.M., & Freeman, S.J. (1995). Counseling survivors of suicide: Implications for group postvention. *The Journal for Specialists in Group Work, 20*(1), 40–48. http://doi.org/10.1080/01933929508411324

Oulanova, O., Moodley, R., & Séguin, M. (2014). From suicide survivor to peer counselor: Breaking the silence of suicide bereavement. *Omega: Journal of Death and Dying, 69*(2), 151–168. http://doi.org/10.2190/OM.69.2.d

Pietilä, M. (2002). Support groups: A psychological or social device for suicide bereavement? *British Journal of Guidance and Counselling, 30*(4), 401–414. http://doi.org/10.1080/0306988021000025600

Pitman, A., Osborn, D., King, M., Erlangsen, A. (2014). Effects of suicide bereavement on mental health and suicide risk. *Lancet Psychiatry, 1*(1), 86–94. http://doi.org/10.1016/S2215-0366(14)70224-X

Portman, T.A.A., & Garrett, M.T. (2006). Native American healing traditions. *International Journal of Disability, Development and Education, 53*(4), 453–469. http://doi.org/10.1080/10349120601008647

Praeger, S.G., & Bernhardt, G.R. (1985). Survivors of suicide: A community in need. *Family and Community Health, 8*(3), 62–72. http://doi.org/10.1097/00003727-198511000-00007

Rath, J. (2008). Training to be a volunteer Rape Crisis counsellor: A qualitative study of women's experiences. *British Journal of Guidance and Counselling, 36*(1), 19–32. http://doi.org/10.1080/03069880701716208

Rawlinson, D., Waegemakers Schiff, J., & Barlow, C.A. (2009). A review of peer support for suicide bereavement as a postvention alternative. *Currents: New Scholarship in the Human Services, 8*(2), 1–20.

Rubey, C.T., & McIntosh, J.L. (1996). Suicide survivors groups: Results of a survey. *Suicide and Life-Threatening Behavior, 26*(4), 351–358.

Sethi, S., & Bhargava, S.C. (2003). Child and adolescent survivors of suicide. *Crisis, 24*(1), 4–6. http://doi.org/10.1027//0227-5910.24.1.4

Shear, K. & Shair, H. (2005). Attachment, loss, and complicated grief. *Developmental Psychobiology, 47*(3), 253–267. http://doi.org/10.1002/dev.20091

Silverman, P. (2004). *Widow to widow: How the bereaved help one another* (2nd ed.). New York, NY: Routledge.

Smith, J. A. (2004). Reflecting on the development of interpretative phenomenological analysis and its contribution to qualitative research in psychology. *Qualitative Research in Psychology, 1*(1), 39–54.

Smith, J. A., Flowers, P., & Larkin, M. (2009). *Interpretative Phenomenological Analysis: Theory, method, research*. London, UK: Sage.

Smith, J. A., Jarman, M., & Osborn, M. (1999). Doing Interpretative Phenomenological Analysis. In M. Murray & K. Chamberlain (Eds.), *Qualitative health psychology: Theories and methods* (pp. 218–240). London, UK: Sage.

Vandecreek, L., & Mottram, K. (2009). The religious life during suicide bereavement: A description. *Death Studies, 33*(8), 741–762. http://doi.org/10.1080/07481180903070467

Van Dongen, C. J. (1993). Social context of postsuicide bereavement. *Death Studies, 17*(2), 125–141. http://doi.org/10.1080/07481189308252610

Visser, V., Comans, T., & Scuffham, P. (2014). Evaluation of the effectiveness of a community based crisis intervention program for people bereaved by suicide. *Journal of Community Psychology, 42*(1), 19–28. http://doi.org/10.1002/jcop.21586

Wagner, K. G., & Calhoun, L. G. (1991–1992). Perceptions of social support by suicide survivors and their social networks. *Omega: Journal of Death and Dying, 24*(1), 61–73.

Chapter 13

After Suicide – Roles of the General Practitioner

Sheila Clark[1] and Louanne Ebert[2]

[1]Unihealth Highbury, Adelaide Unicare network, University of Adelaide, SA, Australia
[2]Bedford Medical Clinic, Adelaide, SA, Australia

Abstract: This chapter describes the potential roles of a general practitioner (GP) or family doctor in suicide postvention in the context of the philosophy and principles of general practice. It is written from the Australian perspective, with reference and relevance to other countries and health systems. The chapter demonstrates that the GP is the professional of choice of the bereaved, that the multimodal form of care provided by the GP is relevant to the needs of the bereaved, and that the GP is an appropriate long-term provider of support and a gateway to other services within the community. The dilemmas faced by the doctor in providing care are described. The chapter examines the expertise of the doctor in providing postvention care and finds an alarming lack of information, training, and support for family doctors. Proposals are made for a postvention-supported general practice pathway to care in collaboration with postvention outreach services, and for a postvention protocol for general practice.

Introduction

A suicide of someone close can change life for the whole family forever: Every domain of life is affected – the emotional, physical, mental, social, behavioral, and spiritual. The general practitioner (GP) is well placed to respond to the person's needs in all of these areas of life. General practice is a unique medical discipline whose principles include commitment to the patient, with a specific focus on understanding their subjective view and the context of their problem, rather than merely relying on a specific body of knowledge. Family doctors can work in a variety of locations including within the person's home, community service centers, and medical care rooms. They see themselves as part of an active community referral network of health care and support agencies. They also have a public health role in the well-being of the general population in which they live and work (McWhinney, 1989). Originally based on the biomedical model, general practice experienced various paradigm changes to become a bio-psycho-social discipline. Indeed, with recent new understandings in the discipline of neuroscience, the scope of general practice can now include reference to such eclectic fields as the arts, complementary therapies, and spirituality (Vermandere et al., 2011).

The GP is trained in a holistic-person approach to provide comprehensive, continuing, collaborative, and coordinated care in a role that is naturally all-encompassing and long term (Royal Australian College of General Practitioners, n.d.). With an intimate knowledge of the individual and their family, the GP can walk alongside the patient for the duration of need. With an understanding of the neuro-psycho-physiological effects of bereavement, the GP can be proactive in initiating appropriate support, and be vigilant for any adverse sequelae. With a wide knowledge of community resources, the GP is also a gateway to a diverse range of other specialized and community assistance. Medical knowledge equips GPs to give authoritative answers to questions about the death. Importantly the GP can be involved in the care of the whole family as well as responding to community needs. From their public health role in suicide prevention and their first-hand experience of working with those bereaved through suicide, family doctors are well placed to contribute to postvention policy making and research. Importantly, they may be the only health professional accessible, especially in rural areas, and perhaps the only affordable practitioner.

Although suicide of a patient is a rare event for a GP, the collective fallout in the general practice population is significant. Around four to five patient suicides occur in a full-time GP's working lifetime (Marquet, Bartelds, Kerkhof, Schellevis, & van de Zee, 2005; Martin, Clark, Beckinsale, Stacey, & Skene, 1997). According to a conservative estimate, six people suffer serious consequences as the result of a single suicide (Shneidman, 1972). Taking account of those people affected in the wider community such as friendship circles, sporting clubs, workplaces, and schools, and the fact that the grieving process may last several years (Cerel, Maple, Aldrich, & van de Venne, 2013; World Health Organization, 2014; Zisook & Shuchter, 1986), the realistic fallout from a single suicide is ten or more bereaved persons. In Australia, which has a current suicide rate of 12/100,000 population, a GP could see 50 or more patients bereaved through suicide in a working lifetime. This figure would vary according to the local and national suicide rates.

Because suicide survivors are more at risk of physical and mental health complications from their grief than the general population (Clark, 2001; Pitman, Osborn, King, & Erlangsen, 2014; Stroebe & Stroebe, 1993; Chapter 2 in this volume), the family doctor is therefore behoven to pursue secondary prevention in this at-risk population as well as the prevention of copycat suicides (Chapter 19 discusses dealing with the aftermath of clustered suicides). The GP is well placed to prevent, detect, and manage physical and mental health problems complicating grief. Importantly, the family doctor is the prime professional to detect depression and prolonged grief disorder (Prigerson et al., 2009) and to refer the person on for specialist care.

Another reason postvention is appropriate to general practice is the congruence between the needs of the bereaved and the GP's mode of practice. Population studies investigating the needs of people bereaved by suicide have consistently demonstrated four characteristics: that help needs to be offered in multiple forms, be offered proactively over and above the usual care, be long term, and be particular to each individual (Dyregrov, 2011; McMenamy, Jordan, & Mitchell, 2008). This is highly relevant to general practice: The family doctor can provide or refer the person to multiple forms of help within community networks; act proactively to prevent and manage complications, especially depression; be available over the long term; and plan individual care. Furthermore, as the two most common barriers to gaining help after a suicide were found to be depression and the lack of information about where to find assistance (McMenamy et al., 2008), early intervention by the doctor may prevent isolation and open the door to ongoing help.

The Roles of General Practitioners in Postvention

Immediate Outreach

The ideal immediate response is a home visit to the whole family. For the bereaved, this offers the comfort and safety of their own familiar surroundings, and for the GP, it provides an opportunity to quickly form multiple relationships, assess the emotional states of family members, and gain an understanding of the differing perspectives of the suicide story. It may provide the only opportunity to observe the family dynamics and living context with a view to assessing possible future needs, such as child care and meals provision. An important role here is to identify those most at risk of severe grief reactions and depression, including the person who found the body. Sometimes such a meeting reveals that the whole family has been severely depressed long before the suicide, while coping with the suicidal family member. Urgent issues such as suicidal ideation and cardiac symptoms can be identified for follow-up. In this sense, the family doctor can be a life-saving presence in preventing serious physical and mental health sequelae. The GP offers sympathy and ongoing support, which may include help through the funeral and coronial procedures. This is also an opportunity to inquire into who else not present may be seriously affected and need help.

Occasionally the GP may be called out to certify death at the site of the suicide. Here a family doctor, in the Australian context, has the opportunity to explain the need for the presence of the police and a coronial investigation, and the requirement to leave the site undisturbed. Importantly, the GP can negotiate with the police for the family to spend some private time alone with the deceased person. This an important opportunity to establish the reality of the death and to facilitate the process of saying goodbye. The GP can prepare the family for what they might see and feel when viewing the body. In circumstances where the body has been severely mutilated, the GP is in a position to counsel the family about the advisability of immediately viewing the deceased because of the possible psychological trauma.

Subsequent Care

The bereaved person often presents with overwhelming need – the need to tell the story, to secure assurance of help, to know that their reactions are normal, for knowledge of how to deal with the practical matters of the death, to find answers to difficult questions, etc. The GP attends to the patient's agenda, and, guided by intuition and experience, assesses and prioritizes what issues need to be dealt with over subsequent appointments. Medical assessment is important to relieve and assure patients about symptoms caused by the grief. With the knowledge of the risks associated with bereavement and the neurophysiology of the allostatic load of trauma, the GP is well placed to plan care and support. People can die from a "broken" heart (Haslam, 2013), and chest pain needs urgent assessment. Existing serious chronic conditions, such as diabetes and asthma, that can be exacerbated by grief, require greater vigilance than usual. Assessment of the emotional and mental states, including depression and anxiety, are important in planning counseling. Additionally, grief may be complicated by other problems related to the suicide, such as family breakdown, alcoholism, and gender issues (see Chapter 4 in this volume). The GP can help instigate healthy coping strategies including sleep, exercise, diet, activities, and socialization. The doctor can also help build new skills to handle thoughts and feelings more effectively. Acknowledgement of spirituality informs the patient the GP is open to discussing the big questions of life, such as "Where is she now?" and "How do I go on from here?"

The GP can support the person with depression or anxiety through counseling and, where appropriate, a trial of medication and referral for psychiatric help. Some severely depressed and suicidal-bereaved people have found great comfort from a time out in a caring psychiatric unit. Importantly also, the doctor can set up an emergency plan with a list of crisis helplines and agencies.

With their knowledge of community supports, GPs are well placed to refer to and collaborate with other services. These may include medical, psychiatric, psychological, financial, legal, and social and community services, and bereavement support groups. So the doctor may be seen as a convenient single source of information and referral to other forms of help.

A unique function of family doctors is in helping the bereaved person in relation to work; negotiating time off work and specific terms for a return to work. In Australia, GPs can provide sickness certification for time off work and for accessing additional sources of finance, such as superannuation or income protection insurance, to enable the bereaved person to take further time off.

Long-Term Care

The GP can provide a sense of a safe home base – a haven to go to when the days get rough. The enduring relationship between doctor and patient can give a sense of security and assist the person to recreate trust that is broken through the suicide. The doctor is vigilant about the effects of adverse events in the years following the suicide, monitoring ongoing physical conditions, mood, lifestyle, and coping abilities. Also, the GP will be aware of anniversary phenomena, which may include physical as well as emotional responses. As the GP walks alongside the patient, the person can feel empowered in finding new life.

Family and Community Care

A GP may have to work vicariously with family members through the attending patient, usually the wife or mother: Males and adolescents tend to drop out of the GP's realm, preferring peer and practical, rather than verbal forms of support (Golden, 2010). Discussing the emerging issues (a common one is how and what to tell the children) and providing reading, storytelling, and other materials that the family can work on collaboratively at home, provides a circular route for assistance. Referral to children and youth practitioners, such as the school counselor, and age- and gender-appropriate groups may also be important (see also Chapter 3 in this volume, which addresses suicide bereavement of adolescents).

Ideally, the GP also has a broad understanding of the public health effects of a suicide and, placed within the community, can provide group interventions – for example, in schools, sporting clubs, and workplaces to counter the ripple effect of grief and the risk of self-harming and copycat suicides. For example, in rural areas that lack formal suicide prevention services, family doctors may collaborate with schools, clubs, and workplaces to identify those most vulnerable and set up appropriate individual support. Public meetings can also be arranged to provide group psychoeducation about grief, self-care, and how to support the bereaved. Sustaining community mental health can be an important service to the community.

Counseling and Psychoeducation

Companioning the bereaved person through their grief is facilitated by an open door policy of availability, openness to the person's agenda, and by the low cost of general practice care.

Listening to and supporting patients in the outpouring of grief and the story of the suicide, assuring people that their grief is normal, and providing psychoeducation about grief and lifestyle to help people get through the difficult days and months ahead, are part of the usual care that most GPs can offer. Compassion, unconditional nonjudgmental positive regard, constructive modeling and destigmatizing suicide and mental health, help people feel accepted and rebuild trust, freeing them up to talk about these issues.

> We were inactive for quite a while. We started to have health issues as a consequence of the grief so the GP was a very important part of it. We had tried several different counsellors and the GP invited us to come down and talk to him and we just used to talk. He later used this as a case for further study. He had lost a child so he was prepared to talk and that was the first time I got some empathic understanding. Empathic understanding is vital in a counsellor. (Bereaved mother, personal communication, 2009)

The GP referred to in this quotation seems to have been inspired to increase his knowledge in this area by engaging in a self-directed continued medical education activity. Continued medical education is a requirement for retaining accreditation with the Australian colleges of general practice.

From their understandings of the neurochemistry of mental illness, GPs can help the bereaved person understand the mental states contributing to the suicide – assisting with the understanding of the "why" question and the "if only" regrets. Similarly, the GP can assist the person understand the coroner's report. Medical terminology can often be frightening and traumatic for close family members: The GP can interpret the cause of death and the dying process and answer common questions such as, "How much pain did she suffer?" and "Could he have changed his mind and not been able to save himself?"

Talking about the person who died, particularly if they were previously known to the GP, reviving memories of their life and joys, discovering what was meaningful to them in life and how they might have liked to be remembered, can introduce new ways for the bereaved of thinking about the loss. This can lead to an understanding of the ongoing influence of the deceased person in the lives of those left behind: That the influence of a life does not end in death. Often this conversation results in feelings of a third person in the room and a sense of joy and new meanings for both doctor and patient.

Depending on their expertise, GPs may also provide or refer people to trauma therapy and forms of cognitive behavior therapy that are helpful in preventing complicated grief (de Groot, Neeleman, van der Meer, & Burger, 2010). Nonjudgmental attitudes of the GP to death and suicide are important in the therapeutic relationship and are vital in aiding the bereaved to reestablish trust. Therefore, the GP needs to have adequate self-knowledge of any personal prejudices originating from their moral or religious belief system. Understanding their limitations to give unbiased support would enable the doctor to refer the patient on so as not to obstruct the healing process.

Dilemmas in Providing Care

Medical "Failure"

A suicide of a patient is often seen as a failure of medical care to detect or cure the mental health condition leading to the suicide. This creates issues for both the bereaved and for the GP. Families have various understandings of the roles and possibilities of the medical profession, including GPs and mental health professionals, in preventing suicide. There are those who recognize the difficulties faced by doctors in keeping the person alive. However, there are others who may feel failed by the profession, feel angry, and have a sense of injustice and even a need for retribution. The consequent loss of trust may render them reluctant to seek the GP's help and to question their expertise in providing support (Pettersen et al., 2015). So the question arises as to what extent those bereaved by suicide may even want help from their family doctor. There is evidence that for many, GPs are a sought-after form of help after a suicide. A population study of 3,004 households in South Australia found that the GP was the professional of choice for support after a bereavement regardless of cause of death (South Australian Health Omnibus Survey, 1993). Further, the GP was also the provider of choice in a survey of 166 persons bereaved by suicide in metropolitan Adelaide (Wilson & Clark, 2004).

A patient's suicide may have major effects both personally and professionally for the treating doctor (Davidsen, 2011; Michel, Armson, Fleming, Rosenbauer, & Takahashi, 1997; Séguin, Bordeleau, Drouin, Castelli-Dransart, & Giasson, 2014; see also Chapter 21 in this volume). Doctors also grieve. Complicating reactions include feelings of guilt, a sense of professional incompetence and personal failure, fear of facing the family, depression, burnout, abandoning a medical career, and even suicide. The doctor may also feel threatened by having to provide a police report and by the possibility of litigation. However, a patient's suicide is also a time for reflecting and learning.

Whether or not to attend the funeral can pose a dilemma and may seem threatening for the doctor. However, attendance is usually appreciated by the mourning family although prior permission is advised for reasons of confidentiality (Kaye & Soreff, 1991; Markowitz, 1990). Attending can be advantageous for the doctor, as a GP colleague found:

> My main recollection is that I attended the funeral and found it difficult, but informative. I was lucky not to experience much hostility. I had a chance to hear more from friends and family and increase my understanding of his life and the events leading up to the death. I may have derived more benefit from going than the family got from me being there, but it seemed that my attendance was appreciated. (GP, personal communication, August 10, 2015)

Support of the doctor is essential. This is where a GP's preexisting support network, such as their peer group, Balint-style small working group, medical indemnity and self-care, can provide assistance. (Balint is a supportive small-group forum that aims to promote GPs' understandings of feelings and interactions generated in the doctor–patient relationship through discussing and reflecting on patients' medical case histories.) With recent understandings of the stress load on GPs and a number of suicides within the medical profession (Soler et al., 2008), self-care and personal support is currently an important topic for medical education. The recent advent of doctors' health services provides in-profession medical care and support. However, in terms of seeking professional help, doctors in most Australian states may confront another dilemma: the fear of being reported to the medical registration board as having a "mental impairment" that "detrimentally affects their practice of the profession" or that their "knowledge, skill or judgement" is "below the standard reasonably expected" (Australian Health Practitioner Registration Agency, 2015).

The American Association of Suicidology provides a list of clinicians who volunteer to support other practitioners who lose a patient to suicide (American Association of Suicidology, 2015; see Box 13.1). A similar peer support service could be provided by family doctors.

Ethical Dilemmas

Confidentiality can cause a number of headaches and heartaches for the GP. The need to keep the confidentiality of separate family members is vital, such as who else from a family attends the practice. It can be difficult to remember who said what, especially when different parties associated with the same suicide are counseled. It can also be difficult to remain neutral in the naming and blaming of others.

Difficult ethical decisions may also be faced by the doctor when the surviving family wish to discuss the cause of death of the GP's deceased patient. In agreeing, the doctor might be placed in the ethical dilemma of whether to uphold the confidentiality of the deceased patient. Does the responsibility to the deceased patient take precedence over any benefit the bereaved family might experience from the knowledge imparted? However, when access to the treating doctor is denied, it is not uncommon for the bereaved to feel let down and lose faith in the medical profession.

Expertise of the General Practitioner

What attitudes do GPs hold toward providing postvention care? A study examining Dutch GPs' attitudes to postvention found that of 488 family doctors, only 44% returned the questionnaire (de Groot, van der Meer, & Burger, 2009). Moreover, of those who responded, only 62% thought that follow-up of patients bereaved by suicide was appropriate in general practice, and 22% thought it was not relevant to professional health care at all. However, previous exposure of the GP to a suicide was associated with higher relevance and supportive action.

How competent are GPs to support people bereaved by suicide? Although population studies of bereaved persons' satisfaction with GPs are very limited, they can give some indication. Goldney, Spence, and Moffit (1986) found a reluctance in GPs to talk about the suicide despite the bereaved wanting them to talk about the death. The Adelaide study (Wilson & Clark, 2004) found that 43% of 166 self-selected suicide-bereaved respondents had sought help from a family doctor for medical and other forms of support, including 10% who had received a home visit. Satisfaction was mixed and participants identified lack of training and inappropriate attitudes as reasons for inadequate care by GPs. The following two examples were typical of the mixed responses received.

> My GP has always been available and supportive to me and I am grateful for the care he has shown.

> Some seemed fearful of my grief, e.g., [my] G.P. wanted to give me sleeping tablets and said, "Don't start crying. I don't know how to help you."

Similar findings were demonstrated by McMenamy et al. (2008) who found that of 63 people bereaved by suicide, only 46% were satisfied with the care received from a primary care doctor.

No research papers could be found to answer the question of the competency of GPs to support their patient bereaved through suicide as measured by controlled trials. However, the research evaluating GPs' proficiency in general bereavement care (García, Landa, Grandes, Pombo, & Moriz, 2015; Ghesquiere, Patel, Kaplan, & Bruce, 2014; Guldin, Vedsted, Jensen, Olesen, & Zachariae, 2013) found a general inadequacy, especially in the GPs' ability to detect prolonged grief disorder.

Finally, what information, education, and training do GPs receive in postvention? A search of the major general practice medical textbooks and manuals of mental health care (Davies, 2003; Murtagh, 2015; Phelps, 2001; Rakel & Rakel, 2015; Taylor, 2001), found no reference to postvention or bereavement care following suicide. Additionally, a PubMed search found no clinical articles in general practice or family medicine journals on postvention, but only the half dozen research papers referenced in this chapter relating to family doctors and postvention care. Furthermore, these focused entirely on very narrow aspects of mental health care without considering physical or other forms of care. As for undergraduate educational programs, a review of Australian universities found only about half of any medical training programs contained any postvention training, which in many cases was minimal (Hazell, Hazell, Waring, & Sly 1999). Further, Hawgood, Krysinska, Ide, and De Leo (2008) found postvention to be the lowest of suicide prevention educational priorities among medical students, GPs, and Australian medical schools. There exist a number of Australian national postvention educational programs for GPs (Martin et al., 1997; Square, 2007; see Box 13.1), but these appear not to have yet filtered through to grassroots practice. However, hot off the press is a new Australian document of postvention guidelines for GPs which may address the alarming deficiency of postvention information for family doctors (General Practice Mental Health Standards Collaboration, 2016; see Box 13.1). Nevertheless, GPs gain much collateral expertise and knowledge through their work with the terminally ill, the dying, and their families, which can contribute to their care of those bereaved by suicide.

Recommendations and Implications for Practice

GP–Postvention Pathway to Care

The authors of this chapter propose the creation of a recognized formal general practice pathway to care for families and communities after a suicide. This should be initiated and supported by the local immediate response team (Australia now has a number of immediate response postvention services nationwide) and would have multiple benefits. Ideally the pathway would be triggered by the postvention facilitator inviting the GP, with the family's permission, to the home outreach visit. The family would then receive expert postvention support together with a familiar professional who can take over long-term care. The GP and the postvention facilitator would be mutually supported by sharing their knowledge and skills. In particular, the GP would be furnished with educational information about suicide bereavement and available postvention resources by the facilitator who would then continue as a source of reference for the GP in providing ongoing care. Inclusion of practice nurses may provide additional support for the family as well as assist the GP. Further research and development of this proposal is required. Educational texts, information sheets, protocols, and therapeutic tools need to be developed for use by the GP. Research is required to evaluate the most effective and acceptable forms of care by GPs.

There also needs to be specific education for GPs about the effects of suicide bereavement and its attendant risks and complications for the individual, family, and community. Further, there is a need for training in appropriate general bereavement management, including counseling skills, attitudes, and the detection of, and therapies for, depression and prolonged grief disorder.

More needs to be done in promoting doctor self-care, in-practice support, and professional support without threat of being reported to the registration board. A peer support service for GPs who have experienced the suicide of a patient, and who are willing to give support to others, is recommended.

Establishing a Practice Postvention Protocol

For the GP, the suicide of a patient is a professional hazard for which every doctor needs to be prepared. A protocol can avoid the agony of what to do in a crisis and bring immediate assistance to both patient and doctor. Unlike the public services, there is no existing standardized postvention strategy in Australian general practice. Every GP practice should adopt a protocol for the management of a patient's suicide (Martin, Clark, Beckinsale, Stacey, & Skene, 1997). This should be threefold: emergency outreach to the bereaved family (ideally by a home visit with follow-up), no-blame support for doctors and practice staff involved, and a case review of the patient's management aimed at preventing a similar occurrence. This may be both daunting as well as reassuring. A study into critical incident debriefing after a suicide in general practices in the United Kingdom found that although this could be intimidating, certain benefits resulted, including an opportunity to reflect on patient care and improved procedures (King et al., 2005). The protocol needs to identify channels of support for the doctor and practice staff affected by the suicide and nominate practice staff (doctors and nurses) to provide the outreach to the family. Careful consideration needs to be given to who does this, because of the emotional load involved. Having supported the family prior to the death, continuing that support can be mutually helpful for both the bereaved and the family doctor.

However, despite all these challenges, there are rewards for the GP in this work. Walking beside the bereaved is a privilege and often a humbling process. Family doctors are often amazed at the strength and resilience of the bereaved which can trigger existential reflection regarding their own lives. There is inherent satisfaction and joy in seeing someone emerge from their grief to lead a new and purposeful life. Although family doctors are not specialized in postvention, they can play a unique and important role as the expert generalist in the long-term care of their bereaved patient and family as well as in the well-being of the community after a suicide.

Box 13.1. Resources for general practitioners

Information resources:
General Practice Mental Health Standards Collaboration (GPMHSC). (2016). *After Suicide: A Resource for GPs*. East Melbourne, Australia: Royal Australian College of General Practitioners. Retrieved from http://www.racgp.org.au/education/gpmhsc/gp-resources/after-suicide/

Commonwealth of Australia. (2007). *Square: Suicide Postvention Counselling: An Education Resource for Primary Health Care, Specialist and Community Settings.* Retrieved from http://www.square.org.au/wp-content/uploads/sites/10/2013/05/Postvention-Counselling_May2013.pdf

After Suicide: Picking Up the Pieces. In G. Martin, S. Clark, P. Beckinsale, K. Stacey, & C. Skene. (1997). *Keep Yourself Alive. Prevention of Suicide in Young People: A Manual for Health Professionals* (pp. 49–79). Adelaide, Australia: Foundation Studios. ISBN 0 646 32424. Retrieved from http://www.familyconcernpublishing.com.au/keep-yourself-alive-suicide-prevention-manual/

Support resource:
American Association of Suicidology. (2014). *Clinicians as Survivors: After a Suicide Loss.* Retrieved from http://mypage.iu.edu/~jmcintos/therapists_mainpg.htm

---

Corresponding author

Sheila Clark
Unihealth Highbury
Adelaide Unicare network
University of Adelaide
Adelaide, SA
Australia
sheila.c@bigpond.net.au

References

American Association of Suicidology. (2015). *Clinicians as survivors of suicide: After a suicide loss*. Retrieved from http://mypage.iu.edu/~jmcintos/contacts.htm

Australian Health Practitioner Registration Agency. (2015). *What can notifications be about?* Retrieved from http://www.ahpra.gov.au/Notifications/What-is-a-notification/What-can-notifications-be-about.aspx

Cerel, J., Maple, M., Aldrich, R., & van de Venne, J. (2013). Exposure to suicide and identification as survivor: Results from a random-digit dial survey. *Crisis, 34*(6), 413–419. http://doi.org/10.1027/0227-5910/a000220

Clark, S. (2001). Bereavement after suicide: How far have we come and where do we go from here? *Crisis, 22*(3), 102–108. http://doi.org/10.1027//0227-5910.22.3.102

Commonwealth of Australia. (2007). *Square: Suicide postvention counselling. An education resource for primary health care, specialist and community settings*. Retrieved from http://www.square.org.au/wp-content/uploads/sites/10/2013/05/Postvention-Counselling_May2013.pdf

Davidsen, A. S. (2011). 'And then one day he'd shot himself. Then I was really shocked': General practitioners' reaction to patient suicide. *Patient Education and Counseling, 85*(1), 113–118. http://doi.org/10.1016/j.pec.2010.08.020

Davies, J. (2003). *A manual of mental health care in general practice*. Canberra, Australia: Commonwealth Department of Health and Ageing.

de Groot, M., Neeleman, J., van der Meer, K., & Burger, H. (2010). The effectiveness of family-based cognitive-behavioural grief therapy to prevent complicated grief in relatives of suicide victims: The mediating role of suicide ideation. *Suicide and Life-Threatening Behavior, 40*(5), 425–437. http://doi.org/10.1521/suli.2010.40.5.425

de Groot, M., van der Meer, K., & Burger, H. (2009). A survey of Dutch GPs' attitudes towards help seeking and follow-up care for relatives bereaved by suicide. *Family Practice, 26*(5), 372–376. http://doi.org/10.1093/fampra/cmp046

Dyregrov, K. (2011). What do we know about needs after suicide in different parts of the world? A phenomenological perspective. *Crisis, 32*(6), 310–318. http://doi.org/10.1027/0227-5910/a000098

García, J., Landa, V., Grandes, G., Pombo, H., & Moriz, A. (2015). Effectiveness of "primary bereavement care" for widows: a cluster randomised controlled trial involving family physicians. *Death Studies, 37*(4), 287–310. http://doi.org/10.1080/07481187.2012.722041

General Practice Mental Health Standards Collaboration (GPMHSC). (2016). *After suicide: A resource for GPs*. East Melbourne, Australia: Royal Australian College of General Practitioners. Retrieved from http://www.racgp.org.au/education/gpmhsc/gp-resources/after-suicide/

Ghesquiere, A. R., Patel, S. R., Kaplan, D. B., & Bruce, M. L. (2014). Primary care providers' bereavement care practices: recommendations for research directions. *International Journal of Geriatric Psychiatry, 29*(12), 1221–1229. http://doi.org/10.1002/gps.4157

Golden, T. (2010). *Swallowed by a snake: The gift of the masculine side of healing* (2nd ed.). Gaithersburg, MD: Golden Healing.

Goldney, R. D., Spence, N. D., & Moffit, P. F. (1986). The aftermath of suicide: A comparison of attitudes of those bereaved by suicide, social workers and a community sample. *Crisis, 7*(1), 38–43.

Guldin, M., Vedsted, P., Jensen, A., Olesen, F., & Zachariae, R. (2013). Bereavement care in general practice: A cluster-randomized clinical trial. *Family Practice, 30*(2), 134–141. http://doi.org/10.1093/fampra/cms053

Haslam, D. (2013). Can you really die from a broken heart? *Practitioner, 257*(1766), 39.

Hawgood, J. L., Krysinska, K. E., Ide, N., & De Leo, D. (2008). Is suicide prevention properly taught in medical schools? *Medical Teacher, 30*(3), 287–295. http://doi.org/10.1080/01421590701753542

Hazell, P., Hazell, T., Waring, T., & Sly, K. (1999). A survey of suicide prevention curricula taught in Australian universities. *Australian and New Zealand Journal of Psychiatry, 33*(2), 253–259. http://doi.org/10.1046/j.1440-1614.1999.00554.x

Kaye, N. S., & Soreff, S. M. (1991). The psychiatrist's role, responses, and responsibilities when a patient commits suicide. *American Journal of Psychiatry, 148*(6), 739–743. http://doi.org/10.1176/ajp. 148.6.739

King, E., Kendall, K., Wiles, R., Rosenvinge, H., Gould, C., & Kendrick, A. (2005). General practice critical incident reviews of patient suicides: benefits, barriers, costs, and family participation. *Quality and Safety Health Care, 14*(1), 18–25. http://doi.org/10.1136/qshc.2003.007344

Markowitz, J. C. (1990). Attending the funeral of a patient who commits suicide. *American Journal of Psychiatry, 147*(1), 122–123. http://doi.org/10.1176/ajp.147.1.122b

Marquet, R., Bartelds, A., Kerkhof, A., Schellevis, F., & van de Zee, J. (2005). The epidemiology of suicide and attempted suicide in Dutch general practice 1983–2003. *BMC Family Practice, 6*, 45. http://doi.org/10.1186/1471-2296-6-45

Martin, G., Clark, S., Beckinsale, P., Stacey, K., & Skene, C. (1997). After suicide: Picking up the pieces. In *Keep Yourself Alive: Prevention of suicide in young people. A manual for health professionals* (pp. 49–79). Canberra, Australia: Department of Health and Ageing. Retrieved from http://www.family-concernpublishing.com.au/keep-yourself-alive-suicide-prevention-manual/

McMenamy, J., Jordan, J., & Mitchell, A. (2008). What do suicide survivors tell us they need? Results of a pilot study. *Suicide and Life Threatening Behavior, 38*(4), 375–389. http://doi.org/10.1521/suli.2008.38.4.375

McWhinney, I. R. (1989). The principles of family medicine. In I. R. McWhinney, *Textbook of family medicine* (pp. 12–26). New York, NY: Oxford University Press.

Michel, K., Armson, S., Fleming, G., Rosenbauer, C., & Takahashi, Y. (1997). After suicide: Who counsels the therapist? *Crisis, 18*(3), 128–139. http://doi.org/10.1027/0227-5910.18.3.128

Murtagh, J. (Ed.). (2015). *John Murtagh's general practice.* North Ryde, Australia: McGraw-Hill.

Pettersen, R., Omerov, P., Steineck, G., Titelman, D., Dyregrov, A., Nyberg, T., & Nyberg, U. (2015). Lack of trust in the health-care system after losing a child to suicide. *Crisis, 36*(3), 161–172. http://doi.org/10.1027/0227-5910/a000312

Phelps, K. (Ed.). (2001). *General practice: The integrative approach.* Chatswood, Australia: Churchill Livingstone.

Pitman, A., Osborn, D., King, M., & Erlangsen, A. (2014). Effects of suicide bereavement on mental health and suicide risk. *Lancet Psychiatry, 1*(1), 86–94. http://doi.org/10.1016/S2215-0366(14)70224-X

Prigerson, H. G., Horowitz, M. J., Jacobs, S. C., Parkes, C. M., Aslan, M., Goodkin, K., … Maciejewski, P. K. (2009). Prolonged grief disorder: Psychometric validation of criteria proposed for DSM-V and ICD-11. PLoS. *Med, 6*(8), e1000121.

Rakel, R. E., & Rakel, D. (Eds.). (2015). *Textbook of family medicine* (9th ed.). Philadelphia, PA: Elsevier Saunders.

Royal Australian College of General Practitioners. (n.d.). *Becoming a GP in Australia: What is general practice?* Retrieved from http://www.racgp.org.au/becomingagp/what-is-a-gp/what-is-general-practice/

Séguin, M., Bordeleau, V., Drouin, M., Castelli-Dransart, D. A., & Giasson, F. (2014). Professionals' reactions following a patient's suicide: review and future investigation. *Archives of Suicide Research, 18*(4), 340–362. http://doi.org/10.1080/13811118.2013.833151

Shneidman, E. S. (1972). Foreword. In A. Cain (Ed.), *Survivors of suicide* (pp. ix–xi), Springfield, IL: Charles C. Thomas.

Soler, J. K., Yaman, H., Esteva, M., Dobbs, F., Asenova, R. S., Katic, M., … Ungan, M. European General Practice Research Network Burnout Study Group. (2008). Burnout in European family doctors: the EGPRN study. *Family Practice, 25*(4), 245–265. http://doi.org/10.1093/fampra/cmn038

South Australian Health Omnibus Survey. (1993). *A research report for Dr Sheila Clark.* Adelaide, Australia: Harrison Market Research.

Stroebe, M. S., & Stroebe, W. (1993). The mortality of bereavement: A review. In M. S. Stroebe, W. Stroebe, & R. O. Hansson (Eds.), *Handbook of bereavement: Theory, research and intervention* (pp. 175–195). Cambridge, UK: Cambridge University Press.

Taylor, R. B. (Ed.). (2001). *Lippincott Manual Series: Manual of family practice* (2nd ed.). Philadelphia, PA: LWWPE.

Vermandere, M., De Lepeleire, J., Smeets, L., Hannes, K., Van Mechelen, W., Warmenhoven, F., … Aertgerts, B. (2011). Spirituality in general practice: A qualitative evidence synthesis. *British Journal of General Practice, 61*(592), 749–760. http://doi.org/10.3399/bjgp11X606663

Wilson, A., & Clark, S. (2004). *South Australian Suicide Postvention Project: Report to Mental Health Services, Department of Health*. Adelaide, Australia: University of Adelaide, Department of General Practice. Retrieved from https://digital.library.adelaide.edu.au/dspace/bitstream/2440/24871/1/South_Australian_Suicide_Postvention_Report.pdf

World Health Organization. (2014). *Preventing suicide: A global imperative*. Retrieved from http://www.who.int/mental_health/suicide-prevention/world_report_2014/en/

Zisook, S., & Shuchter, S. R. (1986). The first four years of widowhood. *Psychiatric Annals, 16*(5), 288–294. http://doi.org/10.3928/0048-5713-19860501-08

Chapter 14

Supporting Families Through the Forensic and Coronial Process After a Death From Suicide

Jane Mowll[1,2], Holly Smith[2], and Colleen Fitzpatrick[2]

[1]The University of Notre Dame, Sydney, NSW, Australia
[2]NSW Department of Forensic Medicine, Health Pathology, Sydney, NSW, Australia

Abstract: Death from suicide brings particular challenges for bereaved relatives and friends, not least because of the statutory requirements of the medicolegal investigation. At the Department of Forensic Medicine, New South Wales Forensic and Analytical Science Service, Sydney branch, an innovative support after suicide program run by the social work team has been developed. The program includes support in the immediate aftermath of a suicide death and a range of services in the longer term. Drawing on practice experience the chapter presents the support needs for people bereaved by suicide and outlines the important components of such support in the context of the death investigation. The strengths of the program and suggested areas of development are discussed.

Introduction

There is increasing literature available on the experience and management of grief after suicide (Andriessen & Krysinska, 2012; McKay & Tighe, 2014; see also Chapter 1 and Chapter 2 in this volume). However, the support needs of family members in the immediate aftermath of a suicide death have had less attention (Botha, Guilfoyle, & Botha, 2009). There are a number of difficulties facing family and friends bereaved in the immediate aftermath of a death from suicide. These difficulties can include distress from learning about the mode of death, which is often violent and disfiguring, or from imagining the suffering leading to the death (Jordan & McIntosh, 2011). Furthermore, the mode of death may be either completely sudden and unexpected, "out of the blue," or the aftermath of a complex mental health history (Wojtkowiak, Wild, & Egger, 2012). There can be intense distress from witnessing the death or finding the body after death (Feigelman, Jordan, & Gorman, 2009). Conversely the requirements of the medicolegal investigation of the death can mean that family members are kept away from the body and not given information about the death (Mowll, Lobb, & Wearing, 2016; see also Chapter 44 in this volume).

Social workers at the Department of Forensic Medicine (DOFM), New South Wales Forensic and Analytical Science Service (NSW FASS) Sydney have developed and refined a unique program of support for family and friends bereaved after a death from suicide. Commencing from the time the death is reported to the coroner on the day of the death, support by the social work team at the morgue in the immediate aftermath is integrated with a model of longer-term care: the support after suicide program (SASP). This chapter draws on the practice experience of the social work team to describe and discuss the rationale for developing the integrated model. The challenges and lessons learned from over 15 years of experience of facilitating this comprehensive service are outlined.

Death Investigation and the Role of the Coroner

In NSW, Australia, suicide death as well as homicide, accidents, and unexplained natural death must be reported to the coroner (Abernethy, Baker, Dillon, & Roberts, 2010). The coroner (a magistrate) has jurisdiction over the body and presides over a medicolegal investigation of the death. The aim of this investigation is to establish the identity of the deceased person, the cause and manner of their death, and the date and place of death (Abernethy et al., 2010). Police report the death to the coroner and undertake an investigation of the death on behalf of the coroner. Police secure and examine the scene of death, establish the identity of the deceased, and seize any evidentiary material such as a suicide note, mobile telephone, and computer. The police also arrange to have a doctor examine the body to certify that life is extinct, before arranging transfer of the body to a forensic facility. Police ensure that the senior next of kin is notified of the death, and they are responsible for the formal identification of the body for the coroner. The coroner does not release the body until an initial investigation, usually an autopsy (post mortem examination), is conducted to establish the cause of death (Abernethy et al., 2010). The DOFM Sydney works alongside the office of the State Coroner NSW and admits around 3,500 coronial deaths a year. Around 1,800 undergo a post mortem examination, and some 380 of the latter are deaths apparent as suicide. Bereaved family members not only deal with the death itself but have to navigate the coronial and forensic system in the wake of the death.

Social Work Role and Support After Suicide at the DOFM Sydney

Specialized forensic counselors (social workers) are employed at the DOFM Sydney to provide support and counseling services to family members in the wake of suicide, accident, homicide, and unexpected natural deaths admitted to the department. The social work team has developed a framework of bereavement services that include proactive information and support in the immediate aftermath of the death and access to counseling in the longer term. In 2000, the social work team developed a support after suicide group (SASG) in response to the expressed needs of family members bereaved from suicide who had come into contact with the DOFM and coroner's system.

At that time (ca. 2000) there were few suicide-specific services available for family members in the months after a suicide death in the Sydney metropolitan area. Specifically, bereaved families identified that they wanted both a safe forum to meet with others bereaved by suicide and professional support that took into account the ongoing nature of the coronial investigation and the impact of this on the family. Now in its 16th year, the support group has expanded to include a comprehensive program of support: the support after suicide program (SASP). One of the key strengths of the SASP is that it is embedded in the support framework provided by the social work team at the DOFM Sydney. This allows for a flexible response that is nuanced to the particular needs of family members and friends bereaved by suicide, both in the immediate aftermath and over the longer term (Stillion, 1996).

Support and Information After a Suicide

Social worker support is available to family and friends of the deceased person via the reporting police officer from the time of the death. A member of the social work team also routinely contacts the next of kin and family soon after the body is admitted to the DOFM. The initial call orients the family to the fact that the body of their relative has been admitted to DOFM, introduces the social work service, and provides information about the forensic autopsy, and coronial requirements. Subsequent calls from the social worker may include information about the initial findings of the autopsy, the identification of the body, coronial processes, funeral planning, psychosocial support, options to view the body, and information about counseling services. In providing this support, the social work team works closely with police and other staff to ensure information is appropriately managed and complements the role of the forensic pathologist, police, and coroner. The social worker also acts as a conduit directing families to other key personnel within the system – such as the police or coronial staff or external services – and conveys relevant information from the family to personnel within the coronial system. The team continue to provide support for specific issues as needed, either over the phone or in a face-to-face meeting with the family in the days and months after a suicide.

In providing these support services, the social work team draws on knowledge of grief, stress, and trauma reactions in the wake of suicide loss (Jordan & McIntosh, 2011). Social workers rely on a body of knowledge that includes responding to the *person in the environment* encompassing a bio-psycho-social-cultural perspective (Pease, 2003). The team are skilled at providing difficult information in the aftermath of the death, which is paced and graduated to the person's capacity and readiness to hear and process information (Mowll et al., 2016). Expertise in communication, and a commitment to compassionate, culturally safe, and competent care is essential (Allan, 2003; Christ & Blacker, 2005; McGrath & Phillips, 2008). Counseling skills such as supportive listening, problem solving, psychoeducation, normalizing, and psychological first aid are also important (Harms, 2007). Above all, social workers respond with respect, gentleness, and compassion to the diverse needs of people in the wake of suicide bereavement.

In the DOFM social work teams experience, family members and friends often seek support for specific areas of concern in the wake of a death from suicide, and these are now briefly outlined. Understanding the cause and mechanisms of the death are often of acute concern for family members (Biddle, 2003), particularly whether the death was quick or there was pain in the last moments of life. The social work team are skilled at explaining medical findings in an understandable way that is attuned to the bereaved persons' sometimes unspoken concerns, such as whether they suffered or not. The team works also with the coroner's office and police to facilitate supported access to the autopsy and coronial reports, and information about the investigation. For those who so request, the team provides support to read, understand, and emotionally process the autopsy results and reports, both in the days after the death and as reports are finalized. The social work team has developed the expertise to discuss evidentiary forensic and coronial material in a supportive way that does not compromise the investigation. The brief of evidence and autopsy report may also reference crime scene photographs and CCTV footage, and some people make requests to the coroner for access to these. Practice experience suggests that, for some, supported access to such material may be an important facet of coming to terms with the death and their grief (Ryan & Giljohann, 2013).

A further concern for many people bereaved by suicide is seeking to understand their own and their family's reactions and feelings in the wake of the death. Bereaved people often report that they want to get a sense of what is normal in the wake of the death. A core part of the social work role is in listening to concerns, providing psychoeducation or normalizing reactions, and discussing coping strategies (Harms, 2007). Family members are also often acutely concerned as to how to tell children about the suicide and death of a family member. The team work from a strengths-based perspective (Saleebey, 1996), and rather than give advice will encourage the family to discuss their thoughts about how and what to tell their children. The social worker engages with the family to provide support, discuss strategies, and facilitate access to resources in supporting their children. Discussion is focused on guidance and strategies nuanced to their particular family and social and cultural situation (Allan, 2003). Support to undertake or express cultural and religious requirements may also be needed. For example, people of Australian Aboriginal heritage may wish to return the body of the deceased person to their community for burial (McGrath, 2007).

An urgent concern for many families is having access to the suicide note, if one has been left (Biddle, 2003). Police sometimes take the note, providing it to the coroner's office without disclosing the contents to the family, perhaps from a fear that it will distress the family, or in following due process. Family members can experience acute distress in seeking to comprehend what happened and both dreading and wanting to see the content of any notes. Social workers have also forged trusted relationships with the coroner's office and staff, and can advocate for family members to access the suicide note, with appropriate support. The team have also built close working relationships with police, who value the expertise of the forensic social work team to provide support to families during the death investigation. This can be particularly important for families who may mistrust or be wary of the involvement of police. Police may also take other property such as the person's mobile phone or computer. These are often a vital link for family to the person who has died and as a way of getting in touch with friends and family. The social worker liaises with the officer in charge of the investigation, providing adjunct support and guidance around the return of property to the family. The social worker also acts as a support and resource for the police and coroner in managing difficult family situations. Support for the identification process, including viewing the body is a major component of the social work service.

Viewing the Body

Support, choice and preparation to view the body of their loved one, including after hours and over weekends, is valued by family members and friends (Mowll, 2007). Viewing the body may be required as part of the formal identification process for the coroner; additionally, family and friends may wish to see the body for their own reasons. There is a growing body of evidence to suggest that viewing the body – even if it is disfigured through injury or decomposition – is important and has profound meaning for families who choose to see it (Chapple & Ziebland, 2010; Drayton, 2013; Harrington & Sprowl, 2011; Mowll, 2007; Mowll et al., 2016). At the same time, more research is needed before definitive recommendations can be made about the efficacy and effects of viewing or not after a suicide (Omerov, Steineck, Nyberg, Runeson, & Nyberg, 2014).

The death investigation effectively takes the body away from the control of the family, at least for a time. Exploring options and timing to see the body in the context of the death investigation is important. In suicide, particular for those who found the body, there may be a need to see the body in a more peaceful setting to help ameliorate the horror of the death (Mowll et al., 2016). Social workers are informed by research suggesting that people who are able to act on their preference to either see or not see the body do not suffer regret and are satisfied with their choice. In practice, rather than a closed question, an open question can elicit preferences and foster further questions (Mowll, 2007; McKissock & McKissock, 2003). For example: "What are your thoughts about whether you would like to see John or not?"

Discussion of the choice to see or not should include provision of support and preparation, including a sensitively paced, graduated description of the body (Mowll et al., 2016; Omerov et al., 2014). Conversely, being given too graphic a description and not discussing the choice may be distressing. Thus an important task for the social worker is to check the family member's preference to see or not, to allow time to decide, permission not to see if they do not wish to, and preparation and support during the viewing. It is important to take into account cultural needs – for example, from an Australian Aboriginal perspective, respecting the broader notion of relationships in determining who can view (McGrath, 2007).

A formal identification of the body usually requires a visual identification by a person who knew the deceased in life. It is important to involve the senior next of kin (parent or partner) in the decision process of who should do this formal identification. Devolving the responsibility for identification to less-upset family members or neighbors can ultimately be more upsetting (Mowll et al., 2016). However, in suicide, the body can be disfigured from injury or decomposition. A visual identification may not be possible, and a report based on a dental examination, finger print comparison, or other evidence is presented by police to the coroner. Differentiating the need for identification with a family member's preference or wish to see the body is important. Once the nonvisual identification has been completed, the family may still wish to see the body. It is helpful to offer options in the timing and presentation of the body – for example, a partial or covered viewing (Mowll et al., 2016).

Referral to the Support After Suicide Program

After the initial information and support, and once the body is released, the family are sent a follow-up letter providing information about how to access the coroner's report and the contact details of the DOFM social work team. Additionally deaths that are considered to be suicide by the family are referred to the SASP for ongoing support. The social worker managing the case refers the file to the SASP coordinator, a social worker who is part of the team. The coordinator enters the case into a SASP database to monitor and manage the referrals. Deaths that the family do not consider as suicide, or where the family have indicated they do not wish for follow-up, are noted as not for follow-up, in the database.

The SASP coordinator mails a letter outlining the services provided by SASP and an information pack (LIFE Communications, 2010) to the available family or friends 6 weeks after the death. The SASP coordinator then follows up with a telephone call 2 weeks later (around 2 months after the death) and provides an opportunity to opt in or out of the various components of the ongoing program. These components include access to the newsletter, attendance at the support group, access to telephone support, and an annual condolence card sent on the anniversary of the death. Around 70% of people contacted elect to receive ongoing mailouts (the newsletter and anniversary card), and 30% choose to opt out of the available services at that time.

The length of the follow-up call varies and is directed by the needs of the bereaved person as they choose to express them. Family members frequently express their appreciation for this call. In particular the timing of the call, some 2 months after the death, is a valued opportunity to talk, ask questions, and discuss needs and access ongoing services. In just one example, a bereaved sister said, *"The phone calls from DOFM were very welcome. Just knowing someone cared and made the effort to follow up."* Families are often searching to make sense of, and come to terms with, the death. For some, the call is an opportunity to understand and normalize their grief reactions, discuss how best to support children and the family, be aware of avenues for support, and know they have a place to turn to should grief or trauma feelings worsen. The model integrated with the forensic social work service means that queries regarding the forensic and coronial process – for example, the progress of the post mortem report – can be answered or appropriately redirected. The mailout pack also includes information about the SASG. Around 5–10 % of those who want to receive ongoing contact express an interest in attending the group.

The Support After Suicide Group

Commencing in February 2000, the SASG has met on the first Tuesday of each month except January, for over 16 years. The group has developed as a counselor-facilitated open support group model. Group membership is constantly evolving and changing; group members come for a number of meetings and may dip in and out of the group as their needs change. The group is managed and attended by the social work team. A SASP coordinator (a social worker) and a social work manager, and/or a member of the social work team are rostered to ensure a continuity of care. The social work manager meets with the coordinator and any team members attending the group, before and after each group to plan and review the meeting. People wishing to attend the group are asked to contact the coordinator before attending a meeting for the first time. This allows the person to decide if the group is suitable for them at the current time, and likewise the coordinator can screen for suitability of the person for the group. People suffering acute mental health or comorbid issues can be referred to specialized services or individual counseling.

The structure includes time for group forming and guidelines, information and psychoeducation, discussion and sharing, rituals and remembrance, and social connection. The role of the social workers is to attend to the group process, facilitate safe introductions and sharing, and to ensure acute grief for trauma is managed sensitively and safely in the context of the needs of other group members. The coordinator follows up group members attending for the first time or who are identified as needing follow-up at the meeting (with their permission). The integration with the social work counseling team means that those who wish it can be referred for individual or family counseling. In the group setting, it is important to balance the needs of the more acutely bereaved with those who are much further down the track. This can sometimes require breaking into two smaller groups. Part of this means attending to the group process to manage acute reactions, and gently challenging people further along in their grief. The shared focus on strategies and information sharing and physical and cognitive reactions, as well as feelings, aims to include men and women and diverse grieving styles (Doka & Martin, 2010).

The social work team takes the stance that the bereaved people are the experts in their own loss. Social workers also use the accumulated *practice wisdom* (Scott, 1990) of working with bereaved families over the years, drawing on stories of survival to balance empathy for the pain of grief, with fostering a sense of hope and future direction. One of the core skills of the team is the ability to be present and sit with grief and pain, occupying the emotional space without needing to fill the silence or fix the pain (Jordan, 2008). Group members are aware that the social workers are part of the same team who provided initial support and may have already met them at the viewing or spoken on the phone in the first days after the death. There is a sense that, for the group members, the social work teams' exposure to death on a daily basis helps both the team members and the bereaved family normalize the trauma of the death. As one of the team observed, *"The bereaved do not have to protect us from the horror, and they can us trust with the pain."* From this, group members gain a sense that they too can survive and even flourish in the wake of acute grief. As one mother whose only child died age 17 through suicide said,

> At first the meetings were a place I could go, knowing there were other people who knew how I felt. Now it is so much more. I feel safe at the meetings. I am free to laugh and cry, as I know everyone understands. No one assumes I have moved on, or thinks I should have. When I am having a bad time, I draw strength from seeing someone who has climbed out of the place I am in now and I know I too will climb out. (Mother; quoted in Mowll, 2014)

A valued aspect of the group is being able to talk, not just about their grief, but about the person who died. This is particularly appreciated by people who experience social isolation or who have not been able to find an audience to really hear their grief and about who the person was to them (McKay & Tighe, 2014). As one mother reflected, *"I like that we can talk about our loved one, the counsellors call them by their names and we can share stories about them."* There is a sense of normalizing differing experiences of grief; some people value a sense of continued bond with their loved one; others may have a spiritual or religious faith; and others may have more of a focus on the impact of their grief on their current relationships. The focus is on tolerating and seeking to understand different experiences within the communal umbrella of suicide bereavement. Rather than imposing a homogenous view of grief, the group process has shown itself to be adaptable to the many and varied needs of suicide bereaved, including men and women, people in same-sex relationships, people from culturally and linguistically diverse backgrounds, and people of differing religious faiths.

The main purpose for many who attend the group is connection and conversations with others who are bereaved by suicide. There is a sense, shared over the years by many in the group, that their family and social networks are sometimes not as supportive as they want or do not know how to support them, particularly over time. For some, the group is a way of both feeling normal in their grief and having meaningful connections with others who can accommodate their ongoing pain and sometimes uncomfortable emotions and thoughts. The team have been touched over the years by the care and compassion that people in the group develop – for themselves, for each other and for others in their communities.

The social work team draw on their expertise and knowledge of the grief literature to balance and respond to the differing needs within the group. The open model means members can drop in and out of the group as they need. Most will come along for a number of group meetings before attending more sporadically. Some return to a group meeting near the anniversary or for the end-of-year meeting. The fact that the group has been meeting without a break 11 times a year for 15 years and still continues with an involved but regularly changing group of bereaved people (and social work staff), is in a sense its own testimonial to a continued need in the community.

One of the interesting evolutions in the group has been the formation of the *newsletter volunteer* group. Volunteers from the group meet every 2 months with the coordinator, over coffee and sandwiches, to help with the mailing of some 1,000 copies of the SASP newsletter (see the next section: "Anniversary Card and SASP Newsletter"). To ensure confidentiality of recipients, the coordinator puts the address stickers on the envelopes after they are stuffed. Over time, this group of volunteers has become a sort of graduation group of suicide bereaved, who are further along in their grief and no longer feel the need to attend the main group. Sharing still happens, but the focus is on families, relationships, hobbies, and work. Grief is still there but more in the background, less intense, woven into the patterns of life now lived in the present.

The newsletter volunteer group members value the chance to get together and to "give back" both to the social work team and to others bereaved by suicide.

Anniversary Card and SASP Newsletter

A condolence card is sent to the next of kin and other family or friends who have provided their contact details, by the SASP coordinator and counseling team. The card is sent annually for 5 years with opt-out options included for those who no longer want to receive it. Similar to the arrangement for the newsletter, that for the card involves the need after 5 years for members to actively opt in to continue to get the card, which some people do. The team has received many acknowledgements of the value of the anniversary card. As one sister wrote in a thank you letter: *"Your caring card arrived on the anniversary when everyone else had forgotten."*

The SASP newsletter comes out every two months and is written by the coordinator and social work managers (the authors of this chapter: H. S., J. M., and C. F.) specifically for the program (sample copy available from authors by e-mail request). It is currently mailed or e-mailed to 1,150 people with an estimated average audience of four readers per newsletter. The banner heading of the newsletter is "you are not alone – shared experiences connect us." For many people, the newsletter is a low-key way of feeling connected to a community that understands their grief. It can even help people feel a bond. As one mother said to us: *"Somehow I can feel my son with me when I read them."* The four-page format has a focus on different aspects of suicide bereavement, shared experiences, poems and excerpts, memorials, grief education, and discussion of support strategies. In addition to information sharing about issues pertaining to suicide, the newsletter articles are a form of bibliotherapy (Jordan, 2008). A number of people report that they keep the newsletters; as one father said, *"I sometimes read them over and over; I always keep them."*

The articles and excerpts written in the newsletter are often about grief and loss, referencing up-to-date literature, which again aims to balance an understanding of the devastating effects of loss with a sense of hope that there is a way through the pain of grief. For example, recent articles have included strategies to deal with anniversaries, understanding the forensic and coronial investigation for death by suicide, and using metaphors to deal with grief. Readers and group attendees often write in to reflect on articles and give feedback. For example, following the publication in the newsletter of an article drawing on Therese Rando's concept of "Is it okay for you to be okay?" (Rando, 2012), a mother and father wrote to thank the team. They wrote that reading the article some 3 years after the death of their son was liberating and gave them permission to reengage with life and let go of some of their feelings of guilt and regret.

Discussion and Implications

In a recent edition of the SASP newsletter, the team reflected on the lessons learned from people bereaved by suicide over the last 16 years of running the SASP, writing on three core themes which have also been reflected in this chapter: Suicide grief is hard, staying connected helps, and there is hope (Mowll & Smith, 2015). In running the program, the team has learned from those who are bereaved that *suicide grief is hard*, particularly the pain of loss, trauma, and a sense of abandonment. While evidence does not as a whole support that suicide bereaved are at higher risk of developing complicated or prolonged grief, there are often aspects of suicide-specific distress, including guilt, blame, anger, stigma, and isolation (Sveen & Walby, 2008). People bereaved by suicide are at risk of suicide themselves, and high suicide ideation may indicate high risk for adverse bereavement outcomes (de Groot, Neeleman, van der Meer, &

Burger, 2010). A recent total population study suggested that parents and fathers in particular may be at a high risk of absenteeism due to psychiatric illness following the suicide death of a child (Wilcox, Mittendorfer-Rutz, Kjeldgård, Alexanderson, & Runeson, 2015). In this context, it is essential to provide comprehensive postvention care (Andriessen & Krysinska, 2012). The requirements of the coronial and death investigation can add to the distress for people bereaved by suicide (Biddle 2003; Harwood, Hawton, Hope, & Jacoby, 2002). For the traumatic experience of confronting deaths such as suicide, skilled support available from the time of death has the potential to ameliorate the distress in the short and longer term (Drayton, 2013; Mowll et al., 2016; Ryan & Giljohann, 2013).

The team also keep learning from bereaved people accessing the program of support that *connection helps,* and the vital importance of providing opportunities for people bereaved by suicide to talk and share with others. The model of support provided by the social work team is a form of the *long-term expert companioning* that is recommended as best practice in suicide postvention support (Jordan, 2008). The team integrates provision of information tailored to individuals' and family's needs along with access to psychosocial support, facilitation of choice, and support to view the body. This is linked to follow-up services including telephone support, group support, the ongoing connection through newsletter, and counseling.

In providing follow-up, team members are mindful of limited available evidence supporting universal counseling interventions for bereaved people (Neimeyer & Currier, 2009). The team balances the need to provide information about services and support in a timely way to acutely bereaved families without encouraging unwarranted therapeutic intervention (Hall, 2014). At the same time, in the wake of a suicide death there is often a complexity of needs and a search for answers and meaning (Jordan, 2008). The practice experience of the DOFM Sydney counseling team in running the program over 16 years suggests that people bereaved by suicide appreciate the opportunity to consider their needs for support 2 months or so after the initial shock, investigation, and funeral. The support and information provided by the program acts as a continuity of care by the social work team following on from the support provided in the days after the death. Suicide grief is not homogenous, and there is a spectrum of reactions and needs, ranging from only needing minimal support and information, to longer-term support, access to group support, and finally to therapeutic counseling. Clients of the service can access support over the course of the death investigation dipping in and out of the service around specific needs to do with forensic and coronial processes.

Crucially the format and structure of the service has been developed by the social work team in collaboration with people bereaved by suicide. This bottom-up approach draws on the experience and insights of people bereaved by suicide to continually adapt the service to the needs of the group and community (Andriessen & Krysinska, 2012). Thus the content, location, and focus of the program have evolved over the years in response to feedback, both informally and from structured evaluations, from the support group members and the wider bereaved-by-suicide community reached in the newsletter. It is important to note that not everyone opts in to the SASP, and one size doesn't fit all. The model of support that the team has developed means that whether or not bereaved people participate in the program, they can still access support from the social work team, or alternative services in the community. The SASP continues to both contribute to and be informed by research and the development of standards of practice, such as the Suicide Bereavement Support Group Standards and Practice Project (2009). Future directions of the service include working with other groups and services in the community to extend the program to a statewide model of service delivery and developing a web-based component of the program.

Conclusions

The final lesson learned from people bereaved by suicide is that *there is hope*. Over and over again the team hears stories of resilience and survival in the face of devastating loss through suicide. Grief can be a transformative experience where people find a new meaning, beauty, and a purpose to their life. Strengthened bonds to friends and family, new relationships, new interests and hobbies can be part of this. Importantly, people have shared how they learn to channel their feelings of loss and grief, honoring the person they loved who died, by forging new hopes and dreams, new meanings, and a new future.

Corresponding author

Jane Mowll
The University of Notre Dame
Sydney, NSW
Australia
jane.mowll@nd.edu.au

References

Abernethy, J., Baker, B., Dillon, H., & Roberts, H. (2010). *Waller's coronial law and practice in New South Wales*. Chatswood, Australia: LexisNexis Butterworths.

Allan, J. (2003). Loss and grief: Weaving the personal and political. In J. Allan, B. Pease, & L. Briskman (Eds.), *Critical social work: An introduction to theories and practices* (pp. 170–184). Crows Nest, Australia: Allen & Unwin.

Andriessen, K., & Krysinska, K. (2012). Essential questions on suicide bereavement and postvention. *International Journal of Environmental Research and Public Health, 9*(1), 24–32. http://doi.org/10.3390/ijerph9010024

Biddle, L. (2003). Public hazards or private tragedies? An exploratory study of the effect of coroners' procedures on those bereaved by suicide. *Social Sciences & Medicine, 56*(5), 1033–1045. http://doi.org/10.1016/S0277-9536(02)00097-7

Botha, K., Guilfoyle, A., & Botha, D. (2009). Beyond normal grief: A critical reflection on immediate post-death experiences of survivors of suicide. *Australian e-Journal for the Advancement of Mental Health, 8*(1), 37–47.

Chapple, A., & Ziebland, S. (2010). Viewing the body after bereavement due to a traumatic death: qualitative study in the UK. *British Medical Journal, 340*, c2032. http://doi.org/10.1136/bmj.c2032

Christ, G., & Blacker, S. (2005). Series introduction: The profession of social work in end-of-life and palliative care. *Journal of Palliative Medicine, 8*(2), 415–417. http://doi.org/10.1089/jpm.2005.8.415

de Groot, M., Neeleman, J., van der Meer, K., & Burger, H. (2010). The effectiveness of family-based cognitive-behavior grief therapy to prevent complicated grief in relatives of suicide victims: The mediating role of suicide ideation. *Suicide and Life-Threatening Behavior, 40*(5), 425–437. http://doi.org/10.1521/suli.2010.40.5.425

Doka, K., & Martin, T. (2010). *Grieving beyond gender: Understanding the ways men and women mourn* (2nd ed.). New York, NY: Routledge.

Drayton, J. (2013). Bodies-in-life/bodies-in-death: Social work, coronial autopsies and the bonds of identity. *British Journal of Social Work, 43*(2), 264–281. http://doi.org/10.1093/bjsw/bct011

Feigelman, W., Jordan, J. R., & Gorman, B. S. (2009). How they died, time since loss, and bereavement outcomes. *Omega: Journal of Death and Dying, 58*(4), 251–273. http://doi.org/10.2190/OM.58.4.a

Hall, C. (2014). Bereavement theory: Recent developments in our understanding of grief and bereavement. *Bereavement Care, 33*(1), 7–12. http://doi.org/10.1080/02682621.2014.902610

Harms, L. (2007). *Working with people: Communication skills for reflective practice*. Melbourne, Australia: Oxford University Press.

Harrington, C., & Sprowl, B. (2011). Family members' experiences with viewing in the wake of sudden death. *Omega: Journal of Death and Dying, 64*(1), 65–82. http://doi.org/10.2190/OM.64.1.e

Harwood, D., Hawton, K., Hope, T., & Jacoby, R. (2002). The grief experiences and needs of bereaved relatives and friends of older people dying through suicide: A descriptive and case-control study. *Journal of Affective Disorders, 72*(2), 185–194. http://doi.org/10.1016/S0165-0327(01)00462-1

Jordan, J.R. (2008). Bereavement after Suicide. *Psychiatric Annals, 38*(10), 679–685. http://doi.org/10.3928/00485713-20081001-05

Jordan, J.R., & McIntosh, J.L. (2011). Is suicide bereavement different? A framework for rethinking the question. In J.R. Jordan & J.L. McIntosh (Eds.), *Grief after suicide* (pp. 115–131). New York, NY: Routledge.

LIFE Communications. (2010). *Information & support pack for those bereaved by suicide or other sudden death. Living is for everyone.* Canberra, Australia: Commonwealth of Australia. Retrieved from http://livingisforeveryone.com.au/Information--Support-pack-for-those-bereaved-by-suicide-or-other-sudden-death

McGrath, P. (2007). Aboriginal cultural practices on caring for the deceased person: Findings and recommendations. *International Journal of Palliative Nursing, 13*(9), 418–425. http://doi.org/10.12968/ijpn.2007.13.9.27389

McGrath, P., & Phillips, E. (2008). Australian findings on Aboriginal culture practices associated with clothing, hair, possessions and use of name of deceased persons. *International Journal of Nursing Practice, 14*(1), 57–66. http://doi.org/10.1111/j.1440-172X.2007.00667.x

McKay, K., & Tighe, J. (2014). Talking through the dead: The impact and interplay of lived grief after suicide. *Omega: Journal of Death and Dying, 68*(2), 111–121. http://doi.org/10.2190/OM.68.2.b

McKissock, M., & McKissock, D. (2003). *Coping with grief.* Sydney, Australia: Australian Broadcasting Corporation.

Mowll, J. (2007). Reality and regret. *Bereavement Care, 26*(1), 3–6. http://doi.org/10.1080/02682620708657676

Mowll, J. (2014). A handrail on my journey: Providing support for people bereaved by suicide in Sydney, Australia. *IASP Bereavement and Postvention Special Interest Group Newsletter, 2*(3), 3–4. Retrieved from https://www.iasp.info/

Mowll, J., Lobb, L., & Wearing, M. (2016). The transformative meanings of viewing or not viewing the body after sudden death. *Death Studies, 40*(1), 46–53. http://doi.org/10.1080/07481187.2015.1059385

Mowll, J., & Smith, H. (2015). Fifteen years of the support after suicide group. *Support After Suicide In-House Newsletter, 91,* 2. Sydney, Australia: Department of Forensic Medicine, NSW Forensic and Analytical Science Service.

Neimeyer, R.A., & Currier, J.M. (2009). Grief therapy: Evidence of efficacy and emerging directions. *Current Directions in Psychological Science, 18*(6), 352–356. http://doi.org/10.1111/j.1467-8721.2009.01666.x

Omerov, P., Steineck, G., Nyberg, T., Runeson, B., & Nyberg, U. (2014). Viewing the body after bereavement due to suicide: a population-based survey in sweden. *PLoS One, 9*(7), e101799. http://doi.org/10.1371/journal.pone.0101799

Pease, B. (2003). Rethinking the relationship between the self and society. In J. Allan, B. Pease, & L. Briskman (Eds.), *Critical social work: An introduction to theories and practices* (pp. 187–201). Crows Nest, Australia: Allen & Unwin.

Rando, T., (2012). Is it Okay for you to be Okay. In R. Neimeyer (Ed.), *Techniques of grief therapy* (pp. 149–151). New York, NY: Routledge.

Ryan, M., & Giljohann, A. (2013). 'I needed to know': imparting graphic and distressing details about a suicide to the bereaved. *Bereavement Care, 32*(3), 111–116. http://doi.org/10.1080/02682621.2013.854542

Saleebey, D. (1996). The strengths perspective in social work practice: Extensions and cautions. *Social work, 41*(3), 296–305.

Scott, D. (1990). Practice wisdom: The neglected source of practice research. *Social Work, 35*(6), 564–568.

Stillion, J.M. (1996). Survivors of suicide. In K. Doka (Ed.), *Living with grief after suicide, homicide, accident, heart attack and stroke* (pp. 41–51). Washington, DC: Hospice Foundation of America.

Suicide Bereavement Support Group Standards and Practice Project. (2009). *Towards good practice: Standards and guidelines for suicide bereavement support. Lifeline Australia 2007–2009.* Retrieved from http://www.livingisforeveryone.com.au/suicide-bereavement-support-group-standards-practice-project.html

Sveen, C. A., & Walby, F. A. (2008). Suicide survivors' mental health and grief reactions: A systematic review of controlled studies. *Suicide and Life-Threatening Behavior, 38*(1), 13–29. http://doi.org/10.1521/suli.2008.38.1.13

Wilcox, H., Mittendorfer-Rutz, E., Kjeldgård, L., Alexanderson, K., & Runeson, B. (2015). Functional impairment due to bereavement after the death of adolescent or young adult offspring in a national population study of 1,051,515 parents. *Social Psychiatry and Psychiatric Epidemiology, 50*(8), 1249–1256. http://doi.org/10.1007/s00127-014-0997-7

Wojtkowiak, J., Wild, V., & Egger, J. (2012). Grief experiences and expectance of suicide. *Suicide and Life-Threatening Behavior, 42*(1), 56–66. http://doi.org/10.1111/j.1943-278X.2011.00070.x

Chapter 15

Workplaces and the Aftermath of Suicide

Sally Spencer-Thomas and Jess Stohlmann-Rainey

Carson J Spencer Foundation, Denver, CO, USA

Abstract: The majority of people who die by suicide are of working age, and almost all of them are employed, previously employed, or a family member of someone employed at the time of death; however, workplaces are often ill-equipped to provide grief and trauma support after such a tragedy. Many workplaces, if they provide grief support at all, have practices built on antiquated models of bereavement needs and do not usually take into account the complexities or duration often needed to cope in the aftermath of suicide.

This chapter stems from the results of a partnership project published as *A Manager's Guide to Suicide Postvention in the Workplace: 10 Action Steps for Dealing With the Aftermath of Suicide*, developed in collaboration with members of the Workplace Task Force of the National Action Alliance for Suicide Prevention and the American Association of Suicidology. In addition to providing a summary of the recommendations from this report, the authors share findings from 13 qualitative interviews from people who had lost loved ones through suicide, who talked about positive and negative responses they received from their employers.

In the night of death, hope sees a star,
and listening love can hear the rustle of a wing.
Robert Ingersoll (1879)

Introduction

Suicide postvention in the workplace focuses on mitigating negative outcomes for individuals and the workplace, and supporting the work community in a healing process (Carson J Spencer Foundation, Crisis Care Network, National Action Alliance for Suicide Prevention, & American Association of Suicidology, 2013). It consists of psychological first aid, crisis intervention, and other support offered after a suicide to affected individuals or the workplace as a whole (Cimini & Smith, 2012).

Vignette 1: Going Through the Motions – When Suicide Postvention Is Superficial

A federal agency of almost 1,000 people experienced a suicide of a high-level, well-liked, well-known, and visible leader. Close to the time of his death he was seen escorted out of the building among gossip of scandal and failed management. In the absence of information from the executive staff, speculation about contributing factors ensued, and rumors ran rampant. Employees looked to senior level of management to provide direction during the crisis; the leaders appeared guarded and unwilling to talk about the fact that it was a suicide. In the days that followed, the response seemed like giving lip service to the confused and grieving employees. As one said,

"We went through the motions but didn't do the work. People didn't want to face the fact that a suicide could happen. Shame prevented us from talking about it at all." (Anonymous, phone interview with Spencer-Thomas, August 13, 2015). *The organization attempted to move back to business-as-usual quickly. No plan was created on how to manage roles the deceased person played; the vacuum created led to more speculation, distrust, anger, and a lack of closure.*

Given that the majority of people who die by suicide are working-age adults, most of whom are employed; hundreds of thousands of workplaces around the globe are affected by the suicide death of an employee each year (Lytle, 2015; Milner, Page, Spencer-Thomas, & Lamontagne, 2015; Paul & Spencer-Thomas, 2012; Spencer-Thomas, 2012; World Health Organization, 2014). Furthermore, knowing that job loss can be a contributing factor, suicide deaths of recently terminated employees can still have a profound effect on their previous places of employment (Milner et al., 2015; Spencer-Thomas, 2014a). When leaders within an organization take their lives, the chaos and trauma resulting from this loss can be immense (Spencer-Thomas, 2011). In addition, suicide deaths of family members of employees, vendors, clients, and associates can all take a toll on employees; the number of workplaces affected is very high. Suicide grief support in the workplace often involves two scenarios: suicide of a work colleague or a suicide death outside the work environment.

Yet, unfortunately, most workplaces do not anticipate needing to respond to suicide death. Models and protocols of how to understand grief, trauma, and suicide contagion are integral to understanding the way workplaces respond, and ought to respond, to suicide death. Though mostly based on experiences of the United States, this chapter creates a framework for understanding and providing effective suicide postvention, provides insight into the way that grief and loss are enacted in workplaces, and offers concrete strategies needed for an effective postvention response at work.

Conceptualizing Grief at Work

Historical conceptualizations of grief stem largely from a Western medical model (see also Chapter 1 in this volume), and have hindered the ability to create meaningful and effective grief support in the workplace. Most often, in Western countries, mourners are given a very short period of time to mourn, and then are expected to return to work, functioning as they had before the death. This response is most likely inspired by stage and task models of grieving. Specifically, two grief models may have had a significant influence on workplace policy, practice, and culture surrounding bereavement: the stages of dying described by Kübler-Ross (1970; Külber-Ross & Kessler, 2007) and tasks of grief, by Worden (1982). Kübler-Ross posits that the five stages of dying outlined in her model – denial, anger, bargaining, depression, and acceptance – are a common set of emotions which a dying or grieving person might feel, rather than an exhaustive list of the emotions a person must feel for effective or healthy grieving. While the stage model considered grief as an extrinsic process that happens to a person, according to the task model the grieving person has agency (Worden, 1982). It postulates a set of tasks through which a person must work to heal and to find resolution, which is achieved by psychologically relocating the deceased person and moving forward (Worden, 1982). In other words, psychological relocating occurs when the person remembering the deceased can maintain emotional distance rather than having an emotionally intense and disruptive experience. Worden's (1982) process assumes that grief is something to "work through" and "get over." Any bereaved person who is unable or unwilling to complete the grief tasks, including the final task of relocating the deceased, is not fully "healed."

Many grief support assistance or programs for workplaces – if existing at all – are often predicated upon this model of "getting through" grief to get back to work. For instance, in the United States, most workplaces only give bereaved workers a very limited paid leave to manage the aftermath of a first-degree relative's death. Psychological support is rarely given after the death of an employee; when it is, it is often in the form of a one-time debriefing with a counselor who comes on site.

Stroebe and Schut's (1999) dual process model of coping with bereavement rejects the "grief work hypothesis" and considers grief as a dynamic process of oscillation between coping with stressors of loss and restoration. Suicide-related stigma may be disruptive of both loss-oriented and restoration-oriented experiences. This disruption, coupled with popular misunderstandings about grief, leaves the suicide bereaved with additional challenges that other grievers may not face.

Finally, a number of circumstances about a suicide may influence traumatic grief reactions and lead to complicated bereavement (Young et al., 2012), even among coworkers (Ambrose, n.d.). For most survivors of suicide loss, the death is unexpected, thus there is no opportunity for goodbyes, unfinished business, resolution of conflict, or answers to questions. Very often the bereaved are left with endless "whys" and "what ifs." When coworkers die from a prolonged illness, by contrast, colleagues have time to prepare themselves for their absence. A sudden death leaves coworkers no time for reallocation of work duties, so in addition to sadness, surviving colleagues may also feel resentment and anger about having to carry the load of extra work. In addition, deaths that involve suffering or extreme pain may cause horrifying traumatic imagery and intrusive thoughts – whether or not coworkers actually witnessed the death or the body. If the death occurred at work, that space will most likely continue to trigger traumatic reactions. The randomness of such a loss can trigger a greater sense of vulnerability and anxiety. This is often the case when there were no apparent warning signs before the person died. Ronnie Janoff-Bulman (1992) talks about how trauma leaves *shattered assumptions* in its wake. Her basic premise is that traumatic events shatter three world views that all people tend to hold: benevolence of the world ("people are generally good"), meaningfulness of the world ("good things happen to good people"), and self-worth ("I am good and can keep myself and those who love me safe and healthy"). If the suicide occurred at a workplace or involved a high-profile employee, the news media might consider the story newsworthy. Being a spokesperson for a story like this can cause additional distress for surviving employees.

Trauma reactions and grief are often at odds with each other. According to the American Psychological Association, "trauma is an emotional response to a terrible event.... Immediately after the event, shock and denial are typical. Longer term reactions include unpredictable emotions, flashbacks, strained relationships and even physical symptoms like headaches or nausea." (American Psychological Association, n.d.). The *trauma* experience can often result in survivors of loss constantly replaying the events surrounding the suicide in their minds. That is, survivors of suicide loss cannot stop thinking about the death scene (even when they are dreaming), and disturbing images may flash before their mind's eye when they least expect it. The horror can be overwhelming, and the natural impulse is to stay away from anything that reminds them of the trauma. Sometimes survivors of suicide loss develop posttraumatic stress disorder in the aftermath of a violent or unexpected death (Young et al., 2012).

By contrast, the *grief* journey for survivors of suicide loss is often a "moving toward" experience. As they come to accept the reality of the loss, and the tendency is to move toward things that remind them of the deceased, holding close memories, places, and mementos that help preserve and honor the life lived. Thus, for coworkers left behind, there is often simultaneously a desire to mourn and openly embrace the memory of the deceased and a desire to suppress the thoughts about the deceased because they are too disturbing, such as the often horrifying notion that someone they cared about died in isolation and despair, often in a violent manner.

Grief in the Workplace

Organizations are often ill-equipped and ill-informed to handle grieving employees. Allotted bereavement leave is typically determined based on relationship to the deceased, not the impact of the death on the employee. The death of any person without a legal relationship, including a close friend, partner, or fiancé, is typically not provided for in bereavement policy (Stein & Winokuer, 1989). It is likely that bereavement policies in the United States fail to account for the grief experiences of employees and that the return to work for many is often marked by distancing or demands rather than compassion (Hazen, 2009). Employees returning to work are often expected to return to work quickly and efficiently, instead of being met with compassion and accommodation. This may be particularly true for the suicide bereaved, who experience the double silencing of workplaces ill-equipped to cope with grieving employees and stigma related to the type of loss.

> **Vignette 2: Mother Whose Son Died by Suicide the Day After He Was Discharged From His Military Service**
>
> *I had only been at my present position for 90 days, my probation period. I was given some money, they had collected. Other than that nothing. I was hurting very much. When the holidays came I put a candy cane, and a note asking for prayers in everyone's mailbox. Nothing. No words, no notes, no nothing. One day I was walking down some steps, and I just wanted to let go of the railing [and fall to my death]. I talked to my supervisor and asked if I could just come in a little later on the Saturday mornings. I said I would stay late and be the last one to leave. She said to me, "I thought you were already over that." I wanted to ask her which one of her three sons she would "be over" in less than 2 years.* (Anonymous, e-mail interview with Spencer-Thomas, August 18, 2015)

Bento (1994) posits that the role of worker and the role of griever are always already at odds. Often these two roles are incompatible – the worker role is about doing, and the grief role is often about being – resulting in disenfranchised grief. According to Doka (1989, p. 4) disenfranchised grief is defined as "the grief that persons experience when they incur a loss that is not or cannot be openly acknowledged, publicly mourned, or socially supported." Disenfranchised grief is associated with a number of negative psychological outcomes, and often exacerbates painful feelings of grieving and prolongs the grief process. The incompatibility of these roles can leave the bereaved person balancing the roles, often in ways that look "troubled" or "inappropriate" to others in the workplace. As the dual process model suggests, grieving employees oscillate between grief work and restoration work. They are not always able to predict or control which role they are occupying at a given moment, so grief can enter the workplace in ways that surprise both the grieving employee and those around them. When the grieving employee loses a loved one to suicide, the silencing and stigma that may accompany that grief can make these surprising moments more uncomfortable and poignant for everyone involved. When grief work is stifled by stigma, the period of time during which these "disruptive" moments of grief surface in the workplace, can be extended even further. **Figure 15.1** illustrates the balancing act in which bereaved employees engage.

Type of death is also associated with disenfranchised grief, suicide being among the most likely types of death to cause disenfranchisement (Bento, 1994). With the compounded risk of disenfranchised grief, the role of the workplace as a supportive environment is paramount for an employee bereaved by suicide. This need can be complicated for workplaces; employers must balance the role of a *productive employee* with a role of a *healing employee*. Many characteristics of grieving are directly at odds with characteristics of productivity, including

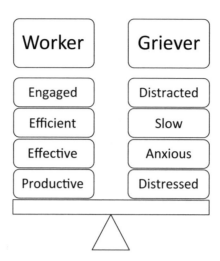

Figure 15.1. Balancing act of bereaved employees. Source: Carson J Spencer Foundation, 2015.

impaired decision making, lack of motivation, inability to concentrate, confusion, higher accident rates, and tardiness (Bento, 1994).

Sometimes bereaved employees believe they can return to their previous level of functioning at work and do not want to take time off, because work provides structure, social support, and a sense of purpose. Thoughtful employers help their grieving staff members find creative ways to balance these competing demands.

Vignette 3: A Parent

I returned to work 1 week after [my son's suicide]. I was under the illusion that I could suppress my pain and go on with my life as if nothing happened. The day I was placed on involuntary leave, I was facilitating a class of about 100 people. Someone interrupted me with an off topic question. Rather than gently deflect and move on, I went into an uncontrollable rage, comparing that person's inane question to my pain over my son's suicide. I was replaced in the classroom immediately. When I went to the corporate offices, they acknowledged my loss; however, I was told to take a month off and see if I could return to full performance. Oddly, now that I've "cleaned up my act," there is a bit of empathy from management. (Anonymous, e-mail interview with Spencer-Thomas, August 13, 2015)

While many employers feel unprepared to support a grieving employee, a number of researchers have made recommendations for workplaces that can be implemented easily. Hazen (2009) recommends that organizations support bereaved employees by providing adequate and flexible leave time with broad definitions of bereavement; providing universal grief and grief support psychoeducation; and connecting bereaved employees to mental health services through employee assistance programs and in the community. Because grieving will happen in the workplace, it is important that the culture in the workplace is supportive of reintegrating bereaved people into the workforce with compassion and flexibility. In the case of an employee who is bereaved by suicide, all of the same recommendations apply. One of the major pitfalls in organizations is to treat an employee bereaved by suicide differently from other bereaved employees. For example, when an employee dies from cancer, a workplace's common practice may be to circulate a sympathy card and attend the memorial service. Feelings of uneasiness in dealing with suicide loss may hinder these otherwise readily available support practices. As a result, a person bereaved by suicide likely in need of support in coping with grief, trauma, guilt, and shame may receive less support.

Supporting a single employee affected by a suicide, which has occurred outside the work context, can usually be accomplished through compassionate response and flexibility with work and expectations. This type of postvention can require much less investment from workplaces than the suicide death of an employee, client/customer, or other important person to the organization. Supporting a single employee comes with some simplicity because the rest of the workplace may not be impacted, and it is likely that the supervisor can occupy the singular role of "support person," instead of needing to balance their own grief response with the wide range of impact a suicide loss will have on different members of the workplace.

One of the most difficult challenges that workplaces face is honoring the competing needs of people significantly affected by a suicide loss and those less affected, while continuing to perform necessary organizational work (**Figure 15.2**). This is particularly true in some of the highest risk occupations. While an individual's suicide risk is the result of a complex interaction between job factors such as work stress, or access to means, and other risk factors such as age, presence of a mental health condition or substance abuse, on a macro level, workplaces with increased suicide risk factors for employees are at increased likelihood to experience a suicide loss (Boxer, Burnett, & Swanson, 1995). Occupations in which employees are likely to experience trauma (transportation, health care, correctional institutions, first responders, the military), have access to and familiarity with lethal means (construction, medicine, law enforcement, the military), feel responsible for the livelihood of others (medicine, the law, financial services), or work in isolation (oil and gas, construction, traveling sales, entrepreneurs) increase employees risk for suicide (Stack, 2001). In many of these industries, workplaces need to be able to continue the work throughout the entire postvention process. Emergency response services, for example, are unable to shut down due to the loss of an employee, even if the decedent's coworkers were required to respond to the scene of their colleague's death. The result is that the highest risk occupations are often unable to focus solely on postvention during the crisis phase, increasing their risk for disenfranchised and complicated grief (Carson J Spencer Foundation, 2015).

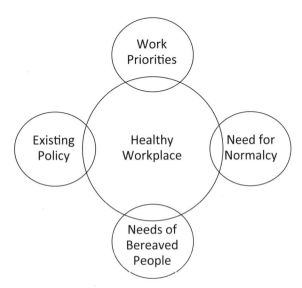

Figure 15.2. Priorities of a healthy workplace. Source: Carson J Spencer Foundation, 2015.

The National Alliance for Mental Illness (NAMI) chapter in New Hampshire, a US leader in suicide postvention, indicates that although suicide postvention includes principles of critical incident response and stress debriefing, it has a larger scope with a narrower focus (National Alliance for Mental Illness, 2006). While critical incident response and critical incident stress debriefing are designed to support workplaces in managing the crisis phase of a workplace incident (Antai-Otong, 2001; Mitchell & Everly, 1995, 2000), suicide postvention is a long-term strategy that addresses the needs of the workplace as a system. After responding to many workplace postvention cases, Elaine DeMello of NAMI New Hampshire shared the observation:

> Because of the intensity, complexity and duration of the grief and trauma reactions, loss survivors are at risk for [their] losing job; what helps is an advocate or conduit who can pave the way for the person to come back to work. (Elaine DeMello, personal communication, August 15, 2015)

Tensions in Postvention in the Workplace

The goals of suicide postvention in the workplace are really not that different from those of other crisis responses (Carson J Spencer Foundation et al., 2013) – that is, to support people through the trauma and help restore functioning to a disrupted system (Survivors of Suicide Loss Task Force, 2015). The process is about managing the inherent balance of needs and safety components that can sometimes be at odds with one another. On the one hand, workplaces acknowledge something really significant happened, while on the other hand, leaders are pressured to get back to business as usual. Grieving employees need to share their stories to mourn and honor a life that was lived, while practices of safe messaging seek to minimize glorification of the deceased and the divulgence of too many details about the death. Also, employees need information that is quick and accurate; however, privacy and investigation concerns can slow down and complicate the process.

Vignette 4: When an Employee Loses a Family Member to Suicide

I am a pharmacist at a grocery store and had been there 8 years when my teenage son died by suicide. I knew all my customers by name and many of them knew my son. When word reached the store, my store manager called everyone together to break the news. With tears streaming down his face he explained that my son was dead. Work was suspended, people were allowed to go home or take the time they needed to "pull themselves together." For a grocery store this is huge as we are all about customer service in a community where the competition is fierce. By the afternoon I had cards, a gift basket and messages from so many of my workplace family. Many of the staff were able to take the day off to attend my son's memorial and the store was generous in their contributions. Since my return to work, I have been given free rein to cry when I need to, hug when I need to, and talk with others when I need to. My store management and fellow staff continue to be a source of support and comfort. (Anonymous, e-mail interview with Spencer-Thomas, August 13, 2015)

The Suicide Postvention Process

In the center of the response are often managers who are guiding bereavement support, trauma reactions, and a transition back to work. In these circumstances, effective managers communicate empathy and respect and offer permission for people to take care of themselves. They offer a range of support options and know that not everyone will need the same types of resources in the same time frame. Many managers find themselves in the middle of complex and competing factors. Just like other employees, leaders are often impacted by the tragic loss and in need of support, but sometimes become targets of anger and blame by other employees. Leaders may feel overwhelmed and immobilized by the shock, and yet they are charged with returning the workplace to health and productivity.

In *A Manager's Guide to Suicide Postvention in the Workplace: 10 Action Steps for Dealing With the Aftermath of Suicide* (Carson J Spencer Foundation et al., 2013), coauthors from the Carson J Spencer Foundation, Crisis Care Network, the National Action Alliance for Suicide Prevention, and the American Association of Suicidology highlight the strategies that will assist workplaces navigating this particular form of crisis response. Upon publication, this guide was disseminated through the hundreds of employee assistance and workplace crisis response programs in the United States, through the partnerships of the National Action Alliance for Suicide Prevention's Workplace Task Force (http://actionallianceforsuicideprevention.org/task-force/workplace).

The guide is broken down into recommendations to guide employers in the immediate aftermath of a suicide, in the short term, and in the long term, sometimes over months and years. The duration of these interventions was intentional because in many workplaces, immediate needs may be considered, but often within just a couple of weeks, bereavement support drops off.

Immediate: Acute Phase

1. *Coordinate*: This involves having the right point person coordinating the efforts around suicide postvention. This person should be decisive and compassionate, knowledgeable about crisis response and suicide grief, and able to juggle many high-stress demands at once.
2. *Notify*: Crisis communication after a suicide is a difficult endeavor. Those left behind have a strong desire for facts, so quick and accurate communication in statements such as "here is what we know, here is what we don't know, and here is what is going to happen moving forward," can do much to quell anxiety and damaging speculation. Still, the workplace must be mindful to protect and respect the privacy rights of the deceased employee and their loved ones during death notification.
3. *Communicate*: As communication regarding the suicide is disseminated, spokespeople should be mindful of the safe and effective messaging guidelines (National Action Alliance for Suicide Prevention, n.d.) to reduce the risk that people who are already vulnerable to suicide might become more at risk for suicide contagion.
4. *Support*: In the immediate aftermath, most people do not benefit from counseling in its traditional format. Instead, what is often needed more is practical assistance. Many grieving families can benefit from the practical support of transportation, food, and everyday life tasks.

Short-Term: Recovery Phase

5. *Link*: After the initial intensity of the crisis has passed, a smaller group of affected individuals usually surfaces. Workplace managers need strategies to identify and link these impacted employees to additional support resources and refer those most affected to professional mental health services.
6. *Comfort*: Usually, what most people need is support, comfort, and an environment that promotes healthy grieving. This can be done within the workplace through professionally facilitated debriefing sessions, or managers can find community resources for employees in the form of suicide grief counselors or suicide loss peer support groups.

7. *Restore*: While providing support, managers are also tasked with restoring equilibrium and optimal functioning in the workplace. Returning to the familiar schedule can be healing for some, but the timing needs to be sensitive to individuals who may not have the capacity to perform their jobs at the levels they did before the tragedy.

8. *Lead*: Leadership messaging is critical during both the immediate and short-term phases of suicide postvention at work. Effective leaders build and sustain trust and confidence in organizational leadership by acknowledging the impact of suicide – on the company, and on them personally – by offering compassion to employees, and by helping the team transition from an immobilization state to a state that returns to, or even supersedes, previous levels of functioning. Impactful leaders are "visible, vocal and visionary" during this time and are able to successfully pull people together to draw upon the collective resilience of the work team culture (Spencer-Thomas, 2014b). Workplace postvention practices should also take into account the fact that leaders need support too.

Longer-Term: Reconstructing Phase

9. *Honor*: With many deaths, the honoring rituals that usually happen at the funeral or memorial service provide sufficient structure to grieving people. For suicide, this intense period of grief and trauma is often protracted (Berkowitz, McCauley, Schuurman, & Jordan, 2011; Eyetsemitan, 1998), and workplaces are advised to prepare for anniversary reactions and other milestone dates. For example, milestone dates might include when a work team completes a major project in which the deceased played a role. Again, this level of response may be just for a handful of employees most affected, but managers are better off preparing for these days than reacting without a plan. Honoring practices for suicide loss are best if they are integrated into the company's overall grief practices.

10. *Sustain*: Finally, managers are charged with providing guidance in transitioning the workforce from a postvention state to suicide prevention. Sometimes, in an acute grief reaction, employees might want to put together an awareness event or start a new suicide prevention training. Thoughtful managers navigate this need to *do something,* with encouragement to create space to move through the oscillating experiences of grief. When an appropriate period of time has past, and the workforce is less reactive and more reflective, managers can help them build a comprehensive and sustained strategy to make suicide prevention a healthy and safety priority.

Evaluation of the Manager's Guide showed how relevant the guide was to the users (Spencer-Thomas & Frey, 2014). Thirty-six workplace leaders participated (executive business leaders = 2.78%, human resources professionals = 2.78%, employee assistance professionals = 52.78%, managers or supervisors = 13.89%, not identified/other = 27.77%). They responded that the most useful features of the guidebook were the checklists for each action step, the roles for managers, and the decision-making flowchart. Additionally, 96% said they would recommend this resource to others, 67% said the guidebook changed their knowledge (e.g., regarding how best to balance grief support and contagion) about how best to support workplaces in the aftermath of suicide, and 42% said the guidebook changed their behavior and/or policies about how best to support workplaces in the aftermath of suicide.

Conclusions

Workplaces are often not well-prepared to respond with a compassionate, long-term strategy of grief and trauma support to employees and surviving family members in the aftermath of a suicide impacting the workforce. New practices and policies are needed to give employers a better plan so the survivors of loss can better manage the oscillating grief and restoration processes that are frequently disruptive to work performance demands and overall health.

In contrast to the opening story of a leadership response of "shutting down," in the aftermath of a leader's suicide, the following story of an insurance company of over 50,000 employees demonstrates a far more compassionate response.

Vignette 5: When Postvention in the Workplace Works

Like in the opening example, the suicide death was of a senior level manager – a man running a 500–700 person division of the company. In the weeks leading up to his death he became distraught and reclusive. "Leaders didn't say much, but they lived every word," said one employee. "Their response was value driven, not just checking a box." Immediately after the death they pulled together all of the managers and briefed them on concrete information about what had happened and that the first priority in the aftermath was to insure the health of all staff. They then assigned Employee Assistance Program staff to specific managers to support all managers and make sure they had what they needed to follow up to provide resources to the employees. The leaders communicated through a press release that was straightforward and honoring of the man who died, using words like "long and distinguished career" and "provided excellent service to customers." "They didn't glorify suicide, but they didn't diminish person," one employee recalled. "This organization was a family, and we became closer through this experience. It was a teachable moment on how we support one another."

Corresponding author

Sally Spencer-Thomas
Carson J Spencer Foundation
Denver, CO
USA
sally@carsonjspencer.org

References

Ambrose, J.T. (n.d.). *Traumatic grief: What we need to know as trauma responders.* Retrieved from http://www.restoringconnections.ca/assets/pdf/ambrose_traumatic_grief.pdf

American Psychological Association. (n.d.). *Trauma.* Retrieved from http://www.apa.org/topics/trauma/

Antai-Otong, D. (2001). Critical Incident Stress Debriefing: A health promotion model for workplace violence. *Perspectives in Psychiatric Care, 37*(4), 125–132. http://doi.org/10.1111/j.1744-6163.2001.tb00644.x

Bento, R.F. (1994). When the show must go on. *Journal of Managerial Psychology, 9*(6), 35–44. http://doi.org/10.1108/02683949410070197

Berkowitz, L., McCauley, J., Schuurman, D.L., & Jordan, J.R. (2011). Organizational postvention after a suicide death. In J.R. Jordan & J.L. McIntosh (Eds.), *Grief after suicide: Understanding the consequences and caring for the survivors* (pp. 157–178). New York, NY: Routledge.

Boxer, P.A., Burnett, C., & Swanson, N. (1995). Suicide and occupation. *Journal of Occupational and Environmental Medicine, 37*(4), 442–452. http://doi.org/10.1097/00043764-199504000-00016

Carson J Spencer Foundation, Crisis Care Network, National Action Alliance for Suicide Prevention, and American Association of Suicidology. (2013). *A manager's guide to suicide postvention in the workplace: 10 Action steps for dealing with the aftermath of suicide.* Denver, CO: Carson J Spencer Foundation. Retrieved from http://www.WorkingMinds.org/

Carson J Spencer Foundation. (2015). *A chink in the armor: Coping with loss. An in-service training for the Denver Fire Department.* Denver, CO: Author.

Cimini, M.D. & Smith, K. (2012, April 17). *Postvention as a prevention tool: Developing a comprehensive campus response to prevent contagion.* Presentation given at GLS Grantee Meeting, Baltimore, MD, USA. Retrieved from http://www.sprc.org/system/files/private/event-training/Campus%201C_Cimini%20Postvention%20as%20a%20Prevention%20Tool.pdf

Doka, K.J. (1989). *Disenfranchised grief: Recognizing hidden sorrow.* Lexington, MA: Lexington Books.

Eyetsemitan, F. (1998). Stifled grief in the workplace. *Death Studies, 22*(5), 469–479. http://doi.org/10.1080/074811898201461

Hazen, M.A. (2009). Recognizing and responding to workplace grief. *Organizational Dynamics, 38*(4), 290–296. http://doi.org/10.1016/j.orgdyn.2009.07.002

Ingersoll, R. (1879, June 4). Eulogy delivered in Washington on June 3, 1879, at the funeral of Ebon C. Ingersoll. *New York Tribune.* Retrieved from http://www.bartleby.com/268/10/9.html

Janoff-Bulman, R. (1992). *Shattered assumptions: Towards a new psychology of trauma.* New York, NY: Free Press.

Kübler-Ross, E. (1970). *On death and dying.* New York, NY: Macmillan.

Kübler-Ross, E., & Kessler, D. (2007). *On grief and grieving: Finding the meaning of grief through the five stages of loss.* New York, NY: Scribner.

Lytle, T. (2015, April 21). Workplace suicide: Companies can take a lead in prevention screenings, well-publicized benefits, transparency about mental health are key. *Society for Human Resource Management.* Retrieved from https://www.shrm.org/resourcesandtools/hr-topics/employee-relations/pages/workplace-suicide-.aspx

Milner, A., Page, K., Spencer-Thomas, S. & Lamontagne, A. (2015). Workplace suicide prevention: A systematic review of published and unpublished activities. *Health Promotion International, 30*(1), 29–37. http://doi.org/10.1093/heapro/dau085

Mitchell, J.T., & Everly, G.S. (2000). Critical incident stress management and critical incident stress debriefings: Evolutions, effects and outcomes. In B. Raphael & J. Wilson (Eds.), *Psychological debriefing: Theory, practice and evidence* (pp. 71–90). Cambridge, UK: Cambridge University Press.

Mitchell, J.T., & Everly, G.S. (1995). Critical Incident Stress Debriefing (CISD) and the prevention of work-related traumatic stress among high risk occupational groups. In G.S. Everly & J.M. Lating (Eds.), *Psychotraumatology: Key papers and core concepts in Post-Traumatic Stress* (pp. 267–280). New York, NY: Springer.

National Action Alliance for Suicide Prevention. (n.d.). *Framework for successful messaging.* Retrieved from http://suicidepreventionmessaging.actionallianceforsuicideprevention.org/

National Alliance for Mental Illness. (2006). *Frameworks youth suicide prevention project: Mental health/substance abuse provider postvention response.* Retrieved from https://www1.maine.gov/suicide/docs/Mental-health-postvention.pdf

Paul, R., & Spencer-Thomas, S. (2012). Changing workplace culture to end the suicide standstill. *National Council Magazine, 2*(1), 126–127.

Spencer-Thomas, S. (2011). High performers and suicide prevention in the workplace. *Psychiatric Annals, 41*(7), 343–344. http://doi.org/10.3928/00485713-20110627-02

Spencer-Thomas, S. (2012). Developing a workplace suicide prevention program. *Journal of Employee Assistance, 42*(1), 12–15.

Spencer-Thomas, S. (2014a, February 20). *After a suicide.* Keynote speech at inaugural construction industry mental health conference. Brisbane, Queensland, Australia. Retrieved from https://www.youtube.com/watch?v=d6MpBsQP7EY

Spencer-Thomas, S. (2014b). *How to be visionary on mental health. Insurance thought leadership.* Retrieved from http://insurancethoughtleadership.com/how-to-be-visionary-on-mental-health/

Spencer-Thomas, S., & Frey, J. (2014, April). *Manager's guide to suicide postvention: 10 Action steps in dealing with the aftermath of a suicide. Results of 2014 evaluation.* Presentation at the American Association of Suicidology's annual conference business meeting, Los Angeles, CA.

Stack, S. (2001). Occupation and suicide. *Social Science Quarterly, 82*(2), 384–396. http://doi.org/10.1111/0038-4941.00030

Stein, A.J., & Winokuer, H.R. (1989). Monday mourning: Managing employee grief. In K. Doka (Ed.), *Disenfranchised grief: Recognizing hidden sorrow* (pp. 91–102). New York, NY: Lexington Books.

Stroebe, M., & Schut, H. (1999). The Dual Process Model of coping with bereavement: Rationale and description. *Death Studies, 23*(3), 197–224. http://doi.org/10.1080/074811899201046

Suicide Prevention Resource Center. (2013). *Postvention as a prevention tool: Developing a comprehensive postvention response for your campus* [Webinar]. Hosted by SPRC, SAMHSA, and EDC. Retrieved from http://www.sprc.org/sites/sprc.org/files/PostventionSlidesFinal.6.8.10.pdf

Survivors of Suicide Loss Task Force. (2015). *Responding to grief, trauma, and distress after a suicide: U.S. National Guidelines*. Washington, DC: National Action Alliance for Suicide Prevention. Retrieved from http://actionallianceforsuicideprevention.org/sites/actionallianceforsuicideprevention.org/files/NationalGuidelines.pdf

Worden, J.W. (1982). *Grief counseling and grief therapy: A handbook for the mental health practitioner.* New York, NY: Springer.

World Health Organization. (2014). *Preventing suicide: A global imperative*. Geneva, Switzerland: Author.

Young, I., Iglewicz, A., Glorioso, D., Lanouette, N., Seay, K., Ilapakurti, M., & Zisook, S. (2012). Suicide bereavement and complicated grief. *Dialogues in Clinical Neuroscience, 14*(2), 177–186.

Chapter 16

The Roles of Religion and Spirituality in Suicide Bereavement and Postvention

Karolina Krysinska[1], Danielle R. Jahn[2], Sally Spencer-Thomas[3], and Karl Andriessen[1]

[1]School of Psychiatry, University of New South Wales, Sydney, Australia
[2]Department of Psychiatry, University of Maryland, Baltimore, MD, USA
[3]Carson J Spencer Foundation, Denver, CO, USA

Abstract: While the need for social, peer, and professional support in the aftermath of suicide is often acknowledged, a "cure for the soul" or religious/spiritual support and its role in the grief journey are often overlooked. However, studies looking at the role of religiosity in bereavement outcomes indicate that religion and/or spirituality are among the resources which can help bereaved people cope with their loss. Strong evidence exists regarding the correlation between religious beliefs or behaviors and positive psychosocial outcomes in bereavement in general, such as adjustment to bereavement, psychological well-being, and sense of meaning.

This chapter presents the role of religion/spirituality in suicide bereavement, including the process of meaning making after the loss, the role of a belief in the afterlife, and the spiritual beliefs of people bereaved by suicide. New findings on intrinsic and extrinsic religiosity, religious coping, spirituality, outreach to faith communities, and online expressions of grief are included. The chapter concludes with implications for clinical work and support of the bereaved, and for postvention more broadly.

> *As you ought not to attempt to cure the eyes without the head, or the head without the body, so neither ought you to attempt to cure the body without the soul.... For the part can never be well unless the whole is well.... And therefore, if the head and body are to be well, you must begin by curing the soul; that is the first thing.*
> Plato, 380 BC

Introduction

Among the psychosocial resources which can help those bereaved by suicide cope with loss are religious faith and spirituality, religious and spiritual practices, and belonging to and participating in faith communities. Spirituality is a set of personal, subjective, and encompassing beliefs that help create meaning and direct purpose in one's life (Zinnbauer & Pargament, 2005). It consists of an awareness that there is something greater than the self, and it involves a deep sense of interconnectedness. Spiritual practices are self-informed through trial and error and vary greatly from individual to individual but allow people to achieve greater insights and may give them a sense of awe and some connection to a divine energy. By contrast, religion is often more formal, ritualized, and institutionalized. Religious traditions are the most common cultural representations of spirituality and are externally prescribed by families and societies (Colucci, 2008).

After a traumatic experience, people may find their worldviews are shattered, including core tenets of their religious faith. For some, the rebuilding process of this faith may take them to a deeper, more personal connection to their spiritual beliefs. Teachings about human ability to live through life traumas are evident in the religious texts of Islam, Judaism, Christianity, Buddhism, and Hinduism (Pargament, 1997). Many refer to the transformational power of trauma. Throughout the world's faith traditions, there is an emphasis on valuing life and turning to faith in times of despair. For example:

- "For our light and momentary troubles are achieving for us an eternal glory that far outweighs them all. So we fix our eyes not on what is seen, but on what is unseen. For what is seen is temporary, but what is unseen is eternal." (2 Corinthians 4:17–18).
- "For one who is born, death is certain and for one who has died, birth is certain. Therefore you should not grieve for that which is unavoidable." (Bhagavad-Gita 2.27).
- "O you who believe! Strengthen yourselves with resolution and prayer. Indeed Allah is with those who persevere in adversity." (Qur'an, Al-Baqara, Surah 2:153).

The tenets of most major faith traditions offer comforting words like these to help people through times of despair (Pargament, 1997). According to Shuchter and Zisook (1993), religion is "one of the most frequently used and effective means of coping with death" (p. 32), and studies looking at the role of different aspects of religiosity/spirituality in bereavement outcomes after different types of death generally confirm this observation. In a systematic review, Becker et al. (2007) found that the majority of studies on bereavement generally found positive effects (68%) or limited positive effects (19%) of spiritual and religious beliefs on adjustment to bereavement. Similar results were reported in an integrative review of the literature by Wortmann and Park (2008), which showed a general positive relationship between many aspects of religion/spirituality and adjustment to bereavement, including bereavement after suicide. In addition, religion/spirituality is one of the mediators of posttraumatic growth in the aftermath of bereavement, along with social support, time since death, and active cognitive coping strategies, such as benefit finding and positive reappraisal (Michael & Cooper, 2013; see also Chapter 5, Chapter 6, Chapter 7, and Chapter 8 in this volume). Positive religious coping, openness, participation, and intrinsic religiousness are the aspects of religion most strongly associated with growth after loss and other traumatic experiences (Shaw, Joseph, & Linley, 2005).

Nonetheless, the complexity and multidimensionality of both religiosity and bereavement outcomes call for caution in interpretation of empirical results (Stroebe, 2004). For example, although there is a relatively strong positive correlation between religious attendance and/or religious coping and adjustment after bereavement, there is not much evidence showing a salutary effect of religious affiliation per se (Wortmann & Park, 2008). The content of individuals' beliefs (e.g., a particular belief in the afterlife) may influence the process of bereavement in a quite complex way. It may be a source of hope and support when providing a prospect of reunion or, on the contrary, may lead to anxiety and guilt if it implies suffering of the deceased in the afterlife. Also, increasing numbers of individuals in Western countries reject organized religions, but create personal religious and/or spiritual belief systems, a phenomenon called "religion à la carte" or "believing without belonging" (Davie, 2007, p. 274). The more central religion is in one's life, the more likely one is to turn to spiritual resources and religious coping when facing negative life events and crisis (Huber & Huber, 2012). No research to date has tackled the role of such individualized belief systems in coping with interpersonal loss, including by suicide.

After Suicide

Although the evidence regarding the positive correlation between religious beliefs or behaviors and positive psychosocial outcomes, such as adjustment to bereavement, psychological well-being, and sense of meaning, is quite strong in the context of interpersonal loss in general, few studies have looked specifically at bereavement after suicide, and most have been conducted from a Western perspective (Jahn & Spencer-Thomas, 2014; Krysinska, Andriessen, & Corveleyn, 2014; Lichtenthal, Neimeyer, Currier, Roberts, & Jordan, 2013; Murphy, Johnson, & Lohan, 2003; Smith, Range, & Ulmer, 1991; Vandecreek & Mottram, 2009, 2011). These studies show quite a complex picture of the role religion/spirituality can play in the aftermath of suicide. Suicide survivors frequently report positive after-death spiritual experiences, such as dreams about the deceased or feeling their presence (Jahn & Spencer-Thomas, 2014), and spontaneously mention religion or spirituality when remembering the deceased (Krysinska et al., 2014). Vandecreek & Mottram (2009) found a new sense of purpose of life and strengthening of spiritual or religious beliefs in the aftermath of suicide, and Smith et al. (1991) reported that belief in the afterlife can enhance bereavement recovery and the well-being of the bereaved. Other studies show that religious or spiritual beliefs can support the process of meaning making after the loss, although this finding does not apply to all bereaved after suicide. For example, in a sample of bereaved parents, Murphy and colleagues (2003) found that religious coping and support group attendance were significant predictors of finding meaning in the child's violent death 5 years after the loss. Eighteen percent of the sample reported a strengthening of their existential beliefs, including a belief in the plan of a deity and perseverance in religious faith; nonetheless, 61% of suicide-bereaved parents in the study were unable to find meaning in the death. Lichtenthal and colleagues (2013) found no significant differences in sense-making and benefit-finding themes, such as acceptance of the death as a part of a deity's plan, and/or belief in afterlife and reunion, between parents who had lost their child due to suicide and those who had lost their child to other violent deaths.

While religiosity and spiritual practices can aid in healing, sometimes people bereaved by suicide can also experience a devastating "loss of faith" (Spencer-Thomas, 2011). In the aftermath of trauma like a loss to suicide, individuals may question their assumptions and closely held beliefs, which may result in anger at God or an abandonment of faith. In particular, adherence to the benevolence and meaningfulness of the world is significantly challenged, and thus the idea that the faithful will be rewarded may no longer be a belief that makes sense (Jannoff-Bulman, 1992). When these changes in worldviews are also met with stigmatizing faith perspectives, people bereaved by suicide can find themselves moving away from their faith communities (Spencer-Thomas, 2011). Because faith traditions can tie family members to one another and to ancestors, this loss may be profound and challenge core identity definitions (Jannoff-Bulman, 1992). Not surprisingly, given the religious condemnation of suicide that can occur in Western culture, there is evidence of spiritual struggles of the bereaved, including their concern about the afterlife of the deceased (Vandecreek & Mottram, 2009; 2011). Some of the bereaved face the stigma surrounding people who die by suicide and the loved ones left behind (Vandecreek & Mottram, 2009; 2011), and the issue of handling moral attitudes, such as the notion of suicide as an unforgivable or mortal sin, can be a concern (Rubey & McIntosh, 1996).

Spirituality and Religiosity After a Loss Through Suicide

A recent study with a large sample of 1,301 suicide survivors (99% of respondents living in the United States; 89% female) explored continuing bonds after a death by suicide (Jahn & Spencer-Thomas, 2014). The study included measures of religiosity and spirituality, and these data have not been previously published. Individuals had a wide variety of religious affiliations in this sample (see **Table 16.1**). A majority of participants (57.9%) would be considered to be affiliated with an organized religion.

Table 16.1. Religious affiliations of study participants

Religion	Number	Percentage
Christian, Protestant/Other	482	37.4%
Spiritual	350	27.2%
Catholic	173	13.4%
No religious affiliation	86	6.7%
Other/multiple religious affiliations	54	4.2%
Agnostic	49	3.8%
Atheist	43	3.3%
Jewish	28	2.2%
Eastern religions (Hindu/Buddhist/other)	24	1.9%

On a scale of 1 *(not at all important)* to 5 *(very important)*, survivors rated the importance of their religious affiliation on average to be somewhat important ($M=3.83$; $SD=1.30$). Nearly half of participants (42%) indicated that their religious affiliation was very important, and 23% identified it as somewhat important. Approximately 10% of participants said their religion was not at all important. Approximately one third of participants (36%) reported that they were more religious/spiritual after their loss, 19% were less religious/spiritual, and 46% did not believe their religiosity/spirituality changed. Collectively, the data indicate that many individuals bereaved by suicide are religious or spiritual, that these religious affiliations are important to them, and that religiousness remains important (and may in fact become more important) after a loss by suicide.

Participants also completed the Duke University Religion Index (Koenig, Parkerson, & Meador, 1997), a measure of organized religious participation, private religious activity, and intrinsic religiosity. In terms of organized religious activity on this measure, one quarter of participants indicated that they were spiritual and regularly participated in organized religion, 26% were spiritual and occasionally participated in organized religion, 40% were spiritual but did not participate in organized religion, and 10% were not spiritual or religious. For private religious activities (e.g., prayer, studying religious texts), 37% of participants reported that they engaged in private religious activities once a day or more, 19% engaged in these activities once or twice a week, 14% engaged in these activities a few times a month, and 31% engaged in these activities rarely or never. Finally, on the intrinsic religiosity items, 56% of participants reported that they had experienced the presence of the divine in their lives, 54% reported that they carried over their religion into all aspects of their lives, and 54% reported that their religious beliefs lay behind their approach to life. This information reiterates the importance of organized and private religious activities, as well as intrinsic religiosity, among the bereaved by suicide, as reported by a majority of study participants.

The study included the Brief Measure of Religious Coping (Brief RCOPE; Pargament, Feuille, & Burdzy, 2011), which measures both positive religious coping (e.g., "Sought help from God in letting go of my anger") and negative religious coping (e.g., "Questioned God's love for me") on a scale of 1 *(not at all)* to 4 *(a great deal)*. The study participants reported an average positive religious coping score ($M=16.89$, $SD=7.11$), slightly lower than the averages reported in nonbereaved samples – for example, older adults in residential care, HIV/AIDS patients, and advanced cancer patients (Pargament et al., 2011) – which is in the middle of the scale, suggesting that suicide survivors engage in positive religious coping some of the time. In terms of negative religious coping, participants reported an average score that suggests that they were engaging in negative religious coping not at all to very little ($M = 12.26$, $SD = 5.66$). This average was higher than in many samples (e.g., HIV/AIDS patients, advanced cancer patients), but lower than in a sample of older adults in residential care (Pargament et al., 2011), Finally, participants responded to the daily spiritual experiences subscale of the Brief Multidimensional Measure of Religiousness/Spirituality (Idler et al., 2003), which is based on how often respondents have spiritual experiences such as connection with a deity. The average score indicated that spiritual experiences were occurring "most days" ($M = 3.39$, $SD = 1.39$), and more frequently in suicide survivors than in validation sample for this measure (Idler et al., 2003). These findings indicate that survivors of suicide have more daily spiritual experiences than a nationally representative sample of adults in the United States. Collectively, the results of these religious and spiritual measures suggest that individuals bereaved by suicide may not utilize religious coping as effectively as others.

Religion and Spirituality in Online Suicide Memorials

A recent qualitative study explored major themes, including religion and spirituality, in 250 memorials written by people bereaved by suicide (Krysinska & Andriessen, 2015; Krysinska et al., 2014). The memorials were randomly selected from two memorial websites (i.e., Faces of Suicide and Gonetoosoon). The study aimed to provide insights into online memorialization – that is, creating and maintaining web pages or websites dedicated to the memory of the deceased, after suicide (Roberts & Vidal, 2000). Although the phenomenon of online memorization has been explored in a number of earlier studies, not much is known about online expressions of grief, including references to religion and spirituality, specifically after suicide (Finlay & Krueger, 2011; Lester, 2012; Williams & Merten, 2009).

The qualitative study found references to religion/spirituality in 14 % of the memorials ($n = 35$) dedicated to individuals who had died by suicide (Krysinska et al., 2014). These memorials were written on average 3 years after the death, possibly reflecting the enduring nature of continuing bonds with the deceased (Klass, Silverman, & Nickman, 1996). There were no significant differences between the memorials with religious and/or spiritual themes and the remaining memorials with regard to age and gender of the deceased, country of origin, type of relationship, type of memorial, or length of time between the suicide and posting of the memorial. The memorials' authors were mostly family members, friends, and (ex-)partners of the deceased, who were living in English-speaking countries, primarily the United States. A similar percentage (15 %) of memorials including religious/spiritual themes was reported by de Vries and Rutherford (2004) in their study of memorials written for people who died from various causes of death, although other studies found that less than 5 % of general memorials included such themes (Roberts & Vidal, 2000). It is possible that the reasons for these differences may be the progressing secularization of Western Europe, which might decrease the likelihood of mentioning a deity and the afterlife in comparison with the more religious North American context (Klaassens & Bijlsma, 2013).

The thematic analysis revealed 10 themes related to religion and/or spirituality in the analyzed suicide memorials (**Table 16.2**). Some memorial authors perceived suicide as an expression of God's will, sometimes even an act of a benevolent deity who could see the pain of the suicidal person and stopped the suffering. Such interpretations of the loss found online may reflect the process of meaning making (Neimeyer & Sands, 2011; Chapter 7 in this volume). Attributing the death to a deity's will, relinquishing control to a benevolent God, and believing in an everlasting life can enable the bereaved to make sense of the death and inform the interpretation of the loss (Vandecreek & Mottram, 2011; Wortmann & Park, 2009). A search for explanations and the desire to understand why the suicide has happened, found in the online memorials, is a common reaction of suicide survivors, shared with individuals bereaved after other sudden and/or violent death. The search for motives and explanations for the death may be a distinguishing feature of online memorials dedicated to individuals who have died a sudden death, including those who have died by suicide (Roberts & Vidal, 2000).

Table 16.2. References to religion and/or spirituality in online suicide memorials

Theme[a]	Examples
God's will (n = 10)	"I'm following the path God laid for me; I took his hand when I heard him call." "It is not where we wanted him/But where god wanted him to be." "God saw he was hurting and took him to rest in his arms for eternity."
Gratitude for peace for the deceased (n = 8) and/or wishing the deceased peace (n = 7)	"I know he is in the loving hands of God." "Rest peacefully in the arms of Jesus"
Continuation of spirit, and/or mention of life after death (n = 7)	"He is in spirits garden now." "Keep up the good work; I know your vibration is growing stronger every day."
Mention of reunion (n = 6)	"Until we meet on that Heavenly shore." "He is in the loving hands of God, and one day we will see him there."
Grief of the survivors (n = 5)	"You are in my heart and in every prayer." "I keep asking God how much does he think is too much for me to bear." "Blessed are those who mourn, for they will be comforted." (Matthew 5:4)
Gratitude for knowing the deceased (n = 3)	"We thank God for this precious gift." "She was my Gift from God."
Description of the deceased (n = 3)	"He loved the Lord and followed his commandments." "You will always be remembered and loved for your kind heart and your devotion to God."
General religious/spiritual (n = 2)	"God bless us all" "Goodnight God bless."
Other, including asking God's forgiveness, asking for a donation, suicide as a sin (n = 4)	"May God forgive you." "I was once told that a person who does this doesn't get into Heaven."

Note. N = 35.
[a]Several of the 35 analyzed memorials contained more than one reference to religion and/or spirituality.

Some of the bereaved in the study of online suicide memorials expressed their gratitude for the deceased or wished the deceased peace in the transcendentally defined afterlife. Other bereaved individuals mentioned the continuation of the deceased's spirit or life after death. The theme of reunion in the transcendental realm (i.e., in heaven or in the "loving hands of God") was found in six memorials. Similar expressions of gratitude, a wish for a peaceful and painless life after death, belief in the continuation of spirit, and hope for reunion have been reported in previous studies of bereavement (Lichtenthal et al., 2013; Musambira et al., 2006–2007; Smith et al., 1991), and may support the process of bereavement recovery in people grieving a suicide loss. In other memorials in the study, religious beliefs were mentioned in the context of the grief reactions of the survivors, such as missing the deceased and holding on to their presence, expression of pain after the loss, and religious consolation for the grieving. Authors of three memorials expressed their gratitude to God for having known the person who died, and in another three online messages, the deceased was described as a religious or pious person. Two memorials contained general references to a deity, and religious beliefs were expressed in other contexts, including asking for forgiveness, asking for a donation to a religious organization, and mentioning the religious prohibition of suicide in four memorials.

In general, the memorials studied contained positive and hopeful expressions of religiosity and spirituality, which may indicate the lessening of religious stigmatization of suicide and loss survivors (Cerel, Fristad, Weller, & Weller, 2000). Nonetheless, it is possible that self-censorship affected the self-disclosure of the authors of the memorials, and only those who felt comfortable and who had a positive experience of online support might have become involved in online memorialization and/or continued maintaining an online memorial. On the other hand, more religious individuals may be more vulnerable to religious struggles and crises following an event that shatters a worldview incorporating a benevolent deity and a predictable life trajectory (Exline & Rose, 2013). Instances of asking God for forgiveness, questioning whether someone who dies by suicide can go to heaven, and expressing ambivalence between accepting the death as "the will of the higher power" and feeling that "it is not where we wanted him," may reflect such spiritual struggles.

Role of Faith Communities

Faith communities can play a critical first responder role in postvention after bereavement by suicide, as well as long-term support in the meaning making process (Doty & Spencer-Thomas, 2009). Many people honor their loved ones who have died by suicide, through funerals and memorial services within their faith communities. Faith leaders are often charged with the challenge of finding a delicate balance between helping families find ways to honor the life that was lived, without disregarding the complex loss involved in suicide (Suicide Prevention Resource Center, 2004; Wilkens, 2003). Faith leaders and those involved in pastoral care are also often aware that congregants and immediate family members left behind may be at increased risk of suicide due to a contagion effect, and therefore, discover the importance of safe messaging while planning memorial services. All of these challenges are complicated when the family of the deceased experiences shame and guilt, which may result in reluctance to address issues of suicide directly. Recommendations exist to assist leaders of faith communities in navigating many of these challenges, such as helping survivors cope with guilt and anger, using accepting language, addressing stigma, and ensuring public memorials are appropriate (Suicide Prevention Resource Center, 2004).

In the previously discussed study of continuing bonds in suicide survivors (Jahn & Spencer, 2014), 68.7% of participants reported that they reached out to their faith communities and/or representatives of these communities after their loss by suicide. A total of 25.1% reached out to their faith community, 24.0% reached out to faith leaders, 21.5% reached out to a deity, and 11.8% reached out to someone else that they defined as part of their faith community. In general, faith communities' responses were supportive or positive (72.6%). However, some responses were negative or indicated stigma or misunderstanding (7.2%), or were neutral or mixed (20.2%).

In longer-term support, faith communities can help provide a sense of belonging and a process for meaning making that help survivors of suicide loss in their grief process. Spiritual and religious practices such as discernment, group prayers, and reflection on religious texts can provide comfort and insight (Young-Eisendrath, 1997). Too often, the roles of mental health service providers and pastoral care are not well integrated in the support of people bereaved by suicide (Spencer-Thomas, 2010). A better understanding of the unique contributions of each role and how they can augment one another in the aftermath of suicide is an excellent area for future study.

Implications for Practice

Religion, spirituality, and faith communities can support the bereaved after suicide and play a significant role in postvention. However, similar to other professionals, faith leaders and pastoral counselors may benefit from postvention training, which can improve their knowledge and skills concerning proactive planning to ensure an appropriate and comprehensive response after a suicide death, providing support to bereaved individuals and communities, and reducing the risk of contagion (Suicide Prevention Resource Center, n.d.; Mason, Geist, Kuo, Marshall, & Wines, 2016).

Therapists and other mental health professionals should be able to assess and utilize the role of religion and spirituality when working with individuals and families bereaved by suicide (Kaslow, Samples, Rhodes, & Gantt, 2011). Assessing the importance of religion, clarifying each client's religious identity and relationships with the faith community, exploring the role of religiosity during past times of stress and difficulties, assessing the conceptualization of suicide in the client's religion, and identifying what may be the value of strengthening their religiosity and religious participation can be of help to clinicians and clients (Gearing & Lizardi, 2009). Given that individuals bereaved by suicide may not use religious coping effectively even when religion is important to them, mental health professionals may foster effective use of positive religious coping when appropriate. It should be noted that some bereaved people, including suicide survivors, are disappointed and enraged at God for "allowing bad things to happen," and report spiritual doubts or even loss of faith (Burke & Neimeyer, 2016, p. 80).

In cases of highly religious clients and families, it may be helpful to involve a clergy member, such as a rabbi, priest, pastor, or imam, in the context of the therapy or as supplementary support (Kaslow et al., 2011). Bibliotherapy, working with a relevant sacred text, incorporating prayer, or stressing religious/spiritual values and virtues (e.g., forgiveness, gratitude) may also be recommended in a psychotherapeutic context. Nonetheless, it is essential that mental health professionals maintain their roles and boundaries and do not take the place of spiritual advisors. According to Kaslow and colleagues (2011), "when appropriate ethical boundaries are maintained, spiritually meaningful interventions can be powerful tools for healing" (p. 317); however, they advise therapists to "be mindful to maintain respect for the tradition and to avoid trivializing the sacred meaning of the ritual or belief" (p. 317).

Conclusions

It is clear that religion, spirituality, and participation in faith communities play complicated and sometimes conflicting roles in the lives of people bereaved by suicide. As communities and mental health professionals seek better ways to support suicide loss survivors, a better integration and understanding of these complexities and opportunities is indicated, including a deeper insight into similarities and differences across religions regarding the spiritual needs of the bereaved and opportunities for support.

Corresponding author

Karolina Krysinska
School of Psychiatry
University of New South Wales
Hospital Road
Randwick 2031 NSW
Australia
k.krysinska@unsw.edu.au

References

Becker, G., Xander, C. J., Blum, H. E., Lutterbach, J., Momm, F., Gysels, M., & Higginson, I. J. (2007). Do religious or spiritual beliefs influence bereavement? A systematic review. *Palliative Medicine, 21*(3), 207–217. http://doi.org/10.1177/0269216307077327

Burke, L. A., & Neimeyer, R. A. (2016). Inventory of Complicated Spiritual Grief (ICSG). In R. A. Neimeyer (Ed.), *Techniques of grief therapy* (pp. 76–80). New York, NY: Routledge.

Cerel, J., Fristad, M. A., Weller, E. B., & Weller, R. A. (2000). Suicide-bereaved children and adolescents: II. Parental and family functioning. *Journal of the American Academy of Child & Adolescent Psychiatry, 39*(4), 437–444. http://doi.org/10.1097/00004583-200004000-00012

Colucci, E. (2008). Recognizing spirituality in the assessment and prevention of suicidal behavior. *World Cultural Psychiatry Research Review, 3*(2), 77–95.

Davie, G. (2007). Religion in Europe in the 21st century: The factors to take into account. *European Journal of Sociology, 47*(2), 271–296. http://doi.org/10.1017/S0003975606000099

de Vries, B. D., & Rutherford, J. (2004). Memorializing loved ones on the world wide web. *Omega: Journal of Death and Dying, 49*(1), 5–26. http://doi.org/10.2190/DR46-RU57-UY6P-NEWM

Doty, T., & Spencer-Thomas, S. (2009). *The role of faith communities in suicide prevention: A guidebook for faith leaders.* Golden, CO: Carson J. Spencer Foundation.

Exline, J. J., & Rose, E. D. (2013). Religious and spiritual struggles. In R. F. Paloutzian & C. L. Park (Eds.), *Handbook of the psychology of religion and spirituality* (2nd ed.; pp. 380–398). New York, NY: Guilford Press.

Finlay, C. J., & Krueger, G. (2011). A space for mothers: Grief as identity construction on memorial websites created by SIDS Parents. *Omega: Journal of Death and Dying, 63*(1), 21–44. http://doi.org/10.2190/OM.63.1.b

Gearing, R. E., & Lizardi, D. (2009). Religion and suicide. *Journal of Religion and Health, 48*(3), 332–341. http://doi.org/10.1007/s10943-008-9181-2

Huber, S., & Huber, O. W. (2012). The Centrality of Religiosity Scale (CRS). *Religions, 3*(3), 710–724. http://doi.org/10.3390/rel3030710

Idler, E. L., Musick, M. A., Ellison, C. G., George, L. K., Krause, N., Ory, M. G., ... Williams, D. R. (2003). Measuring multiple dimensions of religion and spirituality for health research conceptual background and findings from the 1998 General Social Survey. *Research on Aging, 25*(4), 327–365. http://doi.org/10.1177/0164027503025004001

Jahn, D. R., & Spencer-Thomas, S. (2014). Continuing bonds through after-death spiritual experiences in individuals bereaved by suicide. *Journal of Spirituality in Mental Health, 16*(4), 311–324. http://doi.org/10.1080/19349637.2015.957612

Jannoff-Bulman, R. (1992). *Shattered assumptions: Towards a new psychology of trauma.* New York, NY: Free Press.

Kaslow, N. J., Samples, T. C., Rhodes, M., & Gantt, S. (2011). A family-oriented and culturally sensitive postvention approach with suicide survivors. In J. R. Jordan & J. L. McIntosh (Eds.), *Grief after suicide: Understanding the consequences and caring for the survivors* (pp. 301–323). New York, NY: Routledge.

Klaassens, M., & Bijlsma, M. J. (2013). New places of remembrance: Individual web memorials in the Netherlands. *Death Studies, 38*(5), 283–293. http://doi.org/10.1080/07481187.2012.742474

Klass, D., Silverman, P.R., & Nickman, S.L. (1996). *Continuing bonds: New understandings of grief.* Washington, DC: Taylor & Francis.

Koenig, H., Parkerson, G.R., Jr., & Meador, K.G. (1997). Religion index for psychiatric research. *American Journal of Psychiatry, 154*(6), 885–886. http://doi.org/10.1176/ajp.154.6.885b

Krysinska, K., & Andriessen, K. (2015). Online memorialization and grief after suicide: An analysis of suicide memorials on the Internet. *Omega: Journal of Death and Dying, 71*(1), 19–47. http://doi.org/10.1177/0030222814568276

Krysinska, K., Andriessen, K., & Corveleyn, J. (2014). Religion and spirituality in online suicide bereavement: An analysis of online memorial. *Crisis, 35*(5), 349–356. http://doi.org/10.1027/0227-5910/a000270

Lester, D. (2012). Bereavement after suicide: A study of memorials on the Internet. *Omega: Journal of Death and Dying, 65*(3), 189–194. http://doi.org/10.2190/OM.65.3.b

Lichtenthal, W.G., Neimeyer, R.A., Currier, J.M., Roberts, K., & Jordan, N. (2013). Cause of death and the quest for meaning after the loss of a child. *Death Studies, 37*(4), 311–342. http://doi.org/10.1080/07481187.2012.673533

Mason, K., Geist, M., Kuo, R., Marshall, D., & Wines, J.D. (2016). Predictors of clergy's ability to fulfill a suicide prevention gatekeeper role. *Journal of Pastoral Care & Counseling, 70*(1), 34–39.

Michael, C., & Cooper, M. (2013). Post-traumatic growth following bereavement: A systematic review of the literature. *Counselling Psychology Review, 28*(4), 18–33.

Murphy, S. a., Clark Johnson, L., & Lohan, J. (2003). Finding meaning in a child's violent death: A five-year prospective analysis of parents' personal narratives and empirical data. *Death Studies, 27*(5), 381–404. http://doi.org/10.1080/07481180302879

Musambira, G.W., Hastings, S.O., & Hoover, J.D. (2006–2007). Bereavement, gender, and cyberspace: A content analysis of parents' memorials to their children. *Omega: Journal of Death and Dying, 54*(4), 263–279.

Neimeyer, R.A., & Sands, D.C. (2011). Meaning reconstruction in bereavement: From principles to practice. In R.A. Neimeyer, D.L. Harris, H.R. Winokuer, & G.F. Thornton (Eds.), *Grief and bereavement in contemporary society: Bridging research and practice* (pp. 9–22). New York, NY: Routledge.

Pargament, K.I. (1997). *The psychology of religion and coping.* New York, NY: Guilford Press.

Pargament, K., Feuille, M., & Burdzy, D. (2011). The Brief RCOPE: Current psychometric status of a short measure of religious coping. *Religions, 2*(1), 51–76. http://doi.org/10.3390/rel2010051

Roberts, P., & Vidal, L.A. (2000). Perpetual care in cyberspace: A portrait of memorials on the web. *Omega: Journal of Death and Dying, 40*(4), 521–546. http://doi.org/10.2190/3BPT-UYJR-192R-U969

Rubey, T., & McIntosh, L. (1996). Suicide survivors groups: Results of a survey. *Suicide and Life-Threatening Behavior, 26*(4), 351–358.

Shaw, A., Joseph, S., & Linley, P.A. (2005). Religion, spirituality, and posttraumatic growth: A systematic review. *Mental Health, Religion & Culture, 8*(1), 1–11. http://doi.org/10.1080/1367467032000157981

Shuchter, S.R., & Zisook, S. (1993). The course of normal grief. In M.S. Stroebe, W. Stroebe, & R.O. Hansson (Eds.), *Handbook of bereavement: Theory, research, and intervention* (pp. 23–43). Cambridge, UK: Cambridge University Press.

Smith, P.C., Range, L.M., & Ulmer, A. (1991). Belief in afterlife as a buffer in suicidal and other bereavement. *Omega: Journal of Death and Dying, 24*(3), 217–225. http://doi.org/10.2190/HME4-G1XE-9HXL-TJ96

Spencer-Thomas, S. (2010). Spirituality and suicide bereavement Part I: The roles of faith and faith communities [Blog post]. Retrieved from http://sallyspencerthomas.blogspot.com/2010/10/suicide-and-spirituality-part-i-roles.html

Spencer-Thomas, S. (2011). Suicide and spirituality: The role of faith in the aftermath of suicide. Paper presented at the 26th International Association of Suicide Prevention World Congress, Beijing, China. *Chinese Mental Health Journal, 25*(9 Suppl), S80–S81.

Stroebe, M.S. (2004). Commentary: Religion in coping with bereavement: Confidence of convictions or scientific scrutiny? *International Journal for the Psychology of Religion, 14*(1), 23–36. http://doi.org/10.1207/s15327582ijpr1401_2

Suicide Prevention Resource Center. (n.d.). *Suicide intervention and postvention training for faith leaders.* Retrieved from http://www.sprc.org/library_resources/items/suicide-intervention-and-postvention-training-faith-leaders

Suicide Prevention Resource Center. (2004). *After a suicide: Recommendations for religious services and other public memorial observances.* Retrieved from http://www.sprc.org/sites/sprc.org/files/library/aftersuicide.pdf

Vandecreek, L., & Mottram, K. (2009). The religious life during suicide bereavement: A description. *Death Studies, 33*(8), 741–761. http://doi.org/10.1080/07481180903070467

Vandecreek, L., & Mottram, K. (2011). The perceived roles of god during suicide bereavement. *Journal of Psychology and Theology, 39*(2), 155–162.

Wilkens, N. T. (2003). Christian-based counseling for the suicide survivor: A guide for pastoral therapy. *Journal of Pastoral Care & Counseling, 57*(4), 387–394.

Williams, A. L., & Merten, M. J. (2009). Adolescents' online social networking following the death of a peer. *Journal of Adolescent Research, 24*(1), 67–90. http://doi.org/10.1177/0743558408328440

Wortmann, J. H., & Park, C. L. (2008). Religion and spirituality in adjustment following bereavement: An integrative review. *Death Studies, 32*(8), 703–736. http://doi.org/10.1080/07481180802289507

Wortmann, J. H., & Park, C. L. (2009). Religion/spirituality and change in meaning after bereavement: Qualitative evidence for the meaning making model. *Journal of Loss and Trauma, 14*(1), 17–34. http://doi.org/10.1080/15325020802173876

Young-Eisendrath, P. (1997). *The resilient spirit: Transforming suffering into insight and renewal.* Reading, MA: Addison-Wesley.

Zinnbauer, B. J., & Pargament, K. I. (2005). Religiousness and spirituality. In R. F. Paloutzian & C. L. Park (Eds.), *Handbook of psychology of religion and spirituality* (pp. 21–42). New York, NY: Guilford Press.

Chapter 17

Online Suicide Bereavement and Support

Karolina Krysinska and Karl Andriessen

School of Psychiatry, University of New South Wales, Sydney, Australia

Abstract: Since the mid 1990s, due to its increasing availability and ease of use, the Internet has become an important source of (mental) health information and support. Also the bereaved, including those bereaved by suicide – that is, suicide survivors – turn to online resources such as informational websites, social media, forums, chats, and online memorials, to cope with their loss. This chapter provides an overview of online resources available to the bereaved after suicide, and the advantages and challenges of seeking information and support on the Internet. The online resources most frequently used by the bereaved (and most frequently studied by researchers), such as peer support groups, online memorials, and social media, are presented in more detail, along with evidence regarding their impact on the grief process. Finally, the issue of quality and trustworthiness of online information for the bereaved is discussed and recommendations for development of user-friendly and professional websites are provided.

Introduction

Stroebe, van der Houven, and Schut (2008) have observed that the Internet has an enormous potential to become a valuable resource for the bereaved by providing bereavement-related support, such as opportunities for sharing information and networking, bereavement-related activities, such as memorialization (e.g., online cemeteries), and professional psychological interventions. There are many reasons individuals, including the bereaved after suicide, use the Internet. Online bereavement-related activities allow both seeking and maintaining contact with other bereaved, and continuing bonds and connection with the deceased (Bell, Bailey, & Kennedy, 2015; Falconer, Sachsenweger, Gibson, & Norman, 2011; Sofka, NoppeCupit, & Gilbert, 2012). Finding others in the digital space who have gone through a similar experience of loss provides a unique chance to share one's story in a safe and empathic environment. Given the taboo nature of loss by suicide and the social stigma surrounding suicide, online information and help might be particularly attractive to survivors who are often bereft of other support (Berger, Wagner, & Baker, 2005). Online networking and support might be of special appeal to adolescents and young adults (Pennington, 2013), and people with physical handicaps, such as mobility or hearing problems. Online contact, due to the reduced communication channels, might be the medium of choice for those who prefer to write rather than to talk, and those who are afraid or ashamed to show emotions or to cry during a face-to-face contact. Online networking, information, and support are available over geographical and national borders, and may be the only resource for those who live in remote areas where face-to-face help is nonexistent, and for those who are geographically isolated from other mourners (Bocklandt, 2011; Walter, 2015a).

Generally, online resources are continuously available, anonymous, and without the mediation of the third parties, such as referral from a general practitioner or guidance from a mental health professional (Bocklandt, 2011). These factors can significantly reduce the resistance to seek help among individuals who, due to privacy and anonymity concerns, avoid regular mental health services. Participants of online peer support groups, chats, social networks, and online crisis intervention or therapy often have more control over the process and content of the helping intervention than those who use face-to-face facilities. They can more easily decide when to initiate and to break contact, and which content should be shared with others. Nonetheless, due to potentially lower involvement and the ease of ending contact without warning, the dropout rate in an online treatment or peer contact is often higher than in a face-to-face interaction (Bell et al., 2015; Karyotaki et al., 2015).

Categories of Online Resources

A wide range of online mental health resources, including resources for the bereaved, are available for those seeking information and support. Although a detailed discussion of the prerequisites, advantages, and disadvantages of different types of online resources and services is beyond the scope of this chapter, in general, online material can be divided into three broad categories: passive, active, and interactive (Schalken et al., 2013). Passive online resources include websites containing information, tips and advice, links, frequently asked questions, testimonials, and news/media reports. For example, information for the bereaved by suicide is provided online by Befrienders Worldwide (http://www.befrienders.org/bereaved-by-suicide), the American Association of Suicidology (http://www.suicidology.org/suicide-survivors/suicide-loss-survivors), and Healthtalkonline in the United Kingdom (http://www.healthtalk.org/peoples-experiences/dying-bereavement/bereavement-due-suicide/topics) (see also Part IV of this volume). The use of passive resources requires minimum effort; nonetheless, the bereaved have to be able to find the website, evaluate its usefulness, and effectively use the available information (i.e., it requires digital literacy).

Active resources, such as online self-tests, multiple choice tests, and other insight instruments allow the users to better understand the seriousness of their problem and/or the type of help most suited to their needs. For example, PsychCentral, an independent online mental health social network, allows its users to take a self-test measuring complicated grief (http://psychcentral.com/quizzes/grief-quiz.htm). Some active websites allow visitors to upload personal testimonials which can be shared with other users of the site (http://www.save.org). This type of resource requires the user's involvement and readiness to share personal information, such as answering a series of personal questions regarding the nature of loss and emotional, cognitive, and behavioral reactions, which may lead to resistance and anonymity or confidentiality concerns (Schalken et al., 2013).

Interactive resources include online psychological treatments for complicated grief (e.g., Eisma et al., 2015), psychoeducational programs for the bereaved (e.g., Dominick et al., 2009–2010), online forums for suicide survivors (Schotanus-Dijkstra et al., 2014), e-mail help and step-by-step programs, and one-on-one or group chats (Hollander, 2001). The use of interactive resources might require a serious investment of time and energy, sharing personal details, and in case of online therapy and other professional treatments, giving up anonymity (Schalken et al., 2013). Also, social media, online memorials, and interactive blogs can be used by the bereaved coping with their loss (Robinson, Rodrigues, Fisher, & Herrman, 2014; Sofka, Noppe-Cupit, & Gilbert, 2012).

Online Resources Available to Suicide Survivors

Anecdotal and clinical observations, supported by accumulating research evidence, show that the bereaved use the Internet to share their grief, to connect with others, and to maintain their relationship with the deceased. The increasing popularity of the Internet among the bereaved has been described by a bereaved blog writer in the following words: "Maniacal googling is a new stage of grief. After denial and before resignation comes the google stage" (Laura at 11D, 2005; quoted in: Sofka, NoppeCupit, & Gilbert, 2012, p. 52).

More than a decade ago, Vanderwerker and Prigerson (2004) found that approximately half of the bereaved in the United States used the Internet and/or e-mail, and that such online resources seemed to improve their quality of life and could protect against mental problems secondary to bereavement. More recent data show that more than half of the bereaved in North America are currently using online mutual bereavement support, such as e-mail lists, Internet forums, and/or chat rooms (often in combination), while one in five bereaved have used such support in the past (van der Houwen, Stroebe, Schut, Stroebe, & van den Bout, 2010b). A Canadian study showed that 65 % of the bereaved used their computer and the Internet to commemorate, to remember, or to reminiscence about the deceased, for example by digitizing and/or sharing photos, writing about the deceased in e-mails to relatives, or eulogizing the deceased on a memorial website or on Facebook (Massimi & Baecker, 2010). A study conducted in the United Kingdom addressed specifically the use of the Internet by the bereaved by suicide (Chapple & Ziebland, 2011). It showed that suicide survivors use the Internet to find practical information, to inform friends and family about the death, to get online peer support from other bereaved, and to memorialize the deceased through an online memorial.

Despite the abundance and popularity of bereavement-related online material, not much is known about resources available specifically for suicide survivors. To fill in this gap, Krysinska and Andriessen (2010) conducted an Internet search study using several popular search engines to see what type of resources people bereaved by suicide are likely to find online and to describe the quality of such resources. The searches retrieved diverse materials, including personal websites created by suicide survivors themselves and sites developed by bereavement support groups, crisis intervention and mental health services, suicide prevention organizations and helplines, as well as academic and research institutions and educational organizations. Only a relatively modest number of the retrieved websites had been created by professional bereavement and suicide prevention organizations and services. Recupero, Harms, and Noble (2008) in a study on the suicide information available online made a similar observation: mental health organizations' websites were not frequently found through the searches, and the authors suggested implementation of search engine optimization strategies to increase the likelihood of retrieval of professional and trustworthy websites. It is also important to add that the searches did not retrieve any websites and resources which seemed to be offensive or potentially harmful to the bereaved.

Krysinska and Andriessen (2010) also found that there were differences with regard to the recency and amount of information presented, the way the websites were organized, and the search terms which enabled retrieval. Despite such differences, the majority of the sites contained information on suicide bereavement and suicide; referral information for people at risk of suicide and for people bereaved by suicide; resources such as suggested reading, leaflets, and material for sale; and links to other relevant websites. Almost half of the websites also provided opportunities for interactive communication. Of note, the majority of referral resources for the bereaved by suicide which were listed and recommended on the personal bereavement websites, were face-to-face suicide bereavement support groups. Very few websites provided information or encouragement for seeking help from mental health professionals and services or general practitioners. Andriessen, Krysinska, and De fauw (2012), repeated the search study (using the same methodology), to explore resources for the bereaved by suicide available in the Dutch language. Interestingly, in Dutch, they found more websites created by professional bereavement and suicide prevention organizations than personal websites created by survivors (which were most frequently found in English), and the former frequently provided encouragement to seek both professional and peer help and support.

Online Support Groups

Seeking help and support in a group of individuals who share a similar experience of a medical illness, mental health problems, an addiction, trauma, or loss has become a popular manner of coping with the challenges of life and negative life events (Davidson, Bellamy, Guy, & Miller, 2012). Over the last 2 decades, the Internet has become a meeting place for people seeking peer support via mailing lists, newsgroups, discussion forums, and live chatrooms (Ali, Farrer, Gulliver, & Griffiths, 2015; Eysenbach, Powell, Englesakis, Rizo, & Stern, 2004). Also mobile applications, using devices such as smartphones, are being increasingly used to seek and provide peer support (McColl, Rideout, Parmar, & Abba-Aji, 2014). The bereaved, including suicide survivors, are no exception; face-to-face or online peer support has been a treatment of choice for many people not willing or not able to engage in a therapeutic relationship with a professional (Feigelman, Gorman, Beal, & Jordan, 2008; Schotanus-Dijkstra et al., 2014).

Online support forums for persons bereaved by suicide may attract individuals struggling with the mental health problems commonly identified among people bereaved by suicide, such as low well-being, high levels of depressive symptoms, and complicated grief (Kramer et al., 2015). It has been observed that online grief support groups are more popular among women, especially young women, than men, and their participants often also seek face-to-face professional or peer support (Chapple & Ziebland, 2011; Feigelman et al., 2008). Nonetheless, the potentially nonstop access to online support, the anonymity, feeling uncomfortable sharing grief with family and friends, and finding empathy, validation, and understanding in an online group are the most important reasons suicide survivors and other bereaved choose to participated in online groups (Chapple & Ziebland, 2011; Feigelman et al., 2008; Kramer et al., 2015).

A qualitative study by Swartwood, Veach, Kuhne, Lee, and Ji (2011) of the online forum messages exchanged by the bereaved provides an interesting insight into the content and dynamics of the online communication and peer support (unfortunately the study did not extract content specific to communication between suicide survivors and/or the bereaved by suicide with other bereaved). Four major themes, which together can be summarized as an *exchange of hope,* were found: sharing one's personal story, validating the grief experience, offering psychosocial support, and sharing information and resources. Sharing one's story often took place in response to a posted message and followed a certain informal standard. It usually started with an acknowledgement of the other person's loss (e.g., *"I am sorry to hear about your loss"*), followed by a description of one's own loss experience and emotional reactions(e.g., *"My child died as well. Here is my story...."*), and ended with advice or comforting words (e.g., *"Please continue to write about your story. It helps. I will be thinking about you"*). Validation of the grief experience included normalization of the reactions of the other bereaved and permission to feel and behave in the way which felt natural to the person, without guilt, shame, or social stigma (e.g., *"What you describe is normal. Give it time. Just take the time your need for yourself right now"*).

The forum members also offered each other psychosocial support by attending to the emotional difficulties of the others and creating an atmosphere of acceptance and understanding

(Swartwood et al., 2011). Last but not least, the bereaved exchanged information about the process of grieving itself (e.g., expected duration, psychological reactions) and available resources, such as peer support groups, organizations, websites, books, music, or poetry. They also shared advice on how to cope with the loss, including encouragement of self-care activities (e.g., *"Come to this site when you want to cry"*) and religious consolation (e.g., *"You will be in my prayers"*). A qualitative study on what the bereaved by suicide communicate in online support groups run by professional bereavement and suicide prevention organizations in Belgium and in The Netherlands showed similar types of messages and exchanges (Schotanus-Dijkstra et al., 2014). The bereaved used the online forums to share personal experiences, such as emotional expressions of grief, to express support or empathy, to provide advice, and to normalize the grief experience; however, they shared less about their experiences of using health care services.

Online Memorials

Online memorials are web pages or websites dedicated to honoring the dead and are usually used as a supplement to traditional bereavement rituals (Roberts, 2004). They are often created by family members (parents, children) or friends of the deceased, although there are also websites created by funeral homes and other commercial organizations. Online memorials include freestanding web pages dedicated to the deceased (see, e.g., the list of memorials at http://childsuicide.homestead.com/MemorialSites.html), web rings in which individual web pages sharing a common theme such as cause of death or relationship with the deceased are linked together (see, e.g., the web ring of suicide memorial sites at http://hub.webring.org/hub/suicidehurts), web cemeteries (e.g., http://cemetery.org), and formalized online memorial sites (e.g., the Suicide Memorial Wall at http://www.suicidememorialwall.com).

Online memorials are usually created and maintained along with a physical grave, although sometimes due to geographical distance or the nature of the loss, especially in case of a socially unacceptable or unrecognized relationship with the deceased (i.e., disenfranchised grief), they may replace a traditional grave. The type, content, and format of online memorials range from personal letters to the deceased, to formal eulogies, obituaries, or tributes (De Vries & Rutherford, 2004; Roberts & Vidal, 2000). While some online memorial sites or web cemeteries have an uniform format – for example, only the name and birth and death dates are presented (e.g., the Suicide Memorial Wall at http://www.suicidememorialwall.com) – others allow a more individualized approach, and the bereaved can upload photos, videos, flowers, poems, music, or digital candles.

On the one hand, online memorials allow continuing bonds with the deceased, and they can be established many years after the death (De Vries & Rutherford, 2004; Roberts, 2004; Roberts & Vidal, 2000). For example, one study showed that 7% of online memorials were created more than 20 years after the loss (Roberts & Vidal, 2000). Online memorials are often visited regularly and tended with love and care just like traditional burial sites (Roberts, 2004). For some bereaved, online memorialization may be a way to communicate with the deceased via online messages or letters describing recent life events or changes, such as birth of a child or moving home.

On the other hand, online memorialization allows sharing the grief experience with the living (De Vries & Rutherford, 2004; Roberts, 2004; Roberts & Vidal, 2000). The bereaved can share their memories of the deceased, receive or show signs of compassion through signing online guest books, leaving digital flowers, or burning digital candles. Online memorials can be created, maintained, or visited with others, and letting others know about the memorial can be an opportunity to talk about the death with those who knew the deceased as well as with strangers.

Two studies examined specifically the content of online memorials dedicated to people who had died by suicide (Krysinska & Andriessen, 2015; Lester, 2012). In his comparison of the linguistics of suicide memorials and memorials dedicated to those who had died of natural causes, Lester (2012) reported that suicide memorials contained more death-related words, more words reflective of anger and sadness, and fewer references to the self or to the deceased than other types of memorials. Krysinska and Andriessen (2015), found that majority of the memorials' authors were parents, siblings, and children. Other memorials were posted by (ex) partners, members of a stepfamily, other family relations, friends, and acquaintances of the deceased. Approximately half of the suicide online memorials were written during the first 12 months after the suicide, although there were also memorials written 20 years after the loss. A content analysis of online messages revealed that the two most frequent themes were sadness and missing the deceased, and words of love addressed to the deceased. Other common themes (i.e., found in more than 30% of the memorials) included a description of the personality and favorite activities of the deceased, the desire to understand *why* the suicide had happened, and references to the family. (The theme of religion/spirituality in online memorials is presented in Chapter 16 of this volume.)

Social Networks

Given the popularity of social networking sites, especially Facebook, studies have looked at how such sites are used after the death, and at the impact of this type of digital legacy on the bereaved (e.g., Rossetto, Lannutti, & Strauman, 2015), including research specifically on suicide bereavement (Bailey et al., 2015; Bell et al., 2015) (Facebook has a set of procedures for creating a "memorial profile." More information about memorializing an account is available at the Facebook Help Center at http://www.facebook.com/help). There have also been studies exploring other social media, such as Instagram (Gibbs, Meese, Arnold, Nansen, & Carter, 2015), Twitter (Sanderson & Cheong, 2010), and YouTube (Gibson, 2015), in the context of death and bereavement; however, as yet no study has explored how these online media are used by the bereaved by suicide, and whether such use can support or hinder the suicide bereavement process.

Bell, Bailey, and Kennedy (2015) and Bailey et al. (2015) conducted interviews with the suicide bereaved who had set up memorial websites. All respondents except for one used Facebook as a means of online memorialization (either by keeping an account which belonged to the deceased or by creating new memorial pages), although some of the study participants also developed their own memorial websites. The Facebook pages served a number of functions: They were used to inform others about the death, and allowed the bereaved to say final farewells to a deceased who had left suddenly, and they became a means of communication between the person who maintained the Facebook page, and other friends and family members of the deceased person. Users were seeking and providing mutual support, shared information, and communicated their feelings of grief. Some also used the Facebook page to raise awareness – for instance, by including links to suicide prevention organizations, charities, and events. The most common motivation for online memorialization was "keeping the deceased alive" (Bailey et al., 2015, p. 78). Facebook page helped the bereaved to maintain a relationship with the person who had died; it afforded a continuing social presence for the deceased, and allowed the bereaved to feel connected to the deceased. Nevertheless, there were also negative aspects of the online involvement. The study participants were wary of ungenuine expressions of grief and were concerned about the risk of copycat suicides. Some of the suicide bereaved felt angry or hurt when the activity on the memorial Facebook page was diminishing, and for some others, the social online interaction did not help to alleviate the feeling of physical social isolation (Bailey et al., 2015; Bell et al., 2015).

Helpfulness of Online Interventions in Coping With Loss and Bereavement

The bereaved who use online forums, chats, and e-mail lists are mostly young adult women, less likely to be a part of a religious community, and the online resources are used quite frequently: The bereaved spend on average approximately 7–8 hr online (Feigelman et al., 2008; van der Houwen et al., 2010b). Yet, despite an abundance of clinical and anecdotal evidence regarding the popularity of Internet use among the bereaved and the diversity of bereavement-related online activities and resources, there is not much evidence regarding their impact on the grief process and well-being of those who use them. Only a few methodologically sound studies, including controlled randomized trials, have been conducted, and these do show effectiveness of online interventions. These include Internet-based exposure and behavioral activation for complicated grief and rumination (e.g., Eisma et al., 2015) and a brief Internet-based self-help intervention for the bereaved (van der Houwen, Schut, van den Bout, Stroebe, & Stroebe, 2010a). A study of the mental health of visitors of online support forums for the suicide bereaved showed small- to medium-sized positive changes in well-being and depressive complaints (but no changes in levels of complicated grief and suicide risk) over a period of 12 months (Kramer et al., 2015). Still, because of the pre–post design of the study, it was not possible to determine whether there was a causal relationship between visiting the online forum and the observed changes in mental health.

In general, studies show high levels of satisfaction among members of online support groups, mailing lists, and social networking sites, and individuals involved in online memorials. Still, such (mostly qualitative) studies suffer from the problems plaguing research on Internet users, such as positive self-selection of participants (i.e., only people who are satisfied continue to use the websites and participate in research), lack of a comparison group, instability and changing membership of online groups, privacy issues, and lack of follow-up (Eysenbach et al., 2004; Stroebe et al., 2008).

The bereavement literature suggests that involvement in online bereavement-related activities may be a valued addition to traditional bereavement activities as it creates connections with others who have suffered a loss and has a potential for enhancing a relationship with the deceased (Roberts, 2004). The bereaved value the continuous availability, including weekends, holidays, and anniversaries, of online forums and other sites (Swartwood et al., 2011). The online anonymity, often paired with an experience of social stigma and lack of direct social support, attract those who are trying to cope with disenfranchised grief or bereavement after suicide. For some people, expressing their feelings and thoughts writing online can be of therapeutic value (Lattanzi & Hale, 1984–1985; Roberts & Vidal, 2000). The bereaved use the Internet to find practical information, both on informative sites and through other bereaved, and to find support and understanding. Participants of online forums and in social networking sites, as well as those involved in online memorials, evaluate positively their experience and report a sense of online community (Roberts, 2004).

Nonetheless, both professionals and the bereaved have raised concerns about the possible dangers of seeking information and support via the Internet (Chapple & Ziebland, 2011; Swartwood et al., 2011). Suicide survivors using the Internet, for instance, indicate that finding prosuicide sites can be very distressing, and like other bereaved, they warn against treating the online activities as a substitute for (instead of a supplement to) face-to-face contacts.

Anonymous online spaces may encourage disinhibition and result in trolling, stigmatizing, and shaming the bereaved, including suicide survivors (Leonard & Toller, 2012; Walter, 2015b). Participation in a web forum or mailing list can become too time-consuming or too depressing, and there is a risk of finding or offering unhelpful advice and/or misleading information. The impermanence of the Internet material, including online memorials, and changing membership in online groups, and the (frequently) declining numbers of visitors to memorialized Facebook profiles, can be a source of additional stress or loss, including an experience of a "second death" of the deceased person (Falconer et al., 2011). Concerns have also been raised about the reluctance to let go and the ruminative ways of grieving among some of the users and creators of such websites, which may indicate poor adjustment (Stroebe et al., 2008). Last, but not least, dealing with the online legacy of the deceased, such as material left on a social networking site, might be experienced as facing an "online ghost" and may result in additional emotional and cognitive distress (Massimi & Baecker, 2010).

Helpfulness of Social Media

With regard to the helpful and unhelpful aspects of social media involvement during the grief process, Rossetto et al. (2015) conducted a series of interviews with Facebook users who had recently lost someone, to explore their experiences with Facebook communication. The study found three grief-related functions of Facebook communication: news dissemination, preservation, and community; each with its own advantages and disadvantages. Although news dissemination allowed sharing and learning about a death, it could be related to misinformation, including false rumors about someone's death, and depersonalization. The last was reported for instance, when the bereaved person heard about the death from an online source before being informed in person or when the respondent felt that sharing the news on Facebook diminished the seriousness of a person's death.

The function of preservation reported by Rossetto et al. (2015) referred to protecting memories of the person who has died and their continued presence in the lives of the bereaved and on social media. Preservation included positive aspects, such as memorialization and ongoing connection to the deceased; however, it was also related to the existent/nonexistent conundrum – that is, "confusion between the deceased person's death and the deceased person's continued presence" (Rossetto et al., 2015, p. 983). In some cases this conundrum was strengthened by Facebook automatic pop-ups, such as unexpected status updates about the deceased or notifications of messages posted on their wall, which were experienced as intrusive and interfering with grieving.

The third theme related to the Facebook users' connection to and communication with other bereaved people online. The helpful aspects of social network community included facilitation of interpersonal connection, having a space for sharing support, and having witnesses to one's own grief and/or being a witness to someone else's grief. Again, the downside of participating in the community included an encounter with "bandwagon mourners" (or "emotional rubberneckers"; DeGroot, 2014), that is, online voyeurs reading messages and posting on Facebook pages of deceased strangers or distant acquaintances. Some study participants also shared their uncertainty regarding challenges to privacy, such as privacy boundaries and protection of private information about the deceased whom they had known.

Ensuring Quality of Online Information and Support for the Bereaved

A discussion of mental health resources available on the Internet, including bereavement-related material, inevitably leads to questions regarding the quality of online information (Reavley & Jorm, 2011). Information provided on the Internet by professional organizations and services is guaranteed to involve a high level of accuracy and recency of information, but such websites do not come up frequently in searches (Krysinska & Andriessen, 2010; Recupero et al., 2008). A number of initiatives have been implemented internationally to reduce the risk of misinformation when looking for (mental) health information online, such as the Health On the Net Foundation (HON) Code (http://www.hon.ch). The HON Code certificate is awarded to medical and health websites which meet eight criteria. These criteria relate to providing information about authors' qualifications (authority), their valid contact details (transparency), and details of funding received (financial disclosure). The HON Code also requires presentation of justified, balanced, and objective claims (justifiability), citation of sources and dates (attribution), and any advertising being clearly distinguished from editorial content. It is expected that quality medical and health websites are sources of information which support, not replace, contact with a health professional (complementarity), and the websites respect the privacy of site users (confidentiality).

There is also a chart of best practices for online technologies applicable to websites, blogs, Twitter, Facebook, and YouTube, where there is a high probability of encountering online visitors at risk of suicide (http://preventtheattempt.com). This chart offers three levels of response to suicidal ideation or intent: basic (e.g., policies on responding to suicidal content and referral resources), midlevel (e.g., guidelines and automatic preprogrammed system responses to reports of suicidal content), and advanced (e.g., ensuring timely response, outreach, and cultural competency). There are reports on development and qualitative evaluation of websites for the bereaved, including adolescent suicide survivors and their support networks in South Africa (Hoffmann, 2006) and the Internet-based psychoeducational tool Making Sense of Grief for the recently bereaved in the United States (Dominick et al., 2009–2010). Also, quality criteria for health information have been recommended in the bereavement literature (Sofka et al., 2012), and initiatives such as CareSearch (http://www.caresearch.com.au) aim to provide relevant and trustworthy information and resources on bereavement care (Tierman & Hayman, 2016). Still, to date there are no standard quality criteria for suicide bereavement websites, and the quality of available information differs (Andriessen et al., 2012; Krysinska & Andriessen, 2010).

One study which provided information about how to develop a quality and user-friendly bereavement website (http://grieflink.org.au) in collaboration with the bereaved was conducted in Australia (Clark et al., 2004). The authors stressed the need to take into consideration the psychological needs of people who have experienced a recent loss. The grief process often impacts cognitive and emotional functioning, including concentration, memory, and problem solving. In the words of one of the bereaved: "[You] need to make it [the website] very easy for bereaved people – its [sic]very difficult to think clearly and overcome obstacles" (Clark et al., 2004, p. 963). The bereaved can experience high levels of psychological distress and lowered self-esteem. Consequently, emotional support, such as a welcoming paragraph (e.g., "Welcome to GriefLink. We care about you"), should be provided on the home page, and the use of friendly and warm (not only informational) language is recommended. The information provided should be recent and accurate, and at the same time, easy to read, devoid of professional jargon, and presented in small blocks of text, preferably with dot points. While mental health professionals and long-term bereaved value large amounts of information, the more recently bereaved prefer less information as "this is not a time when you can take much information in" (Clark et al., 2004, p. 966). Offering balanced – that is, sufficient but not overwhelming – amounts of information can be achieved by using links offering access to additional resources. **Table 17.1** offers an overview of the recommendations provided by Clark and her colleagues (2004).

Table 17.1. Recommended design for grief-related websites

Technical Aspects	Design, Colors, and Reading Facility	Legal and Ethical Issues	Provision of Emotional Support	Resources, Support Organizations, and Other Information
A home page with search facility	Minimalistic, simple design; no gimmicks, such as flowers or hearts	Provision of information, not advice	Welcoming paragraph[a]	Resources classified,[a] categorized under topic,[a] listed alphabetically by title rather than author[a]
"How to Use This Site" page	Unobtrusive colors compatible with hope, and conveying calm	Provision of quality information, including organizations and resources	Friendly language	A brief description of each book[a] and guidelines for ordering books/DVDs[a]
Side bar containing all functions	Consideration for color blindness	A disclaimer and provision for professional indemnity and intellectual property	Direction to professional assistance	Support organizations listed by topic rather than geographically[a]
Contents and navigation instructions available at the top of each page	Catering for a wide range of users' literacy levels	Liability of a chat site	Chat site or links to chat sites or post-it board	Non-death-related loss information included[a]
No vertical columns with headings	Text in small blocks of print, dot points	Adherence to professional advertising conventions	Vignettes and quotes from real life stories[a]	
	Large, bold type fonts			

Note. Adapted from Clark et al., 2004; reproduced from Krysinska & Andriessen, 2013, with permission of Palgrave Macmillan.
[a]Recommendations provided by the bereaved.

Implications for Practice

Falconer and her colleagues (2011) have observed that "utilizing a combined online-offline approach facilitates the grief process and provides individuals with a broader and more effective set of options" (p. 85), and the clinical literature increasingly includes recommendations to use online tools. For example, creating an online memorial has become a technique of grief therapy, which may be appropriate for adolescents and adults who feel comfortable sharing and expressing their emotions via social media and other online technologies (Stoll, 2016). Other online tools, such as blogs, funeral home online guest books, and online support groups, may also positively contribute to the grieving process. Falconer et al. (2011) used Worden's model of the four tasks of mourning: accepting the reality of loss, working through the pain, readjusting to the environment, and reinvesting in life and forming a continuing bond with the deceased (Worden, 2008), to show how online developments create tools for grief management in clinical practice. **Table 17.2** presents the traditional customs and activities related to the tasks of grieving, and advantages and disadvantages of online tools in the process of grieving.

Table 17.2. Tasks of mourning, traditional customs, and advantages and disadvantages of grieving online

Task of Mourning	Traditional Customs	Advantages of Grieving Online	Disadvantages of Grieving Online
Accepting the reality of loss	Wake, death notices, dealing with remains	Faster communication, i.e., sharing information about the death more quickly and broadly, also online streaming of funeral services	Frozen in time, e.g., the online persona on social media, including photographs, is still present and accessible
Working through the pain	Funerals, support groups	Normalize experience, e.g., in an online support group; and share emotions more freely, e.g., 24/7 availability of online resources and communities	–
Readjusting to the environment	Pastoral care, eulogy and/or obituary	Broader and more durable community to provide connection and social support in spite of geographical distance	Pain in online abandonment, e.g., the memorial site is no longer visited (deterioration of the online persona of the deceased, "second death")
Reinvesting in life and forming a continuing bond	Foundations, mementos, anniversaries	Rich and vibrant place to remember; safe and accessible Starting something positive in a loved one's memory, e.g., an online prevention or awareness initiative	Risk of family members disabling sites, e.g., removal of a deceased's Facebook account or a policy of a time-limited free trial or annual renewal of an online memorial

Note. Based on Falconer et al., 2011.

Falconer et al. (2011) recommend that clinicians be knowledgeable about online technologies and grief support options available to the bereaved. The clinicians should strive to better understand the development of an online persona of the bereaved and the deceased, their double (i.e., offline and online) continuing bond, and the dynamics of the bereaved client's online social interactions. It may also be helpful to integrate Internet-related factors into case conceptualizations by gaining a better understanding of the client's motivation and expectations regarding grief-related online activities.

Conclusions

Many suicide survivors and other bereaved use the Internet to seek information, to freely express their pain, to find others who have experienced a similar loss, and to memorialize and to connect to the deceased. Although more and more studies are looking into the frequency of Internet use in this group and its impact on the grief process, there remain many unanswered questions. The suicide bereavement literature suggests that involvement in personal websites, such as web memorials and memorialized Facebook accounts, may be a valued addition to traditional bereavement activities, as it may create connections with others who have suffered a loss and it has a potential for enhancing a relationship with the deceased. Still, more scientific evidence is needed to determine if creating or consulting suicide bereavement websites is a helpful addition to traditional bereavement activities, or if it hinders the grieving process through rumination and reluctance to let go. The needs of individual survivors differ depending on their age, gender, culture, kinship relationship with the deceased, and where they are in the grieving process. Can everyone find online information and support suited to their individual needs?

There is an issue of digital remains – that is, online content on dead users, and inheritance of personal digital devices used by the deceased (Lingel, 2013; Massimi & Baecker, 2010) – which may create additional, as yet unknown and unexplored, challenges for suicide survivors. The Internet constantly evolves, and new online tools and media are being appropriated by the bereaved, including social media, such as Twitter, YouTube, and Instagram. Clinicians and researchers should remain alert, and be willing and able to explore and utilize these tools to provide high-quality effective treatment and support to the bereaved by suicide. Stroebe et al. (2008) observed that some Internet enthusiasts question the need to evaluate the efficacy of online support for the bereaved as long as the resources are provided for free, people use them voluntarily, and there is assurance that online information does not have adverse effects and is not misleading. However, they caution against accepting these assumptions without proper investigation. Indeed, development of quality standards and further research seem to be necessary steps in providing online support for survivors after suicide.

Acknowledgments

This chapter is a revised and updated version of Krysinska & Andriessen (2013).

Corresponding author

Karolina Krysinska
School of Psychiatry
University of New South Wales
Hospital Road
Randwick 2031 NSW
Australia
k.krysinska@unsw.edu.au

References

Ali, K., Farrer, L., Gulliver, A., & Griffiths, K. M. (2015). Online peer-to-peer support for young people with mental health problems: A systematic review. *JMIR Mental Health, 2*(2), e19. http://doi.org/10.2196/mental.4418

Andriessen, K., Krysinska, K., & De fauw, N. (2012). Wat kunnen nabestaanden na zelfdoding vinden op het internet? Een onderzoek naar het aanbod en de kwaliteit. [What survivors after suicide can find on the Internet: An investigation of the offers and their quality]. *Tijdschrift Klinische Psychologie, 42*(3), 184–193.

Bailey, L., Bell, J., & Kennedy, D. (2015). Continuing social presence of the dead: Exploring suicide bereavement through online memorialisation. *New Review of Hypermedia and Multimedia, 21*(1–2), 72–86. http://doi.org/10.1080/13614568.2014.983554

Bell, J., Bailey, L., & Kennedy, D. (2015). 'We do it to keep him alive': Bereaved individuals' experiences of online suicide memorials and continuing bonds. *Mortality, 20*(4), 375–389. http://doi.org/10.1080/13576275.2015.1083693

Berger, M., Wagner, T. H., & Baker, L. C. (2005). Internet use and stigmatised illness. *Social Science & Medicine, 61*(8), 1821–1827. http://doi.org/10.1016/j.socscimed.2005.03.025

Bocklandt, P. (Ed.). (2011). *Niet alle smileys lachen. Onlinehulp in eerstelijnswelzijnswerk* [Not all smileys are laughing: Online help in frontline well-being services]. Leuven/Den Haag, The Netherlands: Acco.

Chapple, A., & Ziebland, S. (2011). How the Internet is changing the experience of bereavement by suicide: A qualitative study in the UK. *Health, 15*(2), 173–187.

Clark, S., Burgess, T., Laven, G., Bull, M., Marker, J., & Browne, E. (2004). Developing and evaluating the Grieflink web site: Processes, protocols, dilemmas and lessons learned. *Death Studies, 28*(10), 955–970. http://doi.org/10.1080/07481180490512082

Davidson, L., Bellamy, C., Guy, K., & Miller, R. (2012). Peer support among persons with severe mental illnesses: A review of evidence and experience. *World Psychiatry, 11*(2), 123–128. http://doi.org/10.1016/j.wpsyc.2012.05.009

DeGroot, J. M. (2014). "For whom the bell tolls": Emotional rubbernecking in Facebook memorial groups. *Death Studies, 38*(2), 79–84. http://doi.org/10.1080/07481187.2012.725450

De Vries, B., & Rutherford, J. (2004). Memorializing loved ones on the World Wide Web. *Omega: Journal of Death and Dying, 49*(1), 5–26. http://doi.org/10.2190/DR46-RU57-UY6P-NEWM

Dominick, S. A., Irvine, A. B., Beauchamp, N., Seeley, J. R., Nolen-Hoeksema, S., Doka, K. J., & Bonanno, G. A. (2009–2010). An Internet tool to normalize grief. *Omega: Journal of Death and Dying, 60*(1), 71–87.

Eisma, M. C., Boelen, P. A., van den Bout, J., Stroebe, W., Schut, H. A., Lancee, J., & Stroebe, M. S. (2015). Internet-based exposure and behavioral activation for complicated grief and rumination: A randomized controlled trial. *Behavior Therapy, 46*(6), 729–748. http://doi.org/10.1016/j.beth.2015.05.007

Eysenbach, G., Powell, J., Englesakis, M., Rizo, C., & Stern, A. (2004). Health related virtual communities and electronic support groups: Systematic review of the effects of online peer to peer interactions. *British Medical Journal, 328*(7449), 1166–1170. http://doi.org/10.1136/bmj.328.7449.1166

Falconer, K., Sachsenweger, M., Gibson, K., & Norman, H. (2011). Grieving in the Internet age. *New Zealand Journal of Psychology, 40*(3), 79–88.

Feigelman, W., Gorman, B. S., Beal, K. C., & Jordan, J. R. (2008). Internet support groups for suicide survivors: A new mode for gaining bereavement assistance. *Omega: Journal of Death and Dying, 57*(3), 217–243. http://doi.org/10.2190/OM.57.3.a

Gibbs, M., Meese, J., Arnold, M., Nansen, B., & Carter, M. (2015). # Funeral and Instagram: death, social media, and platform vernacular. *Information, Communication & Society, 18*(3), 255–268. http://doi.org/10.1080/1369118X.2014.987152

Gibson, M. (2015). YouTube and bereavement vlogging: Emotional exchange between strangers. *Journal of Sociology.* Advance online publication.

Hoffmann, W. A. (2006). Telematic technologies in mental health caring: A web-based psychoeducational program for adolescent suicide survivors. *Issues in Mental Health Nursing, 27*(5), 461–474. http://doi.org/10.1080/01612840600599978

Hollander, E. M. (2001). Cyber community in the valley of the shadow of death. *Journal of Loss and Trauma, 6*(2), 135–146. http://doi.org/10.1080/108114401753198007

Karyotaki, E., Kleiboer, A., Smit, F., Turner, D. T., Pastor, A. M., Andersson, G., ... Christensen, H. (2015). Predictors of treatment dropout in self-guided web-based interventions for depression: An 'individual patient data' meta-analysis. *Psychological Medicine, 45*(13), 2717–2726. http://doi.org/10.1017/S0033291715000665

Kramer, J., Boon, B., Schotanus-Dijkstra, M., van Ballegooijen, W., Kerkhof, A., & van der Poel, A. (2015). The mental health of visitors of web-based support forums for bereaved by suicide. *Crisis, 36*(1), 38–45. http://doi.org/10.1027/0227-5910/a000281

Krysinska, K., & Andriessen, K. (2010). On-line support and resources for people bereaved through suicide: What is available? *Suicide and Life-Threatening Behavior, 40*(6), 640–650. http://doi.org/10.1521/suli.2010.40.6.640

Krysinska, K., & Andriessen, K. (2013). Suicide bereavement online: Sharing memories, seeking support, and exchanging hope. In B. Mishara & A. Kerkhof (Eds.), *Suicide prevention and new technologies* (pp. 150–165). New York, NY: Palgrave Macmillan.

Krysinska, K., & Andriessen, K. (2015). Online memorialization and grief after suicide: An analysis of suicide memorials on the Internet. *Omega: Journal of Death and Dying, 71*(1), 19–47. http://doi.org/10.1177/0030222814568276

Lattanzi, M., & Hale, M. E. (1984–1985). Giving grief words: Writing during bereavement. *Omega: Journal of Death and Dying, 15*(1), 45–52.

Leonard, L. G., & Toller, P. (2012). Speaking ill of the dead: Anonymity and communication about suicide on MyDeathSpace.com. *Communication Studies, 63*(4), 387–404.

Lester, D. (2012). Bereavement after suicide: A study of memorials on the Internet. *Omega: Journal of Death and Dying, 65*(3), 189–194.

Lingel, J. (2013). The digital remains: Social media and practices of online grief. *The Information Society, 29*(3), 190–195.

Massimi, M., & Baecker, R. M. (2010, April). A death in the family: opportunities for designing technologies for the bereaved. In *Proceedings of the SIGCHI Conference on Human Factors in Computing Systems* (pp. 1821–1830). ACM.

McColl, L. D., Rideout, P. E., Parmar, T. N., & Abba-Aji, A. (2014). Peer support intervention through mobile application: An integrative literature review and future directions. *Canadian Psychology/PsychologieCanadienne, 55*(4), 250.

Pennington, N. (2013). You don't de-friend the dead: An analysis of grief communication by college students through Facebook profiles. *Death Studies, 37*(7), 617–635.

Reavley, N. J., & Jorm, A. F. (2011). The quality of mental disorder information websites: A review. *Patient education and Counseling, 85*(2), e16–e25.

Recupero, P. R., Harms, S. E., & Noble, J. M. (2008). Googling suicide: Surfing for suicide information on the internet. *Journal of Clinical Psychiatry, 69*(6), 878–888.

Roberts, P. (2004). The living and the dead: Community in the virtual cemetery. *Omega: Journal of Death and Dying, 49*(1), 57–76.

Roberts, P., & Vidal, L. A. (2000). Perpetual care in cyberspace: A portrait of memorials on the Web. *Omega: Journal of Death and Dying, 40*(4), 47–70.

Robinson, J., Rodrigues, M., Fisher, S., & Herrman, H. (2014). *Suicide and social media study: Report of the stakeholder consultation*. Melbourne, Australia: Orygen Youth Health Research Centre, Community Works.

Rossetto, K. R., Lannutti, P. J., & Strauman, E. C. (2015). Death on Facebook: Examining the roles of social media communication for the bereaved. *Journal of Social and Personal Relationships, 32*(7), 974–994.

Sanderson, J., & Cheong, P. H. (2010). Tweeting prayers and communicating grief over Michael Jackson online. *Bulletin of Science, Technology & Society, 30*(5), 328–340.

Schalken, F., & Stichting E-hulp.nl. (2013). *Handboek online hulpverlening. Hoe onpersoonlijk contact heel persoonlijk wordt* [Handbook of online help: How impersonal contact becomes very personal] (2nd ed.). Houten, The Netherlands: Bohn Stafleu van Loghum.

Schotanus-Dijkstra, M., Havinga, P., van Ballegooijen, W., Delfosse, L., Mokkenstorm, J., & Boon, B. (2014). What do the bereaved by suicide communicate in online support groups? *Crisis, 35*(1), 27–35.

Sofka, C. J., NoppeCupit, I., & Gilbert, K. R. (Eds.). (2012). *Dying, death, and grief in an online universe. For counselors and educators*. New York, NY: Springer.

Stoll, E. J. (2016). Online memorials. In R. A. Neimeyer (Ed.), *Techniques of grief therapy* (pp. 244–247). New York, NY: Routledge.

Stroebe, M. S., van der Houven, K., & Schut, H. (2008). Bereavement support, intervention, and research on the Internet: A critical review. In M. S. Stroebe, R. O. Hanson, H. Schut, & W. Stroebe (Eds.), *Handbook of bereavement research and practice. Advances in theory and intervention* (pp. 551–554). Washington, DC: American Psychological Association.

Swartwood, R. M., Veach, P. M., Kuhne, J., Lee, H. K., & Ji, K. (2011). Surviving grief: An analysis of the exchange of hope in online communities. *Omega: Journal of Death and Dying, 63*(2), 161–181. http://doi.org/10.2190/OM.63.2.d

Tierman, J., & Hayman, S. (2016). Finding the evidence. Use of the CareSearch site in bereavement care. In R. A. Neimeyer (Ed.), *Techniques of grief therapy* (pp. 30–35). New York, NY: Routledge.

van der Houwen, K., Schut, H., van den Bout, J., Stroebe, M., & Stroebe, W. (2010a). The efficacy of a brief internet-based self-help intervention for the bereaved. *Behaviour Research and Therapy, 48*(5), 359–367. http://doi.org/10.1016/j.brat.2009.12.009

van der Houwen, K., Stroebe, M., Schut, H., Stroebe, W., van den Bout, J. (2010b). Online mutual support in bereavement: An empirical investigation. *Computers in Human Behavior, 26*(6), 1519–1525. http://doi.org/10.1016/j.chb.2010.05.019

Vanderwerker, L. C., & Prigerson, H. G. (2004). Social support and technological connectedness as protective factors in bereavement. *Journal of Loss and Trauma, 9*(1), 45–57. http://doi.org/10.1080/15325020490255304

Walter, T. (2015a). Communication media and the dead: From the Stone Age to Facebook. *Mortality, 20*(3), 215–232. http://doi.org/10.1080/13576275.2014.993598

Walter, T. (2015b). New mourners, old mourners: online memorial culture as a chapter in the history of mourning. *New Review of Hypermedia and Multimedia, 21*(1–2), 10–24. http://doi.org/10.1080/13614568.2014.983555

Worden, J. W. (2008). *Grief counseling and grief therapy* (4th ed.). New York, NY: Springer.

Chapter 18

A Vibrant Living Process

Art Making and the Storying of Suicide

Mic Eales[1] and Erminia Colucci[2]

[1]Littlecreek Studio, Mallanganee, NSW, Australia
[2]Centre for Psychiatry, Queen Mary University of London, UK

Abstract: Art making in whatever form is a vibrant living process. Art informs and communicates. The arts are integral to our sense of identity as individuals and communities. Art enriches our lives and helps increase our understanding of the world, including our identity and culture. It is a process through which the artist expresses thoughts, feelings, ideas, and emotions. Art as a vehicle for expression provides opportunities for increased public awareness and education and to encourage different types of dialogue to occur within environments that are generally nonthreatening. Bridging the two seemingly opposite worlds of suicidology and art, suicidologist Erminia Colucci and artist Mic Eales, an artist with personal experience of suicide, have forged new ground in expressing and representing the complex realities and emotional pain of the suicide phenomena. Their collaborations are an example of what is possible using an interdisciplinary approach to gaining insight and researching the issue of suicide. In creating artworks and films that re-present original voice narratives of suicide, these researchers have been exploring alternative approaches in the understanding and reaction to suicide. This chapter is based on the author's personal experiences and presents their engagement with art and art making in their practice of suicide research and prevention.

> *What is art? Art grows out of grief and joy, but mainly grief.*
> *It is born of people's lives.*
> Edvard Munch (quoted in Stang, 1979, p. 15)

Mic

Ghosts From the Past

Memories are funny things. They can appear or reappear from seemingly nowhere and for no obvious or apparent reason. One particular memory has haunted me for many years. It is so vivid, and remembered in minute detail the more that it appears. The incident occurred around the age of 5 or 6. In an outer suburb of Adelaide in an empty paddock next to our house the *neighborhood gang* decided that it would be great fun to ride their bikes as fast as they could up and over a timber ramp to see how far they could *fly*. Remember this was in the late 1950s. No BMX bikes around then. To raise the stakes, my brother, aged 12 or 13 at the time, told me to lie down at the front of the ramp. Bike after bike whizzed over my body as six or more of the older boys each took their turn. Gradually more and more of us younger siblings were placed next to each other on the ground, face down, to be ridden over. My brother always placed me in the most dangerous position – at the outer reaches, closest to where the wheels would eventually land. There was the noise of the boys cheering each other on, the sound of the bikes racing to the ramp, the sound of bike on ramp and then the point where sound stopped as the rider became airborne. Hushed silence. And then there was the fear and trepidation. I would hold my breath while waiting for the bike to land. Would I be….? There were at least four of us lying there on the bike path before our neighbor saw what was happening and came out of her house screaming. At the time I felt important and as much a daredevil as those riding over me, while simultaneously feeling somehow worthless. Was my life expendable in my brother's eyes? Were these the beginnings of my feelings of worthlessness and eventual suicidality? It is odd but the 13th anniversary of my brother's suicide occurred just a few days ago without my realizing it. Memories and anniversaries are funny things.

My brother was 56 when he took his own life. He died in May 2002. In late September of that year, his partner called, finally deciding to inform me of his death. The coroner was about to deliver his findings. When the report arrived it gave no indication as to why my brother had taken the action he had. It was a sterile matter-of-fact document that left me empty and cold. On the other hand, I had gleaned most of the more painful and traumatic details from his partner. My brother and I had never been close, but that is not to say that I did not love him. I respected certain aspects of his life, but conversely, I also found it difficult to forgive specific incidents that had occurred throughout our lives.

When I received that phone call, I was studying contemporary art at Southern Cross University in northern New South Wales, in Australia. Several months later, in fact during May of the following year, I descended into my own suicidal crisis. It was almost 1 year to the day that my brother had taken his own life. Memories and anniversaries are funny things.

The Art of Understanding

Reaching out for help is not easy for me, nor is it for many men, but eventually I did contact a counselor and a psychologist, yet neither was the right "fit" for me. Finding the right person to trust can be difficult. My experience as an adventure-based therapist although did help me navigate through the worst of my pain. In addition, art became a way for me to begin a process of expressing emotions of grief and anger and frustration in ways that words simply failed to achieve. Art acted as a catalyst for me to begin a process of self-discovery. In a desire and an attempt to understand what drove my own suicidality and my brother's, I immersed myself in my art practice and began to create visual representations of my inner dialogues. An integral component of the art-making process at university is the use of the *crit*. The crit is the critical analysis of artworks from conception through to exhibition. Staff and students come together at varying stages to discuss ideas and processes relating to a particular project. The feedback offered during these sessions is invaluable and helps students identify strengths and weaknesses within the work being discussed. It is a process that helps individuals clarify their ideas and research and how best to present them.

> Creative arts research is often motivated by emotional, personal and subjective concerns, it operates not only on the basis of explicit and exact knowledge, but also on that of tacit and experiential knowledge. (Barrett, 2007, p. 115)

Art is by any measure a rich and complex interlacing of imagination and human sensory, tacit knowledge that makes visible (or audible), that which was hitherto unseen. Art for me is primarily about telling a story. So how does one go about telling the story of the lived experience

Figure 18.1. Too Few Ladders, 2008, Artist/Photographer: Mic Eales. Exhibited at Southern Cross University, Lismore, NSW, Australia.

of suicide? What are the benefits of using art-based research in storying the lived experience of suicide?

Why my brother's death provoked such an intense desire to begin expressing, in a creative way, issues relating to suicide from a range of perspectives, I have no idea. What was undeniable was that I needed to communicate and express my feelings and emotions. It was also apparent that if I was to continue living and embrace life, my artistic expressions would need to have a life-affirming quality to them, as previously argued by Riggs (2010, p. 47).

> Artists whose concerns lie with human connection and disconnection move towards, rather than turn away from, the complexities of humanity; they grapple with and attempt to express the layers of human nature and behaviour. Through contemplation and imagination, the artist reveals what cannot always or easily be said. As an enabler, the artist transforms an idea, feeling or the internal world by giving form to, revealing and offering a physical object that can be touched, as well as seen and felt.

What I found was that the utter complexity and unspeakable nature of the trauma of suicide and the lived experience of it, when examined through art, allowed me to offer back to an audience a form of narrative that went way beyond everyday speech. It was important for me to begin by creating artworks that had an embodied sense of honesty within them, were spiritually motivated and incorporated elements of naïvety and playfulness. By listening to my inner voice, I began to observe that the only time I ever felt free of emotional pain was as a small child prior to going to school. It was an observation that caused me to reflect that childhood innocence might be seen within my own life as an opposite of suicide. The result has been that I now consciously incorporate childlike or playful aspects into each of my artworks about suicide. Focusing on the darker aspects and pain of suicide is easy but would have provided little or no new understanding of my desire to end my own life and in all probability would have only hastened my descent into self-destructive behaviors. Nor would it have shed any light on my relationship with my brother or in the understanding of his suicide. Lexi Cutcher states:

> It is in this intimate and individual connection between artwork and audience that empathy, dialogue and understanding can occur. The audience is able to come to the information embedded in the works in their own, idiosyncratic ways, enabling interpretations that are peculiar to each individual's experience and subsequent engagement with the works. This is a powerful way to communicate to the field of suicidology and, importantly, to those of us as yet untouched by suicide, the psychache present in the minds of those who feel suicide is the only option. Yet embedded in the works, because of Mic [Eales]'s assertion regarding play and innocence as essential elements in his work, there is also hope. (Eales & Cutcher, 2015, p. 75)

It is absolutely crucial that we make a place for innovative and alternative research practices if we are to more fully comprehend the phenomena of suicide from a lived experience perspective. By humanizing the issue of suicide, the stories of those who have attempted or those who are bereaved by it, expressed in whatever form, will provide insight into the trauma of being a survivor. We need to hear those stories to discover what is required to help and support them on their healing journey. Anne Riggs in her thesis and work with sexual abuse victims sums it up best: "Victims of trauma benefit and grow when they are guided towards expressing all their emotions" (Riggs, 2010, p. 249). It is essential that support for anyone suffering trauma be empathetic, compassionate, and carried out in a trusting and supportive environment.

Storying Through Art

In 2010, Tony Gee from the Life Is... Foundation invited me to participate in the exhibition *Pieces: Suicide the Aftermath*. It was an exhibition that dealt with the impact and loss that suicide has upon those left behind. Through Compassionate Friends of Victoria and the community artists' group stART, Tony teamed up individuals bereaved by suicide with community artists. Being an artist bereaved by my brother's suicide, I was qualified for both roles. Working collaboratively over an extended period, a range of artworks, using an assortment of media, were created. Tony's request provided me with a unique opportunity to examine and express the relationship I had with my brother. The suicidal crisis that I experienced after my brother's death I have since witnessed in others after the suicide or attempted suicide of a loved one.

What emerged was the installation *Paper Shadows* (**Figure 18.2**). It evolved through a series of internal conversations between my deceased brother, his dog Ralf and myself. As odd as that may sound it was just one of the strategies I used to come to terms with my brother's suicide and the manner in which he took his own life. Together the three of us relived their last moments, the notes he left, the music he played, and we recalled his pain and humiliation. As a means to represent the notes that he left, I created two large sheets of handmade paper from the fabric of an old futon that my brother had slept on and the fiber of a plant known as cottonweed. Cottonweed is an extremely difficult fiber to work with, and I have a love/hate relationship with it, just like the relationship between my brother and me. As I sprayed the paper pulp onto a large silk screen, I embedded red thread within each sheet as a way to represent our blood connection. Barely visible, the threads are noticed as they extend beyond the paper's deckle edges. Suspended from the ceiling, the sheets float, one above the other, an acknowledgement that for much of my childhood I lived in his shadow. The handmade paper helped to signify that a few pieces of paper are sometimes the only reminders we have of someone's existence. There are of course, memories – but even those can be extremely lonely melancholic experiences if no

Figure 18.2. Paper Shadows, 2010, Artist/Photographer: Mic Eales. Exhibited at The Dax Centre, Melbourne, VIC, Australia.

one else was witness to them. *"For all of our differences in age and in attitude, he and I were bound by blood, yet strangely, we led such parallel lives"* (Eales, 2013, p. 83).

> Those who go through the experience of trauma know that it is one of deadening and reduction, whereas creative spaces are alive and full of promise. (Riggs, 2010, p. 9)

As an artist researcher I have previously suggested (Eales, 2013, p. 105) that the artist's intention is to invite audiences to take a journey within an exhibition space or with a particular artwork. My own art practice actively encourages this process. The gallery space provides opportunities for individuals to respond, interpret, and communicate with artworks on their own terms but many people can be intimidated or overwhelmed especially when viewing trauma based art. However, once permission is granted to interact and even touch the artworks, the viewer's apprehension and disquiet diminishes and allows the senses and imagination an opportunity to experience alternative translations within each story/artefact.

> The artist's intent is very likely part of the linguistic, cultural, and artistic conventions of the times during which the artist was working, and thus intent would play a part in the interpretation, but the artist intent does not determine an artworks sole meaning. (Barrett, 2003, p. 214)

Touching the Senses

Listening to the stories of suicide loss survivors was the starting point for Irish artist Seamus McGuinness, in making the works *21 grams* and *One Hundred Lived Lives* and *Lost Portraits* (McGuinness, 2012). In collaboration with psychiatrist Dr. Kevin Malone, suicide loss survivors were interviewed: the family and friends of young people under the age of 35 who had taken their own lives. The installation *21 grams* featured 92 torn, white shirt collars each weighing 21 g (the weight reportedly lost from a body when it dies) that were suspended at various heights within a room. Their research with the bereaved identified a dilemma about what to do with the material remains of their deceased family member. The work was used to highlight the increasing suicide rates among young Irish males over the past 2 decades. McGuinness hoped that the artwork would emphasize the effect of suicide on the living and of the constant presence that absence created. He mentioned the case of one mother who kept some of her son's dirty clothes in a sealed plastic bag. Periodically she would open the bag to smell and remember.

The Right Fit

> Talking about suicide therefore takes all of us to a most vulnerable place in ourselves. When we are faced with such a painful reality we would usually withdraw or retreat to protect ourselves, to survive. The space that can be created by art can help us to move out of our psychic retreat to find the courage to embrace our vulnerability, and to confront the painful reality of trauma, loss, death and grief. (Dr. Eugen Koh; cited in Middleton & Colucci, 2012, p. 3)

Much of my own research efforts have been with the support of, or in collaboration with, suicidologist Dr. Erminia Colucci. My initial efforts to engage with researchers in the field of suicidology failed dismally. Although attitudes are slowly changing, I find it disturbing that suicide attempt survivors and the bereaved are still subject to attitudes of bias, prejudice, and discrimination. Fortunately there are many researchers who see the value in meaningfully engaging with the lived experience of suicide. Serendipity, as in many of my art and research projects, played its role in helping to meet Erminia. That relationship, first forged in 2008, has now become an example of what is possible using multidisciplinary and interdisciplinary approaches to research into understanding the trauma and pain associated with suicide.

Mic and Erminia

Other authors have explored the link between arts and suicide, usually looking at the way suicide has been represented though the history in visual arts (e.g., Cutter, 1983; Brown, 2004), and/or literature and films (e.g. Stack & Lester, 2009). However, although including important works in the field, this exploration has generally been limited to well-known artists rather than looking at artistic-expressive representations and understanding of suicide among "living and real" people who deal on a daily basis with the pain and traumas that were represented in classic artworks. Furthermore, these discourses around arts and suicide seemed to seat somehow outside academic and clinical practices and may be seen as interesting intellectual exercises of scholars interested in the matter rather than becoming an integral part of our understandings around suicide and a way to challenge mainstream biomedical perspectives on suicide, the will to die and the will to live.

Early on in our association, we developed a series of creative, experiential workshops in an attempt to use art-based initiatives as vehicles for expressing what words often fail to do, communicating what is happening in the psyche and articulating emotions that are often difficult using verbal language. As observed by Dr. David Webb, the first known suicide attempt survivor to write a PhD dissertation about his lived experience of attempted suicide, "Art, music, dance, play and other creative methods of enquiry are required. We especially need to create safe spaces where these stories can be told both to inform our enquiry but also and more importantly, as healing spaces" (Webb, 2003, p. 13).

One of the workshops we organized is featured in the documentary film *Different Voice Different Perspective: The Art of Understanding Suicide* (Eales, 2012). Using biography as a tool for introspection, we began by asking workshop participants – some of whom had been bereaved by suicide, while others were dealing with their own suicidality – to creatively recon-

Figure 18.3. Columbus Cubes, 2009, Artist/Photographer: Mic Eales. Exhibited at nextart Gallery, Lismore, NSW, Australia.

struct their life stories as artworks on six sheets of paper. The pages were then folded origami-style to form a Columbus cube (i.e., a cube with one corner indented) in an attempt to provide participants with an opportunity to delve into, express, and examine their own lives and their lived experiences of suicide (**Figure 18.3**).

> His [Mic Eales's] art is quite beautiful and thought provoking. And the workshop full of heart, he created a space that enabled vulnerability with gentleness and openness. Being fairly new to a therapeutic community I hadn't realised that many therapists come from these places, holding brokenness; emerging from woundedness. Why would it necessarily be otherwise? (Anonymous workshop participant, personal correspondence, May 18, 2009)

By creating stories embedded within many other stories and combining remnants of memory and personal artefacts, our aim was to create a quilted tapestry of information and experiences that could be used and easily accessed by individuals and families alike as part of the difficult process of healing trauma.

> A creative practice by its very nature pushes against boundaries, barriers and preconceptions. As participants pushed, they discovered an opening into the "outside world" and, at the same time, into the internal world; this observation suggests one reason why art can be such an effective counterweight to trauma. (Riggs, 2010, p. 12)

Erminia

Artists have always been driven to create work in response to trauma and other painful experiences, in an effort to seek meaning, and to bear witness, as recently indicated in a special issue of the *World Cultural Psychiatry Research Review* dedicated to arts, media, and mental health (Colucci & Bhui, 2015). There are various reasons and a complexity of paths that bring people to arts in mental health and to mental health through arts, as observed by Bayles and Orlando (1993), who stated:

> Some people who make art are driven by inspiration, others by provocation, still others by desperation. Artmaking grants access to worlds that may be dangerous, sacred, forbidden, seductive,

or all of the above. It grants access to worlds you may otherwise never fully engage. It may in fact be the engagement – not the art – that you seek. The difference is that making art allows, indeed guarantees, that you declare yourself. Art is contact, and your work necessarily reveals the nature of that contact. In making art you declare what is important. (Bayles & Orlando, 1993, p. 108)

In 2012 I undertook an ethnographic photo and film documentary project about human rights violations against people with mental health issues in Indonesia: *Breaking the Chains* (http:// movie-ment.org/breakingthechains). This documentary project aimed to contribute to an understanding of the practice of *pasung*. Pasung describes the use of shackles, rope, wooden stocks, and cages, and the practice of locking individuals who show certain attitudes, behaviors, and emotional expressions that depart from culturally defined *normality*, into confined spaces. It also aimed to tell an original story about the social and political activism being carried out at several levels (from consumer volunteer organizations to the pasung survivors and their communities) to eradicate this form of human rights abuse and give freedom and dignity to people with a mental illness (Anto & Colucci, 2015).

During the ethnographic fieldwork, I met a young man on the east side of Java, Agus [Anto is his artistic name] and I went to spent a few days in his house with him and his parents. From this encounter, the short collaborative documentary *Breaking the Chains: Anto's Story* (codirected by Agus) was born. This testimony-style documentary depicts the subjective lived experience of Agus, a young man who was restrained but was then released and reintegrated into the community as a self-taught artist and English student. Agus tells his first-hand story using a combination of narration, drawings, painting, and poetry. Both in the documentary and the article we later coauthored, Agus provides an introspective recount of how he understood his experiences and tried to make sense of how others in his surroundings, including his own family, related to him and responded to his mental distress. Although in the initial recounting of his story, Agus does not talk about suicide, progressively through his visual arts, prose, and poetry, he starts to reveal his experience of being saved at the last moment from jumping to his death from a boat. Upon reflection on these experiences, he produced the following poem, and today, Agus continues to write and paint, while also completing a degree in English. He continues to be involved as a human rights and mental health advocate with the mission of helping others who, like himself, have been chained and risk death because of their mental health condition.

A New Meaning

Day by day passes
Choice by choice
I know I had to survive
it's about learning to live
I choose to be free
I choose to survive
I choose to forgive
I choose to rise
Once again
I embrace this life
A life full of possibilities
A life with an new meaning

Agus Sugianto

In spite of the existence of cultural differences in suicide (Colucci & Lester, 2013), as Riggs (2010) states, "Art, like trauma, transcends boundaries of language, sex, education, culture, abilities, family and age" (p. 51), and this has certainly been my experience in Indonesia, as in the other countries where I have carried out my suicide research and prevention activities.

My collaboration and friendship with Mic, and later Agus, have helped me appreciate the importance of using a variety of channels and "languages" to understand and communicate about suicide and loss by suicide. My own desire to engage in filmmaking and photography was born from a sense of dissatisfaction, and of the incompleteness I increasingly felt, in relation to scholarly writing about suicide. For as much as various academics and professionals are very careful and sensitive in their description of the *suicidal mind, suicidal behavior,* and so on, there was always a sense that something was missing, a distance between what is written and what is lived. This dissatisfaction comes also from my own personal experience with suicidal behavior within my own family.

The arts offers a space of mutual exchange, an opportunity to challenge our preconceptions, the preconstructed, and be provoked by different sets of beliefs, insights, and understandings. *Inspired Lives: Discovering Life in Imagination,* an exhibition about and from people who had made a suicide attempt and/or had lost someone through suicide that Mic and I were involved in, at the Dax Centre in Melbourne (with me as initiator and cocurator and Mic as artist), became that space for many who viewed the exhibition (Middleton & Colucci, 2012). This happened in spite of the (understandable) concerns expressed by members of the gallery that hearing about someone else's suicidal attempts or losses could instigate suicidal thoughts in the visitors or that there might not be interest in the subject. On the contrary, attendance figures indicated that the gallery received a fivefold increase in visits during the 3 months that the exhibition ran (http://movie-ment.org/inspired-lives/) (A. Middleton, personal communication, January 11, 2013).

> It is nearly impossible not to be changed when working with humans; we see their struggles, experience their vulnerabilities, and better understand ourselves through listening to their narratives. (Quaye & Pope, 2008, p. 147)

Conclusions

To fully understand the issue of suicide and loss by suicide from a lived experience perspective, it is essential to look at the person and their experience holistically. We have tried to consciously incorporate, within the core of our respective research (artworks, documentaries, and workshops), what we see as a spiritual quality. As a way of demonstrating this inclusion, it is important to understand that we speak about the works in terms of their having a heart, spirit, or soul. We have come to see the artworks as taking on a life of their own.

> If you turn a story told into a story analyzed ... you sacrifice the story at the altar of traditional sociological rigor. You transform the story into another language, the language of generalization and analysis, and thus you lose the very qualities that make a story a story. (Ellis & Bochner, 2006, p. 440)

The arts and creative methods offer an opportunity to engage differently and more deeply with the lived experiences of suicide, to learn from one's *mal de vivre* and turn trauma and pain into an external object, a materialization of feelings that can be shared and understood. We would like to conclude with the words of Prof. Baden Offord, whose family history with suicide extends back several generations, and with whom Mic collaborated during his research:

One of the most important questions for me about surviving suicide in my family and in my own life has been about how it has absolutely deepened my love of life and shown me how precious it is. Suicide has been probably one of the most powerful narrative currents in my life and has impacted on how I think and feel every day and every moment I breathe. I have survived suicide to live. Your project has been a remarkable intervention into my family's tragic story of suicide; through our discussions; and through the collaboration you brought about; and the way in which you have helped me translate core intimate reflections. Although I was already sensitive to the transformative nature of suicide in my life, psychologically and emotionally, your work as a translator of feeling, bafflement and loss has inspired me immensely in the way I now approach the story of suicide through my life. You have brought coherence (happiness as defined by Toni Morrison) to this taboo subject. (B. Offord, personal communication, August 3, 2012)

Through our artworks, videos, workshops, and collaborations, we believe that we have shown that art, in its many forms, can act as a vehicle for expressing what words often fail to do. Our research demonstrates that art can reach across the void that we believe exists within the field of suicidology, to express the experience of suicide as it is lived, be it for attempt survivors or those bereaved by suicide, in all of its complexity, and act as a tool for healing and recovery. Anniversaries and memories remain odd occurrences but they remind us of our journey and how each of us has been marked and changed by the paths that we have traversed.

Corresponding authors

Mic Eales
Littlecreek Studio
Mallanganee, NSW
Australia
littlecreek@aapt.net.au

Erminia Colucci
Centre for Psychiatry
Queen Mary University of London
UK
e.colucci@qmul.ac.uk

References

Anto SG, & Colucci, E. (2015). Free from pasung: A story of chaining and freedom in Indonesia told trough painting, poetry and narration. *World Cultural Psychiatry Research Review, 10*(3/4), 149–167.

Barrett, E. (2007). Experiential learning in practice as research: context, method, knowledge. *Journal of Visual Art Practice, 6*(2), 115–124. http://doi.org/10.1386/jvap.6.2.115_1

Barrett, T. (2003). *Interpreting art: Reflecting, wondering, and responding.* New York, NY: McGraw-Hill.

Bayles, D., & Orlando, T. (1993). *Art and fear: Observations on the perils (and rewards) of Artmaking.* Santa Cruz, CA: Image Continuum.

Brown, R. (2004). *Art of suicide.* London, UK: Reaktion Books.

Colucci, E., & Bhui, K. (Eds.). (2015). WCPPR Special issue on Arts, media and cultural mental health. *World Cultural Psychiatry Research Review, 10*(3/4).

Colucci, E., & Lester, D. (Eds.). (2013). *Suicide and culture: Understanding the context.* Götingen, Germany: Hogrefe.

Cutter, F. (1983). *Art and the wish to die.* Chicago, IL: Nelson/Hall.

Eales, M. (2012). *Different voice different perspective: The art of understanding suicide* [Film documentary]. Retrieved from https://vimeo.com/116125821

Eales, M. (2013). *Different voice different perspective: An arts-based and evocative research response to original voice narratives of suicide* (Doctoral thesis, Southern Cross University, Lismore, Australia). Retrieved from http://epubs.scu.edu.au/theses/368/

Eales, M., & Cutcher, A. (2015). Researching suicide from an original voice, collaborative, arts-based perspective: Issues for doctoral research, supervision and examination. *Creative Approaches to Research, 8*(2), 70–85.

Ellis, C., & Bochner, A. P. (2006). Analyzing analytic autoethnography: An autopsy. *Journal of Contemporary Ethnography, 35*(4), 429–449. http://doi.org/10.1177/0891241606286979

McGuinness, S. (2012). *Lived lives: Materializing stories of young Irish suicide 2003–2008.* Retrieved from http://www.3ts.ie/wp-content/uploads/2012/09/Lived-Lives-Overview-July-12.pdf

Middleton, A., & Colucci, E. (2012). *Inspired lives: Discovering life in imagination.* Melbourne, Australia: The Dax Centre.

Quaye, S. J., & Pope, B. (2008). Fearless leadership: R. Michael Fisher's story. In D. T. Jacobs (Ed.), *The authentic dissertation: Alternative ways of knowing, research, and representation* (pp. 143–148). London, UK: Routledge.

Riggs, A. (2010). *The creative space: Art and wellbeing in the shadow of trauma, grief and loss* (Unpublished doctoral dissertation). Victoria University, Melbourne, Australia. Retrieved from http://vuir.vu.edu.au/16014/1/Riggs_PhD_thesis.pdf

Stack, S., & Lester, D. (Eds.). (2009). *Suicide and the creative arts.* Hauppage, NY: Nova Science.

Stang, R. T. (1979). *Edvard Munch: The man and his art.* New York, NY: Abbeville Press.

Webb, D. (2003, June 12–15). *Self, soul and spirit: Suicidology's blind-spots?* Paper presented at the conference Finding Meaning to Sustain Life: The Place of Spirituality in Suicide Prevention, Suicide Prevention Australia (SPA), Brisbane, Australia.

Part III

Suicide Bereavement Support in Different Populations

Chapter 19

Emerging Survivor Populations

Support After Suicide Clusters and Murder–Suicide Events

Ella Arensman and Sean McCarthy

[1]National Suicide Research Foundation, Department of Epidemiology and Public Health, University College Cork, Ireland
[2]Suicide Prevention, HSE South St Patrick's Hospital, Waterford, Ireland

Abstract: This chapter presents postvention for two emerging, yet understudied, suicide survivor populations. More specifically, the chapter addresses the needs and requirements related to bereavement, support, and evidence-informed interventions after suicide clusters and murder–suicide. Internationally, there is professional and public interest in suicide clusters. There are indications of an increasing trend in suicide clusters associated with the rise of modern communication systems. Yet, the research in this area and information on effective responses to those affected are limited. Murder–suicide events are also relatively rare, but internationally there has been a noticeable increase over the last 10 years. The effects of murder–suicide are extremely intense and long lasting for those who are left behind. Intensive specialized support is required to support survivors, in particular in coping with their posttraumatic reactions.

Introduction

Suicide clusters and murder–suicide are rare events. However, both events involve several victims, and therefore the impact on bereaved individuals, families, and communities can be severe and long lasting. Often, the media tends to report extensively on such, statistically speaking, rare events, which may put the events and the bereaved in the spotlight, and which may increase the risk of copycat behavior (Pirkis & Nordentoft, 2011). Regarding both types of events, well-planned responses and evidence-informed interventions are needed to identify the survivors and to provide appropriate support on a short- and long-term basis.

Support After Suicide Clusters

Over the past number of years there has been increasing interest in how to respond to and prevent clustering of suicides, both from the general public and from professionals. There are some indications that there is an increase in clustering and contagion effects in suicidal behavior associated with the rise in modern communication systems (Larkin & Beautrais, 2012; Robertson, Skegg, Poore, Williams, & Taylor, 2012). Suicide clusters have been referred to in various ways, such as a temporary increase in the frequency of suicides within a small community or institution, relative to both the baseline suicide rate before and after the point cluster, and the suicide rate in neighboring area (Gould, Wallenstein, & Davidson, 1989). An operational definition is provided by Larkin and Beautrais (2012):

> A suicide cluster is a series of three or more closely grouped deaths within a three month period that can be linked by space or social relationships. In the absence of transparent social connectedness, evidence of space and time linkages are required to define a candidate cluster. In the presence of a strong demonstrated social connection, only temporal significance is required. (Larkin & Beautrais, 2012, p. vi)

Suicide clusters have a significant impact across a whole community leading to anxiety and fear within that community of further suicides. This can be a result of a contagion effect in that suicidal behavior may facilitate the occurrence of subsequent suicidal behavior, either directly (via contact or friendship with the index suicide) or indirectly (via the media) (Haw et al., 2013). Incidents of clustering are associated with significant trauma for the bereaved at an individual, familial, and community level. This impact spans across all spheres of society, within schools, colleges, workplaces, sports, and community organizations (Arensman & McAuliffe, 2015).

Suicide Clusters Identified by the Irish Suicide Support and Information System

The Suicide Support and Information System (SSIS) developed by the National Suicide Research Foundation in Ireland combines proactive facilitation of support for families bereaved by suicide, with information gathering on consecutive cases of suicide and open-verdict deaths following the conclusion of a coroners' inquest (Arensman et al., 2013). The SSIS identified two independent suicide clusters in the Cork region in 2011 (Arensman et al., 2013). One cluster involved 13 suicides occurring over a 3-month period from April to June 2011, with a second cluster involving seven cases between September and October 2011. For the first cluster, the expected number of suicides for the same period and geographic area would have been 1.86. However, the observed cluster represented a 6.9-fold increase in suicides. For the second cluster, the expected number of cases for the same time period and geographic area would have been 0.52, while the observed cluster represented a 13.4-fold increase in cases.

In the first of those identified suicide clusters, with the exception of one individual, all were male ($n = 12$), with a mean age of 47 years. The majority of the deceased were married or cohabiting, while nearly half were living with a partner and children, and the majority were unemployed. Regarding work sector, nearly half had worked in sales or business or in the construction or production sector. More than one third had received a psychiatric diagnosis and two thirds had been diagnosed with a physical illness.

The second cluster involved seven people – three men and four women – with a mean age of 39 years. Of these, almost half were married or living with a partner and children; the others were single. All of the deceased were in paid employment, with nearly half working in the construction and production sector, followed by nearly one third in the agricultural sector. Over half had a history of self-harm as well as a psychiatric diagnosis. The information gathered with respect of gender, relationships, work status, and place of work, along with psychiatric and physical well-being, can inform responders in targeting services to where they may be needed, and in identifying those who may need support.

Identifying the Survivors and Meeting Their Needs

To be bereaved by suicide is a hugely traumatic experience for any individual, family, or community, and can impact an individual in many ways. The manifestations of grief touch on their feelings and cognitions, along with influencing their behaviors and resulting in physical sensations (Jordan & McIntosh, 2011). As a result of the numbers of persons dying, and the number of the bereaved, a suicide cluster has an even greater impact across a community (Arensman & McAuliffe, 2015). Manifestations of grief impact on people at different levels of intensity, ranging from those who are mildly impacted by a suicide death within their community, to those who are directly bereaved by the death and may experience complicated grief. Shear et al. (2011) suggested that complicated grief may derail or impede healing after loss and lead to a period of prolonged and intensified acute grief which may lead to significant distress and impairment in work and social functioning. It is important to understand that within a cluster of suicides there is a pattern of numerous individual suicides, with each individual contributing to the collective trauma experienced by the whole community (Arensman & McAuliffe, 2015), which results in a need to respond at an individual, familial, and community level.

When responding to clusters of suicide, or indeed murder–suicide events – that is, the unlawful killing of one or more individuals, followed by the suicide of the perpetrator – a range of supports and interventions will be required to be able to comprehensively meet the needs of all of those affected. Using the iceberg analogy, there may be differences in the needs among people within a community. A service delivery model (**Figure 19.1**) is appropriate to responding to a suicide that has an impact on a community (Petrus Consulting, 2006). This includes the death of a well-known person within a community, a celebrity, sports person, or other person whom people from the community may identify with. It may also inform responders as to what is needed to support the community after a cluster of suicides.

The service delivery model (Petrus Consulting, 2006) distinguishes different intervention levels, ranging from a broad population-based approach, including education and training in areas of mental health promotion and suicide prevention, to delivering comprehensive information on support services and information relating to depression and other mental health difficulties within the workplace, schools, and colleges, sports organizations, and community services. The population level also includes informing and training media professionals, as there is growing evidence that irresponsible reporting of suicide in the media can potentially lead to copycat suicides and could thus act as a tipping point on which a cluster could begin or be exacerbated (Pirkis & Blood, 2001; Stack, 2005). This broad population-based approach should be implemented across communities and is also considered to contribute to preventing suicide. Moreover, it is considered that there are four levels of support required to address the needs of people suffering from mild distress up to complicated grief reactions.

Level 1 addresses the provision of directories of services, booklets, other relevant literature, web-based resources rituals, helplines, and texting support services. Level 2 ensures that community support organizations and self-help groups are available and that their existence and availability is highlighted and advertised. Level 3 is about ensuring that appropriate counseling services for adults, children, and families are available, and that those delivering such services are appropriately trained and accredited, with required supervision and professional indemnity insurance in place. Finally, level 4 is about having available and accessible mental health services and psychotherapy in place for the cohort of bereaved who may require these services as

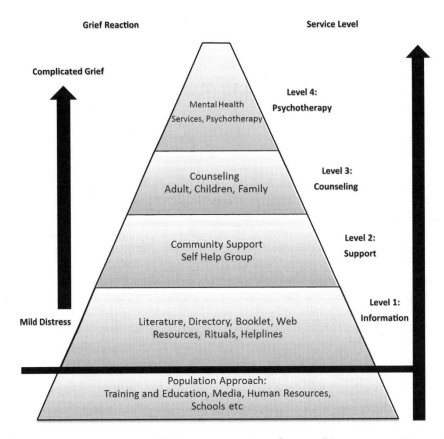

Figure 19.1. Service delivery model. Source: *Review of General Bereavement Support and Specific Services Following Suicide Bereavement,* by Petrus Consulting, 2006, Dublin, Ireland: National Office for Suicide Prevention. © 2006 by Petrus Consulting. Reproduced with permission.

a result of their complicated grief reactions, which have the potential to impact on both their physical and mental well-being. During the occurrence of a suicide cluster, movement and referral between the differing levels of support should be seamless, with open and clear communication between all services providing support at times of crisis.

Responding to Potential Suicide Clusters

Box 19.1 summarizes the key elements in responding to suspected suicide clusters. One of the key elements is preparedness. It is suggested that communities should plan for three overlapping phases of action to prevent and respond to suicide clusters (Commonwealth Australia, 2012). These phases address preparedness, intervention/postvention and follow-up, which are further broken down into eight recommended steps across the three phases.

Box 19.1. Responding to suicide clusters

Phase 1: Preparedness
- Identify a lead agency or steering committee to develop and host the plan
- Identify relevant available contacts and resources

Phase 2: Intervention and/or postvention
- Establish the facts
- Provide ongoing and accurate information
- Identify individuals, groups, and areas of greater risk
- Respond to risks and immediate support needs

Phase 3: Follow-up
- Link with longer-term suicide prevention work
- Revise and update the community plan

When a suicide cluster is identified, it is crucial that there is an agreed multiagency, interdisciplinary approach taken to respond to and support the community in such circumstances. Proper structures to ensure the activation, implementation, and wind down of such approaches must be in place. It is also important that responses to clusters or murder–suicide are designed for the circumstances of the specific event, as they will be different as a result of scale, impact on a community, and resources available. An agreed template for responding to suicide clusters, such as a recent practice resource (Public Health England, 2015), provides additional evidence-informed guidance.

The identification of all people and groups in a community who may be impacted by a suicide cluster is central to responding, and there are many templates available that can be used to identify where resources and responses should be targeted. One such model used is that of circles of vulnerability (Lahad & Cohen, 2004; Public Health England , 2015), which can assist in identifying those in a community who may be at elevated risk of developing mental health difficulties or engaging in suicidal behavior. The circles of vulnerability model looks at varying types of proximity people may have had to the deceased, and particularly focuses on geographic, psychological, and social proximity.

The more vulnerability factors identified for an individual, the greater the possible risk the person is placed at. The closer to the intersecting circles the person moves, the greater the risk and the more acute the need for support and referral to appropriate services. Identifying those at potential risk and providing support and intervention may reduce the possibility of copycat deaths or contagion. In this context, Berkowitz and colleagues (2011) recommend screening for suicide risk and presence of depression among young people affected by the suicide of a friend or somebody close.

Geographic proximity refers to the physical distance between a person and the incident, such as for eyewitnesses, those who found the deceased, first responders, and exposure through extensive media coverage (Lahad & Cohen, 2004). *Social proximity* refers to the relationship with the deceased, such as family members, friends, romantic partners, social circle, close working colleagues, and close connections through social media (Lahad & Cohen, 2004). *Psychological proximity* covers the psychological closeness a person feels to the deceased irrespective of kinship (family ties) or other type of relationship (e.g., colleagues or friends) and may include, for example, people with similar cultural and/or religious beliefs, or role models (Lahad & Cohen, 2004).

Obtaining information on the psychological and social proximity of a survivor in relation to the deceased is particularly important as what is implemented at this juncture can be very beneficial for the bereaved in the medium to long term. According to Andriessen (2009), the provision of support to the survivors is a form of suicide prevention among those who are bereaved by suicide. The provision of support, information, and signposting to services is beneficial and welcomed by the bereaved. Hawton et al. (2008) found that assistance on practical matters, such as ways of coping, arranging funerals, and supporting children, can be beneficial for the bereaved. Similarly, providing outreach on a proactive basis has been shown to lead to earlier uptake on treatment among the bereaved and greater attendance to survivor group meetings (Cerel et al., 2008). By responding at an individual, familial, and community level to suicide clusters, support and information can be provided to those immediately affected by the loss of their loved one. At a community level, by taking a public health approach targeting schools and colleges, workplaces, sports organizations, and other areas where people are impacted either by an individual suicide or a cluster, appropriate support can be provided.

Support After Murder–Suicide Events

There is a paucity of research that systematically examines the phenomenon of murder–suicides (or homicide–suicide) in contemporary society (Joiner, 2014; Samaritans, 2014). Yet, paradoxically, when these events occur they often receive extensive media coverage. Murder–suicide is commonly referred to as a two-stage sequential act in which a person kills one or more individuals and then takes their own life thereafter (Logan et al., 2008). In line with Nock and Marzuk (1999), the suicide should take place within 24 hr of the murder(s) for an event to be considered murder–suicide. International research reports prevalence rates of murder–suicide ranging from 0.05 to 0.52 per 100,000 (Flynn et al., 2009; Krulewitch, 2009). A review by Eliason (2009) showed that people involved in murder–suicide were commonly male perpetrators, older male caregivers, and those with depression and substance abuse issues.

Marzuk, Tardiff, and Hirsch (1992) classified different types of murder–suicide, including *familial suicide,* which refers to the killing of one's child(ren) and spouse or partner, followed by suicide. *Filial suicide* refers to the killing of one's child(ren) followed by suicide. Such deaths may also be referred to as *filicide,* when involving children aged 1 to 18 years; *infanticide,* when involving children up to 1 year; and *neonaticide,* when involving children within the first 24 hr of birth. Furthermore, *extrafamilial suicide* refers to the killing of one or more others (usually not related) followed by suicide.

Impact on Survivors

Research into the impact of murder–suicide on survivors is limited. However, there is growing evidence for specific aspects of sudden violent deaths, including murder–suicide, which contribute to the long-lasting impact of these tragic events on survivors (Boelen, 2015; Boelen, de Keijser, & Smid, 2015; Joiner, 2014; Jordan, 2008; Nakajima, Ito, Shirai, & Konishi, 2012). These studies address the impact on survivors of various sudden violent deaths, including survivors of murder–suicide.

Traumatic Aftermath

Loss of a family member or multiple family members by murder–suicide is often sudden, violent, and usually unexpected. Depending on the situation, survivors may need to deal with the police or handle press inquiries. While they are still in shock, they may be asked whether they want to visit the death scene. Sometimes officials will discourage the visit as too upsetting. However, the impact of the traumatic experience can be compounded if people feel that they do not have a choice (Jordan, 2008; Zisook & Shear, 2009).

Stigma and Isolation

Murder–suicide and individual suicide can isolate survivors from their community and even from other family members. This is further compounded by the stigma around mental disorders, which are often associated with murder–suicide and suicide, in particular in countries where suicide is still criminalized (World Health Organization, 2014). Therefore, survivors may be reluctant to acknowledge or disclose the circumstances of such a death. Differences among family members regarding how to publicly discuss the death, can further complicate providing mutual support among family members, which may prolong the grieving process (Jordan, 2008).

Mixed Emotions

Murder–suicide can evoke intense anger from survivors directed toward the perpetrator. Often there are conflicting emotions due to the perpetrator having suffered from a mental disorder, but at the same time having engaged in an extremely violent act, such as in filicide suicide. This may induce intense feelings of anger, rejection, and abandonment (Jordan, 2008; Zisook & Shear, 2009).

Research showed that survivors of violent and unexpected loss, such as cases of murder–suicide, had more symptoms of prolonged grief disorder (PGD) and posttraumatic stress disorder (PTSD) compared with people losing a family member due to illness (Boelen, 2015). This study also provided evidence for factors mediating the impact of violent loss and the sudden nature of loss on the severity of PGD, PTSD, and depression, such as peritraumatic distress – that is, distress at the time of the trauma, dissociation, and helplessness. In this regard, increased levels of dissociative responses and acute helplessness may explain exacerbation of postloss psychopathology (Boelen, 2015). In a related study, Boelen et al. (2015) identified specific cognitive behavior processes mediating between violent loss and elevated PTSD severity, including unrealness, catastrophic misinterpretations, depressive and anxious avoidance, and negative cognitions about the self and the future.

Consistent with these outcomes, Kaltman and Bonanno (2003) found that violent loss was more strongly associated with severe PTSD symptoms and enduring depression over 25 months following bereavement. However, this association was not found for suddenness of the loss. A review by Nakajima et al. (2012) reported that the prevalence of complicated grief among survivors of violent death, including murder–suicide, ranged from 12.5 % to 78 %. Severity of complicated grief was associated with more comorbid mental disorders, greater lack of readiness for the death, greater difficulty in making sense of the death, higher level of negative appraisal about the self and others, and more social stressors (Nakajima et al., 2012).

While the biological basis of the symptomatology of PTSD is still unclear, the interplay of somatic and environmental factors can increase the severity and duration of PTSD and complicated grief (Nakajima et al., 2012). PTSD in particular, was considered to contribute to the development of complicated grief by suppressing function of the medial prefrontal cortex and the anterior cingulate cortex, which works at facilitating the normal mourning process (Nakajima et al., 2012).

Impact on Communities

So far, limited research has been conducted into the impact of murder–suicide on communities, including schools, workplaces, and health and social services (Joiner, 2014; Logan et al, 2008). However, a number of studies addressing sudden violent deaths and suicide clusters have highlighted the impact of these events on communities. In this context, the circles of vulnerability model (Public Health England, 2015) can also assist in identifying those within a community who may be at elevated risk of developing mental health difficulties or engaging in suicidal behavior after an incident of murder–suicide.

In cases of filicide suicide, surviving siblings and peers can be severely impacted by the sudden and violent loss of their brother or sister or friend. Specific challenges for surviving siblings and peers are how to cope with feelings of guilt and responsibility following the death, difficulties in interpreting warning signs, recognizing reactions to grief, and directing affected children and adolescents to appropriate services for help, should they feel suicidal themselves (Hazell, 1991; Hacker, Collins, Gross-Young, Almeida, & Burke, 2008). Professionals who are directly or indirectly involved in the aftermath of a murder–suicide, such as mental health and primary care professionals, representatives from a local crisis center, and law enforcement, may be at increased risk of developing PTSD symptoms, in particular if they have not received relevant training (Everly & Flynn, 2006; Hacker et al, 2008; Jordan, 2008).

Impact of Media Reporting of Murder–Suicide

Feelings of depression and hopelessness present before the homicide and suicide are often the impetus for both (Gould, 2001). In covering murder–suicides, it is important to be aware that the tragedy of the homicide can mask the suicidal aspect of the act. Importantly, research identifies the need for sensitive and factual reporting to minimize harm and increase awareness (Samaritans, 2014). First of all, the graphic nature of reporting incidents of murder–suicide can trigger copycat cases: The effects of exposure on suicidal behavior and violence are well-documented. Secondly, there is a risk that sensationalized media reporting of murder–suicide can distort the facts. Finally, media professionals should consider the vulnerable reader who might be in crisis when they read the story: Coverage should not be glorified or romanticized, should emphasize consequences of the event for others, and list sources of help (Joiner, 2014).

Responding to Murder–Suicide and Recommended Interventions

With regard to recommended supportive interventions for survivors of murder–suicide, so far, no controlled evaluations have been conducted. Therefore, it is currently only possible to rely on uncontrolled evaluations for survivors of a range of violent deaths. An element of the grieving process that is considered to be particularly important is *sense making* in violent loss, such as murder–suicide, in particular when a father or mother takes the lives of his or her child(ren) (Gillies & Neimeyer, 2006; Keesee, Currier, & Neimeyer, 2008; see also Chapter 7 in this volume). Sense making relates to a constructivist conceptualization of bereavement and proposes that (a) individuals bring a set of existing beliefs about themselves and the world to the loss experience; (b) the experience of loss can violate or fracture these basic assumptions; (c) restoration entails a struggle to adapt one's personal world of meaning to make sense of the loss, with violent losses being more challenging to comprehend; (d) complications in grieving result when the bereaved individual is unable to make sense of the loss within the context of their current system or meaning (Gillies & Neimeyer, 2006; Neimeyer, Baldwin, & Gillies, 2006).

Keesee et al. (2008) identified that among mothers and fathers who had lost a child due to violent and unnatural death, including murder–suicide, reduced sense making was a significant predictor of concurrent, complicated grief symptoms, independent of the level of violence involved. Increased symptoms of complicated grief were strongly associated with increased levels of distress. Specific challenges in the process of making sense of the losses following murder–suicide are associated with trying to find an answer as how a parent can take the lives of their own child(ren) and feelings of extreme anger associated with a child or children being taken away from the surviving parent or other family members (Joiner, 2015).

Considering the link between violent death and complicated grief, eye movement desensitization and reprocessing (EMDR) is a recommended intervention for alleviating trauma, which is strongly associated with loss due to violent death (Jordan & McIntosh, 2011; Solomon & Rando, 2007). EMDR was developed by Shapiro (1995) who identified that bilateral stimulation – that is, stimulation on both sides of the body, whether in the form of eye movements, tapping, sound, or other forms, released traumatic material from the brain in a way that made the material workable (Shapiro, 1995; Solomon & Rando, 2007). Parnell (2007) underlines that survivors of violent deaths, including murder–suicide, may benefit from EMDR in that this may provide some relief from recurrent traumatic intrusions, and therefore may contribute to stabilizing the survivor to engage in bereavement counseling or other psychotherapeutic interventions. However, as indicated before, research is lacking to identify best practice and effective psychotherapeutic interventions for survivors of murder–suicide.

Conclusions and Implications for Research and Practice

Reviewing the literature on the impact and aftermath of suicide clusters and murder–suicide for survivors and other persons who may be affected, there is a need to prioritize high-quality research addressing the short- and long-term effects of these events on those affected. The available research shows a number of commonalities in responding to suicide clusters and murder–suicide; however, there are also important differences between these two phenomena. Community response plans are recommended, addressing key stages, such as preparedness, evidence-informed intervention/postvention, and follow-up up to at least a year after the deaths, to improve the response to suicide clusters and murder–suicide. The circles of vulnerability model can assist in identifying those within a community who may be at elevated risk of developing mental health difficulties or engaging in suicidal behavior. In terms of grief reactions including prolonged and complicated grief, little is known about best practice and evidence-informed interventions, in particular for survivors of murder–suicide. So far, sense making and EMDR have been the only interventions developed for survivors of murder–suicide based on the available literature, with limited evaluation in terms of outcomes for survivors.

It is recommended to prioritize research into developing and evaluating the efficacy of specific interventions for survivors of murder–suicide based on high-quality studies, including randomized controlled trials.

Corresponding author

Ella Arensman
National Suicide Research Foundation
Department of Epidemiology and Public Health
University College Cork
Cork
Ireland
earensman@ucc.ie

References

Andriessen, K. (2009). Can postvention be prevention? *Crisis, 30*(1), 43–47. http://doi.org/10.1027/0227-5910.30.1.43

Arensman, E., & McAuliffe, C. (2015). Clustering and contagion of suicidal behaviour. In U. Kumar (Ed.), *Suicidal behaviour: Underlying dynamics* (pp. 110–120). London, UK: Routledge.

Arensman, E., Wall, A., McAuliffe, C., Corcoran, P., Williamson, E., McCarthy, J., ... Perry, I. J. (2013). *Second report of the Suicide Support and Information System*. Cork, Ireland: National Suicide Research Foundation.

Berkowitz, L., McCauley, J., Schuurman, D. L., & Jordan, J. R. (2011). In J. R. Jordan & J. L. McIntosh (Eds.), *Grief after suicide: Understanding the consequences and caring for the survivors* (pp. 3–18). New York, NY: Routledge.

Boelen, P. A. (2015). Peritraumatic distress and dissociation in prolonged grief and posttraumatic stress following violent and unexpected deaths. *Journal of Trauma & Dissociation, 16*(5), 541–550. http://doi.org/10.1080/15299732.2015.1027841

Boelen, P. A., de Keijser, J., & Smid, G. (2015). Cognitive-behavioral variables mediate the impact of violent loss on post-loss psychopathology. *Psychology Trauma, 7*(4), 382–390. http://doi.org/10.1037/tra0000018

Cerel, J., Jordan, J. R., & Duberstein, P. R. (2008). The impact of suicide on the family. *Crisis, 29*(1), 38–44. http://doi.org/10.1027/0227-5910.29.1.38

Commonwealth Australia. (2012). *Developing a community plan for preventing and responding to suicide clusters*. Melbourne, Australia: University of Melbourne.

Eliason, S. (2009). Murder-suicide: A review of the recent literature. *Journal of the American Academy of Psychiatry and Law, 37*(3), 371–376.

Everly, G. S., & Flynn, B. W. (2006). Principles and practical procedures for acute psychological first aid training for personnel without mental health experience. *International Journal for Emergency Mental Health, 8*(2), 93–100.

Flynn, S., Swinson, N., While, D., Hunt, I. M., Roscoe, A., Rodway, C., ... Shaw, J. (2009). Homicide followed by suicide: a cross-sectional study. *Journal of Forensic Psychiatry & Psychology, 20*(2), 306–321. http://doi.org/10.1080/14789940802364369

Gillies, J., & Neimeyer, R. A. (2006). Loss, grief and the search for significance: Toward a model of meaning reconstruction in bereavement. *Journal of Constructivist Psychology, 19*(1), 31–65. http://doi.org/10.1080/10720530500311182

Gould, M. S. (2001). Suicide and the media. In H. Hendin & J. J. Mann (Eds.), *Suicide prevention: Clinical and scientific aspects (Annals of the New York Academy of Sciences)* (pp. 200–224). New York, NY: New York Academy of Sciences.

Gould, M. S., Wallenstein, S., & Davidson, L. (1989). Suicide clusters: A critical review. *Suicide and Life-Threatening Behavior, 19*(1), 17–29. http://doi.org/10.1111/j.1943-278X.1989.tb00363.x

Hacker, K., Collins, J., Gross-Young, L., Almeida, S., & Burke, N. (2008). Coping with youth suicide and overdose: One community's efforts to investigate, intervene, and prevent suicide contagion. *Crisis, 29*(2), 86–95. http://doi.org/10.1027/0227-5910.29.2.86

Haw, C., Hawton, K., Niedzwiedz, C., & Platt, S. (2013). Suicide clusters: A review of risk factors and mechanisms. *Suicide and Life-Threatening Behaviour, 43*(1), 97–108. http://doi.org/10.1111/j.1943-278X.2012.00130.x

Hawton, K., Simkin, S., & Rees, S. (2008). Help is at hand for people bereaved by suicide and other traumatic death. *Psychiatric Bulletin, 32*(8), 309–311. http://doi.org/10.1192/pb.bp.107.018242

Hazell, P. (1991). Postvention after teenage suicide: An Australian experience. *Journal of Adolescence, 14*(4), 335–342. http://doi.org/10.1016/0140-1971(91)90002-9

Joiner, T. (1999). The clustering and contagion of suicide. *Current Directions in Psychological Science, 8*(3), 89–92. http://doi.org/10.1111/1467-8721.00021

Joiner, T. (2014). *The perversion of virtue: Understanding murder-suicide*. Oxford, UK: Oxford University Press.

Jordan, J. R. (2008). Bereavement after suicide. *Psychiatric Annals, 38*(10), 670–685. http://doi.org/10.3928/00485713-20081001-05

Jordan, J. R., & McIntosh, J. L. (2011). *Grief after suicide: Understanding the consequences and caring for the survivors.* New York, NY: Routledge.

Kaltman, S., & Bonanno, G. A. (2003). Trauma and bereavement: Examining the impact of sudden and violent deaths. *Journal of Anxiety Disorders, 17*(2), 131–147.

Keesee, N. J., Currier, J. M., & Neimeyer, R. A. (2008). Predictors of grief following the death of one's child: The contribution of finding meaning. *Journal of Clinical Psychology, 64*(10), 1145–1163. http://doi.org/10.1002/jclp.20502

Krulewitch, C. J. (2009). *Epidemiology of intimate partner homicide-suicide events among women of child-bearing age in Maryland, 1994–2003. American Journal of Forensic Medicine and Pathology, 30*(4), 362–365.

Lahad, M., & Cohen, A. (2004). 25 years community of stress prevention and intervention. In O. Ayalon, A. Cohen, & M. Lahad (Eds.), *Community stress prevention* (Vol. 5). Kiryat Shmona, Israel: The Community Stress Prevention Center.

Larkin, G., & Beautrais, A. (2012). *Geospatial mapping of suicide clusters.* Auckland, New Zealand: Te Pou o Te Whakarro Nui.

Logan, J., Hill, H. A., Lynberg Black, M., Crosby, A. E., Karch, D. L., Barnes, J. D., & Lubell, K. M. (2008). Characteristics of perpetrators in homicide-followed-by-suicide incidents: National Violent Death Reporting System, 17 US States, 2003–2005. *American Journal of Epidemiology, 168*(9), 1056–1064. http://doi.org/10.1093/aje/kwn213

Marzuk, P. M., Tardiff, K., & Hirsch, C. S. (1992). The epidemiology of murder suicide. *Journal of the American Medical Association, 267*(23), 3179–3190. http://doi.org/10.1001/jama.1992.03480230071031

Nakajima, S., Ito, M., Shirai, A., & Konishi, T. (2012). Complicated grief in those bereaved by violent death: The effects of post-traumatic stress disorder on complicated grief. *Dialogues in Clinical Neuroscience, 14*(2), 210–214.

Neimeyer, R. A., Baldwin, S. A., & Gillies, J. (2006). Continuing bonds and reconstructing meaning: Mitigating complications in bereavement. *Death Studies, 30*(8), 715–738. http://doi.org/10.1080/07481180600848322

Nock, M. K., & Marzuk, P. M. (1999). Suicide and violence. In K. Hawton & K. van Heeringen (Eds.), *The international handbook of suicide and attempted suicide* (pp. 437–446). New York, NY: Wiley.

Parnell, L. (2007). *A therapist's guide to EMDR: Tools and techniques for successful treatment.* New York, NY: W. W. Norton.

Petrus Consulting. (2006). *Review of general bereavement support and specific services following suicide bereavement.* Dublin, Ireland: National Office for Suicide Prevention.

Pirkis, J., & Blood, R. W. (2001). Suicide and the media. Part II: Portrayal in fictional media. *Crisis, 22*(4), 155–162. http://doi.org/10.1027//0227-5910.22.4.146

Pirkis, J., & Nordentoft, M. (2011). Media influences on suicide and attempted suicide. In R. O'Connor, S. Platt, & J. Gordon (Eds.), *International handbook of suicide prevention: Research, policy and practice* (pp. 531–544). New York, NY: Wiley-Blackwell.

Public Health England. (2015). *Identifying and responding to suicide clusters and contagion: A practice resource* (pp. 26–29). London, UK: Author.

Robertson, L., Skegg, K., Poore, M., Williams, S., & Taylor, B. (2012). An adolescent suicide cluster and the possible role of electronic communication technology. *Crisis, 33*(4), 239–245. http://doi.org/10.1027/0227-5910/a000140

Samaritans. (2014). *Media guidelines for reporting suicide.* Retrieved from http://www.samaritans.org/sites/default/files/kcfinder/files/press/Samaritans%20Media%20Guidelines%202013%20UK.pdf

Shapiro, F. (1995). *Eye movement desensitization and reprocessing: Basic principles, protocols, and procedures.* New York, NY: Guilford Press.

Shear, M. K., Simon, N., Wall, M., Zisook, S., Neimeyer, R., Duan, N., ... Gorscak, B. (2011). Complicated grief and related bereavement issues for DSM-5. *Depression and Anxiety, 28*(2), 103–117. http://doi.org/10.1002/da.20780

Solomon, R. M., & Rando, T. A. (2007). Utilization of EMDR in the treatment of grief and mourning. *Journal of EMDR Practice and Research, 1*(2), 109–117. http://doi.org/10.1891/1933-3196.1.2.109

Stack, S. (2005). Suicide in the media: A quantitative review of studies based on nonfictional stories. *Suicide and Life-Threatening Behavior, 35*(2), 121–133. http://doi.org/10.1521/suli.35.2.121.62877

World Health Organization. (2014). *Preventing suicide: A global imperative.* Geneva, Switzerland: Author. Retrieved from http://apps.who.int/iris/bitstream/10665/131056/1/9789241564779_eng.pdf

Zisook, S., & Shear, K. (2009). Grief and bereavement: What psychiatrists need to know. *World Psychiatry, 8*(2), 67–74. http://doi.org/10.1002/j.2051-5545.2009.tb00217.x

Chapter 20

Lack of Trust in the Health Care System by Suicide-Bereaved Parents

Rossana Pettersén

Department of Clinical Neuroscience, Karolinska Institute, Stockholm, Sweden

Abstract: Approximately 62 % of individuals who die by suicide had contacted the health care system within a year prior to their death. It is conceivable that bereaved parents, who have lost a child to suicide, lose trust in the health care system. This may prevent them from seeking professional treatment when needed, and reduce their prospect of recovery. This chapter presents the construct of trust in the health care system and a review of empirical evidence regarding the level of trust in the health care system in suicide-bereaved parents. It concludes with recommendations for future research in this area.

Introduction

The suicide of a child can be a devastating event that puts parents at high risk of developing psychological problems, such as depression, anxiety, and posttraumatic stress disorder (Murphy, Johnson, Chung, & Beaton, 2003). Suicide-bereaved parents are also at high risk of taking their own lives (Qin, Agerbo, & Mortensen, 2002) and dying prematurely (Tal Young et al., 2012). Research shows that an average of 62 % of suicide victims, aged 35 or less, had contacted the health care system within a year before their suicide (Luoma, Martin, & Pearson, 2002). After losing a child to suicide, it is conceivable that some parents' trust in the health care system will be shaken or that they will have low expectations regarding clinicians' ability to help, especially if their child had had contact with health professionals. This attitude may prevent the bereaved to seek help when needed, and consequently, reduce their chances of recovery. To date, there is scarce research regarding trust in the health care system in suicide-bereaved populations.

Trust in the Health Care System

Trust in the health care system is an attitude that refers to the patient's confidence that clinicians will provide their services competently, responsibly, honesty, ethically, and with concern (Hall, Dugan, Zheng, & Mishra, 2001). The construct of *trust in the health care system* intrinsically includes the elements of the patient's vulnerability and their expectation that health care providers will act in the patient's best interests. When measuring the performance of clinical interventions, the scientific literature uses the words *trust, satisfaction,* and *faith* as synonymous;

however, trust is not equivalent to satisfaction. *Satisfaction* is also used to assess performance, but in contrast to *trust,* it refers to a personal assessment of past events. *Trust* implies a future-oriented evaluation of an individual or a system.

Why the Study of Trust in the Health Care System Matters

The study of trust in the health care system is important because trust promotes the use of health services and favors patients' behaviors that are essential for effective treatment, such as disclosure of symptoms, adherence to therapy, medication compliance, and behavioral changes necessary to promote recovery (Gilson, 2003; Hall et al., 2001). Obversely, a very low level of trust or no trust at all in the health care system is associated with an increased risk of psychological distress (Ahnquist, Wamala, & Lindström, 2010), low self-rated health (Armstrong et al., 2006), increased risk of daily smoking (Lindström & Janzon, 2007), and decreased likelihood to undergo screening for life-threatening diseases (Yang, Matthews, & Hillemeier, 2011). In summary, lack of trust in the health care system can be a significant barrier to health service use, which increases the likelihood of negative health outcomes.

What Predicts Lack of Trust in the Health Care System?

So far, studies show inconsistent results with respect to the determinants of trust in the health care system. Only age seems to have a modest, positive correlation with trust (Hall et al., 2001), but it is not known if this correlation is due to a generational effect or to the fact that older people have more contact with health professionals. A patient's personality is not a strong predictor of trust (Kao, Green, Davis, Koplan, & Cleary, 1998; Thom, Ribisl, Stewart, & Luke, 1999), and racial minority groups are more distrustful of the health services (Jacobs et al., 2011).

Lack of Trust in the Health Care System in Suicide-Bereaved Populations

Research regarding the association between suicide bereavement (or bereavement in general) and trust in the health care system is scarce. A systematic search of scientific literature conducted in November 2015 identified only one large study in suicide-bereaved populations: a Swedish, nationwide population-based survey of 569 suicide-bereaved parents and a matched comparison group of 326 nonbereaved parents, both identified from national registers (Pettersén, Omerov, Steineck, Titelman et al., 2015). Lack of trust in the health care system was considerably more prevalent in suicide-bereaved parents (47%) than in nonbereaved parents (18%). In the bereaved group, the variables associated with lack of trust in the health care system were high scores of current depression as measured by the Patient Health Questionnaire – ninth version (Arroll et al., 2010), living in a big city (>200,000 inhabitants), and being single.

Given that lack of trust in the health care system in the general population is associated with 59% increased risk for psychological distress in men and 83% in women (Ahnquist et al., 2010), the researchers argued that this may be an explanation for the observed association between lack of trust in the health care system and depression. Pettersén, Omerov, Steineck, Titelman et al., (2015) also found that even after excluding parents who reported psychological morbidity 10 or more years before the study (a potential confounder), currently depressed individuals were the most distrustful of the health care system, both in the bereaved and non-bereaved groups. Furthermore, the higher the level of depression, the higher the reported level of lack of trust in the health care system. This was true in both suicide-bereaved and non-bereaved parents.

Living in a big city (>200,000 inhabitants) was another variable associated with lack of trust in the health care system in the suicide-bereaved parents. There was a statistically significant trend where the more populous the place of residence, the greater the lack of trust in the health care system in the suicide bereaved. Also, the deceased child's contact with the health care system was more prevalent in more populous than in less populous places of residence. Previous research has shown that confidence in the health system's provision of effective treatment is higher in rural areas than in urban areas (Haven, Celaya, Pierson, Weisskopf, & Mackinnon, 2013). Based on this observation, Pettersén, Omerov, Steineck, Titelman et al. (2015) suggested that a number of factors present in big urban areas, such as lower sense of community, more socioeconomic disparities, and higher expectations in the quality of health services, may contribute to the bereaved parents' lack of trust in the health care system.

Moreover, suicide-bereaved single parents reported lower trust than the bereaved who were married or who had a romantic partner. It is possible that bereaved single parents experience additional stressors, such as economic difficulties and negative interactions with governmental institutions, and studies have shown that singlehood is associated with negative grief outcomes (Ostfeld, Ryan, Hiatt, & Hegyi, 1993).

As mentioned above, studies concerning suicide bereavement and trust in the health care services are scarce. However, there are previous studies that corroborate the results that Pettersén, Omerov, Steineck, Dyregrov et al. (2015) found in their Swedish population-based study. An US-based study looked at attitudes toward, and perceptions of, the clinicians who were treating their loved one before the suicide in a group of 71 suicide-bereaved relatives and friends (Peterson, Luoma, & Dunne, 2002). The participants were asked to describe how their attitudes and beliefs regarding mental health care changed as a consequence of their loss, and the category "lack of faith in clinicians/mental health care system" was endorsed by 27% of the participants. Similarly, one of the themes coming from the interviews in a Swedish qualitative study of 18 suicide-bereaved siblings' perception of health services was that siblings did not trust the health services' ability to help (Pettersén, Omerov, Steineck, Dyregrov et al., 2015). This attitude was based on the perceived negative experiences that the deceased sibling had had with health services before their suicide. When the bereaved perceived the professional care provided to the deceased sibling as less than optimal, they did not seek professional help for themselves, even when they needed it.

Previous disappointments and negative encounters with health providers are reasons for some bereaved persons not to trust health professionals' ability to help, and to refrain from seeking professional care (Dyregrov & Dyregrov, 2008). In the previously mentioned nationwide study, Pettersén, Omerov, Steineck, Titelman et al., (2015) found that suicide-bereaved parents whose children had been in contact with health care services, were more disappointed with the quality of care than suicide-bereaved parents whose children did not contact the health care system. It is possible that the suicide shattered expectations of a fair and benevolent world (Janoff-Bulman, 1989) in parents who trusted the health care system before their loss.

Lack of Trust as a Criterion for Complicated Grief

The bereaved persons' inability to trust others has been recognized as a diagnostic criterion of complicated or prolonged grief (Boelen & Prigerson, 2013). Two criteria sets to diagnose complicated grief were proposed for the inclusion of this condition in the *Diagnostic and Statistical Manual of Mental Disorders*, 5th Edition (DSM-5), and these criteria refer to difficulties trusting others:

a. Prolonged grief disorder (Prigerson et al., 2009): The diagnostic criteria for prolonged grief disorder include (under "Cognitive, Emotional and Behavioral Symptoms") the item "inability to trust others since the loss," which the bereaved person must experience daily or to an impairing degree. To diagnose prolonged grief disorder, the symptoms and impairment must be present for at least 6 months.

b. Complicated grief (Shear et al., 2011): The diagnostic criteria for complicated grief include "persisting difficulty trusting or caring about other people or feeling intensely envious of others who have not experienced a similar loss" (Boelen & Prigerson, 2013, p. 93). To diagnose complicated grief, the symptoms and impairment must be present for at least 1 month.

There is an increased likelihood of complications in the course of grief after sudden, violent, and unexpected deaths (Nakajima, Ito, Shirai, & Konishi, 2012), and the incidence of complicated grief is high in suicide-bereaved individuals (Mitchell, Kim, Prigerson, & Mortimer-Stephens, 2004; Tal Young et al., 2012). In some cases, the suicide-bereaved person's inability to trust the health care system may reflect complicated grief; however, more research is needed to clarify this potential association.

Restoring Trust in the Health Care System in the Suicide-Bereaved

Can health professionals restore trust in the health care system in the suicide-bereaved, and if yes, how? Trust occurs in the context of a relationship between the "trustor," in this case, the suicide-bereaved individual, and the "trustee," the health care system. Trust cannot be elicited from the trustor per se, and the trustee should show trustworthiness in the first place. Trustworthiness is the quality of being reliable, and it is one of the main reasons people contact mental care providers (Jesse, Dolbier, & Blanchard, 2008). Since negative portrayals of the trustworthiness of mental health providers are constructed based on previous experiences, they may be overcome by more trustworthy behaviors by clinicians (Brown & Calnan, 2012). For instance, a physician's communication style and interpersonal skills are consistently associated with trust (Aruguete & Roberts, 2002). There is also evidence that satisfaction, continuity of care, doctor's reliability, valued listening time (Laugharne, Priebe, McCabe, Garland, & Clifford, 2012), and clear communication, are positively associated with trust (Maidment, Brown, & Calnan, 2011).

Recommendations for Future Research

The study of trust in the health care system in suicide-bereaved populations is incipient. Further research in this area is crucial, as the lack of trust increases the risk of negative health outcomes, and suicide-bereaved relatives are at risk for mental and physical ill-health. Fine-grained information is needed to better understand whether the distrust experienced by the bereaved concerns the entire health care system, psychiatric services only (institutional trust), or specific categories of health providers such as nurses, doctors, or psychologists (interpersonal trust). Furthermore, it should be further explored whether the bereaved persons are able to trust the therapeutic efficacy of professional interventions, especially when the person who died by suicide received professional help.

Despite the high self-perceived need for mental health care, the suicide-bereaved receive less professional support than needed, and in addition, the received support may not be satisfactory (Wilson & Marshall, 2010). An important factor to measure in future research is the association between trust and help-seeking behavior. There is evidence that distrust of professionals is a barrier to seeking professional help in suicide-bereaved adults (McMenamy, Jordan, & Mitchell, 2008). Studies are needed to clarify whether this lack of trust hinders help-seeking behavior in all age groups, whether it refers to both mental and physical care, and for how long it prevails. Also, since trust in the health care system refers to institutional trust, future research could investigate if persons bereaved by suicide lack trust in other institutions that could potentially facilitate the bereavement process, such as peer support groups, insurance companies, the legal system, the school system, and religious institutions.

Another research question is whether distrust in the health care system is a phenomenon unique to the suicide-bereaved or is shared by other bereaved, especially those who have experienced other types of sudden and violent losses. For instance, there is evidence that perception of poor efforts and distrust in the quality of care provided to a parent dying due to cancer, increases the risk of depressive symptoms in bereaved youngsters (Bylund-Grenklo et al., 2013). Moreover, complicated grief may induce inability to trust others, and future research could explore whether lack of trust in suicide-bereaved populations reflects complicated grief.

Since current research on trust in the health care system in the suicide-bereaved is cross-sectional, longitudinal studies are needed to determine if the reported lack of trust might have existed even before the suicide, and if it persists over time.

Implications for Practice

At present, there is no identified optimal clinical approach to restore trust in the health care system in the suicide-bereaved. However, clinicians who encounter suicide-bereaved individuals could start by elucidating their patients' attitudes toward health care services (see also Chapter 13 on the possible roles of general practitioners). Do they think that the procedures to get access to care and the interventions offered to the deceased loved one had a negative impact on their trust in clinicians and the health care system? What about their previous experiences with health care providers? Clinicians could also assess if low trust in the health services translates to detrimental attitudes, such as the reluctance to take psychiatric medication or to undergo clinical examinations. Clinicians could then help the nontrusting suicide-bereaved persons to reframe these attitudes by helping them to solve specific areas of concern. For example, if, regarding the suicide of their loved one, bereaved individuals mention "the clinicians' failure to assess suicide risk" or "the prescription of the wrong medication" as reasons for not trusting the health services, clinicians could, without being disrespectful, help patients to gain a better perspective by discussing, for instance, the nonexistence of a 100 % reliable instrument to predict suicide or that finding the right psychotropic and dose can be difficult.

So far, studies show that a high level of depression, living in a big city, and being single are variables related to lack of trust in the health care system in parents bereaved by suicide (Pettersén, Omerov, Steineck, Titelman et al., 2015). Unfortunately, the direction of this association remains unknown. On the one hand, clinicians could take special care to assess and target depression in the suicide-bereaved and, on the other hand, be observant of those living in big cities and those who are single because they may be more distrustful of the health care system.

Corresponding author

Rossana Pettersén
Department of Clinical Neuroscience
Karolinska Institute
Stockholm
Sweden
rossana.pettersen@ki.se

References

Ahnquist, J., Wamala, S. P., & Lindström, M. (2010). What has trust in the health-care system got to do with psychological distress? Analyses from the national Swedish survey of public health. *International Journal for Quality in Health Care, 22*(4), 250–258. http://doi.org/10.1093/intqhc/mzq024

Armstrong, K., Rose, A., Peters, N., Long, J. A., McMurphy, S., & Shea, J. A. (2006). Distrust of the health care system and self-reported health in the United States. *Journal of General Internal Medicine, 21*(4), 292–297. http://doi.org/10.1111/j.1525-1497.2006.00396.x

Arroll, B., Goodyear-Smith, F., Crengle, S., Gunn, J., Kerse, N., Fishman, T., … Hatcher, S. (2010). Validation of PHQ-2 and PHQ-9 to screen for major depression in the primary care population. *Annals of Family Medicine, 8*(4), 348–353. http://doi.org/10.1370/afm.1139

Aruguete, M. S., & Roberts, C. A. (2002). Participants' ratings of male physicians who vary in race and communication style. *Psychological Reports, 91*(3), 793–806. http://doi.org/10.2466/PR0.91.7.793-806

Boelen, P. A., & Prigerson, H. G. (2013). Prolonged grief disorder as a new diagnostic category in DSM-5. In M. S. Stroebe, H. Schut, & J. van den Bout (Eds.), *Complicated grief: Scientific foundations for health care professionals* (pp. 85–98). New York, NY: Routledge.

Brown, P. & Calnan, M. (2012). Braving a faceless new world? Conceptualizing trust in the pharmaceutical industry and its products. *Health, 16*(1), 57–75.

Bylund-Grenklo, T. B., Kreicbergs, U. C., Valdimarsdóttir, U. A., Nyberg, T., Steineck, G., & Fürst, C. J. (2013). Communication and trust in the care provided to a dying parent: a nationwide study of cancer-bereaved youths. *Journal of Clinical Oncology, 31*(23), 2886–2894.

Dyregrov, K., & Dyregrov, A. (2008). *Effective grief and bereavement support. The role of family, friends, colleagues, schools, and support professionals*. London, UK: Jessica Kingsley Publishers.

Gilson, L. (2003). Trust and the development of health care as a social institution. *Social Science & Medicine, 56*(7), 1453–1468. http://doi.org/10.1016/S0277-9536(02)00142-9

Hall, M. A., Dugan, E., Zheng, B., & Mishra, A. K. (2001). Trust in physicians and medical institutions: what is it, can it be measured, and does it matter? *The Milbank Quarterly, 79*(4), 613–639. http://doi.org/10.1111/1468-0009.00223

Haven, K., Celaya, M. F., Pierson, J., Weisskopf, A. J., & Mackinnon, N. J. (2013). Comparison of health confidence in rural, suburban and urban areas in the UK and the USA: a secondary analysis. *BMJ Open, 3*(5), e002640. http://doi.org/10.1136/bmjopen-2013-002640

Jacobs, E. A., Mendenhall, E., McAlearney, A. S., Rolle, I., Whitaker, E. E., Warnecke, R., & Ferrans, C. E. (2011). An exploratory study of how trust in health care institutions varies across African American, Hispanic and white populations. *Communication and Medicine, 8*(1), 89–98. http://doi.org/10.1558/cam.v8i1.89

Janoff-Bulman, R. (1989). Assumptive worlds and the stress of traumatic events: Applications of the schema construct [Special issue]. *Social Cognition, 7*(2), 113–136. http://doi.org/10.1521/soco.1989.7.2.113

Jesse, D. E., Dolbier, C. L., & Blanchard, A. (2008). Barriers to seeking help and treatment suggestions for prenatal depressive symptoms: focus groups with rural low-income women. *Issues in Mental Health Nursing, 29*(1), 3–19. http://doi.org/10.1080/01612840701748664

Kao, A. C., Green, D. C., Davis, N. A., Koplan, J. P., & Cleary, P. D. (1998). Patients' trust in their physicians: Effects of choice, continuity, and payment method. *Journal of General Internal Medicine, 13*(10), 681–686. http://doi.org/10.1046/j.1525-1497.1998.00204.x

Laugharne, R., Priebe, S., McCabe, R., Garland, N., & Clifford, D. (2012). Trust, choice and power in mental health care: Experiences of patients with psychosis. *International Journal of Social Psychiatry, 58*(5), 496–504. http://doi.org/10.1177/0020764011408658

Lindström, M., & Janzon, E. (2007). Social capital, institutional (vertical) trust and smoking: a study of daily smoking and smoking cessation among ever smokers. *Scandinavian Journal of Public Health, 35*(5), 460–467.

Luoma, J. B., Martin, C. E., & Pearson, J. L. (2002). Contact with mental health and primary care providers before suicide: a review of the evidence. *American Journal of Psychiatry, 159*(6), 909–916. http://doi.org/10.1176/appi.ajp.159.6.909

Maidment, I. D., Brown, P., & Calnan, M. (2011). An exploratory study of the role of trust in medication management within mental health services. *International Journal of Clinical Pharmacy, 33*(4), 614–620. http://doi.org/10.1007/s11096-011-9510-5

McMenamy, J. M., Jordan, J. R., & Mitchell, A. M. (2008). What do suicide survivors tell us they need? Results of a pilot study. *Suicide and Life-Threatening Behavior, 38*(4), 375–389. http://doi.org/10.1521/suli.2008.38.4.375

Mitchell, A. M., Kim, Y., Prigerson, H. G., & Mortimer-Stephens, M. (2004). Complicated grief in survivors of suicide. *Crisis, 25*(1), 12–18. http://doi.org/10.1027/0227-5910.25.1.12

Murphy, S. a., Johnson, L. C., Chung, I.-J., & Beaton, R. D. (2003). The prevalence of PTSD following the violent death of a child and predictors of change 5 years later. *Journal of Traumatic Stress, 16*(1), 17–25. http://doi.org/10.1023/A:1022003126168

Nakajima, S., Ito, M., Shirai, A., & Konishi, T. (2012). Complicated grief in those bereaved by violent death: The effects of post-traumatic stress disorder on complicated grief. *Dialogues in Clinical Neuroscience, 14*(2), 210–214.

Ostfeld, B. M., Ryan, T., Hiatt, M., & Hegyi, T. (1993). Maternal grief after sudden infant death syndrome. *Journal of Developmental and Behavioral Pediatrics, 14*(3), 156–162. http://doi.org/10.1097/00004703-199306010-00005

Peterson, E. M., Luoma, J. B., & Dunne, E. (2002). Suicide survivors' perceptions of the treating clinician. *Suicide and Life-Threatening Behavior, 32*(2), 158–166. http://doi.org/10.1521/suli.32.2.158.24406

Pettersén, R., Omerov, P., Steineck, G., Dyregrov, A., Titelman, D., Dyregrov, K., & Nyberg, U. (2015). Suicide-bereaved siblings' perception of health services. *Death Studies, 39*(6), 323–331. http://doi.org/10.1080/07481187.2014.946624

Pettersén, R., Omerov, P., Steineck, G., Titelman, D., Dyregrov, A., Nyberg, T., & Nyberg, U. (2015). Lack of trust in the health-care system after losing a child to suicide. *Crisis, 36*(3), 161–172. http://doi.org/10.1027/0227-5910/a000312

Prigerson, H. G., Horowitz, M. J., Jacobs, S. C., Parkes, C. M., Aslan, M., Goodkin, K., … Maciejewski, P. K. (2009). Prolonged grief disorder: Psychometric validation of criteria proposed for DSM-V and ICD-11. *PLoS Medicine, 6*(8), e1000121. http://doi.org/10.1371/journal.pmed.1000121

Qin, P., Agerbo, E., & Mortensen, P. (2002). Suicide risk in relation to family history of completed suicide and psychiatric disorders: a nested case-control study based on longitudinal registers. *The Lancet, 360*(9340), 1126–1130. http://doi.org/10.1016/S0140-6736(02)11197-4

Shear, M. K., Simon, N., Wall, M., Zisook, S., Neimeyer, R., Duan, N., … Keshaviah, A. (2011). Complicated grief and related bereavement issues for DSM-5. *Depression and Anxiety, 28*(2), 103–117. http://doi.org/10.1002/da.20780

Tal Young, I., Iglewicz, A., Glorioso, D., Lanouette, N., Seay, K., Ilapakurti, M., & Zisook, S. (2012). Suicide bereavement and complicated grief. *Dialogues in Clinical Neuroscience, 14*(2), 177–186.

Thom, D. h., Ribisl, K. M., Stewart, A. L., & Luke, D. A. (1999). Further validation and reliability testing of the Trust in Physician Scale. The Stanford Trust Study Physicians. *Medical Care, 37*(5), 510–517. http://doi.org/10.1097/00005650-199905000-00010

Wilson, A., & Marshall, A. (2010). The support needs and experiences of suicidally bereaved family and friends. *Death Studies, 34*(7), 625–640. http://doi.org/10.1080/07481181003761567

Yang, T.-C., Matthews, S. A., & Hillemeier, M. M. (2011). Effect of health care system distrust on breast and cervical cancer screening in Philadelphia, Pennsylvania. *American Journal of Public Health, 101*(7), 1297–1305. http://doi.org/10.2105/AJPH.2010.300061

Chapter 21

Impact of Client Suicide on Health and Mental Health Professionals

Dolores Angela Castelli Dransart[1], Marta Treven[2], Onja T. Grad[3], and Karl Andriessen[4]

[1]School of Social Work Fribourg, University of Applied Sciences and Arts Western Switzerland, Givisiez, Switzerland
[2]Slovenian Association for Suicide Prevention, Ljubljana, Slovenia
[3]University Psychiatric Hospital, Ljubljana, Slovenia
[4]School of Psychiatry, University of New South Wales, Sydney, Australia

Abstract: This chapter addresses the personal and professional impact of a client suicide on health and mental health professionals (the phrase client suicide refers to client and patient suicide). It is based on a review of the literature, and on the research and clinical experience of the authors. On a personal level, professionals can experience emotional turmoil or disruption, stress reactions ranging from acute stress to posttraumatic stress disorder, or grief and bereavement. They can also doubt their professional judgment, their competence and skills in assessing and supporting suicidal people, and fear legal consequences. Client suicide is also likely to cause changes in their professional practices such as increased awareness of suicidality issues and more cautious practices. The severity of the reactions following a client suicide depends on a variety of factors, related to the professional, the client, their relationship, and the context of the suicide, along with the support sought and received. Support and training for professionals are protective factors, which should be provided on a regular basis. Recommendations for dealing with the event of a client suicide both at the institutional and individual level are suggested.

Introduction

A substantial number of health and mental health professionals have experienced the suicide of a client. Studies indicate that between 51% and 82% of psychiatrists (Chemtob, Hamada, Bauer, Kinney, & Torigoe, 1988; Chemtob, Bauer, Hamada, Pelowski, & Muraoka, 1989; Dewar, Eagles, Klein, Grey, & Alexander, 2000; Grad, Zavasnik, & Groleger, 1997; Henry, Séguin, & Drouin, 2003), between 22% and 39% of psychologists (Chemtob, Hamada, Bauer, Torigoe, & Kinney, 1988; Chemtob et al.,1989), 55% of nurses (Takahashi et al., 2011), 68% of general practitioners (Halligan & Corcoran, 2001), and 33% of social workers (Jacobson, Ting, Sanders, & Harrington, 2004) have experienced the suicide of a client. Yet, only a minority (approximately one third) of health professionals receive training regarding the professional and personal impact of client suicide, and many report a lack of emotional and/or of institutional support (Mangurian, Harre, Reliford, Booty, & Cournos, 2009; Pilkinton & Etkin, 2003).

Since the landmark investigations of Chemtob and colleagues (1988, 1989) in the 1980s, the suicide of a client has been considered as a professional hazard for mental health professionals. Indeed, a client suicide seems to be a relatively frequent and potentially very stressful event; for some, even the most disturbing event in their career (Hendin, Lipschitz, Maltsberger, Haas, & Wynecoop, 2000). Professionals can react in a similar way as families bereaved by suicide and experience a grief process. Professionals who lose a client to suicide can react on different levels and with various degrees of severity. Some will experience emotional turmoil, without experiencing intense grief (which usually presupposes the severance of a significant tie or attachment and a reframing of personal identity and daily life), others will experience more or less significant stress levels (e.g., acute stress) for a period of time (mostly days or weeks); a minority will experience grief, bereavement, and/or traumatic stress in the clinical range (Castelli Dransart, Gutjahr, Gulfi, Kaufmann Didisheim, & Séguin, 2013).

Professionals may experience disenfranchised grief – that is, grief that is denied the right to exist because the loss is not recognized and socially supported (Doka, 1989) or cannot be eased by common rituals of consolation (McWilliams, 2004). Professionals are often expected to maintain their professional role and its boundaries, and to repress their personal responses. Organizational procedures may also contribute to the difficulties experienced by professionals if they focus on investigative and disciplinary actions (Clark, 2014).

Emotional Impact

A client suicide is likely to have an emotional impact. Health and mental health professionals often experience similar feelings or ask questions similar to those of the bereaved relatives and friends: *"Why? How is that possible? Should I have done something more or something different?"* The most frequent reactions and feelings include shock, sadness, guilt, anger at oneself, the deceased and/or their family, a feeling of betrayal, frustration, helplessness, failure, shame, anxiety, denial, relief, and fear of legal action (Grad, 2011; Gutin, McGann, & Jordan, 2011; Ruskin, Sakinofsky, Bagby, Dickens, & Sousa, 2004). The severity of the emotional reactions and their persistence reported across studies are difficult to compare as the studies have had a different scope and used a variety of measures (Séguin, Bordeleau, Drouin, Castelli Dransart, & Giasson, 2014). Nonetheless, some studies reported intense emotional reactions (Grad et al., 1997; Hendin, Haas, Maltsberger, Szanto, & Rabinowicz, 2004; Ruskin et al., 2004; Wurst et al., 2011), others found moderate or low levels of emotional disruption (Henry et al. 2003; Castelli Dransart et al., 2013), and the emotional responses after a client suicide usually decrease over time (Wurst et al., 2011).

Predictors of emotional impact include emotional closeness to the deceased client (Campbell & Fahy, 2002; Castelli Dransart et al., 2013; Chemtob et al., 1989; Hendin et al., 2000), a feeling of responsibility for the client, and insufficient support available to the treating professional (Castelli Dransart et al., 2013). In some studies, female professionals (Grad et al., 1997; Hendin, et al., 2004; Henry, Séguin, & Drouin, 2008) and younger and/or less experienced professionals (Chemtob, Hamada, Bauer, Kinney, & Torigoe, 1988; McAdams & Foster, 2000) reported greater emotional distress. Attendance at the death scene as a coroner, living in the same environment as a client, and knowledge of the client's emotional distress may affect the emotional impact of the death on a general practitioner (GP) (Treven, Rotar Pavlič, & Grad, 2013). The reactions may also be more intense if the client had not been diagnosed with mental illness.

A study of GPs during the period 2012–2013 showed a range of beliefs regarding the impact of a client suicide: from an understanding that a suicide will affect a professional, to beliefs that one has to limit intensity, duration, and expression of one's own emotional response and even a denial of any emotional reactions (Treven et al., 2013) (Chapter 13 discusses the possible roles of GPs regarding bereavement support after a suicide). According to some study participants, a GP can be more affected than a psychiatrist because of the long-standing relationship with the client and their family (see Vignette 1), whereas others believed that a psychiatrist will be more distressed, because a client suicide will imply a greater professional failure for a mental health professional than for a GP. All GPs reported self-scrutiny about their role in the suicide and an attempt to understand the reasons for the death. In approximately two thirds of suicide cases, the GPs believed that there was nothing they could have done differently to prevent the death, although for some, this might have been a psychological self-defense mechanism.

Vignette 1

A GP working in a small isolated town described a case of client suicide for which he felt responsible. Several cognitive and emotional reactions, as well as factors influencing these reactions, transpired through his words: "I could not understand that one cardiologic examination could push him into completing suicide. I felt somehow as if I had contributed to this act because I had forced him to go on this examination in a way....

And then you have to live with it. His family members are also my patients, I keep meeting them all the time, and I know that it was very difficult for his wife for some time.... You wish you could withdraw to some different place, but you are there, you keep meeting relatives and it reminds you constantly of the suicide. In fact, you are so connected to these people because you have lived among them for so long, and you do not only have a rational but also an emotional relationship, that such things affect you more. Even if rationally you could explain to yourself that it is not just your fault, the feeling that you contributed remains.... I felt powerless. You are angry with yourself for not having thought of it, expected it, for having been caught by surprise. Because as a doctor, especially after so many years of practice, you should be able to anticipate these kinds of reactions [suicide].... Also anger toward the patient – why did he do this.... You think about many things, you analyse, you clarify with yourself whether you maybe did not inquire sufficiently, connect with the patient's feelings enough to be able to suspect and prevent this outcome, although you probably could not."

Only after months was this GP able to work again with the same concentration and motivation as before the suicide. He considered the suicide of his patient as a life ordeal which made him stronger, with a different perspective on people and better abilities to draw nearer to them.

Stress and Traumatic Reactions

A client suicide may trigger stress or traumatic reactions, such as intrusive thoughts or images, anxiety, lack of concentration, indecisiveness, avoidance of people or situations reminiscent of the suicide, impaired coping strategies (including substance abuse and suicidal ideation), reduced effectiveness in dealing with daily matters, insomnia, loss of appetite, or overreactions to suicide-related situations (Campbell & Fahy, 2002; Gaffney et al., 2009; Gutin et al. 2011; Henry et al., 2003; Treven et al., 2013). However, only a number of studies have investigated stress or traumatic reactions with validated instruments, such as the Impact of Event Scale (IES; Horowitz, Wilner, & Alvarez, 1979) or the Impact of Event Scale-Revised (IES-R; Weiss & Marmar, 1997), and findings concerning the intensity and the prevalence of stress or traumatic reactions are quite heterogeneous (Séguin et al., 2014).

Predictors of stress or traumatic reactions include psychological closeness, high level of intensity of the professional–client relationship (Castelli Dransart et al., 2013; Chemtob et al., 1989; Henry et al., 2003), feeling responsible for the treatment and care. Being a woman (Grad et al., 1997; Henry et al., 2003), less experienced (Chemtob, Hamada, Bauer, Kinney, & Torigoe, 1988; Ruskin et al., 2004), and receiving insufficient support after client suicide (Castelli Dransart et al., 2013) also increase the risk of stress and traumatic relations. Other predictors include professionals' personality traits (Ratkowska, Grad, De Leo, & Cimitan, 2014), work setting (Grad, 2009), previous experience of personal traumatic bereavement, and having visited the suicide scene (Gutin et al., 2011; Schultz, 2005). The interplay of these predictors is a key in differentiating professionals with regard to stress reactions (Castelli Dransart, Heeb, Gulfi, & Gutjahr, 2015). The most strongly impacted professionals seem to be those who felt close to the deceased client, were exposed to a higher number of suicides, received less support and training (both theoretical and clinical) in suicide risk assessment, and sought out help but did not find it. Of interest, many of these professionals were women and nurses. In summary, professionals who accumulated a high number of risk factors and were not offered sufficient support and resources experienced the greatest impact.

Grief After a Client Suicide

The grief of the professional after a client suicide is a process involving the above-mentioned emotional, stress, and traumatic reactions, influenced by the setting and/or the circumstances of the death. Caregivers react both as professionals and as human beings, and their responses vary according to a range of subjective (affective, traumatic, interaction with colleagues, and personal worldview) and objective factors (related to the treatment), as well as liability concerns (Gutin et al., 2011; Tillman, 2006). Some authors describe "a narcissistic injury" (Maltsberger, 1992) or a damage to "grandiose professional ideal" (O'Neill & Kueppenbender, 2012) as a part of mental health professional's grief after a client suicide. These refer to a therapist's assumption that if they do everything necessary in terms of treatment, a client will be safe and protected, or at least will disclose suicidal thoughts early enough to prevent a suicide.

A professional's grief and bereavement reactions depend on their personality traits, ways of coping with stress, availability of professional (supervision, supportive colleagues) and personal (family, friends) support, and extent of responsibility toward the client – that is, being a part of a treatment team or working in a private practice (Grad, 2009). The intensity and depth of the therapeutic involvement between the client and the professional is also an important factor. The reactions may be stronger in case of a long-term psychotherapeutic connection with a client than in the case of shorter or less frequent professional encounters – for example, in an emergency room. The clinicians' belief and understanding regarding the suicide triggers will either support the process of acceptance of the client's decision or add to the pain of guilt and a feeling of incompetence. Also, the professional's willingness to disclose their personal feelings, informal support available, and the institution's policy for dealing with the impact of client suicide will affect the grief process and outcomes. Client suicide might result in long-lasting negative consequences for clinicians and their clients or over time may lead to professional growth (Gulfi, Castelli Dransart, Heeb, & Gutjahr, 2016).

Impact on Professional Practice and Professional Competence

1e suicide of a client may challenge feelings of self-confidence and professional competence. nay trigger self-doubt, lead to decreased self-esteem and questioning of one's own professial skills and professional identity, and may even result in leaving the profession. Some clinicians report fear or avoidance of working with suicidal clients and being anxious about public or legal repercussions (Campbell & Fahy, 2002; Gulfi et al., 2016; Gutin et al., 2011; Treven et al., 2013). Professionals may also be concerned about reactions of the family or significant others of the deceased (Wurst et al., 2011). In a study involving GPs, some of them never spoke to the bereaved relatives about the death, even if the relatives were their patients (Treven et al., 2013). Nevertheless, feeling sufficiently supported and integrated in professional networks may reduce negative reactions concerning one's professional competence (Gulfi, Heeb, Castelli Dransart, & Gutjahr, 2015; Ruskin et al., 2004).

A client suicide may impact the professional practice in two ways: It may offer an opportunity for professional growth, or it may hinder it (Gulfi et al., 2016; Ratkowska et al., 2014). The former includes increased sensitivity to warning signs and risk factors for suicide, increased knowledge about effective interventions, such as offering patients more time or involving relatives, and increased awareness that suicide can occur within institutions. It may also provide insights regarding one's own clinical competence, encourage consultations with colleagues or supervisors, and over time lead to posttraumatic growth. The latter includes questioning one's own clinical judgment and competence in assessment of suicide risk, becoming more prudent in reporting and dealing with suicide risk, becoming overcautious and frequently hospitalizing low-risk patients for extended periods of time, and prescribing more psychopharmacological treatments. Some clinicians start to perceive suicide as less preventable, find it difficult to trust a suicidal client or refuse to treat them (Schultz, 2005), or decline to take care of suicidal clients (Gulfi et al., 2016; Gutin et al., 2011; Hendin et al., 2000; Henry et al., 2003). Some professionals report diminished work performance and difficulties in being fully present or genuinely empathic during clinical encounters. A client suicide can also have a negative impact on an institution, such as disturbed or even conflictual (i.e., scapegoat dynamics) relationships among teams or colleagues, communication difficulties, high staff turnover, absenteeism, or burnout (Joyce & Wallbridge, 2003; Pommereau, 2004).

A number of factors determine the impact of client suicide on professional practice and feelings of competence. Again, the impact seems stronger for clinicians who feel closer to the clients, have had a longer relationship with them (Henry et al., 2003; Gaffney et al., 2009; Gulfi, Castelli Dransart, Heeb, & Gutjahr, 2010; Gulfi et al., 2016), or have felt responsible for care, and received insufficient support (Gulfi et al., 2015). In some studies, female (Gaffney et al., 2009; Gulfi et al., 2010, 2016; Henry et al., 2008) and less experienced professionals (McAdams & Foster, 2000) reported more changes to their practices than male or more experienced professionals. The interplay of factors is more influential than single predictors. In a study by Gulfi et al. (2015), a long and close relationship with a client resulted in greater changes in practices only for professionals who needed and sought support after the suicide.

Work Context

Some professionals report insensitive or unsupportive reactions from colleagues or within the institution (Hendin et al., 2000). A suicide can be interpreted as a mismanagement or a failure in delivery of professional care (Jobes & Maltsberger, 1995), and a psychological autopsy (or any other institutional procedure following a death) may be experienced as an inquest instead of a supportive measure (Gutin et al., 2011; see also Chapter 15 regarding postvention in the workplace). This can obstruct communication, increase (self-)isolation and the risk of scapegoating among the professionals involved (Gutin et al., 2011). Some caregivers may avoid seeking much needed help for fear of criticism from colleagues and supervisors (Ruskin et al., 2004).

Possible legal consequences may dissuade professionals from talking freely about their experience. It is not uncommon for attorneys or managers to advise professionals to limit communication with, and any disclosure of facts and emotions to families, or even within the institution, for fear of litigation or adverse consequences. These fears seem to be more pronounced in the United States, where suicidal death is the most common cause of medical malpractice claims (Bongar, 2002), than, for example in Switzerland, where only a few professionals have faced liability issues (Castelli Dransart et al., 2013). Empirical findings on institutional reactions and legal consequences are still scarce, and further research could provide more insights into these consequences of client suicide.

Support for Health and Mental Health Professionals

Support can be a protective factor for professionals who have experienced a client suicide and is a predictor for adaptive coping and lower levels of emotional turmoil and stress (Castelli Dransart et al., 2013; Gulfi et al., 2015, 2016). Although lack of support can contribute to feelings of isolation and guilt, a significant number of professionals do not receive the support they want or need (Gaffney et al., 2009; Halligan & Corcoran, 2001). Only one study reported that 78 % of professionals received sufficient support, both formal and informal, following a client suicide and were satisfied with the support received (Castelli Dransart et al., 2013). Of interest, professionals working in institutions were more supported than their colleagues in private practice, and were mainly supported by superiors and colleagues.

The types of support and their effectiveness have rarely been investigated in a systematic way. Nevertheless, findings suggest that both formal and informal support provided by colleagues, teams, family, and friends are important and usually found to be helpful (Dewar et al., 2000; Gaffney et al., 2009; McAdams & Foster, 2000; Ruskin et al., 2004). Support provided by supervisors may sometimes be considered inappropriate (Linke, Wojciak, & Day, 2002; Pieters, Gucht, Joos, & Heyn, 2003). The forms of support most appreciated are discussions within a team or with colleagues, post mortem case reviews or reviews of care provided (if they conducted in a sensitive and constructive manner) (Castelli Dransart et al., 2007). Participation in the patient's funeral can be helpful, although a personal visit to the bereaved family may be less helpful (Campbell & Fahy, 2002; Hendin et al., 2000; McAdams & Foster, 2000).

Institutional Postvention Procedures

Various professionals may be impacted by a client suicide, including psychiatrists, nurses, therapists, clinical psychologists, other members of a care team, and GPs. It is important that their needs are acknowledged, the necessary support is provided as soon as possible, and the health professionals feel safe to ask for and accept help. If a suicide happens inside the hospital, during a weekend leave, or immediately after a discharge, the institution should have a comprehensive protocol (or a procedure) covering a range of administrative, institutional, educational, and emotional areas and needs in order to protect other clients and the staff (Grad, 2012; Gutin et al., 2011). Some of these measures should be compulsory, and some should be optional for the professionals to choose.

When planning and delivering support, it is important to understand the various roles the health professionals played in the deceased client's care, what their responsibility was for the client, how intense and long-lasting their relationship was, and what their transference and countertransference was like (Grad, 2009). The suicide of a client may shatter the basic goal of therapeutic work, which is to heal and help or support the client. This is also true for those professionals (social workers, occupational therapists, etc.) whose task is not primarily therapeutic, but who are in contact with clients and work with them occasionally. The suicide of a client disrupts the working alliance and the therapeutic bond with professionals, and contaminates the relationship with guilt and a sense of involvement on the side of the caregivers. Their responsibility for the patient can thus turn into a sense of a failure, incompetence and betrayal. This might be quite devastating and calls for support (Grad, 2012).

If there are no accepted rituals and procedures after the suicide of a client, many professionals may dismiss or overlook their need for support and continue working as if nothing had happened (Gutin et al., 2011). Such denial may lead to traumatic consequences. Accepting the limitations of their work and working through a range of reactions is necessary for health professionals to recover after a client suicide.

Implications for Practice

The suicide of a client is an eventuality which health and mental health professionals working with persons suffering from serious mental distress have to take into account. In Brown's (1987, p. 103) words, there are only two kinds of therapists: those who have already experienced the suicide of a client, and those who will. It is extremely important to include more education on suicide prevention in the training curriculums for those working with populations at risk for suicide. Caregivers should be aware of the warning signs of suicide and be skilled in assessing and reassessing clients for suicidal risk as frequently as possible. However, mastering these skills will not prevent every suicide. It is necessary for young (and other) professionals in training to be prepared for the possibility of a client suicide in their practice, and relevant procedures, especially those regarding supervision and support must be available to them.

The impact of suicide and the reactions of the health professionals vary, depending on many factors. Some experience and share their intense and immediate reactions, whereas others are deeply impacted but do not express their emotions. Some experience stress-related reactions and posttraumatic stress, and some are deeply affected emotionally. Others do not react emotionally to the suicide (or deny any reactions), and consider the death as a side effect and an occupational hazard. The intensity of the professionals' responses depends not only on the nature of their relationship with the client, but also on the depth, closeness, and the importance of the relationship (Castelli Dransart et al., 2013; Cerel, Maple, Aldrich, & van de Venne, 2013). When a suicide occurs, the professionals react both on a professional and on a personal level. Therefore, professionals faced with the suicide of a client should not be considered as a homogeneous group. Research on various subgroups should be carried out more systematically to provide tailored support.

Because the needs of professionals are highly individual, it is important that postvention guidelines and protocols offer comprehensive and easily available help and support. Every institution working with highly distressed or suicidal individuals should have protocols and guidelines prepared in advance, and the procedures should be well known to the staff.

Conclusions

Although the impact of client suicide has been investigated for 30 years, findings are still incomplete and sometimes contradictory (Séguin et al., 2014). More qualitative and quantitative studies on the experiences of professionals after the suicide of a client are needed to enrich the knowledge in this field and to produce solid data on what professionals need after the suicide of a client, and to evaluate existing postvention practices. Comparative studies including a range of professional groups and the sequelae of experiencing a client death through suicide and through other types of death would also be helpful in understanding the shared and unique features of an impact of client suicide on health and mental health professionals.

Corresponding author

Dolores Angela Castelli Dransart
School of Social Work Fribourg
University of Applied Sciences and Arts Western Switzerland
Givisiez
Switzerland
angela.castelli@hefr.ch

References

Bongar, B. (2002). *The suicidal patient: Clinical and legal standards of care* (2nd ed.), Washington, DC: American Psychological Association. http://doi.org/10.1037/10424-000

Brown, H. B. (1987). The impact of suicide on therapists in training. *Comprehensive Psychiatry, 28*(2), 101–112. http://doi.org/10.1016/0010-440X(87)90075-7

Campbell, C., & Fahy, T. (2002). The role of the doctor when a patient commits suicide. *Psychiatric Bulletin, 26*(2), 44–49. http://doi.org/10.1192/pb.26.2.44

Castelli Dransart, D. A., Gutjahr, E., Gulfi, A., Kaufmann Didisheim, N., & Séguin, M. (2013). Patient suicide in institutions: Emotional responses and traumatic impact on Swiss mental health professionals. *Death Studies, 38*(5), 315–321. http://doi.org/10.1080/07481187.2013.766651

Castelli Dransart, D. A., Heeb, J.-L., Gulfi, A., & Gutjahr, E. (2015). Stress reactions after a patient suicide and their relations to the profile of mental health professionals. *BMC Psychiatry, 15*, 265. http://doi.org/10.1186/s12888-015-0655-y

Castelli Dransart, D. A., Kaufmann Didisheim, N., Gulfi, A., & Gutjahr, E. (2007). *Conséquences du suicide d'un client sur les professionnels de l'action socio-sanitaire. Impact individuel, répercussions sur les pratiques professionnelles et modalités de gestion* [Consequences of the suicide of a client on health and social care professionals: Individual impact, repercussions on professional practices and management]. Givisiez, Switzerland: Haute Ecole Fribourgeoise de Travail Social.

Cerel, J., Maple, M., Aldrich, R., & van de Venne, J. (2013). Exposure to suicide and identification as survivor. *Crisis, 34*(6), 413–419. http://doi.org/10.1027/0227-5910/a000220

Chemtob, C. M., Bauer, G., Hamada, R. S., Pelowski, S. R., & Muraoka, M. Y. (1989). Patient suicide: Occupational hazard for psychologists and psychiatrists. *Professional Psychology: Research and Practice, 20*(5), 294–300. http://doi.org/10.1037/0735-7028.20.5.294

Chemtob, C. M., Hamada, R. S., Bauer, G., Kinney, B., & Torigoe, R. Y. (1988). Patients' suicide: Frequency and impact on psychiatrists. *American Journal of Psychiatry, 145*(2), 224–228. http://doi.org/10.1176/ajp.145.2.224

Chemtob, C. M., Hamada, R. S., Bauer, G., Torigoe, R. Y., & Kinney, B. (1988). Patient suicide: Frequency and impact on psychologists. *Professional Psychology: Research and Practice, 19*(4), 416–420. http://doi.org/10.1037/0735-7028.19.4.416

Clark, J. (2014). Engaging in ritual after client suicide: The critical importance of linking objects for therapists. *Bereavement Care, 33*(2), 70–76. http://doi.org/10.1080/02682621.2014.933574

Dewar, I., Eagles, J., Klein, S., Grey, N., & Alexander, D. (2000). Psychiatric trainees' experiences of, and reactions to, patient suicide. *Psychiatric Bulletin, 24*(1), 20–23. http://doi.org/10.1192/pb.24.1.20

Doka, K. (1989). *Disenfranchised grief: Recognizing hidden sorrow.* New York, NY: Lexington Books.

Gaffney, P., Russell, V., Collins, K., Bergin, A., Halligan, P., Carey, C., & Coyle, S. (2009). Impact of patient suicide on front-line staff in Ireland. *Death Studies, 33*(7), 639–656. http://doi.org/10.1080/07481180903011990

Grad, O. (2009). Therapists as survivors of suicide loss. In D. Wasserman & C. Wasserman (Eds.), *Suicidology and suicide prevention: A global perspective* (pp. 609–613). Oxford, UK: Oxford University Press.

Grad, O. (2011). The sequelae of suicide. In R.C. O'Connor, S. Platt, & J. Gordon (Eds.), *International handbook of suicide prevention: Research, policy and practice* (pp. 561–577). Chichester, UK: Wiley Blackwell.

Grad, O.T. (2012). *Guidelines to assist clinical staff after the suicide of a patient.* Retrieved from http://www.iasp.info/pdf/postvention/guidelines_to_assist_clinical_staff_after_suicide_patient_grad.pdf

Grad, O.T., Zavasnik, A., & Groleger, U. (1997). Suicide of a patient: Gender differences in bereavement reactions of therapists. *Suicide and Life-Threatening Behavior, 27*(4), 379–386.

Gulfi, A., Castelli Dransart, D.A., Heeb, J.L., & Gutjahr, E. (2016). The impact of patient suicide on the professional practice of Swiss psychiatrists and psychologists. *Academic Psychiatry, 40*(1), 13–22. http://doi.org/10.1007/s40596-014-0267-8

Gulfi, A., Castelli Dransart, D.A., Heeb, J.-L., & Gutjahr, E. (2010). The impact of patient suicide on the professional reactions and practices of mental health caregivers and social workers. *Crisis, 31*(4), 202–210. http://doi.org/10.1027/0027-5910/a000027

Gulfi, A., Heeb, J.-L., Castelli Dransart, D.A., Gutjahr, E. (2015). Professional reactions and changes in practice following patient suicide: What do we know about mental health professionals' profiles? *Journal of Mental Health Training, Education and Practice, 10*(4), 256–267. http://doi.org/10.1108/JMHTEP-11-2014-0034

Gutin, N., McGann, V.L., & Jordan, J.R. (2011). The impact of suicide on professional caregivers. In J.R. Jordan & J.L. McIntosh (Eds.), *Grief after suicide: Understanding the consequences and caring for the survivors* (pp. 93–111). New York, NY: Routledge.

Halligan, P., & Corcoran, P. (2001). The impact of patient suicide on rural general practitioners. *British Journal of General Practice, 51*(465), 295–296

Hendin, H., Haas, A.P., Maltsberger, J.T., Szanto, K., & Rabinowicz, H. (2004). Factors contributing to therapists' distress after the suicide of a patient. *American Journal of Psychiatry, 161*(8), 1442–1446. http://doi.org/10.1176/appi.ajp.161.8.1442

Hendin, H., Lipschitz, A., Maltsberger, J.T., Haas, A.P., & Wynecoop, S. (2000). Therapists' reactions to patients' suicide. *American Journal of Psychiatry, 157*(12), 2022–2027. http://doi.org/10.1176/appi.ajp.157.12.2022

Henry, M., Séguin, M., & Drouin, M.-S. (2003). L'impact du décès par suicide d'un patient chez des professionnels en santé mentale [The impact of the death by suicide of a patient among mental health professionals] *Revue Québécoise de Psychologie, 24*(1), 227–242.

Henry, M., Séguin, M., & Drouin, M.-S. (2008). L'impact du suicide d'un patient chez des professionnels en santé mentale. Différences entre les femmes et les hommes [The impact of a patient suicide among mental health professionals: Differences between women and men]. *Frontières, 21*(1), 53–63. http://doi.org/10.7202/037874ar

Horowitz, M., Wilner, N., & Alvarez, W. (1979). Impact of Event Scale: A measure of subjective stress. *Psychosomatic Medicine, 41*(3), 209–218. http://doi.org/10.1097/00006842-197905000-00004

Jacobson, J.M., Ting, L., Sanders, S., & Harrington, D. (2004). Prevalence of and reactions to fatal and nonfatal client suicidal behavior: A national study of mental health social workers. *Omega: Journal of Death and Dying, 49*(3), 237–248. http://doi.org/10.2190/HPKQ-T700-EPQL-58JQ

Jobes, D.A., & Maltsberger, J.T. (1995). The hazards of treating suicidal patients. In M.B. Sussman (Ed.), *A perilous calling: The Hazards of psychotherapy practice* (pp. 126–141). New York, NY: Norton.

Joyce, B., & Wallbridge, H. (2003). Effects of suicidal behavior on a psychiatric unit nursing team. *Journal of Psychosocial Nursing and Mental Health Services, 41*(3), 14–23.

Linke, S., Wojciak, J., & Day, S. (2002). The impact of suicide on community mental health teams: Findings and recommendations. *Psychiatric Bulletin, 26*(2), 50–52. http://doi.org/10.1192/pb.26.2.50

Maltsberger, J.T. (1992). The implications of patient suicide for the surviving psychotherapist. In D. Jacobs (Ed.), *Suicide and clinical practice* (pp. 169–182). Washington, DC: American Psychiatric Press.

Mangurian, Ch., Harre, E., Reliford, A., Booty, A., Cournos, F. (2009). Improving support of residents after a patient suicide: A residency case study. *Academic Psychiatry, 33*(4), 278–281. http://doi.org/10.1176/appi.ap.33.4.278

McAdams, C.R., & Foster, V.A. (2000). Client suicide: Its frequency and impact on counselors. *Journal of Mental Health Counseling, 22*(2), 107–121.

McWilliams, N. (2004). Occupational hazards and gratifications in the practice of psychotherapy. *Psychotherapy in Australia, 10*(2), 14–19.

O'Neill, S.M., & Kueppenbender, K. (2012). Suicide in group therapy: Trauma and possibility. *International Journal of Group Psychotherapy, 62*(4), 586–611. http://doi.org/10.1521/ijgp.2012.62.4.586

Pieters, G., Gucht, V.D., Joos, G., & Heyn, E.D. (2003). Frequency and impact of patient suicide on psychiatric trainees. *European Psychiatry, 18*(7), 345–349. http://doi.org/10.1016/j.eurpsy.2003.02.003

Pilkinton, P., & Etkin, M. (2003). Encountering suicide: The experience of psychiatric residents. *Academic Psychiatry, 27*(2), 93–99. http://doi.org/10.1176/appi.ap.27.2.93

Pommereau, X. (2004). Suicide et institution: Deuil et travail de deuil [Suicide and institution: Grief and bereavement]. *Revue Française de Psychiatrie et de Psychologie Médicale, VII*(76), 55–57.

Ratkowska, K.A., Grad, O., De Leo, D., & Cimitan, A. (2014). Traumatic bereavement for the therapist: The aftermath of a patient suicide. In D. De Leo, A. Cimitan, K. Dyregrov, O. Grad, & K. Andriessen (Eds.), *Bereavement after traumatic death. Helping the survivors* (pp. 105–113). New York, NY: Hogrefe.

Ruskin, R., Sakinofsky, I., Bagby, R.M., Dickens, S., & Sousa, G. (2004). Impact of patient suicide on psychiatrists and psychiatric trainees. *Academic Psychiatry, 28*(2), 104–110. http://doi.org/10.1176/appi.ap.28.2.104

Schultz, D. (2005). Suggestions for supervisors when a therapist experiences a client's suicide. In K.M. Weiner (Ed.), *Therapeutic and legal issues for therapists who have survived a client suicide: Breaking the silence* (pp. 59–69). New York, NY: Haworth Press.

Séguin, M., Bordeleau, V., Drouin, M.S., Castelli Dransart, D.A., & Giasson, F. (2014). Professionals' reactions following a patient's suicide: Review and future investigation. *Archives of Suicide Research, 18*(4), 340–362. http://doi.org/10.1080/13811118.2013.833151

Takahashi, C., Chida, F., Nakamura, H., Akasaka, H., Yagi, J., Koeda, A., & Sakai, A. (2011). The impact of inpatient suicide on psychiatric nurses and their need for support. *Bio Med Central, 11*(38), 1–8.

Tillman, J.G. (2006). When a patient commits suicide: An empirical study of psychoanalytic clinicians. *The International Journal of Psychoanalysis, 87*(1), 159–177. http://doi.org/10.1516/6UBB-E9DE-8UCW-UV3L

Treven, M., Rotar Pavlič, D., & Grad, O. (2013). *General practitioners' reactions to patients' suicides* [Abstract]. Proceedings of the XXVII world congress of the International Association for Suicide Prevention: Suicidologi: Final programme and book of abstracts (pp. 231–232). Oslo, Norway: IASP.

Weiss, D.S., & Marmar, C.R. (1997). The Impact of Event Scale–Revised. In J.P. Wilson & T.M. Keane (Eds.), *Assessing psychological trauma and PTSD* (pp. 399–411). New York, NY: Guilford Press.

Wurst, F.M., Kunz, I., Skipper, G., Wolfersdorf, M., Beine, K.H., & Thon, N. (2011). The therapist's reaction to a patient's suicide. Results of a survey and implications for health care professionals' well-being. *Crisis, 32*(2), 99–105. http://doi.org/10.1027/0227-5910/a000062

Chapter 22

Promoting a Way of Life to Prevent Premature Death

Ojibway First Nation (Anishinaabe) Healing Practices

Edward A. Connors[1], John Rice[2], and Antoon A. Leenaars[3]

[1]Onkwatenro'shon'a Health Planners, Orillia, Ontario, Canada
[2]Canadian Mental Health Association, First Nations Métis Inuit Healer, Barrie, Ontario, Canada
[3]Private Practice, Windsor, Ontario, Canada

Abstract: Indigenous peoples around the world have the highest suicide risk of any culture (or ethnic) identifiable group. It is a young people crisis. This is largely due to colonization and acculturation; this continues with the imposition of nonindigenous suicide prevention programs, including postvention, on indigenous people. This chapter describes Ojibway First Nation (Anishinaabe) healing practices employed with family and community survivors of unnatural premature death(s), a concept that includes suicides. It also presents the Ojibway worldview of postvention which uses concepts of Ojibway healing approaches. Culturally competent care is outlined, illustrated by the deaths of two young men from an Anishinaabe community. Decolonized from Christian dogma, our approach is revealed by rituals and releasing songs acknowledging the young men's lives and preparing them for a spiritual journey. Through the guidance of a Mide (a healer and spiritual leader of the Midewiwin society), the sacred sundown and sunrise rituals and interment practices are presented. The final send off, the memorial feast, is described. It is concluded that much of the rebuilding that needs to be done will occur by enhancing the traditional and cultural Ojibway life. In the words of our Elders: "Creator has given us all that we need to live good lives."

Introduction: Suicide Among Indigenous People

Suicide is a multidimensional event (Shneidman, 1985). Indigenous people around the world have the highest suicide risk of any identifiable culture (or ethnic group) (Hunter & Leenaars, 2002; Krug, Dahlberg, Mercy, Zwi, & Lozano, 2002). In a special report, *Suicide Among Indigenous Peoples: The Research*, published in the *Archives of Suicide Research,* researchers (Leenaars, EchoHawk, Lester, Leenaars, & Haramic, 2006) presented the first international effort examining the global epidemic. Scholars, indigenous and nonindigenous, reported from the Arctic, Canada, Australia, Greenland, the United States, New Zealand, Brazil, and Siberia. It is a young people crisis. What was also learned is that some communities within these nations have low rates, and most noteworthy, for example, that within Norway, the Sami people have significantly lower rates than the nonindigenous population. International studies found that suicide is multidetermined in indigenous people; simple answers and their solutions are fabrications (Chandler & Proulx, 2006; EchoHawk, 2006; Hunter & Milroy, 2006; Leenaars, Anawak, Brown, Hill-Keddie, & Taparti, 1999; Leenaars, EchoHawk, Lester, & Leenaars, 2007). Colonialism and its associated acculturation are, however, cited as a common factor worldwide.

Finally, it was concluded that although much greater cooperative international efforts among indigenous peoples are needed to understand the crisis, it is also understood that each indigenous people needed to approach the solutions from their own worldviews. By *worldview,* we refer to a person's way of making meaning of themselves, others, the world around, all of creation, and the Creator. (In this chapter, we prefer to use the personal pronouns *we* and *us* as this is how we, First Nations people, usually share our knowledge. We own the knowledge that we share.) This approach would be true within postvention, the focus of our chapter from the Ojibway (First Nations) worldview. (Farberow, 1994, presents an excellent history of nonindigenous care after an untimely death.) Of course, we recognize that other peoples may have different ways of promoting life; however, we also believe that we may be able to make a different contribution to this current much-needed volume on postvention.

First Nations are an indigenous people living in Canada, who at one time, were referred to as "Indians." In Canada, the rate of suicide amongst First Nations communities ranges from 5 to 7 times that of the nonnative population (Chandler & Proulx, 2006; Hunter & Leenaars, 2002). This range runs from no suicides in many First Nations communities to 7 times the national average in many others. At different points in time, some First Nations communities have reported suicides as much as 800 times the national average. The causes of these elevated rates have been linked to colonization and acculturation (Chandler & Proulx, 2006; Hunter & Leenaars, 2002; Sinclair, 1998). It has also been noted that communities where no suicides are occurring typically exhibit strong self-governance and elements of cultural renewal (Chandler & Proulx, 2006; Leenaars, 1995; Ross, 1992).

A First Nations Worldview

Most of the approaches to preventing suicide amongst First Nations populations have been developed from a colonizer's worldview. To date, the reemergence of First Nations worldviews through revival of cultures and languages has encouraged the redevelopment of First Nations healing practices. This chapter describes Ojibway First Nations (Anishinaabe) healing practices employed with family and community survivors of two young men who died due to unnatural premature deaths (suicides) that occurred within 1 month during a recent year. It also presents an Ojibway worldview of suicide postvention which will include the use of concepts and healing approaches that align with an Ojibway First Nations worldview.

We will begin our description by reconceptualizing efforts to prevent death into concepts consistent with promoting life. We believe that the use of culturally appropriate healing practices contributes to improved health outcomes within First Nations communities. Evidence supporting this belief will be documented within this chapter. While it is true that a higher percentage of First Nations and Inuit people experience the negative effects of trauma and loss compared with the nonnative population, there are a large number of First Nations communities and individuals who have the capacity to cope effectively with *Maazhise* (an Anishinaabe word for "things turning in a bad way" to a crisis or tragedy) and to minimize the negative effects of trauma and loss. These communities and people offer examples of resilience. These are the communities and people that we must learn from, when attempting to reduce the negative impact of trauma and loss on indigenous communities.

Since first contact with Europeans, First Nations people have recognized that there were two worldviews or perceptions of reality between themselves and the newcomers to this land. These worldviews consisted of different languages, cultures, beliefs, values, and lifestyles (Ross, 1992). Colonization of First Nations people, which has included residential schools and the child welfare system, resulted in loss of language, culture, teachings, beliefs, lands, and self-determination. All of this has contributed to the progressive disconnection from First Nations worldviews and weakened the ability to cope with tragedy, leaving us, First Nations people, vulnerable to the negative effects of crisis. Moreover, colonization in itself has been a traumatizing experience that has negatively impacted the health of indigenous populations for generations. The ongoing onslaught of assimilating policies and colonial forces has led to the transmission of trauma through generations (Wesley-Equimaux & Smoleski, 2004). Since 1884, Section 141 of the Indian Act prohibited the practices of First Nations ceremonies and rituals. Revision to this section created further restrictions until amendments were made in 1951 to comply with the UN Declaration of Human Rights (Leslie, 2002; United Nations, 1948).

Crisis (or tragedy) often creates increased risk for more crises (Figley, 1985; Meichenbaum, 2012: Ross, 1992; Krug et al., 2002). Trauma, we know, may result in prolonged and pervasive physical, mental, emotional, and spiritual harm. These imbalances may lead to suicide. The Truth and Reconciliation Commission of Canada (2015), for example, identified a relationship between early childhood trauma experienced in residential schools and higher suicide rates in First Nations communities. It has been postulated that these effects have been passed intergenerationally. In addition, colonization has weakened our positive connections and relationships within family, and community. These losses have also contributed to depleting our capacity to cope with tragedy and loss. A study conducted in 2012 supports these observations (Elias et al., 2012).

Current Western research supports the positive benefits of First Nations knowledge, recognizing that indigenous communities that maintain and support traditional cultural practices, beliefs, values, and self-determination experience less crisis and trauma and cope more effectively with these events (Chandler & Lalonde, 2008; Levy, 1965; Van Winkle & May, 1986; Warren, 1885/1984). In other words, First Nations worldviews appear to increase our capacity to cope with and benefit from *Maazhise*, a reality in all lives, so that trauma and loss occur less, and when they do happen they are less likely to produce enduring harmful effects. Simply put, we learn good things from bad experiences. Ritual follows a structure that allows the whole person – mind, body, and spirit – to adjust to the experience. Today, we refer to this capacity as resilience. Resilience is a multidimensional concept. The well-known Canadian psychologist, Dr. Donald Meichenbaum (2012), no stranger to the study of suicide, defines resilience as "the capacity to adapt successfully in the presence of risk and adversity" (p. 3). Perhaps, the concept of resilience was best captured by Anishinaabe spiritual teacher, Arthur Solomon (1990, p. 24), when he taught:

My brothers and sisters, this too the vision gave:
Those prisons of soul and mind are fashioned
By cutting off the true knowledge, from the Great Mystery,
And replacing it with mistaken ways of seeing
And understanding that don't belong.
There, my people, is where we start.
We must turn back to the wheel of life again
And help it to renew.
I give thanks for the new day.
Kitchi meegwetch.

In short, traditional indigenous cultures contain the strengths that create the capacity to cope effectively with crisis, trauma, and loss.

Culturally Competent Care

Recent developments in health care have included the promotion of *culturally competent care* (or what is also called *cultural safety*). Culturally competent care is defined as follows: "Cultural safety (or cultural competency) within an indigenous context means that the educators/ practitioners/professionals, whether indigenous or not, can communicate competently with a patient in that patient's social, political, linguistic, economic, and spiritual realms" (National Aboriginal Health Organization, 2008, p. 4). This concept promotes recognition of the person's/patient's/client's personal worldview and supports providing care that is also consistent with, and respectful of, that worldview. Research into culturally competent care indicates that this approach to care results in improved health outcomes (National Aboriginal Health Organization, 2008).

Nonaboriginal prevention programs have not been developed with cultural competency or safety. One ongoing onslaught of culturally not competent care has been the imposition of nonaboriginal prevention programs onto our communities (Martin, 2002; Ross, 1992; National Aboriginal Health Organization, 2008). It is important to note, in fact, that recent research into suicide prevention gatekeeper programs concludes that there is no evidence that these programs prevent suicide and caution academics and organizations not to overstate the positive impacts of these programs when the evidence is lacking (Wei, Kutcher, & Leblanc, 2015). Also of concern is a relatively recent research finding that nonindigenous suicide prevention assist training with First Nations populations where suicide rates are high, might be contraindicated because of a trend toward increased suicidal ideation among participants who receive this training (Sareen et al., 2013). We believe, like many indigenous people around the world, these nonindigenous programs may even be suicidogenic (causing or promoting suicide), in fact. Considering this outcome, researchers caution against the widespread implementation of these programs with high-risk First Nations communities, until evidence to support safe use is produced (Sareen et al., 2013).

In light of these developments, we propose that additional approaches to suicide postvention with indigenous populations be explored. We offer another approach to suicide postvention, from a First Nations worldview. This perspective presents a *life promotion lens* to replace a suicide prevention viewpoint. Accompanying the life promotion lens is a language that supports this perspective. For example, it is proposed that *suicide* be replaced with *preventing premature unnatural death*. This concept refers to life that ends in advance of its fullest potential and the fact that this early death is contributed to by the individual's behaviors. By definition, this includes death that occurs as a result of behaviors that fail to protect and promote optimum health or life-promoting conditions (e.g., addictions such as alcoholism, smoking, and overeating). Through this life promotion lens, we also act to encourage relatives of those who die a premature and unnatural death to enhance their connection to life (Connors, 1996; Connors & Maidman, 2001).

The Anishinaabe People

There are 617 First Nations. As of the 2006 census over 1 million Canadians identified themselves as indigenous. Within First Nations, there are more than 50 indigenous languages. Although there is a common holistic worldview that binds indigenous populations together, there is also great diversity in languages, beliefs, and cultural practices throughout the country. The Anishinaabe people are a group of related First Nations tribes who share languages that have evolved from the Algonquin language. It is believed that these people migrated from the Atlantic coast and separated into distinct tribal groups who inhabited vast territories of central Canada and the United States extending as far west as the Rocky Mountains (Anthony, 2007). The Ojibway (also known as Chippewa) are the largest group of the Anishinaabe peoples and the second largest First Nation in Ontario, next only in number to the Cree Nation. The Algonquin, Odawa, Oji-Cree, and Potawatomi are also branches of the Algonquin language family who are considered Anishinaabe-speaking peoples.

Within the Anishinaabe worldview, the teachings that reinforce a life promotion lens and accompanying behaviors are referred to as the Miikaans teachings. One of the times when these teachings are provided to community members is in a ceremony that is conducted in the wake of premature unnatural deaths. The Miikaans teachings identify that the journey through life consists of many natural transitions during which one's spirit can be tempted to leave life and return to the spirit world. It is the teachings that help individuals to become aware of this possibility and to recognize what steps they and their relatives can take to hold their spirit to life so that they can complete their full life journey.

Send Off

The Anishinaabe *send-off ritual* occurs over 1 calendar year and involves three elements: assisting/encouraging the spirit on its journey to the spirit world, interment of the vessel (body) that has carried the spirit through life's journey, and a final release of the spirit to the spirit world. The ritual follows the Anishinaabe belief that the spirit journeys through life in physical form and that there are three parts to life: prelife, life, and postlife. The spirit is immortal.

Prelife

The spirit has a conversation with the Creator. The content of this conversation is unique to each individual spirit. When the spirit is satisfied that it is prepared for life, it leaves the Creator and enters the human body created for it in its birth mother's womb. The birth is regarded as the doorway into life and is chosen by the spirit.

Life

Birth begins the spirit's physical journey through life. Life is viewed as being made up of seven main physiological changes. Each change brings about a change in perception as the mind adjusts to each physiological change. At each change, an individual may ponder, "Why am I here?" This question is viewed as spiritual, and the individual is questioning the purpose of their life. The seven stages of life teachings state that when an individual takes only what the natural earth offers, they live long enough to see Haley's comet three times (i.e., 150 years: Haley's comet is visible from earth every 75–76 years).

Postlife

Death occurs when the Creator sends an emissary to call the individual home. When an individual spirit leaves the Creator to come to life they receive a spirit name, this is the name that the Creator calls when the life journey is finished. Usually an individual will have a naming ceremony during life, and if not, a naming ceremony is performed postlife. Knowing one's spirit name is important to the spirit journey. As close to the moment of death as possible the ritual to release the spirit from where the body fell is performed to release the spirit from the vessel to begin the spirit journey.

Obituaries for Anishinaabe and aboriginal people will wish "a safe spirit journey." The spirit remains in life for 4 days, and it is incumbent upon the bereaved to prepare the spirit for the 4-day spirit journey back to the Creator. The ritual generally takes 8–10 days in total. The first four days of the ritual ensures a safe spirit journey.

The Premature Unnatural Deaths

Two young men from an Anishinaabe community who were first cousins and very close friends died premature deaths in a recent year. The 27-year-old succumbed to a drug overdose, and the 30-year-old took his life on the evening of the 27-year-old's interment. At that time, there were statements by the family that the older cousin may have been the last one to see his younger cousin alive. In both events, lives ended suddenly and the deaths were self-inflicted.

In recent years, this community has revived rituals and ceremonies and decolonized from Christian dogmas. The grief process has moved from condemning the method of death to preparing the spirit for its journey back to the spirit world regardless of the manner of death. In the past, Christian dogmas often prevented the conducting of last rites rituals and interment in sacred ground when death occurred by suicide. In both of these instances, the family requested the traditional rituals over Christian burial rites.

Vignette 1: First youth – Male, 27 years

Releasing Song: In a recent year, the 27-year-old man was discovered in the morning, collapsed in a basement recreation room. A family member (a Mide, a healer and spiritual leader of the Midewiwin Society: the Midewiwin are the formalized spiritual teachings of the Anishinaabe.) schooled in rituals was summoned, and songs were sung acknowledging the young man's life and preparing him for his spirit journey.

Consultation With the family: The Midewiwin Mide consulted with the family, asking their input for the 4-day send-off ritual. The community has roots in three Anishinaabe nations: Ojibway, Potawatomi, and Odawa. Families in this community have varying recollections of life rituals. This meeting was held to encourage inclusivity and participation by family and community. The family agreed to follow the process described below. The family was encouraged to allow the grief to be immediate and flow from the nature of each individual.

First Sundown: The Anishinaabe regard men as firekeepers. Men in attendance from the family and community lit a sacred fire to give the spirit a reference point that it soon will be walking away from, towards the west – to the spirit world. A significant number of family and community attended (estimated 50–60 out of a community of 400). Explanation was given that day and night reverse for the departed – our day is now their night, and our night is their day. A song encouraging the spirit to attend a feast in his honor was sung, and a spirit dish was burned (the spirit dish is a small dish of the person's favorite foods prepared by family members and placed in the sacred fire for the spirit to enjoy and feast with living relatives). Attendees feasted and were encouraged to tell good stories about the young man. Men stepped forward volunteering to tend to the fire at all times over the next 4 days.

First Sunrise: A song was sung to encourage the spirit to rest for the day, and tobacco offerings were burned. Immediate family attended. Tobacco is a sacred medicine that when burned is believed to carry our prayers to the Creator as the smoke rises.

Second Sundown: Similar to the first night, a feast was prepared, a spirit dish was offered, and good stories were encouraged. Newcomers to the ritual exhibited deep grief and in turn were consoled by participants who had attended the night before.

Second Sunrise: A song was sung to encourage the spirit to rest for the day, and tobacco offerings were burned. Immediate family attended.

Third Sundown: A feast was prepared, a spirit dish was offered, and good stories were encouraged. Again, newcomers were consoled by those who had attended previously. The mood changed as participants understood that the young man's spirit was preparing to leave this plane and embark on his spirit journey. There was now a sense of purpose among the participants.

Third Sunrise: A song was sung to encourage the spirit to rest for the day, and tobacco offerings were burned.

Fourth Sundown: This night the family gathered in a circle preparing to share a feast with their beloved for the last time in this part of the send-off ritual. Community members in attendance prepared plates of food for family members, demonstrating the community's caring for the family during this time of grief. A spirit dish was prepared and offered to the fire to feast the spirit of the departed. Participants in this feast were encouraged to forgive past transgressions done by the departed and petition for forgiveness from the departed if they had hurt the departed in the past. This "final forgiveness" ritual released the departed from any remaining obligations to this life. The departed were given instructions by the Mide. This prepared the spirit of the departed for the 4-day journey to the spirit realm.

Fourth Sunrise: Final songs were sung at the fire, final tobacco and prayers were offered to the sacred fire, and the fire was built up one last time. The fire was allowed to die out naturally.

Fifth Day – Interment: A great many friends and community joined the family in the interment service at the local community center which has a capacity of 250 people; as there were people standing, that number was easily exceeded. Attendees were encouraged to let the spirit of the departed go and if possible try not to speak about him by name for a year. This practice is related to spiritual teachings that the spirit is journeying back to the Creator for 1 year after the death and that in speaking of them by name, we interfere with the journey. It is also believed that this assists the family in their "letting go" during the year. Thus, this action is meant to enable the spirit to continue its journey into the spirit world and not hold it unnaturally to this physical world. In a year, there would be a memorial feast acknowledging the young man's safe journey to the spirit world. This is why their name is called once again at the releasing ceremony and can be used after that because we know at that point that the spirit has completed this journey back to Creator.

The mood after the interment service appeared to be one of relief, and participants commented that the young man was safely on his way.

Vignette 2: Second youth – Male, 30 years

The second youth, first cousin and a very close friend to the youth whose interment was completed earlier in the day, ended his own life later that evening. Family later made a statement that this young man was the last one to see his cousin alive. As the family and community had returned to the activities of an average summer weekend, the news of this suicide was shocking, and reaction to the news of the event was extreme. A contingent of family and friends undertook to check in on community members advising them to keep each other safe and let no one be alone during this time. The fear was that the spirits of other youths may be tempted to leave life upon hearing the news. Anishinaabe beliefs indicate that the spirits of close relations can be tempted to follow their departed at these times.

Releasing Song: Due to the nature of the death, this ritual could not be attended to until the morning following the death. Immediately family gathered at daybreak when the body was released by the police. Two songs were sung acknowledging the young man's life and his preparation for the spirit journey. With the recent death of the first young man and now, the death of his cousin in such a short passage of time, the grief experienced by all in attendance was at an extreme.

Consultation With the Family: Later in the morning after the family had been encouraged to rest, a meeting was held to discuss the rituals involved in summoning the spirit of the young man from that place in between life and death where it is believed that spirits go who have left from life by ending their lives prematurely. The family was encouraged by the belief that the Great Spirit is a loving and forgiving spirit. With the love and efforts of the surviving relatives, their rituals would petition the Creator to accept the young man's spirit regardless of the manner of his death. The family agreed to follow the process described below. The family was encouraged not to dwell on the manner of death but to focus on the task of preparing for the spirit journey.

Sundown – Retrieval: Family and community gathered to light the ceremonial sacred fire, and again within a week of the first death, men from the community lit the fire that would burn for the remainder of this part of the send-off. A song to call the spirit of the young man from that place between life and death was sung, and participants were encouraged in their own way to pray or think thoughts that would encourage the young man's spirit to leave that place and come to his sacred fire. During and after the song, participants stated that they felt him come to his sacred fire. The regular 4-day ritual for the sending off to the spirit world could now be followed. Again, it was mentioned that the work is the responsibility of family and friends.

First Feast: The first feast was not considered the normal part of the send-off ritual; rather, it was an acknowledgement of the spirit's journey from that place between life and death back to this world from the spirit world for the purposes of the send-off ritual. Participants were encouraged not to dwell upon the manner of the death and that that would be a conversation between the young man and the Creator when the young man makes it back to the Creator. The purpose of his relatives within the ceremony was to fulfill elements of the send-off ritual that support their relatives' spirit journey.

Ritual: The 4-day send-off ritual, as described above, was employed for this young man, with the added element that participants were encouraged not to dwell upon the manner of death and that the purpose was to prepare the body for interment and prepare the spirit for its spirit journey. This sense of purpose appeared to facilitate the process of healthy grieving as the 4 days passed.

Fifth Day – Interment: A great many friends and community joined the family in the interment service. Attendees were encouraged to let the spirit of the departed go and if possible, try not to speak about him by name for a year. The atmosphere at this ceremony was solemn, and participants exhibited signs of fatigue. At the interment the final instructions for the spirit's journey were given, and the spirit was encouraged to continue on his spirit journey. At this time, the relatives and friends were also instructed to turn their attention back to their life journey and their life purpose. Family and community were reminded that in a year there would be a memorial feast acknowledging the young man's safe journey to the spirit world.

Final Send-Off – The Memorial Feast: The Memorial Feast completes the send-off ritual occurring on the 1-year anniversary of the death of the departed one. (To be mindful of other cultures, there are more similarities than differences between 1-year rituals that appear to be universal. The differences likely lie in the meaning associated with the rituals by different cultures.) Since the interment, family and friends of the departed were encouraged not to think too much or speak about the departed loved one as this may interfere with the departed's adjustment to being a spirit again.

Food is prepared for this feast. Individuals who might carry a heavier grief prepare an individual dish to speak to their grief at the feast. The feast is held after sundown, acknowledging that for the spirit our night becomes their daytime. The ritualistic songs and prayers acknowledge that while the loved one has left this realm and is missed, they will never be forgotten. The songs and prayers encourage the spirit to be present. Before the food is eaten, individuals are encouraged to speak about the departed. For some, this is the first time that they have done so in a year. The speeches include stories about life's struggles without the loved one, to humorous anecdotes about the departed. Generally there is a range of emotions and sentiments expressed. After the speaking, a spirit dish is prepared to be offered to a sacred fire lit for this ritual. Participants share this feast with the spirit of the departed. When the feasting is complete, the family of the departed *will have a giveaway ceremony. Possessions of the departed, sacred and personal, are distributed to those in attendance. This sharing of material items reinforces the belief that the departed spirit has finished the life journey.*

The memorial feast concludes with a dance. The lights in the venue are turned off, and a song is sung to encourage the spirit of the departed to dance one last time with family and friends. Participants will see or sense the presence of the loved one dancing with them. The loved one is dressed in their finest clothes/regalia and appears shining or glowing. The completion of the song concludes the ceremony. The spirit dances out of life at the conclusion of the song, life's journey finished. The spirit of the loved one will not come back into life; however, they may look in at times through "window" dreams. The fulfillment of this ritual gives the family and friends of the departed reassurance that the spirit has completed the journey to the spirit world safely. It also reinforces to individuals that they may continue their life journeys with the knowledge that they will someday be reunited with their loved ones.

Memorial Feast: In the instances of the death of the two cousins, the family elected to have a simple feasting. Family and close friends gathered at the home of an uncle to feast on food that was prepared for the day. A spirit dish made of birch bark was made for each of the young men. Participants each placed a tiny portion of the feast food into each dish. An invitation song was sung to invite the spirits of the two young men to be present, and spirit dishes were offered to a sacred fire. The conversation was light and convivial. The manner of the deaths of these two men did not enter the conversation; rather, the stories covered about how the upcoming hockey and hunting season would be good ones with these two spirits watching over the lives of their relatives. Participants appeared to have a peaceful resolve and reassurance that the two spirits were safely with the Creator and that the life journeys of their relatives could continue now.

In the past when Christian burial rites were prominent in this community, suicides were often experienced in clusters, suggesting that a contagion effect might have occurred. Since the community has reintroduced traditional grieving and burial ceremonies, it has become uncommon for clusters of suicide to occur among families who have been living an Anishinaabe worldview.

The Time of Healing

Despite the many assaults that have occurred on the Aboriginal families of North America during the past five hundred years, native people have survived and are ... [recovering from the impact of colonization]. While it is a travesty that some First Nations did not survive to see this time of healing, it is a testament of the resilience and strength of the tribal family that so many Aboriginal families remain. Today, many Aboriginal people are beginning to realize that most of the strengths that enabled our survival lie within our cultures. Those ways that the colonizers regarded as primitive and from which they attempted to separate Native people are what many First Nations and Non-native people now realize contain the tools that will likely ensure the survival of all peoples and all of creation on this planet. This is why today there is a strong resurgence of native culture and native pride. Aboriginal families are now coming full circle to redefine the principles from our past that will help us to form a healthier future. (Connors & Maidman, 2001, p. 415).

Conclusions

In short, much of the rebuilding that we need to do is from within ourselves, in balance with some of what is offered from others. Some First Nations people refer to this process as decolonization or "reclaiming much of what we have lost." This reclamation also includes incorporation of our cultural practices and knowledge into our community programs and policies, which will enhance our ability to be self-governing and self-determining. Our Elders often remind us that the "Creator has given us all that we need to live good lives. We need only to attend to these gifts and use them well for our benefit and the benefit of all of creation."

Corresponding authors

Edward A. Connors
Onkwatenro'shon'a Health Planners
Orillia, Ontario
Canada
econnors0507@gmail.com

John Rice
Canadian Mental Health Association
First Nations Métis Inuit Healer
Barrie, Ontario
Canada
jrice@cmhastarttalking.ca

Antoon A. Leenaars
Private Practice
Windsor, Ontario
Canada
draalee@sympatico.ca

References

Anthony, D. (2007). *The Horse, the wheels and language*. Princeton, NJ: Princeton University Press.

Chandler, M., & Lalonde, C. (2008). Cultural continuity as a protective factor against suicide in First Nations youth. *Horizons – A special Issue on Aboriginal Youth, Hope or Heartbreak: Aboriginal Youth and Canada's Future, 10*(1), 68–72.

Chandler, M., & Proulx, T. (2006). Changing selves in changing worlds: Youth suicide on fault-lines of colliding culture. *Archives of Suicide Research, 10*(2), 125–140. http://doi.org/10.1080/13811110600556707

Connors, E. (1996). The healing path: Suicide and self-destructive behaviour in North American native people. In A. Leenaars & D. Lester (Eds.), *Suicide & the unconscious.* (pp. 259–269). Northvale, NJ: Jason Aronson.

Connors, E., & Maidman, F. (2001). A Circle of Healing: Family wellnesss in aboriginal communities. In I. Prilletensky (Ed.), *Promoting family wellness and preventing child maltreatment* (pp. 349–416). Toronto, Canada: University of Toronto Press.

EchoHawk, M. (2006). Suicide prevention efforts in one area of Indian Health Service, USA. *Archives of Suicide Research, 10*(2), 169–176. http://doi.org/10.1080/13811110600558224

Elias, B., Mignone, J., Hall, M., Hong, S., Hart, L., & Sareen, J. (2012). Trauma and suicide behaviour histories among a Canadian indigenous population: An empirical exploration of the potential role of Canadian residential school system. *Social Sciences & Medicine, 74*(10), 1560–1569. http://doi.org/10.1016/j.socscimed.2012.01.026

Farberow, N. (1994). The Los Angeles survivors' after-suicide program. In E. Shneidman, N. Farberow, & R. Litman (Eds.), *The psychology of suicide* (pp. 171–186). Northvale, NJ: Jason Aronson.

Figley, C. (Ed.). (1985). *Trauma and its wake*. New York, NY: Brunner/Mazel.

Hunter, E., & Leenaars, A. (2002). Suicide among indigenous peoples: the cases of Australia and Canada. In E. G. Krug, L. L. Dahlberg, J. A. Mercy, A. B. Zwi, & R. Lozano (Eds.), *World report on violence and health* (p. 190). Geneva, Switzerland: World Health Organization.

Hunter, E., & Milroy, H. (2006). Aboriginal and Torres Strait Islander suicide in context. *Archives of Suicide Research, 10*(2), 141–157. http://doi.org/10.1080/13811110600556889

Krug, E. G., Dahlberg, L. L., Mercy, J. A., Zwi, A. B., & Lozano, R. (Eds.). (2002). *World report on violence and health.* Geneva, Switzerland: World Health Organization.

Leenaars, A. (1995). Suicide in the Arctic: A few stories. *Archives of Suicide Research, 1*(2), 131–140. http://doi.org/10.1080/13811119508258981

Leenaars, A., Anawak, J., Brown, C., Hill-Keddie, T., & Taparti, L. (1999). Genocide and suicide among indigenous people: The north meets the south. *Canadian Journal of Native Studies, 19*(2), 337–363.

Leenaars, A., EchoHawk, M., Lester, D., & Leenaars, L. (2007). Suicide among Indigenous peoples: What does the international knowledge tell us? *Canadian Journal of Native Studies, 27*(2), 479–501.

Leenaars, A., EchoHawk, M., Lester, D., Leenaars, L., & Haramic, E. (Eds.). (2006). Suicide among indigenous peoples: The research. *Special issue, Archives of Suicide Research, 10*(2), 101–224. http://doi.org/10.1080/13811110600556590

Leslie, J. F. (2002). The Indian Act: An historical perspective. *Canadian Parliamentary Review, 25*(2), 23–27. Retrieved from http://www.revparl.ca/25/2/25n2_02e_Leslie.pdf

Levy, H. (1965). Navajo suicide. *Human Organization, 24*(4), 308–318. http://doi.org/10.17730/humo.24.4.hp3460lp4w556730

Martin, D. (2002). Two-eyed seeing: A framework for understanding indigenous and non-indigenous approaches to indigenous health research. *Canadian Journal of Nursing Research, 44*(2), 20–42.

Meichenbaum, D. (2012). *Road map to resilience.* Clearwater, FL: Institute Press.

National Aboriginal Health Organization. (2008). *Cultural competency and safety: A guide for health care administrators, providers, and educators.* Ottawa, Canada: Author.

Ross, R. (1992). *Dancing with a ghost: Exploring Indian reality.* Markham, Canada: Reed Books Canada.

Sareen, J., Isaak, C., Bolton, S., Enns, M., Elias, B., Deahn, F., … Katz, L. (2013). Gatekeeper training for suicide prevention in First Nations community members: A randomized controlled trial. *Depression and Anxiety, 30*(10), 1021–1029.

Shneidman, E. (1985). *Definition of suicide.* New York, NY: Wiley.

Sinclair, C. (1998). Suicide in First Nations People. In A. Leenaars, S. Wenckstern, I. Sakinofsky, R. Dyck, M. Kral, & R. Bland (Eds.), *Suicide in Canada.* (pp. 165–178). Toronto, Canada: University of Toronto Press.

Solomon, A. (1990). *Songs for the people: Teachings on the natural way.* Toronto, Canada: NC Press Limited.

Truth and Reconciliation Commission of Canada. (2015). *Final Report.* Ottawa, Canada: Author.

United Nations. (1948, December 10). *Universal declaration of human rights.* New York, NY: Author.

Van Winkle, N., & May, P. (1986). Native American suicide in New Mexico, 1957–1979: A comparative study. *Human Organization, 45*(4), 296–309. http://doi.org/10.17730/humo.45.4.f1159w1x64k164t4

Warren, W. (1984). *History of the Ojibway People.* St. Paul, MN: Minnesota Historical Society Press. (Original work published in 1885).

Wei, Y., Kutcher, S., & Leblanc, J. (2015). Hot ideas or hot air: A systematic review of evidence of two widely marketed youth suicide prevention programs and recommendations for implementation. *Journal of Canadian Academy of Child & Adolescent Psychiatry, 24*(1), 5–16.

Wesley-Equimaux, C., & Smoleski, M. (2004). *Historic trauma and aboriginal healing.* Ottawa, Canada: Aboriginal Healing Foundation.

Part IV

Help for the Bereaved by Suicide in Different Countries

Part IV.1

The Americas

Chapter 23

Brazil – The Development of Suicide Postvention

Karen Scavacini

Instituto Vita Alere de Prevenção e Posvenção do Suicídio, São Paulo, Brasil

Abstract: Brazil does not have high suicide rates compared with other countries. However in the last 10 years, suicide rates have increased more than rates of homicides and traffic accidents. Prevention efforts have improved, but not at the necessary pace. Suicide postvention activities are provided mostly through support groups in major cities. This chapter presents the situation of suicide postvention in Brazil, and the importance of the services. It discusses what could be accomplished in Brazil to effectively support those bereaved through suicide and to raise awareness for suicide postvention activities.

Introduction

The suicide of a significant other often causes grief and pain in the survivors. International studies have found poor social outcomes, psychological morbidity, and an increase of suicidal behavior in the bereaved (Ellenbogen & Gratton, 2001; Jordan, 2001; Scavacini, 2011). Suicide can be considered one of the most painful types of death, and families might have to deal with a financial impact as well (Andriessen, 2009; Jaques, 2000; Jordan, 2001; Kovács, 1992). Ample research has revealed the needs and the huge effects that a suicide poses to the bereaved in their grief (Jaques, 2000; World Health Organization [WHO], 2008). The bereaved can deal with their grief with or without professional help. However, postvention is increasingly recognized as an important component of mental health care systems and suicide prevention programs. It can be offered by health professionals, educators, survivors, and gatekeepers, as it includes a range of activities and resources of support (Grad, 1996; WHO, 2008). Unfortunately, suicide bereavement support is particularly difficult to find in Brazil.

Given the increasing suicide rates in Brazil, the tremendous social and economic costs of suicide, and the risk of poor mental health for many survivors, the public health authorities and agencies, the scientific community, and the mental health care providers in Brazil face an important challenge to develop and support mental health promotion, suicide prevention, and postvention strategies.

Suicide in Brazil

In 2014, Brazil had more than 202 million habitants (Fundação Instituto Brasileiro de Geografia e Estatística, 2014). Even though the national suicide rate (5.3 per 100,000) is not high compared with the world suicide rate (11.4 per 100,000), the country holds the eighth position in the global ranking for suicide in absolute numbers (Waiselfisz, 2014). This represents one suicide in Brazil every 45 min or 11,821 Brazilians who died by suicide in 2012 (WHO, 2014). Underreporting is estimated to be up to 20 % because of the low quality of information in death certificates and nonregistered cases (Botega, 2010).

The suicide rates in Brazil increased by 62.5 % from 1980 to 2012, and the greatest increase was reported for the years between 2002 and 2012 (33.6 %). This was more than the population increase (11 %) or the increase in traffic accidents (24.5 %) and homicides (2.1 %) (Waiselfisz, 2014). A history of relatively low national suicide rates, the taboo surrounding suicide, and a lack of governmental interest may partially explain why support for the bereaved by suicide has not been adequately developed in Brazil.

Suicide Postvention in Brazil

The suicide survivors' population is growing as the number of suicide deaths increases. Applying the average proposed by WHO (2008) – that is, at least 5 to 10 people are severely affected by each suicide – it is estimated that in 2012, there were at least 59.105 Brazilian people who began their suicide grief journey. In 2006, the National Strategy for Suicide Prevention, which included education and care for survivors, was developed in the country in accordance with Ordinance Number 1876, dated August 14, from the Ministry of Health (Ministério da Saúde [Brazilian Ministry of Health], 2006). The Projeto ComViver (To Live Project) designed to provide support and promote awareness of survivors' needs was established in Rio de Janeiro and was run until 2008. The Projeto ComViver prepared a report identifying suicide prevention activities and research in Brazil; however, none of those focused exclusively on suicide bereavement.

The term *postvention,* coined by Shneidman (1969) and used in the international literature, has just started to be used in Brazil in the last few years, in the context of dissertations, courses, groups, books (such as this book for children: Scavacini, 2014), and private institutions for prevention and suicide bereavement support. Although the terms *postvention* and *suicide survivors* have been appropriately used in the scientific literature (Andriessen, 2009), their translation to Portuguese has been confusing, as it seems to refer both to people bereaved by suicide and to people who have survived a suicide attempt. The term *survivors of a suicide loss* seems to be less confusing in the Brazilian context.

Although the National Strategy for Suicide Prevention was never fully implemented, it has positioned suicide as a public health problem and opened discussions regarding what types of services should be developed. In 2013, the Ministry of Health signed the WHO Mental Health Action Plan 2013–2020 (WHO, 2013) to reduce suicide rates by 10 % by 2020; however, no action followed to reach that goal. Also, the majority of the curricula of psychology, public health, medicine, and education at universities do not offer classes on suicide prevention or suicide grief and bereavement.

Regarding support for the bereaved and individuals in a suicidal crisis, the Centro de Valorização a Vida (CVV; the Valuing Life Center), a helpline volunteer organization linked to the Befrienders International, has been covering most of the states in Brazil and includes Internet-based support. From the 26 states and the federal district, just seven states (São Paulo, Espírito Santo, Rio de Janeiro, Alagoas, Ceará, Rio Grande do Sul, and Mato Grosso) have specific suicide bereavement activities, mostly support groups or psychotherapy. Other states have plans to start similar initiatives. The Associação Brasileira de Estudo e Prevenção do Suicídio (ABEPS; Brazilian Association for Suicide Studies and Prevention) was created in June 2015, during the Latin-American Suicide Prevention Symposium and was intended to set up a postvention task force. The first International Survivors of Suicide Loss Day was held on November 21, 2015, in São Paulo at the Instituto Vita Alere de Prevenção e Posvenção do Suicídio (Vita Alere Institute for Suicide Prevention and Postvention) in partnership with the American Foundation for Suicide Prevention. In June 2016, the first National Suicide Survivors meeting, with almost 80 participants, took place during the 1st Brazilian Congress of Suicide Prevention – a milestone in the history of postvention activities in the country.

An increase of public interest and media communication about suicide can be seen on the World Suicide Prevention Day (September 10). Social media and online networks have been playing an important role in the development of the postvention culture in Brazil, as they have opened the possibilities for suicide survivors to freely search for information about suicide and suicide grief support. A number of suicide prevention and postvention discussion groups are now available online, including a Facebook online survivor support group called Grupo Virtual de Enlutados pelo Suicídio – Sobreviventes (Survivors: Suicide Bereaved Virtual Group) which has members all around the country.

Implications for Support and Research

Based on a survey of services for suicide survivors available in Brazil and internationally, Scavacini (2011, p. 47) developed and proposed the *suicide postvention center model* (**Figure 23.1**) to address the needs of suicide survivors for support and postvention. This model of provision of services is based on collaborations between professional groups, survivor groups, and universities, with funding provided by the government and private companies. The model is regionally adapted.

There are numerous challenges to the development of postvention in Brazil. Services have to be adapted and connected in a huge country with a multicultural population. Most service providers lack knowledge, empathy, and/or experience to help people bereaved by suicide. Provision of services in rural and remote areas with no Internet access is especially challenging as well as the overall difficulty to talk about death in Brazil. Also, there appears to be a lack of interest from the government, private companies, the media, and society to address suicide survivors issues, including a paucity of scientific literature and research on postvention in Brazil. Recommendations are related to further work and progress in three main areas:

1. Research is needed regarding sociodemographic characteristics and needs of suicide survivors, including culturally sensitive service delivery, and connection of the population to the services. Studies should also look at the interaction between suicide stigma and taboo regarding death, and how this can influence openness and help-seeking behavior among survivors and in postvention as a whole. In general, there is a need to promote further studies about the implementation of postvention services in Brazil from the local to the national level with survivors' involvement, and, for example, scholarships and grants for postvention evidence-based research and outcome measures.
2. Education and awareness raising is needed to increase the dialogue among the general population, media, academics, school systems, professionals, and survivors. The bereaved should be included in scientific meetings, and boards of health and education professionals should take steps concerning the importance of suicide prevention and postvention training for students as part of their graduate studies. Existing support groups may increase with better disclosure, reciprocal help, survivor empowerment, and expansion of services around the country. Increasing public awareness and the power of the survivors, gained either through support groups or other means, may pressure the government to take responsibility and truly work for a national strategy to reduce the suicide rate by 10 % by 2020.
3. Regarding the provision of support, society should be better informed about the existing services, as a large number of survivors are not aware of their existence. To this aim, the

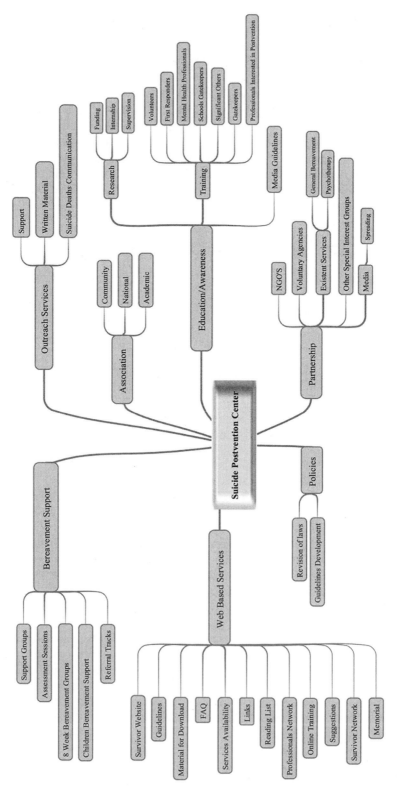

Figure 23.1. Suicide postvention center model. Source: Scavacini, 2011, p. 42.

profiles of online services and helplines to reach people living in remote areas or who do not want to attend traditional support groups should be improved. The bereaved themselves should be trained and included as service providers; and proactive services, which offer services rather than wait to be contacted by the bereaved should be installed.

Conclusions

Although much remains to be done regarding postvention in Brazil, and governmental help is lacking, some activities, programs, and services have been developed and implemented in the country. The proposed suicide postvention center model seems to offer a feasible solution to deliver effective support to suicide survivors and to raise awareness of suicide postvention. Postvention can reduce the risk of negative bereavement outcomes, including risk factors for suicide, and is a fundamental part of comprehensive suicide prevention strategies. Although the suicide rate in Brazil is relatively low, it has been increasing over recent years, and suicide prevention and postvention deserve attention and integration into public health policies. Suicide survivors and the scientific community need to join forces and share knowledge and wisdom, to increase the number of activities and services available in Brazil, to create new venues of support, and to influence the government and the society to become a part of the solution and not a part of the problem.

Corresponding author

Karen Scavacini
Instituto Vita Alere de Prevenção e Posvenção do Suicídio
São Paulo
Brasil
karen.scavacini@uol.com.br

References

Andriessen, K. (2009). Can postvention be prevention? *Crisis, 30*(1), 43–47. http://doi.org/10.1027/0227-5910.30.1.43

Botega, N. (2010). Comportamento suicida em números [Suicide behaviour in numbers]. *Debates – Psiquiatria Hoje, 2,* 11–15.

Ellenbogen, S., & Gratton, F. (2001). Do they suffer more? Reflections on research comparing suicide survivors to other survivors. *Suicide and Life-Threatening Behaviour, 31*(1), 83–90. http://doi.org/10.1521/suli.31.1.83.21315

Fundação Instituto Brasileiro de Geografia e Estatística. (2014). Resolução n.2, de 26 de agosto de 2014 [Resolution no. 2, from 26 of August, 2014]. *Diário Oficial da União* (p. 98). Retrieved from http://pesquisa.in.gov.br/imprensa/jsp/visualiza/index.jsp?jornal=1&pagina=98&data=28/08/2014

Grad, O.T. (1996). Suicide: how to survive as a survivor? *Crisis, 17*(3), 136–142.

Jaques, J.D. (2000). Surviving suicide: The impact on the family. *The Family Journal, 8*(4), 376–379. http://doi.org/10.1177/1066480700084007

Jordan, J.R. (2001). Is suicide bereavement different? A reassessment of the literature. *Suicide and Life-Threatening Behavior, 31*(1), 91–103. http://doi.org/10.1521/suli.31.1.91.21310

Kovács, M.J. (1992). *Morte e desenvolvimento humano* [Death and human development]. São Paulo, Brazil: Casa do Psicólogo.

Ministério da Saúde (Brazilian Ministry of Health). (2006). *Portaria n. 1.876/GM, de 14 de agosto de 2006* [Ordinance No. 1876 of 14 August 2006]. Brasília, Brazil: Ministério da Saúde. Retrieved from http://bvsms.saude.gov.br/bvs/saudelegis/gm/2006/prt1876_14_08_2006.html

Scavacini, K. (2011). *Suicide survivors support services and postvention activities: The availability of services and an interventions plan in Brazil* (Master's thesis). Stockholm, Sweden: Karolinska Institutet, Program in Public Health Sciences.

Scavacini, K. (2014). *E Agora? Um livro para crianças lidando com o luto por suicídio* [What now? A book for children dealing with suicide bereavement]. São Paulo, Brazil: All Print Editora.

Shneidman, E. (1969). Prologue: Fifty-eight years. In E. Shneidman (Ed.), *On the nature of suicide* (pp. 1–30). San Francisco, CA: Jossey-Bass.

Waiselfisz, J. J. (2014). *Mapa da violência: Os jovens do Brasil* [Violence map: The young in Brazil]. Brasilia, Brazil: Flacso Brasil. Retrieved from http://www.mapadaviolencia.org.br/pdf2014/Mapa2014_JovensBrasil.pdf

World Health Organization. (2008). *Preventing suicide: How to start a survivors group*. Geneva, Switzerland: Author.

World Health Organization. (2013). *Mental health action plan 2013–2020*. Geneva, Switzerland: Author.

World Health Organization. (2014). *Preventing suicide: A global imperative*. Geneva, Switzerland: Author.

Chapter 24

Canada – Hope After Loss

Suicide Bereavement and Postvention Services of Suicide Action Montréal

Jean-Claude Daoust

Suicide Action Montréal, QC, Canada

Abstract: Suicide Action Montréal (SAM) is a volunteer-based nongovernmental organization located in Montréal, Québec, Canada. Founded in 1984, its mission is to prevent suicide and to reduce its impact by offering quality services to suicidal people, their friends and relatives, and people bereaved by suicide, as well as professionals and organizations affected by suicide. SAM operates a telephone helpline which receives approximately 40,000 suicide-related calls per year. People touched by suicide can call the helpline to get immediate support from trained volunteers and follow-up support from a variety of services. This chapter describes SAM postvention services based on a fictional case study, and examines the positive impact and outcomes these services can have on individuals who use them.

Introduction

In 1984, a group of individuals who were very committed to the Montréal community and pre-occupied by the rising number of suicides, created Suicide Action Montréal (SAM). Over the years, SAM has become one of the leading suicide prevention initiatives in Canada. The service answers over 40,000 calls per year, including more than 600 calls from grieving individuals. SAM is also involved in development of clinical tools regarding intervention practices and provides training to its own volunteers, as well as employees of health and social services of the island of Montréal, the most populated area of the mostly French-speaking Québec province in Canada.

Established in 1991, SAM's suicide bereavement services offer guidance and a meeting place for the bereaved to express, acknowledge, and validate their experience, while promoting the positive progression of the personal grieving process and the work it entails. The suicide bereavement services receive intakes through the SAM helpline, from funeral homes, law enforcement officials, and other government and nongovernment organizations. The SAM staff includes both paid employees and volunteers, and for the purpose of this chapter, both groups will be referred to as *counselors*. The first step for the bereaved is a call to the 24/7 SAM helpline. The counselors take the time to support the grieving callers and encourage them to express thoughts and emotions. They usually ask questions regarding what happened to the deceased person in order to better understand what the caller went through before, during and after the suicide, and to find out about the relationship the caller had with the deceased. The stronger and the psychologically closer the bond, the more repercussions a suicide might have on the grieving person's life (Fauré, 2007). Using a solutions-oriented approach which helps rekindle hope of a better future (Fiske, 1998) by putting more focus on possible solutions instead of the problematic situation (O'Hanlon & Weiner-Davis, 1995), and by using SAM's *Grille d'estimation de la dangerosité d'un passage à l'acte suicidaire* (Suicide risk assessment scale; Lavoie, Lecavalier, Angers, & Houle, 2012), the counselors are there to listen, to validate, and to acknowledge emotions and reactions related to the loss, and to support and help bereaved callers who have suicidal thoughts. The following section presents the fictional case of Alice, to illustrate the range of services offered by SAM to the bereaved.

First Contact and Assessment

As an illustrative case, Alice, a fictional 40-year-old woman, calls the SAM helpline about 2 weeks after she has lost her husband to suicide. She is still in a state of shock when she makes the call, and the counselor talks for a good half hour with her. The counselor asks Alice questions about her husband's death, whether he left a suicide note, and whether she found the body. Although often difficult, research and clinical practice suggest that talking about the morbid details can help the bereaved, as it allows taking a certain weight off their shoulders and reduces the feeling of isolation (Fauré, 2007). Alice says that she did not see the suicide coming, that her husband was indeed going through a rough patch at work, but she had no idea that his distress had gotten to that point. The counselor explores Alice's reactions: feeling disorganized and disconnected from reality, sadness, anger, and her inability to process what has happened. After giving her time to talk and to express herself, the counselor asks Alice about self-care: Who is there to support her? How does she spend her time? Are there moments when she feels better? At the end of the call, the counselor asks Alice if she would like to receive a follow-up call from the SAM bereavement services.

As Alice's initial call was answered by a volunteer who works limited hours at the helpline, the follow-up call a few days later is made by the bereavement services' head counselor. The counselor performs a needs assessment to verify what Alice would like to work on if she decides to use SAM's face-to-face services, asks questions to better understand her, and assesses whether the services will be right for her. Alice explains that occasionally she has had suicidal ideas since her husband passed away, but that she does not have a suicide plan. However, she had attempted suicide after a difficult breakup when she was in her 20s. Since people who have attempted suicide are more likely to reattempt (Lavoie et al., 2012), the counselor points out to Alice that SAM is there as an ally to help her protect herself. Although Alice has a family and friends, she feels that they do not understand well what she has been going through. Before her husband's suicide, she consulted a psychiatrist regarding her symptoms of depression and anxiety, and she wants to continue treatment as her anxiety is getting worse. Based on this conversation, the counselor decides that Alice could benefit from individual and group sessions for the bereaved offered by SAM.

Alice is willing to attend the group sessions and to continue her meetings with the psychiatrist. She agrees to call the SAM helpline again if she needs to talk or when her suicidal thoughts worsen or overwhelm her. The counselor explains to her that she could benefit from one to five individual sessions (described below). The objective of these sessions is to share her story and to solidify her strengths. The sessions will give her time and space to express herself; to ask questions; to explore her feelings of guilt, anger, and sadness; and perhaps help her to better understand the suicidal process and her own grieving and recovery process. In general, the individual sessions are tailored and adapted to the rhythm and needs of each particular bereaved person, and in some cases, one or two sessions can be sufficient.

Individual Sessions

Alice is given an appointment with a SAM grief counselor. Important messages are communicated during the first session. Although a grieving process may take a year or two (Séguin et al., 2004), not everything will be painful during that period. As weeks and months pass, the intensity and the frequency of intense emotions and reactions are likely to diminish (Fauré, 2007). The counselor tries to help Alice find a balance between experiencing grief-related emotions, and giving herself a break from those emotions by keeping busy, getting her mind off things, and if possible, doing something pleasurable (Séguin et al., 2004). Finding a balance may give Alice much needed break periods and rest, and will allow her to continue evolving in her grieving process (Lane, Archambault, Collins-Poulette, & Camirand, 2010).

Although SAM does not provide psychotherapy, the counseling process includes elements of psychotherapy. In 2010, based on clients' feedback, SAM developed the tool Ce qui m'aide à vivre [What helps me to live]. This questionnaire-type tool can be used with all of SAM's clients and not just the bereaved, and explores seven issues: what the person appreciates in life, important others in the person's life, what the person can offer to other people, plans and projects for the future, dreams worth living for, enjoyable activities, and what beliefs help the person go on.

Group Meetings

Some of the bereaved attend the individual sessions offered by SAM and can call the helpline, if needed, once the sessions have been completed. Still, others, like Alice, may opt to attend a support group. There are eight group sessions, followed by a ninth session approximately 1 month later to see how the participants are doing after the group has finished. The groups are structured to include six to eight participants in order to provide an intimate, confidential, and supporting environment conducive to creating interpersonal relationships.

Once a week, for 2 hrs, Alice meets seven other people bereaved by suicide. The group members are encouraged to think about their goals in 8 weeks' time and how they will know they are achieving their goals. They share strategies they use to find comfort and reassurance. While experiencing and reexperiencing emotions related to their grief, the group participants explore how they see themselves in the future, and start focussing step-by-step on moments of the week when they felt a bit better. For example, Alice mentions that a friend of hers invited her for coffee and that she was actually able to relax and have a good time. Using metaphors and images, some sessions focus on specific aspects of the grief process. In this way, Alice and the other participants can see more clearly where they are in their grieving process and can better understand that grieving is a dynamic process, involving progress and setbacks. Other sessions focus on particular themes, such as guilt and anger, and personal well-being strategies.

Postvention Services for the Community

SAM offers support services for organizations such as schools, companies, other NGOs, or businesses to help employees cope with the death by suicide (or a suicide attempt) of a colleague or a client. Based on the work of Séguin et al. (2004), these specific postvention services were created to reduce the negative impact of a suicide by detecting and preventing postsuicide crisis reactions, alleviating stress reactions, and supporting grieving processes of those affected. Building on an analysis of needs of the affected organization, SAM can provide a variety of interventions, such as a debriefing or coaching session for the management team (i.e., directors, managers, and/or counselors) who might be called upon to provide support to employees. For example, SAM can coach a manager on how to inform employees of the suicide of a colleague and how to detect distress signs in employees. SAM counselors can also intervene directly and facilitate a debriefing session with a manager and the staff. Such a session allows the employees to express their reactions after a suicide and to have their emotions acknowledged and validated. The employees also receive information on the grieving process, as well as an opportunity to share as a group and explore how they can support each other. The debriefing sessions are confidential and participation in such a session are on a voluntary basis. After careful analysis of needs, before and after the session, SAM determines whether or not another type of follow-up is necessary. Organizations are always invited to contact SAM again if they have any questions or if other issues should arise.

Conclusions

The wide range of services offered by SAM creates a security net by offering support for at-risk individuals and coaching of their friends and family. This security net is just as important when it comes to those bereaved by suicide. It is important to help the bereaved reconnect with their reasons for living and to support their sources of strength while they are coping with the loss.

Corresponding author

Jean-Claude Daoust
Suicide Action Montreal
Montreal, QC
Canada
jcdaoust@suicideactionmontreal.qc.ca

References

Fauré, C. (2007). *Après le suicide d'un proche: Vivre le deuil et se reconstruire* [After the suicide of a loved one: To live the grief and to reconstruct oneself]. Paris, France: Éditions Albin Michel.

Fiske, H. (1998). Application of solution-focused brief therapy in suicide prevention. In D. De Leo, A. Schmidtke, & R. F. W. Diekstra (Eds.), *Suicide prevention: A holistic approach* (pp. 185–197). Dordrecht, The Netherlands: Kluwer Academic.

Lane, J., Archambault, J., Collins-Poulette, M., & Camirand, R. (2010). *Guide de bonnes pratiques en prévention du suicide à l'intention des intervenants des centres de santé et de services sociaux* [Good practices in suicide prevention for counselors of health and social services]. Québec, Canada: Communication Department, Ministry of Health and Social Services.

Lavoie, B., Lecavalier, M., Angers, P., & Houle, J. (2012). *Grille d'estimation de la dangerosité d'un passage à l'acte suicidaire: Fondements théoriques et pratiques* [Suicide risk assessment scale: Theoretical and practical foundations]. Montréal, Canada: Centre Dollard-Cormier – Institut Universitaire sur les Dépendances [University Institute on Addictions] and Suicide Action Montréal.

O'Hanlon, W. H., & Weiner-Davis, M. (1995). *In search of solutions: A new direction in psychotherapy.* Bruxelles, Belgium: SATAS.

Séguin, M., Roy, F., Bouchard, M., Gallagher, R., Raymond, S., Gravel, C., & Boyer, R. (2004). *Programme de postvention en milieu scolaire: Stratégies d'intervention à la suite d'un suicide* [Postvention programs in schools: Intervention strategies after a suicide]. Montréal, Canada: Éditions AQPS.

Chapter 25

Uruguay – Working With Suicide Survivors

Silvia Peláez, Patricia Wels, and Isaías Valencia

Último Recurso, Montevideo, Uruguay

Abstract: This chapter discusses the therapeutic dynamics in postvention groups organized and coordinated by mental health specialists in Uruguay. It explores a number of suicide-related notions, such as crisis, the identity of the bereaved (i.e., suicide survivors), and the process of mourning after suicide, from a psychoanalytic perspective, and from suicidology and social psychology. It looks into the technical and methodological aspects involved in the reconstruction of the identity of suicide survivors who look for meaning in the death of a loved one. Postvention groups represent a privileged therapeutic resource. Nevertheless, there remain many challenges and unanswered questions surrounding postvention groups, in particular regarding accessibility, visibility, and the demystification of suicide in society.

Even if only two people show up.... It is worth it!
Airi Värnik (2002)

Introduction

Uruguay is a small Latin American country situated in the Southern Cone. Uruguay's population is composed mainly of immigrants of European descent, especially Spanish and Italian, although there are also Afro-American and Native American communities. According to the 2011 census, Uruguay's population is 3.29 million (Instituto Nacional de Estadistica, 2011), and almost half of the population lives in the capital, Montevideo. Due to the low population density, there is a great social cohesion, expressed in the popular saying "in Uruguay everybody knows everybody." This may generate ambiguous feelings among an emotionally vulnerable population, such as the bereaved by suicide, since one may receive a lot of support from neighbors and family, but also the level of social control is high.

Suicide as a Crisis

According to Moffatt (1982), crisis is manifested as a paralyzing experience of discontinuity in the process of life. In these conditions, the future looks empty and the present frozen. When the intensity of disturbance increases, one may begin to feel disconnected from self, in a state resembling a depersonalization syndrome (*International Statistical Classification of Diseases and Related Health Problems* [ICD-10] code F48.1). Moreover, beyond the pain suffered by suicide survivors, it is the unexpectedness of the new situation that causes the most damage and has the highest impact. The unexpected situation that one faces when dealing with a powerful crisis, such as suicide, feels unreal and strange. This may result in an alienation effect, which manifests itself in the sense of being invaded by an "other" not recognized by ourselves (Moffatt, 1982).

The Experience of Suicide Survivors

Suicide survivors frequently experience shame, guilt, and anger. However, worse than guilt and shame, they may suffer from the unsolicited birth of a new identity (e.g., the "woman who 'allowed' her husband to kill himself"), and may feel that this new identity will prevail. They may feel that this "special" bereavement is a sort of punishment, because of their loved one's death. Many times, they consider suicide as a crime and themselves as criminals. The members of postvention groups must help each other to analyze and to change the new identity created by bereavement. Only then can the bereaved feel they may heal in a healthy way. What is striking when working with groups of the bereaved, is how suicide survivors become alienated, strangers to themselves. This is why the crisis is mainly seen as an identity crisis.

The loss of a loved one by suicide and the crisis that may follow can be studied under the basic equation: "love plus death equals madness" (Moffatt, 1982). This is because, according to the Freudian perspective (Freud, 1917; García, 2009), people's reaction when facing loss demands the representation, or the symbolization, of that which has been lost and is now absent. Given the difficulty of accepting the death of a loved one, hallucinations may appear in the early stages of mourning. If the crisis is not resolved appropriately, the person may function in a disintegrated way or even become psychotic (González de Rivera y Revuelta, 2001).

Nonetheless, it is possible to successfully resolve the loss of a loved one. There are at least two possible alternatives. One of them involves placing the suicide survivor in their previous state of being before the crisis. The second one implies empowering the person to become a new Ego (Slaikeu, 1996). (When dealing with patients with few internal and/or external resources, the crisis is usually resolved through a passive adaptation to reality; see Pichon-Riviere, 1981, p. 66. In contrast, if the patient counts on adequate and varied resources, the new self that emerges after the crisis may operate in a healthier way and even with more freedom than before the crisis.) It is precisely in the crisis of identity that comes after loss, that a new character may appear to restore (even if only partially) the cohesion of the Ego. This new character's role – for instance, the "mother of the one who died by suicide" or the "groom of the one who killed herself" – comes at a cost. The price of this new identity makes the postvention patient the depositary of social condemnation expressed in rumors, suspicions, and superstitions. This may place the person in the role of murderer or at least a scapegoat for the "crime" that suicide means to society (Robertt, 1997). One must remember that once upon a time, suicide was called self-murder.

Postvention Groups

To process the loss, it is necessary in the therapeutic context to avoid repeating the judgment that the bereaved have already been experiencing since their new identity as a suicide survivor was assigned to them. This will be possible if a group participant feels respected and equal to other participants. In this way, each postvention group participant may act as a similar or symmetrical figure, providing mirror images with which others, who are experiencing the same kind of pain, may identify and feel understood. A group of suicide survivors provides this dimension as a starting point because no judgmental attitude is allowed.

These groups represent the crucible where a healthier new identity shall be forged. From now on, being the "father of the one who killed herself" shall be one aspect of the suicide survivor but not their most defining identity feature. Moreover, at this point, it will be necessary to explore what the suicide of a loved one means for each survivor. It is useful to remember the idea that "nobody wants to die ... but they want to stop living the way they are living" (Garma, 1973, pp. 105–114) and that death takes on different meanings depending on the circumstances and personal characteristics of those who have died by suicide (Garma, 1973). If there is suicidal ideation in the survivor, it will be essential to work on the meaning of this fantasized death. Is it to punish oneself? Is it to ask the dead one about their death by suicide? To apologize or to blame the deceased?

Occasionally, when those who have died by suicide had exhausted the emotional and material resources of their environment, because of repeated suicide attempts, hospitalization, care requirements, behavior being seen as manipulative, etc., their death can be seen as a relief. In these cases, it is vital to work with the guilt feelings of the bereaved to avoid depression or increased vulnerability.

Furthermore, the possibility of organizing postvention groups in terms of self-help should be dismissed, given the nature of these sessions' objectives. The access to a new, healthy and chosen identity requires supervised hard technical work with a determined strategy and treatment plan. Moreover, in the context of the groups' dynamics, it is common for multiple testimonies to come out – for example, related to guilt, one of the most intense feelings experienced by many survivors. These must be identified, interpreted, and worked through by a qualified mental health professional. To this aim, it is often a good idea for the mental health professional to illustrate the historical development of the significance of suicide and the sense of place of the survivor through informative interventions. Role playing is one of the most widely used techniques, as it promotes reconstruction of identity and working with experiences related to grief. The mental health professional may also work with the interpretation of Sophocles' *Antigone* (Lester, 2002) by exploring its meaning together with participants.

Postvention Groups in Uruguay

Último Recurso (the Last Resort) is a nongovernmental organization operating in Uruguay since 1989, aiming to prevent suicide through a telephone helpline and other activities, such as clinical attention, workshops, and postvention groups. These groups are usually coordinated by two suicidologists trained in group psychotherapy and social psychology. To date, Último Recurso has served about 300 people, and the community services provided are accessed through suicide prevention activities in Montevideo and other locations in the country.

Since 2002, the groups organized by Último Recurso have had an open format for the first 2 months, and later they become closed groups. Experience shows that if a group remains open, the members who attend more frequently feel abandoned by those who leave early.

Closure in therapeutic terms may appear after 12–18 months, depending on various circumstances, such as the speed of the process, desertion of more than 40% of the members, and repeated and unresolved conflicts that can lead to shortening of the group's processes, and moving to another modality of work. Even though unusual, it is possible to change the therapeutic model once the group has started. Some bereaved require individual therapy and pharmacotherapy. The frequency of the group's meetings is weekly or fortnightly, depending on the circumstances and abilities of the participants. In rural areas, for instance, meetings occur fortnightly. The recommended duration is 2 to 2.5 hr per session. An important condition is that suicide survivors who participate in a group are not related. If the bereaved are related to the same person who died by suicide, they may not speak and express themselves honestly or wholeheartedly. The size of the group may vary between 2 and 25 participants.

The first meeting usually includes an introduction involving pair or individual presentations, and there is an opportunity to get acquainted with each other. Each member may be presented by a peer. Afterwards, there is a brief break, and snacks are provided. After the break, free expression by those who wish to speak is encouraged. By the third or the fourth meeting, the members bring drinks and food to share, as it promotes networking among participants and helps to build confidence and self-knowledge.

Conclusions

Working with suicide survivors in postvention groups helps the bereaved. One of the positive aspects is the rapid acceptance of the collective format of these groups and the establishment of therapeutic links between the participants. Most probably, this is related to a sense of security and increased confidence granted by contact with other bereaved. However, unlike other group therapies, such as Alcoholics Anonymous, the therapeutic model presented in this chapter is not yet well established. This limits the accessibility of postvention groups as a therapeutic resource. Further work on promoting this therapy format among mental health professionals is needed along with the demystifying of suicide in society.

Corresponding author

Silvia Peláez
Último Recurso
Montevideo
Uruguay
spelaez@ultimorecurso.com.uy

References

Freud, S. (1917). *Works on metapsychology, mourning and melancholy* Buenos Aires, Argentina: Amorrortu.
García, J. (2009). La muerte y el objeto [Death and the object]. *Revista Uruguaya de Psicoanálisis, 108*, 90–107.
Garma, A. (1973). The representation of death in the suicide. In M. Abadi, Á. Garma, E. Garma, A. Gazzano, E. Rolla, & N. Yampey (Eds.), *La fascinación de la muerte* [The fascination of death] (pp. 105–114). Buenos Aires, Argentina: Paidos.
González de Rivera y Revuelta, J.L. (2001). Psicoterapia de la crisis [Crisis psychotherapy]. *Revista de la Asociación Española de Neuropsiquiatría, 21*(79), 35–53.
Instituto Nacional de Estadistica. (2011). *Results of the population census 2011: Population growth and structure by sex and age* [In Spanish]. Retrieved from http://www.ine.gub.uy/c/document_library/get_file?uuid=12d80f63-afe4–4b2c-bf5b-bff6666c0c80&groupId=10181
Lester, D. (2002). Sophocles: The first great suicidologist. *Crisis, 23*(1), 34–37.
Moffatt, A. (1982). *Terapia de crisis* [Crisis therapy]. Buenos Aires, Argentina: Búsqueda.
Pichon-Riviere, E. (1981). *El proceso grupal: Del psicoanalisis a la psicologia social* [The group process: From psychoanalysis to social psychology]. Buenos Aires, Argentina: Nueva Vision.
Robertt, P. (1997). El suicidio en el Uruguay. Un análisis histórico [Suicide in Uruguay: An historical analysis]. *UdelaR – Research Report* (23). Montevideo, Uruguay: Department of Sociology, Faculty of Social Sciences.
Slaikeu, C. (1996). *Intervención en crisis: Manual para práctica e investigación* [Crisis Intervention: A handbook for practice and research]. Mexico City, Mexico: El Manual Moderno.
Värnik, A. (2002). *Surviving a suicide*. Presentation at the suicide prevention conference, December 6, 2002. Montevideo, Uruguay: Último Recurso.

Chapter 26

USA – Suicide Bereavement Support and Postvention

Jerry Reed[1], John R. Jordan[2], and John L. McIntosh[3]

[1]Suicide Prevention Resource Center, Education Development Center, Washington DC, USA
[2]Private Practice, Pawtucket, RI, USA
[3]Academic Affairs, Indiana University South Bend, South Bend, IN, USA

Abstract: As a result of the selfless service of those bereaved by suicide loss who were willing to tell their stories and recommend programmatic and policy objectives to advance suicide prevention in the United States, policymakers have heard the call for more action to address the 10th leading cause of death in the nation. Legislative resolutions have been passed, national strategies have been written, guidelines on postvention have been established, support services for survivors of suicide loss have been developed, and a national research agenda inclusive of postvention research has been published. This chapter will trace the past, current, and future of postvention in the United States and present key advances in postvention that are making these vital programs an integral part of the national network of suicide prevention services.

Past Postvention Efforts in the United States

The focus on postvention in the United States began in the second half of the 20th century. Postvention began as a recognized area of interest in the field of suicidology as an indirect result of psychological autopsy work, which made clear that survivors of suicide loss needed to speak about their losses and the emotional and psychological responses that followed (Chapter 9 in this volume; Jobes et al., 2000; Spencer-Thomas & Jahn, 2012). It was also learned that exposure to suicide actually confers increased risk of suicide on those left behind (Jordan & McIntosh, 2011a).

Suicide prevention gained significant national attention in the United States in the mid-1990s when survivors mobilized to bring attention to the fact that suicide was a leading cause of death and that many suicides might be preventable if the national resolve were strengthened. Indeed, survivors have been one of the driving forces behind suicide prevention efforts in the United States. Grassroots advocacy groups launched a survivor-driven campaign to encourage the development of a national strategy. Their efforts resulted in two congressional resolutions recognizing suicide as a national problem and calling for suicide prevention to be treated as a national priority. Shortly after these resolutions passed, a major conference was held in 1998 in Reno, Nevada, bringing suicide loss and attempt survivors, policymakers, clinicians, researchers, state leaders, and advocates together to review the knowledge about suicide prevention and where the field's collective actions should be directed. This conference helped prompt the *Surgeon General's Call to Action to Prevent Suicide* (US Public Health Service, 1999) and soon thereafter in 2001, the release of the first *National Strategy for Suicide Prevention*

(US Department of Health and Human Services [HHS], 2001). In 1999, a resolution was passed in the US Congress declaring the Saturday before the US Thanksgiving holiday, which is always on the fourth Thursday in November, National Survivors of Suicide Day. Events have been held annually since the resolution passed, and the observance has expanded to become International Survivors of Suicide Loss Day.

The first National Strategy for Suicide Prevention (NSSP) contained two objectives relevant to postvention policy (HHS, 2001). Objective 7.5 called for the provision of training and support to key *first responders* (e.g., police, emergency medical personnel, funeral directors, etc.) who might be impacted by their work with survivors. Objective 8.7 called for the development of national guidelines for effective and comprehensive support programs for suicide survivors (see Chapter 27 in this volume).

Launched in 2010, the National Action Alliance for Suicide Prevention has as its mission to serve as the national coordinating body for suicide prevention in the United States. Among its early actions were a call for the revision of the NSSP and the creation of several task forces, including one on Survivors of Suicide Loss. The revised NSSP (HHS, 2012) was released on World Suicide Prevention Day in 2012, and it spoke much more directly to postvention. Goal 10 of the new strategy is to "provide care and support to individuals affected by suicide deaths and attempts to promote healing and implement community strategies to help prevent further suicides" (HHS, 2012). A document recently released by the Survivors of Suicide Loss Task Force, *Responding to Grief, Trauma, and Distress After a Suicide: US National Guidelines* (see Chapter 27 in this volume), is the fulfillment of the original call for national postvention guidelines in the United States mentioned above.

Current Postvention Efforts in the United States

Presently, in addition to traditional therapeutic and grief counseling approaches for postvention, there are support groups for survivors of suicide loss in communities around the nation (see Chapter 10 in this volume). The American Association of Suicidology (AAS) lists over 450 such groups in its online directory (http://www.suicidology.org). As described in Chapter 10 of this volume, these support groups vary in their characteristics and may include peer mutual support among survivors, facilitation by mental health professionals, and/or specially trained facilitators including survivors. Reflecting technological advances, there are now several online support communities for suicide loss survivors, including e-mail Listservs, chat rooms, blogs, and electronic memorials. A particularly noteworthy postvention approach is the Active Postvention Model (Campbell, 2011). Provided first by the Baton Rouge Crisis Intervention Center, the Local Outreach to Suicide Survivors (LOSS) Team facilitates cooperation between the coroner's office and trained team members (often survivors of suicide themselves) who respond at the scene of a death to provide immediate assistance and support to the survivors there and to make them aware of available support group resources.

Significant contributions to the understanding of suicide loss and the development of postvention protocols have been made by national organizations. The oldest of these, noted above, is AAS, a national membership organization with a goal to understand and prevent suicide. AAS now includes a dedicated Loss Survivor Division. Another national organization is the American Foundation for Suicide Prevention (AFSP; http://www.afsp.org; Chapter 28 in this volume). This foundation funds research, provides educational programming, supports survivors of suicide, and – since merging with the Suicide Prevention Action Network USA (SPAN USA; established by parents who had lost a daughter to suicide, see https://www.whitehouse.gov/champions/suicide-prevention/the-suicide-prevention-action-network-(span-usa) for their web page) – advocates for public policy on suicide. AFSP has 75 local chapters across the nation and a Loss and Bereavement Council that oversees the foundation's survivor and postvention activities.

AAS hosts an annual national conference at which workshops, papers, invited addresses, and sessions on survivors are included. A special component of the annual AAS gathering is the Healing After Suicide Conference cosponsored by AAS and AFSP. This day-long event includes a joint plenary session shared with the annual professional conference, as well as a unique schedule of sessions specifically for those attending the Healing Conference.

Among the activities it sponsors each year, AFSP, through its local chapters, conducts Out of the Darkness Walks in communities across the nation and on college campuses. In addition, Overnight Walks are held annually. In these fund-raising events, walkers are sponsored for their participation by friends, family, and others. The funds raised support the suicide prevention efforts of the AFSP, including research and educational programs as well as advocacy efforts. Another important aspect of the walks for those who take part is to honor their lost loved ones by supporting suicide prevention. In cooperation with AAS and other organizations, AFSP sponsors International Survivors of Suicide Loss Day, with a nationally distributed program either via webcast or on DVD, as well as events and activities, such as panels of survivors and national experts in mental health as well as local programming to comfort loss survivors and promote healing in local communities.

Both AAS and AFSP give annual awards to recognize outstanding efforts by suicide loss survivors (AAS has the Survivor of the Year Award and AFSP the Survivor of Suicide Loss Award), create educational and other resources on survivors and postvention, and maintain lists of support groups across the nation. In addition to the specific activities noted here, both AAS and AFSP are among the seven organizations that make up the National Council for Suicide Prevention (http://www.thencsp.org). This national leadership group encourages and assists in efforts for effective suicide prevention and works particularly to advance the goals and objectives, including those related to postvention, of the *National Strategy for Suicide Prevention.*

Future Directions for Postvention in the United States

The most recent, and perhaps the most important, development in postvention in the United States is intended to help shape the direction of postvention efforts for the next ten or more years: the release of *Responding to Grief, Trauma, and Distress After a Suicide: US National Guidelines,* by the Survivors of Suicide Loss Task Force of the National Action Alliance for Suicide Prevention (National Action Alliance for Suicide Prevention, 2015). The guidelines make a compelling and empirically based case for the need for postvention and lay out a rationale for the types of assistance that will be useful for suicide loss survivors. The guidelines also outline 15 specific postvention goals for the nation across four different *strategic directions.* The guidelines are a major step forward in the effort to raise awareness of the serious impact of suicide, and to build *postvention infrastructure* (Jordan et al., 2011). The guidelines are described in Chapter 27 of this volume (available online at: http://actionallianceforsuicideprevention.org/sites/actionallianceforsuicideprevention.org/files/NationalGuidelines.pdf).

In concert with recommendations set forth in the guidelines, there are a number of changes in postvention practices in the United States that seem likely to grow in impact over the coming years. One is an emerging and crucial conceptual shift among policymakers and program administrators to realize that, as Shneidman (1972) noted years ago, postvention with suicide loss survivors *is* a direct form of suicide prevention with a population of people known to be at elevated risk for suicide themselves (Jordan & McIntosh, 2011b; Pitman et al., 2014). Incorporation of this key understanding into suicidology means that policy and programs will increasingly include postvention as a fundamental element of *all* suicide prevention efforts.

Second, postvention programs will increasingly strive to produce a systematic and coordinated response when a suicide occurs in a given community. Such a response includes the universal provision of psychoeducational information about the nature of suicide and grief after suicide to the newly bereaved. It also includes the delivery of directories of support resources where survivors can obtain further assistance. These coordinated responses will entail the development of multiple types of support services within communities for survivors with differing and complex needs. These services may include outreach teams of peer survivors (such as a LOSS Team), bereavement support groups, online sites for contact with other survivors, and skilled and "survivor-knowledgeable" mental health professionals to help with issues of traumatization, complicated grief, and suicidality in the survivor (see Jordan & McIntosh, 2011a, for examples of existing programs).

Third, efforts will expand to provide training for caregivers who have contact with new survivors. The training of police, emergency and medical personnel, funeral professionals, clergy, and even mental health professionals, in suicide prevention and postvention skills is often sorely lacking. It is important to change this situation, so that new survivors receive compassionate and knowledgeable support from people to whom they can reliably turn in a time of great personal crisis.

Fourth, research into the elevated risk of suicide among survivors, and into the effectiveness and efficacy of support interventions for them, should increase as awareness of the needs of survivors grows. The vast majority of research in suicidology has focused on the causes of suicide, and to a much lesser extent, on treatments for suicidal individuals. The field has barely begun to study suicide loss survivors as an at-risk population, and to develop a solid empirical base for postvention efforts with survivors. It is expected that this will change as the needs and vulnerabilities of people exposed to the suicide of a loved one become better understood.

Lastly, efforts to make postvention programs more culturally nuanced and customized will also likely grow in the next decade. The majority of postvention services in the United States (e.g., peer-to-peer bereavement support groups) appear to be utilized primarily by female, White, and middle-class individuals. Certain specific populations in the United States that have been exposed to high rates of suicide loss or that have typically not utilized postvention services (e.g., Native Americans, military personnel, males in general) may need more culturally relevant and focused programs. The effort to develop such "culturally competent" services is just beginning in the United States, but will hopefully expand rapidly in the future.

Conclusions

This chapter has traced the past, current, and future of postvention services in the United States and presented key advances in postvention to highlight the ways these vital services are integral to the national network of suicide prevention services. Postvention efforts in the United States include work at the policy level as well as the individual and community levels, and touch on the need for resource development, enhanced service delivery, guideline development, cultural competence, research, and evaluation. These efforts are founded on the premise that postvention is prevention (Shneidman, 1972), and this important focus should continue to be a part of the evolving field.

Corresponding author

Jerry Reed
Suicide Prevention Resource Center
Education Development Center
Washington DC
USA
jreed@edc.org

References

Campbell, F. R. (2011). Baton Rouge Crisis Intervention Center's LOSS Team active postvention model approach. In J. R. Jordan & J. L. McIntosh (Eds.), *Grief after suicide: Understanding the consequences and caring for the survivors* (pp. 327–332). New York, NY: Routledge.

Jobes, D. A., Luoma, J. B., Hustead, L. A. T., & Mann, R. E. (2000). In the wake of suicide: Survivorship and postvention. In R. W. Maris, A. L. Berman, & M. M. Silverman (Eds.), *Comprehensive textbook of suicidology* (pp. 536–561). New York, NY: Guilford Press.

Jordan, J. R., & McIntosh, J. L. (2011a). *Grief after suicide: Understanding the consequences and caring for the survivors.* New York, NY: Routledge.

Jordan, J. R., & McIntosh, J. L. (2011b). Suicide bereavement: Why study survivors of suicide loss? In J. R. Jordan & J. L. McIntosh (Eds.), *Grief after suicide: Understanding the consequences and caring for the survivors* (pp. 3–17). New York, NY: Routledge.

Jordan, J. R., McIntosh, J. L., Bolton, I. M., Campbell, F. R., Harpel, J. L., & Linn-Gust, M. (2011). A call to action: Building clinical and programmatic support for suicide survivors. In J. R. Jordan & J. L. McIntosh (Eds.), *Grief after suicide: Understanding the consequences and caring for the survivors.* (pp. 523–534). New York, NY: Routledge.

National Action Alliance for Suicide Prevention. (2015). *Responding to grief, trauma, & distress after a suicide: U. S. national guidelines.* Washington, DC: Author.

Pitman, A., Osborn, D., King, M., & Erlangsen, A. (2014). Effects of suicide bereavement on mental health and suicide risk. *Lancet Psychiatry, 1*(1), 86–94. http://doi.org/10.1016/S2215-0366(14)70224-X

Shneidman, E. S. (1972). Foreword. In A. C. Cain (Ed.), *Survivors of suicide.* Springfield, IL: Charles C. Thomas.

Spencer-Thomas, S., & Jahn, D. R. (2012). Tracking a movement: US milestones in suicide prevention. *Suicide and Life-Threatening Behavior, 42*(1), 78–85. http://doi.org/10.1111/j.1943-278X.2011.00072.x

US Department of Health and Human Services. (2001). *National strategy for suicide prevention: Goals and objectives for action.* Rockville, MD: Author.

US Department of Health and Human Services, Office of the Surgeon General and National Action Alliance for Suicide Prevention. (2012). *2012 National strategy for suicide prevention: Goals and objective for action.* Washington, DC: HHS.

US Public Health Service. (1999). *The Surgeon General's call to action to prevent suicide.* Washington, DC: Author.

Chapter 27

USA – National Postvention Guidelines

John R. Jordan

Private Practice, Pawtucket, RI, USA

Abstract: It is being recognized that suicide postvention is a crucial part of suicide prevention. The United States has recently released new guidelines for developing postvention services in the nation. This chapter offers a summary of these guidelines, as well as a discussion of the implications of the guidelines for postvention services for people exposed to suicide.

Introduction

While initially a slow process, the development of postvention in the United States has been accelerating in recent years (Chapter 26 in this volume; Jordan, 2015; Jordan & McIntosh, 2011a). The original US National Strategy for Suicide Prevention (NSSP) barely made mention of postvention or the needs of the bereaved by suicide (US Public Health Service, 2001). The more recent update of the NSSP (US Department of Health & Human Services [HHS], Office of the Surgeon General, & National Action Alliance for Suicide Prevention, 2012) did include a greater focus on the needs of suicide loss survivors, and issued a call to "develop guidelines for effective comprehensive support programs for individuals bereaved by suicide and promote the full implementation of these guidelines at the state/territorial, tribal, and community levels." (US Department of Health & Human Services [HHS], Office of the Surgeon General, & National Action Alliance for Suicide Prevention, 2012, p. 63). This chapter describes the fulfillment of this objective in the form of guidelines that were released by the Survivors of Suicide Loss Task Force (SOSL TF) of the National Action Alliance for Suicide Prevention in April, 2015. The National Action Alliance for Suicide Prevention (NAASP) is a public-private partnership begun in 2010 to further the goals of the original US National Strategy for Suicide Prevention (US Public Health Service, 2001), which called for the formation of such a partnership. The guidelines are titled *Responding to Grief, Trauma, and Distress After a Suicide: US National Guidelines* (the full text of the guidelines is available at the Action Alliance website or at: http://actionallianceforsuicideprevention.org/sites/actionallianceforsuicideprevention.org/files/NationalGuidelines.pdf), and this chapter describes the development, organization, and rationale for the guidelines. It also outlines the four strategic directions, the three appendices, and the implications of the recommendations in the guidelines for the development of "support infrastructure" for people exposed to suicide.

Development and Organization of the Guidelines

As a result of the growing recognition that suicide can leave significant psychological and so-cial damage in its wake, including an elevated risk for suicide (Jordan & McIntosh, 2011b), the SOSL TF was created by the Action Alliance and charged to develop guidelines for postvention services at all levels of government and community in the United States. The guidelines begin with a careful exposition of the rationale for providing postvention support for people exposed to suicide. They introduce a new answer to the question, Who is a survivor? called the *con-tinuum model of survivorship* (Cerel, Mcintosh, Neimeyer, Maple, & Marshall, 2014; National Action Alliance for Suicide Prevention, 2015). The guidelines also provide a thoughtful discus-sion of the ways that grief after suicide may differ from other bereavement as a result of the perceived intentionality to die on the part of the deceased (Jordan, 2008; McIntosh, & Jordan, 2011). Likewise, the social context of stigmatization and social isolation also adds additional burdens for loss survivors (Cvinar, 2005; Feigelman, Gorman, & Jordan, 2009; Feigelman, Jordan, McIntosh, & Feigelman, 2012). The guidelines provide an extensive review of the em-pirical evidence that people exposed to, and bereaved by, suicide suffer significantly elevated psychiatric and social problems that range from increased risk for suicide, to depression and complicated grief reactions, substance abuse, and social strain, isolation, and stigmatization. The guidelines also comment on the needs of suicide loss survivors in the immediate aftermath of a death, as well as the longer term.

Goals and Objectives

Mirroring the organizational structure of the updated NSSP (US Department of Health & Hu-man Services et al., 2012), the guidelines are organized around the four *strategic directions* of the NSSP. Under each direction, there are several goals, and within each of the goals, there are specific objectives.

   The first strategic direction, *healthy and empowered individuals, families, and communities,* corresponds in a public health model to universal interventions for promoting health accom-plished on behalf of an entire population. The first direction has four goals:

1. Integrate and coordinate effective suicide postvention activities across jurisdictions, or-ganizations, and systems through increased communication, collaboration, and capacity building.
2. Communicate accurate and useful information about the impact of suicide on individuals, organizations, and communities; the availability of services for people affected by suicide; and the nature and importance of suicide postvention.
3. Work to ensure that media, entertainment, and online communications about suicide and its aftermath do not contribute to the distress of people bereaved by suicide or to the risk of suicidal behavior among people exposed to a fatality.
4. Create the infrastructure and delivery systems for training a wide array of service provid-ers in suicide bereavement support and treatment, and in minimizing the adverse effects of exposure to a suicide.
   Strategic direction 2, *Clinical and community preventive services,* maps onto selective public health interventions that target people who are at elevated risk for developing disor-ders after exposure to a suicide. Its goals are:
5. Develop and implement protocols in communities and across caregiving systems for effectively responding at the scene and in the immediate aftermath of all suicides.
6. Ensure that people exposed to a suicide receive essential and appropriate information.

7. Develop and implement effective postvention practices in organizational, workplace, and school settings.
Strategic direction 3, *Treatment and support services,* relates to indicated interventions in a public health approach that attempt to reach people who are currently experiencing negative outcomes as a result of a suicide. Its goals are:
8. Ensure that all support and treatment services delivered to the suicide bereaved are accessible, adequate, consistent, and coordinated across systems of care.
9. At the level of support services, provide an array of assistance, programs, and resources that help bereaved individuals and families cope with and recover from the effects of their loss to suicide. Services at this level may include information, emotional support, guidance; psychoeducation about suicide, grief, trauma, and effective self-care; and participation in peer help and other community-based services.
10. At the level of professional clinical services, provide an array of treatment, programs, and resources that help people affected by unremitting or complicated grief, posttraumatic stress disorder (PTSD), depression, suicidality, and other acute or potentially debilitating conditions.
Strategic direction 4, is *Surveillance, research, and evaluation.* Its goals are designed to increase the knowledge base about the aftermath of suicide to guide the implementation of effective treatment and support:
11. Design studies of suicide loss survivors using appropriate scientific methods.
12. Establish valid and reliable estimates of the number of people exposed to suicide and the immediate and longer-term impact of exposure. This includes people (a) exposed to and (b) affected by a given suicide, as well as those who suffer (c) short-term and (d) long-term bereavement difficulties after a suicide.
13. Identify common and unique impacts of suicide bereavement, as well as individual difference variables that function as risk factors for or buffers to such effects.
14. Study the utilization and efficacy of interventions and services designed to assist people bereaved by suicide.
15. Promote bridging of research and practice by soliciting engagement of relevant stakeholders in scientific studies of suicide loss and intervention.

Finally, the national guidelines include three appendices. Appendix A delineates a set of overarching principles for postvention programs and services. Appendix B provides a comprehensive list of key resources for survivors and for those who care for them. Appendix C identifies specific action steps that can be taken by officials at the local, tribal, state, and national levels to strengthen postvention efforts in their jurisdiction.

Implications of the Guidelines

The release of the US Guidelines is a signal event in the advancement of postvention in the United States, offering clear and focused goals for improving the support infrastructure for people impacted by suicide. There are several outcomes that can be hoped for from the publication of this important document.

The guidelines expand the range of persons to whom postvention resources should be directed. They identify a much larger circle of people who may have difficulty after a suicide than has previously been identified. Recent research supports the proposition that there are many more people who self-identify as having been impacted by suicide than earlier postvention research and interventions have recognized (Cerel et al., 2016). The guidelines also note that a subset of suicide loss survivors (i.e., the long-term bereaved) may require long-term services that go far beyond the short-term and crisis-oriented postvention efforts of the typical postvention service in the United States.

The guidelines explicitly call for the integration of postvention services into *all* levels of the national effort to reduce suicide. Historically, suicide loss survivors have been the "caboose" of suicidology – a population which has evoked compassion from the field, but has been viewed by many in academic suicidology as having little to do with suicide prevention efforts. In direct contrast, the US Guidelines make a forceful case for postvention as a crucial form of suicide prevention with a population that is known to be at elevated risk for suicide.

The guidelines strongly encourage communities and states to develop an organized and co-ordinated response to suicide. The literature suggests that many new loss survivors are too trau-matized, depressed, and/or acutely bereaved to be able to seek needed services for themselves, and have difficulty finding services when they do search for them. (Dyregrov, 2002; Dyregrov, Plyhn, Dieserud, & Oatley, 2012; McMenamy, Jordan, & Mitchell, 2008). While examples of well-developed postvention responses in the United States exist (Archibald, 2011; Campbell, 2011; Harrington-LaMorie, & Ruocco, 2011; Koenig, 2011), they are few and far between. The guidelines call for the development of support infrastructure throughout the United States, as well as the coordination of these services at a local level, so that all survivors are informed by first responders of where and how to access services, and are supported in their efforts to do so. Of particular promise are outreach teams of survivors and/or mental health professionals that proactively visit new survivors. Research has suggested that this kind of *active postven-tion* response is both effective and helps to link new survivors to additional services that are needed (Campbell, 2011; Campbell, Cataldie, McIntosh, & Millet, 2004; UnitedSynergies, 2009, 2011).

The guidelines call for improved training for people who care for suicide loss survivors. For example, the great majority of US mental health professionals receive only cursory training in providing grief therapy of any kind. The guidelines call for training in crisis response and be-reavement care to be a regular component of the training, licensure, and continuing education requirements of all mental health professionals. Likewise, the guidelines call for an improve-ment in the quantity and quality of training for other types of caregivers and first responders to suicide, including police, emergency medical personnel, clergy, funeral professionals, and government authorities.

Conclusions

It is hoped that the new US Guidelines will serve as a potent catalyst for the inclusion of post-vention services into *all* suicide prevention efforts in the United States. They can also initiate vital collaboration among clinicians, researchers, policymakers, and loss survivors – with each other and with the larger fields of inquiry in which postvention is rooted. These domains in-clude not only the obvious sphere of suicidology, but also the fields of traumatology, thanatol-ogy, and public health. The guidelines provide a blueprint for the development of effective and universal bereavement and trauma support for all people affected by suicide. As was observed at their release (Cook, Padgett, Jordan, Marshall, & Berkowitz, 2015), the guidelines can hope-fully lead to a nation where

> communities and organizations provide everyone who is exposed to a suicide access to effec-tive services immediately – and for as long as necessary – to decrease their risk of suicide, to strengthen their mental health, and to help them cope with grief. (Cook et al., 2015, p. i)

Corresponding author

John R. Jordan
Private Practice
Pawtucket, RI
USA
jjordan50@gmail.com

References

Archibald, L. (2011). HEARTBEAT Survivors after Suicide, Inc. In J.R. Jordan & J.L. McIntosh (Eds.), *Grief after suicide: Coping with the consequences and caring for the survivors* (pp. 349–356). New York, NY: Routledge.

Campbell, F.R. (2011). Baton Rouge Crisis Intervention Center's LOSS Team Active Postvention Model Approach. In J.R. Jordan & J.L. McIntosh (Eds.), *Grief after suicide: Understanding the consequences and caring for the survivors* (pp. 327–332). New York, NY: Routledge.

Campbell, F.R., Cataldie, L., McIntosh, J.L., & Millet, K. (2004). An active postvention program. *Crisis, 25*(1), 30–32. http://doi.org/10.1027/0227-5910.25.1.30

Cerel, J., Maple, M., van de Veene, J., Moore, M., Flaherty, C., & Brown, M. (2016). Suicide exposure in the community: Prevalence and correlates in one US state. *Public Health Reports, 131*(1), 100–107. http://doi.org/10.1177/003335491613100116

Cerel, J., Mcintosh, J.L., Neimeyer, R.A., Maple, M., & Marshall, D.S. (2014). The continuum of survivorship: Definitional issues in the aftermath of suicide. *Suicide and Life-Threatening Behavior, 44*(6), 591–600. http://doi.org/10.1111/sltb.12093

Cook, F., Padgett, J.H., Jordan, J.R., Marshall, D.S., & Berkowitz, L. (2015). *Responding to grief, trauma, and distress after a suicide: Introducing new U.S. national guidelines.* Paper presented at the American Association of Suicidology, 48th annual conference, Atlanta, GA.

Cvinar, J.G. (2005). Do suicide survivors suffer social stigma: A review of the literature. *Perspectives in Psychiatric Care, 41*(1), 14–21. http://doi.org/10.1111/j.0031-5990.2005.00004.x

Dyregrov, K. (2002). Assistance from local authorities versus survivors' needs for support after suicide. *Death Studies, 26*(8), 647–668. http://doi.org/10.1080/07481180290088356

Dyregrov, K., Plyhn, E., Dieserud, G., & Oatley, D. (2012). *After the suicide: Helping the bereaved to find a path from grief to recovery.* London, UK: Jessica Kingsley.

Feigelman, W., Gorman, B.S., & Jordan, J.R. (2009). Stigmatization and suicide bereavement. *Death Studies, 33*(7), 591–608. http://doi.org/10.1080/07481180902979973

Feigelman, W., Jordan, J.R., McIntosh, J.L., & Feigelman, B. (2012). *Devastating losses: How parents cope with the death of a child to suicide or drugs.* New York, NY: Springer.

Harrington-LaMorie, J., & Ruocco, K. (2011). The Tragedy Assistance Program for Survivors (TAPS). In J.R. Jordan & J.L. McIntosh (Eds.), *Grief after suicide: Understanding the consequences and caring for the survivors* (pp. 403–411). New York, NY: Routledge.

Jordan, J.R. (2008). Bereavement after suicide. *Psychiatric Annals, 38*(10), 679–685. http://doi.org/10.3928/00485713-20081001-05

Jordan, J.R. (2015). Grief after suicide: The evolution of suicide postvention. In J.M. Stillion & T. Attig (Eds.), *Death, dying, and bereavement: Contemporary perspectives, institutions, and practices* (pp. 349–362). New York, NY: Springer.

Jordan, J.R., & McIntosh, J.L. (2011a). *Grief after suicide: Understanding the consequences and caring for the survivors.* New York, NY: Routledge.

Jordan, J.R., & McIntosh, J.L. (2011b). Suicide bereavement: Why study survivors of suicide loss? In J.R. Jordan & J.L. McIntosh (Eds.), *Grief after suicide: Understanding the consequences and caring for the survivors* (pp. 3–17). New York, NY: Routledge.

Koenig, M. (2011). Friends for Survival. In J.R. Jordan & J.L. McIntosh (Eds.), *Grief after suicide: Understanding the consequences and caring for the survivors* (pp. 357–362). New York, NY: Routledge.

McIntosh, J.L., & Jordan, J.R. (2011). The impact of suicide on adults. In J.R. Jordan & J.L. McIntosh (Eds.), *Grief after suicide: Understanding the consequences and caring for the survivors* (pp. 43–79). New York, NY: Routledge.

McMenamy, J. M., Jordan, J. R., & Mitchell, A. M. (2008). What do suicide survivors tell us they need? Results of a pilot study. *Suicide and Life-Threatening Behavior, 38*(4), 375–389. http://doi.org/10.1521/suli.2008.38.4.375

National Action Alliance for Suicide Prevention. (2015). *Responding to grief, trauma, & distress after a suicide: U. S. national guidelines*. Washington, DC: Author.

UnitedSynergies. (2009). *StandBy replication project: Final evaluation report*. Noosa Heads, Australia: Author.

UnitedSynergies. (2011). *Economic evaluation of the StandBy Response Service: Final report*. Buddina, Australia: Griffith University.

US Public Health Service. (2001). *National strategy for suicide prevention: Goals and objectives for action*. Washington, DC: Author.

US Department of Health & Human Services, Office of the Surgeon General & National Action Alliance for Suicide Prevention. (2012). *National strategy for suicide prevention: Goals and objectives for action*. Washington, DC: Author.

Chapter 28

USA – The American Foundation for Suicide Prevention's Support of People Bereaved by Suicide

Robert Gebbia and Christine Moutier

American Foundation for Suicide Prevention (AFSP), New York, NY, USA

Abstract: The American Foundation for Suicide Prevention (AFSP) approaches suicide bereavement as a journey – a process of surviving, connecting, and healing. While this process never ends, one can move forward, and one can grow. AFSP acknowledges that survivors of suicide loss do not all grieve in the same way and that a wide array of approaches should be available to reach those bereaved by suicide. This chapter presents the various postvention initiatives developed by AFSP, such as Out of the Darkness Walks, Survivor Day, the Survivor Outreach Program, and the digital Memory Quilts Project.

Introduction: Becoming Part of a Community

This notion of multiple access points for loss survivors was part of the thinking of the American Foundation for Suicide Prevention (AFSP) since the launch of the Out of the Darkness Walks in 2004. At that time, some AFSP board members and other colleagues of the organization had concerns that the walks would not be a good fit for those bereaved by suicide. They worried that suicide was still too taboo, and that many families would not feel comfortable talking about the loss of their loved one to suicide, let alone participate in a public event like a walk.

But survivors of suicide loss did come out that first year – several thousand. And they kept showing up, in greater numbers year after year. Twelve years later, there are close to 300,000 walkers, and an additional 700,000 people supporting those who walk. While not all walkers are loss survivors, an estimated 70% are, and they often find that the friends, coworkers and classmates they ask to support them have also lost someone to suicide, but had never shared this – until they started the conversation about the walk.

This experience of being part of a large gathering of peers creates a powerful sense of community and a safe space to talk about the loss and to share the survivors' stories. For many walkers, it is comforting to know that they are not alone. For many, it is also a way to turn their grief into action by raising money for research, advocacy, education, and programs for fellow loss survivors – a way to help prevent others from experiencing a similar tragic loss.

In retrospect, such a response to the Out of the Darkness Walks seems inevitable. Suicide has been a major health problem for countless generations, affecting up to 55% of US Americans based on a recent public opinion poll (Preidt, 2015). However, misinformation and discrimination has historically masked the scope of the problem and marginalized those affected (National Action Alliance for Suicide Prevention, 2015). This is changing in large measure because of the engagement and activism of growing numbers of loss survivors. Through the walks, many loss survivors are at last finding understanding and acceptance, and in the process, a path to healing.

Gaining a New Perspective: International Survivors of Suicide Loss Day

If it is true that loss survivors need multiple options for engagement to find the best way forward, then it's equally true that walks are not for everyone. Offering opportunities to gain new perspectives about suicide loss and how others survived their loss can be beneficial, especially for the recently bereaved. It was with this goal in mind that AFSP asked Senator Harry Reid, a survivor of his father's suicide, to introduce a US Senate Resolution declaring that the Saturday before the US holiday of Thanksgiving (held on the fourth Thursday of November) each year be known as National Survivors of Suicide Day. The year was 1999, and there were very few resources or programs for loss survivors (see Chapter 9 in this volume). The day's purpose was, and still is, to have friends and family of those who have died by suicide join together at local *healing conferences*, for information and support for their healing journey. The day was later renamed International Survivors of Suicide Loss Day to reflect the growing expansion to countries around the world. There were a handful of AFSP organized conferences that first Survivor Day, as it is informally known. Today, Survivor Day has grown to involve more than 360 sites in 18 countries, with more hosting a program every year.

In 2014, AFSP created a dedicated website (https://afsp.org/find-support/ive-lost-someone/survivor-day/) and a host of new promotional and event materials for Survivor Day program organizers. This had a dramatic impact on attendance with an estimated 12,000 participants. For some, there may not be a conference in their community or they are not ready to attend in person. An additional 18,000 people viewed *Survivor Day Live,* an online program that includes experts on loss, a film, and interactive discussion between online participants and experts, in the privacy of their home or a friend's home. The focus of the online *Survivor Day Live* program, like the in-person program, is to provide information on suicide loss, but even more importantly, a safe sense of community, to support individuals' and families' grieving and healing.

A major part of the 2014 Survivor Day was the premiere of a new AFSP documentary film, *The Journey*, the first in a series of planned films that explore the breadth of experiences people face after a loss. The film delves into the complicated emotions and experiences of survivors alongside expert commentary by AFSP's chief medical officer, Dr. Christine Moutier. *The Journey* is a 30-min documentary film meant to provide information and hopeful messages with a high level production quality, and the end result is a truly moving film which AFSP translated into 16 languages to reach loss survivors around the world (NarrativeLab Communications, 2014).

Family Journeys, the second in *The Journey* documentary film series, was released on Survivor Day in 2015, and traces the ripple effects of a suicide through the eyes and experiences of three families. This film shows how the members of each family, together and as individuals, are weathering the loss of their loved one, as well as how they are healing and finding new meaning after living through a loss. *Life Journeys: Reclaiming Life after Loss*, the third in this series, premiered for 2016 Survivor Day. This film highlights the longer-term path and features survivors whose loss occurred more than 10 years ago. *The Journey* series films can be viewed online at https://afsp.org/find-support/ive-lost-someone/survivor-day/survivor-day-documentaries/.

For many loss survivors, attending a Survivor Day event is the first time they realize they are not alone. Hearing from people at all stages of their journey, about what they experienced, what they did to continue on after their loss, and to understand more about suicide as a complication of health conditions, helps survivors along their journey.

Feedback from organizers and attendees alike has been overwhelmingly positive with comments like, "many people have that moment of realizing they are not struggling alone," and "attendees may not speak up in front of the group, but in the quiet conversations that follow, there are always knowing smiles and kind words exchanged between strangers."

Peer-to-Peer Support: Survivor Outreach Program

For many recently bereaved, there is a powerful role for one-to-one peer support. AFSP provides this service through its Survivor Outreach Program, which links those newly bereaved with trained volunteers who are long-term loss survivors themselves. This encounter is a more private one, which can take place in-person through a visit to the home by the volunteers. It can also take place through video chat, by phone, or via e-mail exchanges. The intention is that every person interested in having this more personal connection with a fellow survivor feels comfortable and has the interaction that best meets their needs in the aftermath of a suicide loss.

AFSP's Survivor Outreach Program is based in large measure on the pioneering work of Iris Bolton, founder of The Link's National Resource Center for Suicide Prevention and Aftercare in Atlanta, Georgia (Marshall & Bolton, 2011), and Dr. Frank Campbell, developer of the active postvention model known as The LOSS Team, in Baton Rouge, Louisiana (Campbell, 2011; Campbell, Cataldie, McIntosh, & Millet, 2004), both in the United States (Chapter 9 presents an overview of the history of survivor support).

Today, AFSP's Survivor Outreach Program has reached more than 1,000 families in many communities throughout the United States, and the goal is to take the initiative nationwide in the next couple of years to provide information, resources, and social support to loss survivors on a scale not seen before.

Putting a Face on Suicide: Memory Quilts

Another new way to support loss survivors is through AFSP's new Digital Memory Quilt. This online "quilt" makes it possible for survivors to keep the memory of their loved one alive, while also putting a face on the tragedy of suicide. In the first year of its launch, over 1,000 loss survivors shared their photos and stories on the digital quilt. The Digital Memory Quilt is a version of the Lifekeeper Memory Quilts, founded in 1995 by the late Sandy Martin following the loss of her son Tony to suicide.

Today, AFSP offers survivors the option of placing their loved one's photo and other information on either the new online quilt, featured on the AFSP website, or on a traditional Lifekeeper cloth quilt, which is often displayed at healing conferences and suicide prevention programs and events.

Memorial quilts have successfully raised public awareness about other leading causes of death such as HIV/AIDS and cancer (Names Project Foundation, n.d.; Quilts of the Women's Cancer Program, n.d.), and about the need for prevention by moving beyond statistics and showing that each death is a person lost. Likewise, these memory quilts do the same for suicide, while also sharing the memory of those we have lost.

Resources: Current and Future

AFSP believes no one should have to face their loss alone. Therefore, additional ways to engage and/or support survivors of suicide loss have been developed, and new ones are being planned. Existing resources include an updated directory (https://www.afsp.org/coping-with-suicide-loss/find-support/find-a-support-group) of more than 800 nationwide loss survivor support groups, where loss survivors can find support groups in communities; and training sessions for those who currently facilitate, or would like to learn how to facilitate, a loss survivor support group. The training sessions are offered by experts in the field, and are recommended for mental health professionals and loss survivors at least 2 years from their loss.

There is also an online resource to assist schools when they lose a student or someone in the school community to suicide. *After a Suicide: A Toolkit for Schools* (AFSP & National Suicide Prevention Resource Center [SPRC], 2011) was jointly developed by AFSP and the National Suicide Prevention Resource Center. National experts on suicide loss and bereavement worked together to create the toolkit, which shows schools how to respond to the crisis, help students cope with the loss, and mitigate suicide contagion. This free resource on the AFSP website and SPRC website gives practical guidance on memorialization and social media, as well as how to bring in outside help and support. Customized toolkits for other settings, like medical training programs and hospitals, have also been developed.

Resources in development include training for mental health clinicians to help them better understand and work with individuals and families bereaved by suicide. The Suicide Bereavement Clinician Training Program was developed by suicide loss expert, Dr. John Jordan in cooperation with AFSP, and has been conducted in several communities to date. The goal is to expand the number of training programs in the future, and therefore the number of clinicians trained throughout the United States. Also, in 2016, AFSP convened the first national conference for long-term survivors of suicide loss called *Our Journey Continues*. The theme of the conference was *Engage, Enrich, Empower,* which AFSP believes is an important message to survivors who are several years from their loss.

Through AFSP's involvement in the suicide research field and a priority on growing the area of survivor studies, several large research studies have been initiated. One example is AFSP's funding of a multisite study of complicated grief following suicide loss. For an estimated 43 % of suicide loss survivors (3 to 4 times the rate of other types of loss), engagement, educational programs, or peer-to-peer support may not be sufficient, as a complicated, diagnosable form of grief can occur (Mitchell, Kim, Prigerson, & Mortimer-Stephens, 2004). When acute grief becomes prolonged and unrelenting for years, this complicated form of grief can lead to extreme distress, a sense of emptiness punctuated by intense pangs of yearning, rendering the loss survivor "stuck" in the grief process. These individuals require specialized treatment known as complicated grief therapy, which has been shown to be effective in research studies (Shear, Frank, Houck, & Reynolds, 2005).

Loss survivor research is, and will continue to be, a priority for AFSP, as the field needs more evidence regarding effective ways for survivors of suicide loss to heal. Each survivor's journey is different, and each path varies greatly, but one thing is certain: It is vital to bring hope to those affected by suicide loss and to walk with them on their lifelong journey.

Corresponding authors

Robert Gebbia
American Foundation for Suicide Prevention (AFSP)
New York, NY
USA
rgebbia@afsp.org

Christine Moutier
American Foundation for Suicide Prevention (AFSP)
New York, NY
USA
cmoutier@afsp.org

References

American Foundation for Suicide Prevention and SPRC Suicide Prevention Resource Center. (2011). *After a suicide: A toolkit for schools.* Newton, MA: Education Development Center. Retrieved from www.afsp.org/content/download/1603/27543/file/toolkit.pdf

American Foundation for Suicide Prevention. (2016). *Find a support group* [Website]. Retrieved from https://www.afsp.org/coping-with-suicide-loss/find-support/find-a-support-group

Campbell, F. R. (2011). Baton Rouge Crisis Intervention Center's LOSS Team Active Postvention Model Approach. In J. R. Jordan & J. L. McIntosh (Eds.), *Grief after suicide: Understanding the consequences and caring for the survivors* (pp. 327–332). New York, NY: Routledge.

Campbell, F. R., Cataldie, L., McIntosh, J., & Millet, K. (2004). An active postvention program. *Crisis, 25*(1), 30–32. http://doi.org/10.1027/0227-5910.25.1.30

Marshall, D. & Bolton, I. (2011). The Link Counseling Center and The Link's National Resource Center for Suicide Prevention and Aftercare. In J. R. Jordan & J. L. McIntosh (Eds.), *Grief after suicide: Understanding the consequences and caring for the survivors* (pp. 333–340). New York, NY: Routledge.

Mitchell, A. M., Kim, Y., Prigerson, H. G., & Mortimer-Stephens, M. K. (2004). Complicated grief in survivors of suicide. *Crisis, 25*(1), 12–18. http://doi.org/10.1027/0227-5910.25.1.12

Names Project Foundation. (n.d.). *AIDS memorial quilt* [Website]. Retrieved from http://www.aidsquilt.org/

NarrativeLab Communications. (2014). *The Journey: A Story of Healing and Hope* [DVD]. Bullseyedisc DVD. Retrieved from http://www.survivorday.org/survivor-day-documentaries/

National Action Alliance for Suicide Prevention. (2015). *Responding to grief, trauma, and distress after a suicide: U.S. National Guidelines.* Washington, DC: Author. Retrieved from http://actionallianceforsuicideprevention.org/sites/actionallianceforsuicideprevention.org/files/NationalGuidelines.pdf

Preidt, R. (2015, September 1). Many say mental health care is vital, but often tough to get. *U.S. News & World Report.* Retrieved from http://health.usnews.com/health-news/articles/2015/09/01/many-say-mental-health-care-is-vital-but-often-tough-to-get

Quilts of the Women's Cancer Program. (n.d.). *Mayo Clinic website.* Retrieved from http://www.mayo.edu/pmts/mc1600-mc1699/mc1604-48.pdf

Shear, K., Frank, E., Houck, P. R., & Reynolds, C. F. (2005). Treatment of complicated grief: A randomized controlled trial. *Journal of the American Medical Association, 293*(21), 2601–2608. http://doi.org/10.1001/jama.293.21.2601

Chapter 29

USA – Collaboration of Volunteers and Professionals in Suicide Bereavement Support

The EMPACT Experience

Sandra McNally, Jill McMahon, and Denis Thirion

EMPACT – Suicide Prevention Center, Tempe Office, Tempe, AZ, USA

Abstract: Every year, approximately 1 million people die by suicide worldwide. In the wake of these numbers are the loved ones who are left behind. Providing services for the bereaved by suicide is crucial for their healing, yet many communities are challenged by limited financial resources to provide needed services. This chapter will highlight a collaborative postvention model that has been sustained for the past 28 years in Arizona (USA) at EMPACT – Suicide Prevention Center. This model utilizes volunteers who have been bereaved by suicide as a primary resource. The chapter reviews key components and outcomes of this model, demonstrating program effectiveness.

Introduction

Suicide has a profound impact on a community. Whether exposed to suicide or intimately affected by it, suicide can have a devastating effect on those left behind – the *bereaved by suicide*. Recent US data suggest that more than 800,000 individuals are affected each year by suicide loss (Berman, 2011) and, according to a recent review of the literature (Pitman, Osborn, King, & Erlangsen, 2014), the effects of suicide bereavement include an increased risk of depression and suicide. This number represents the lives of real individuals who have been forever transformed by the tragedy of suicide. Although that research indicates a clear and definite need to provide services for those bereaved by suicide, service development and implementation have been challenging due to limited financial resources.

While some researchers have debated whether suicide bereavement differs from other forms of bereavement (Jordan & McIntosh, 2011), it can be suggested, from the perspective of those bereaved by suicide, that the grief is different because of the stigma, trauma, and shame that often are associated with a suicide. In 1988, a year after EMPACT – Suicide Prevention Center was founded, an existing employee who had lost her husband to suicide and was working in a capacity unrelated to suicide bereavement, came to the conclusion that, in her case, traditional grief counseling was ineffective in helping her process her husband's death. Her healing journey eventually led her to explore the Survivors of Suicide (SOS) movement in the United States and to start an SOS support group in Arizona in 1988. She did not take this initiative as a result of her role as an employee, but out of her passion to help others bereaved by suicide. Thus, the EMPACT model of postvention began: one survivor helping another. EMPACT, which stands for Emergency Mobile Pediatric and Adolescent Crisis Teams, is a nonprofit behavioral health organization in Arizona that has been providing suicide prevention/postvention and crisis services in the community for the past 29 years.

Volunteer Involvement

Since 1988, EMPACT has been committed to postvention and providing a comprehensive program for those bereaved by suicide. However, the financial challenges of operating such a program forced the agency to be creative in exploring other resources. It was discovered that utilizing volunteers who were survivors of suicide could be a valuable, cost-effective resource while providing the benefits of a peer-led model. As a result, the EMPACT model of postvention became one of collaboration between behavioral health professionals and volunteers; approximately 40 active volunteers are involved in program activities on an annual basis.

At the core of this partnership is the belief that those who have lost a loved one to suicide have a unique opportunity to give back to their community by helping others who have suffered a similar loss. This action creates hope for the newly bereaved, as well as gives purpose for those volunteering. Although having a behavioral health, crisis-focused agency such as EMPACT as the service provider is advantageous in providing oversight and supervision of the program, the backbone of the program truly is the volunteers who help to make program decisions, provide program services, and develop new program components to expand and improve existing services.

In developing the EMPACT model of postvention, which is an original model that was created by program staff, the vision was to build a comprehensive program for those bereaved by suicide expanding beyond the original support group that was started 28 years ago. The result of ongoing program development was a continuum of services, reaching survivors at all levels, from initial crisis to sustainability. Immediate services include a Local Outreach to Suicide Survivors (LOSS) program for the newly bereaved, individual counseling, and weekly support groups that provide an opportunity for survivors to process their grief and develop new coping skills. In addition, there is an annual SOS conference, and other community events that allow survivors to stay connected to the survivor community, and provide opportunities for ongoing support.

Each year, over 4,000 individuals bereaved by suicide benefit from the services provided. At the sustainability stage, when these individuals are ready, they are given the opportunity to give back through various volunteer opportunities, such as serving on a LOSS Team, becoming an SOS group facilitator, or assisting at community events.

Components of the Model

The EMPACT model of postvention, which can be replicated by other communities, includes the following fundamental components necessary to create a successful SOS program: volunteer recruitment, training, supervision, appreciation, and innovation, as well as retention.

The recruitment and training of volunteers, which is conducted by the behavioral health professionals at EMPACT, is the initial step in creating a successful SOS program. Recruitment of the right volunteers is vital, choosing an individual who is in a healthy place in their own grief journey and who can be of assistance to others. When selecting a volunteer, asking key questions can gauge where the person is in their grief recovery: "Where do you think you are in your grief process? How do you view suicide? What do you think about a person who dies by suicide? What has helped you cope with the loss of your loved one?" These questions help to determine if the survivor is ready to take on this new role. Furthermore, the training model suggests that a minimum of 2 years must have passed since the potential volunteer lost their loved one to suicide. During this period of time, the individual must have been involved in some type of counseling or support program.

Training of volunteers is essential. The model is focused on a combination of education and experiential learning. Group facilitation skills are crucial since so many of the volunteers are involved in support group facilitation. A separate training is offered to those volunteers who are involved in a LOSS Team to learn about what behavior is acceptable at the scene of a suicide. In both training programs, there is a focus on how to provide support, maintain healthy boundaries, be a healthy role model, and use effective communication skills.

Regarding the supervision of volunteers, this model emphasizes a team approach, with mental health professionals offering support and guidance to the volunteers. The model includes meeting regularly with volunteers to provide group cohesion and improved communication. Problem solving is accomplished by discussing challenging group members or difficult situations. Ongoing continuing education is offered on a regular basis to provide the volunteers with the tools they need to be effective in their volunteer role. Participation in statewide suicide prevention/postvention conferences is one opportunity for volunteers to grow professionally. Additionally, an annual refresher training is offered to focus on key areas of group facilitation and self-care.

Volunteer appreciation is an important part of this model. Though potentially very rewarding, their work is extremely emotionally taxing. While volunteers are passionate about what they do, it is important to remind them of the incredible impact they have on fellow survivors and the community. From tangible gifts to celebrations to an annual retreat, it is demonstrated to volunteers that they are cared about and valued. This increases volunteer retention, but more importantly, it shows volunteers that they are needed and appreciated within the program itself and within the greater family of those bereaved by suicide.

Innovations in Support Formats

Volunteers are the heart and soul of this program and are at the core of its success. As survivors, they bring genuine empathy, heartfelt compassion, and true understanding of grief after suicide. To have a successful community-based SOS program, the volunteers need to have a voice, a chance to be innovative, and the opportunity to make creative programmatic additions to the services currently being offered. When the program first started, the only services that were offered were support groups. Today, there are numerous offshoots, due in large part to the passion and innovation of the volunteers who wanted to make a difference. For example, due to the vision and passion of one volunteer who had lost his son to suicide, an annual day of remembrance for survivors was started in 2007, a day for survivors to come together to honor their loved ones who have died by suicide. After his own painful journey of trying to cope with the loss, this survivor decided he wanted to give back to EMPACT in a meaningful way because of the support he had received from the SOS program. This idea evolved into a community 5-km walk/run and fund-raiser for SOS, including a candlelight ceremony with inspirational stories, poems, and words of encouragement, followed by a symbolic balloon release and walk/run. This has become an annual, all-day event. Since its inception in 2007, this 5-km walk/run has tripled in attendance and contributions.

Inspired by the AIDS Memorial Quilt, another volunteer started the Arizona Lifekeeper Memorial Quilt program. This survivor realized the impact that a memorial quilt could have on a group of people by raising awareness and putting a face to the statistics of those we have lost to suicide. To date, these quilts have gained attention at events in our state of Arizona, as well as nationwide.

Another volunteer with a passion for keeping the survivor community connected was instrumental in creating the program's online quarterly newsletter. This newsletter, which is listed on the program's website (http://www.empactsos.org) shares program updates, upcoming events, inspirational stories, and new research in the field with the survivor community. It is collaborative, with volunteers contributing to each edition. Former SOS group members report that this newsletter has the benefit of extending and perpetuating the feeling of support they received while active in the program.

Meeting the Needs of the Bereaved

While one can speculate that the EMPACT model of postvention meets the needs of the bereaved by suicide due to the comprehensive services that are offered and based on the former members' personal feedback, years of data collection have validated the work that the volunteers are doing in terms of meeting the needs of the survivor community, in particular those who have attended an SOS support group. For the past 13 years, client satisfaction surveys have been distributed to support group attendees quarterly to obtain feedback about program services, resulting in the outcomes shown in **Box 29.1**.

Box 29.1. Feedback about program services

96 % Attendees reporting the SOS group is a safe place
79 % Attendees reporting feeling better prepared to deal with the loss of their loved one after attending the SOS support group
100 % Attendees reporting feeling welcome in the SOS support group
100 % Attendees reporting satisfaction with their SOS support group experience

Note. SOS = Survivors of Suicide.

In addition to this objective outcome data, subjective reports have been offered from suicide loss survivors who have been able to describe how the SOS program provided emotional healing and facilitated the ability to cope with their loss. These narratives further confirm the positive impact of this comprehensive model.

Conclusions

The EMPACT model of postvention involves the ongoing collaboration between professionals and volunteers, a partnership formed through a common bond of suicide and dealing with its aftermath. With passionate professionals and volunteers who share the life-altering experience of having lost a loved one to suicide, and with proper training, an effective program can be created and sustained in every community.

Corresponding author

Sandra McNally
EMPACT – Suicide Prevention Center
Tempe, AZ
USA
sandra.mcnally@lafrontera-empact.org

References

Berman, A. L. (2011). Estimating the population of survivors of suicide: Seeking an evidence base. *Suicide and Life-Threatening Behavior, 41*(1), 110–116. http://doi.org/10.1111/j.1943-278X.2010.00009.x

Jordan, J. R., & McIntosh, J. L. (2011). Is suicide bereavement different? A framework for rethinking the question. In J. R. Jordan & J. L. McIntosh (Eds.), *Grief after suicide: Understanding the consequences and caring for the survivors* (pp. 19–42). New York, NY: Routledge.

Pitman, A., Osborn, D., King, M., & Erlangsen, A. (2014). Effects of suicide bereavement on mental health and suicide risk. *Lancet Psychiatry, 1*(1), 86–94. http://doi.org/10.1016/S2215-0366(14)70224-X

Part IV.2

Europe

Chapter 30

Austria – Suicide Postvention

Regina Seibl

Pro Mente Tirol, Innsbruck, Austria

Abstract: The aim of this chapter is to provide an overview of suicide postvention activities in Austria, with a focus on family and clinician survivors, from the late 1990s to the present. The growing number of suicide survivor services, increased awareness for the needs of the bereaved, and the inclusion of suicide postvention goals in a national suicide prevention strategy are major positive steps. Nonetheless, a lot of work remains to be done to sustain and further improve suicide survivor support in Austria.

Introduction

According to the latest report on suicidal behavior issued by the Austrian Ministry of Health (Grabenhofer-Eggerth & Kapusta, 2016), Austrian suicide rates have decreased significantly in the past 3 decades (from a rate of 28/100,000 inhabitants in 1986 to 15/100,000 in 2014). This has been a positive development; still approximately 1,300 Austrians end their lives every year, which is three times the number of individuals killed in traffic accidents (Grabenhofer-Eggerth & Kapusta, 2016). Each suicide leaves behind a varying number of survivors, the lives of many of them forever altered by the loss of their loved one. Some survivors are even at risk for suicidal behavior (Jordan & McIntosh, 2011; Seibl, 1999; Seibl, Antretter, & Haring, 2001). With Austria being a country that holds a strong Catholic tradition, many family member survivors also face the burden of stigmatization and social isolation, especially in rural areas (Seibl, 1999).

Development of Postvention in Austria

When the author cofounded a support group for suicide survivors in Innsbruck (Seibl, 2001) and worked on her master thesis on grief after suicide in 1998, literature on bereavement after suicide in German was sparse, let alone available support services or groups for survivors in Austria (Seibl, 1999). One exception was the Vienna Kriseninterventionszentrum (Center for Crisis Intervention) founded by Erwin Ringel in 1948, which since its inception has offered counseling for those at risk of suicidal behavior and for those bereaved by suicide (http://www.kriseninterventionszentrum.at). Fortunately, suicide survivor support in Austria has improved since then.

The European Directory of Suicide Survivor Services compiled for the International Association for Suicide Prevention (IASP) at the beginning of the new millennium listed eight support groups for suicide survivors in Austria (Andriessen & Farberow, 2002). By 2016, the number of support groups for suicide survivors has grown to a total of 12 (Österreichische Gesellschaft für Suizidprävention [Austrian Association for Suicide Prevention], 2016, http://www.suizidpraevention.at/selbsthilfe.html). These groups specifically address the needs of suicide survivors and can be found in six out of the nine federal states of Austria. Most of them are open-access groups, facilitated either by peers or professionals, some by a combination of both. Many of them are volunteer-based and struggle to find sufficient support in terms of funding or training.

Considering that thousands of Austrians annually are severely affected by the loss of a loved one, 12 support groups seem inadequate to meet their needs. However, two groups have paused their activities due to a lack of requests by suicide survivors. Even if those who attend support groups may greatly benefit from doing so (Jordan, 2011; Seibl et al., 2001), apparently the majority of suicide survivors in Austria never find their way to a support group. This might be due to the lack of support groups in many regions of Austria, and/or a lack of access to information on their availability. Also, some survivors may be reluctant to use this kind of service for various reasons, including shame and self-stigmatization. Whatever reasons may be involved, a lot of work still needs to be done in the domain of suicide survivor support.

Fortunately, a number of projects and initiatives have started during the past few years, one of them being a very successful suicide prevention and community mental health project in the federal state of Styria (GO-ON Suizidprävention Steiermark, http://www.suizidpraevention-stmk.at). It was launched in 2011 as a response to high suicide rates in the region, and in the course of its implementation the team became aware of the needs of the bereaved by suicide. This led to a modification of the program and the establishment of a support group for suicide survivors (Mayerdorfer, 2015). In agreement with the German organization Angehörige um Suizid (Suicide Survivors; AGUS; http://www.agus-selbsthilfe.de), the GO-ON team adapted and now distributes their booklets developed for survivors (Mayerdorfer, 2015). Additionally, the team collaborates with a local artist whose work focuses on bereavement after suicide in order to raise awareness for the needs of suicide survivors in the general public. These accomplishments may be viewed as a successful integration of suicide postvention in the course of a suicide prevention project.

Since 2011, the website of the Austrian Association for Suicide Prevention (ÖGS) provides information on grief after suicide, a regularly updated directory of suicide support groups, and a list of relevant literature for survivors of suicide. Help is also offered to anyone who intends to start a new support group (http://www.suizidpraevention.at/selbsthilfe.html).

Integration of Postvention in the National Suicide Prevention Program

In May 2013, the Plattform Trauernde nach Suizid Oesterreich (Platform for the Bereaved by Suicide in Austria) was founded by facilitators of suicide support groups and experts in the field of suicide prevention (Seibl, 2015). Its main goals are to connect and to establish cooperation between the local suicide support groups. Also, the initiative wants to offer support, encouragement, and knowledge to individuals who intend to found new support groups. Moreover, it aims to promote integration of services for suicide survivors in the network of community mental health services (Seibl, 2015). Since its inception, the platform has been working in close cooperation with the German organization for suicide survivors (AGUS).

In the fall of 2013, the platform and its goals were integrated into the concept of Suizidpraevention Austria (SUPRA; Seibl, 2015). SUPRA is a national suicide prevention program, designed and implemented by a group of experts in the field of suicide research and prevention, which was launched in 2012 on behalf of the Ministry of Health (Haring et al., 2011). SUPRA promotes networking and collaboration between individuals and organizations that are working in the field of suicide prevention. Since the improvement of suicide survivor support has been on the agenda of SUPRA, a booklet for survivors and those who care for them was issued in 2015, providing information on grief after suicide and suicide survivor support groups. To further raise awareness of the situation of suicide survivors, their needs (Seibl, 2015), and the suicide postvention activities of GO-ON (as mentioned above) were presented at the first SUPRA conference in September 2014 (Mayerdorfer, 2015). Currently, a SUPRA website presents information on grief after suicide and makes a directory of support services available to the public.

The fifth biennial conference, Tabu Suizid – Wir reden darueber (The Taboo of Suicide – We Talk About It), hosted by the European Alliance Against Depression, took place in Innsbruck in November 2016 (in cooperation with SUPRA for the first time). Initially, the conferences were organized for suicide survivors; however, over the years, they have received increasing attention from mental health professionals. The 2016 program aimed at meeting the interests of survivors and those of mental health professionals, and offered both groups a platform to meet and learn from each other. The contributions to the conference focused on aspects of suicide prevention, grief after suicide (of family, friends, and clinician survivors), and different approaches to suicide postvention.

Postvention for Specific Groups: Workplace, Schools, Health Clinics

Support for suicide survivors in the workplace is facilitated by different organizations, such as the Austrian Red Cross. The support can be requested by concerned employees after a suicide in the workplace. In the days after the event, a team of mental health professionals hosts a meeting for all employees of a given company. Those attending are encouraged to address their thoughts and feelings surrounding the death, and receive information on mental health services. Employees who show signs of severe psychological distress or mental illness are offered further support in a one-to-one setting, and they are encouraged to seek additional help from the mental health care system. For example, the Austrian Red Cross offers crisis intervention (in terms of acute stress reduction) after suicide for train drivers of the OEBB (Austrian Federal Railway Company). Additionally, they receive ongoing support by trained peers as well as by psychologists who work for the OEBB (Mag. Dietmar Kratzer, Department of Psychology at University of Innsbruck, and European Red Cross/Red Crescent Network for Psychosocial Support, personal communication, April 27, 2016).

Suicide postvention in school settings across the country has been implemented by school psychologists who have received special training (Mag. Dr. Beatrix Haller, National Coordinator for Health Promotion in Schools, Ministry of Education and Women´s Affairs, personal communication, March 22, 2016). When a suicide occurs in a school setting, the headmaster, teachers, and psychologists hold a meeting to discuss the event and to agree on how to deal with the aftermath of the suicide in a responsible and caring manner. The psychologists support and accompany the teachers when they inform the students about the suicide, and help to discuss the students' reactions, and carry out a grief ritual in the classroom. If the family of the deceased agrees, all students receive a letter to inform their parents of the suicide. After 5 to 7 days, the psychologists return to the classroom to answer any questions that may have arisen in the meantime. Students and teachers, who show severe symptoms of distress following the suicide, are referred to the mental health care system (Mag. Waltraud Schennach, Oesterreichisches Zentrum fuer psychologische Gesundheitsvorsorge [Austrian Center for Psychological Health Care], personal communication, May 4, 2016).

Even though the loss of a client or patient to suicide is not uncommon for mental health professionals (Gutin, McGann, & Jordan, 2011, Jacobson, Ting, Sanders, & Harrington, 2004), there is often a lack of awareness of the detrimental effects a client suicide can have on a professional caregiver`s ability to function and their need for support (see Chapter 21 in this volume). Implementation of guidelines and training should prepare and strengthen the capacity of the clinicians to deal with possible reactions to a client suicide, their own needs following the event, and the needs of other (fellow) clients and family members of the deceased (Grad, 2012; Jacobson et al., 2004, McGann, Gutin, & Jordan, 2011; Ting, Jacobson, & Sanders, 2008). Adequate care for clinicians in the aftermath of client suicide can also help promote mental health professionals' suicide prevention skills (Gutin et al., 2011; Seibl, 2014).

Pro Mente Tirol is a large community mental health service provider in Innsbruck, similar to many others of its kind in Austria. However, it may be the first service provider in the country that has made a special effort to focus on suicide postvention, initiated and implemented by the author of this chapter. Between 2012 and 2013, the organization trained their entire staff of about 250 professionals working with psychiatric patients in different settings (together 28 teams). Shortly after the training, tailor-made guidelines to deal with fatal and nonfatal suicidal behavior were designed for each of the teams (Seibl, 2014). Since 2014, the standard procedure after suicidal events of clients includes immediate crisis response (e.g., phone consultation) and support for the teams and professionals involved who were in charge of the deceased client. An internal consultant attends the team meeting in the days following the suicide to address the needs of the team members, allow them to talk about their reactions to the suicide, and review the events that may have led to the fatal event. An individual session is offered to the clinicians who were directly involved with the deceased client. If necessary, follow-up sessions are offered to the team or the individual clinicians.

Conclusions

As recently as about 20 years ago, suicide survivors in Austria could not find adequate support and care, other than from family members and friends. Over the years, several support groups have been installed, and there have been substantial developments in the field of postvention for professional caregivers and other groups of survivors. At a national level, significant progress has been made to implement strategies to improve suicide survivor support. However, a lack of public funding for suicide bereavement support may hinder the success of these initiatives. What remains to be done, now and in the future, is to continuously increase awareness among the general public, mental and other health professionals, and policymakers, of the importance and necessity of support for all the bereaved by suicide. Suicide postvention is an important part of suicide prevention and general mental health care in Austria.

Corresponding author

Regina Seibl
Spokesperson of Plattform Trauer nach Suizid Österreich
(Platform Grief After Suicide Austria)
Pro Mente Tirol
Innsbruck
Austria
gina_seibl@hotmail.com

References

Andriessen, K., & Farberow, N. (Eds.). (2002). *The European Directory of Suicide Survivor Services*. Le Baradé–Gondrin, France: International Association for Suicide Prevention.

Grabenhofer-Eggerth, A., & Kapusta, N. (2016). *Suizid und Suizidpraevention in Oesterreich. Bericht 2015* [Suicide and suicide prevention in Austria: Report 2015]. Vienna, Austria: Bundesministerium fuer Gesundheit.

Grad, O. T. (2012). *Guidelines to assist clinical staff after the suicide of a patient*. Retrieved from http://www.iasp.info/pdf/postvention/guidelines_to_assist_clinical_staff_after_suicide_patient_grad.pdf

Gutin, N., McGann, V., & Jordan, J. R. (2011). The impact of suicide on professional caregivers. In J. R. Jordan & J. L. McIntosh (Eds.), *Grief after suicide: Understanding the consequences and caring for the survivors* (pp. 93–111). New York, NY: Routledge.

Haring, Ch., Sonneck, G., Gollner, G., Kapusta, N., Niederkrotenthaler, T., Stein, C., ... Wolf, J. (2011). *Supra – Suizidpraevention Austria* [SUPRA – Suicide Prevention Austria]. Vienna, Austria: Bundesministerium fuer Gesundheit.

Jacobson, J., Ting, L., Sanders, S., & Harrington, D. (2004). Prevalence and reactions to fatal and nonfatal client suicidal behaviour: A national study of mental health social workers. *Omega: Journal of Death and Dying, 49*(3), 237–248. http://doi.org/10.2190/HPKQ-T700-EPQL-58JQ

Jordan, J. R. (2011). Group work with suicide survivors. In J. R. Jordan & J. L. McIntosh (Eds.), *Grief after suicide: Understanding the consequences and caring for the survivors* (pp. 283–300). New York, NY: Routledge.

Jordan, J. R., & McIntosh, J. L. (2011). Is suicide bereavement different? A framework for rethinking the question. In J. R. Jordan & J. L. McIntosh (Eds.), *Grief after suicide: Understanding the consequences and caring for the survivors* (pp. 19–42). New York, NY: Routledge.

Mayerdorfer, R. (2015). Entstehungsprozess des Angebotes für Angehoerige und Trauernde nach Suizid am Beispiel Murau, GO-ON Suizidpraevention Steiermark [Development of suicide survivor services in Murau, GO-ON Suicide prevention Styria]. In A. Grabenhofer-Eggerth & N. Kapusta (Eds.), *Suizid und Suizidpraevention in Oesterreich, Bericht 2014* (pp. 42–43). Vienna, Austria: Bundesministerium fuer Gesundheit.

McGann, V., Gutin, N., & Jordan, J. R. (2011). Guidelines for postvention care with survivor families after the suicide of a client. In J. R. Jordan & J. L. McIntosh (Eds.), *Grief after suicide: Understanding the consequences and caring for the survivors* (pp. 133–155). New York, NY: Routledge.

Österreichische Gesellschaft für Suizidprävention. (2016). *Selbsthilfegruppen*. Retrieved from http://www.suizidpraevention.at/selbsthilfe.html

Seibl, R. (1999). *Das Erbe des Suizids – Von den Schwierigkeiten Suizid-Hinterbliebener und der Notwendigkeit, sie zu unterstuetzen* [The legacy of suicide: On the difficulties of suicide survivors and the necessity to support them] (Unpublished master's thesis). University of Innsbruck, Innsbruck, Austria.

Seibl, R. (2001). Hinterbliebene von Suizidopfern auf der Suche nach Antworten und Wegen aus der Krise [Survivors of suicide victims searching for answers and ways out of the crisis]. *Psychiatrische Praxis, 28*(7), 348–350

Seibl, R. (2014). *Auswirkungen eines Klientensuizids auf Helfer im außerstationaeren sozialpsychiatrischen Arbeitsfeld. Untersuchung zu den Folgen dieses Ereignisses und adaequaten Formen der Unterstuetzung fuer betroffene Helfer* [The impact of client suicide on therapists in the field of social psychiatry] (Unpublished doctoral dissertation). University of Innsbruck, Innsbruck, Austria.

Seibl, R. (2015). Trauer nach Suizid und Angebote für Angehoerige – eine Einfuehrung [Grief after suicide and suicide survivor services: An introduction]. In A. Grabenhofer-Eggerth & N. Kapusta (Eds.), *Suizid und Suizidpraevention in Oesterreich, Bericht 2014* (pp. 39–41). Vienna, Austria: Bundesministerium fuer Gesundheit.

Seibl, R., Antretter, E., & Haring, Ch. (2001). Konsequenzen eines Suizids für Personen im Umfeld des Suizidenten [The consequences of a suicide for the bereaved, current knowledge, unresolved questions and tasks of future research]. *Psychiatrische Praxis, 28*(7), 316–322. http://doi.org/10.1055/s-2001-17776

Ting, L., Jacobson, J., & Sanders, S. (2008). Available supports and coping behaviors of mental health social workers following fatal and nonfatal suicidal behavior. *Social Work, 53*(3), 211–221. http://doi.org/10.1093/sw/53.3.211

Chapter 31

Belgium – Support Groups for Children and Adolescents Bereaved by Suicide

Liselot Willems and Leen Hoebrechts

Victim Care Unit, Centre for Social Welfare, Brussels, Belgium

Abstract: This chapter presents a support program for traumatically bereaved children and adolescents, 4–18 years old. The program consists of group meetings with the bereaved children and their siblings, and a parallel group for the parents. The chapter describes the beneficial effects of group participation, such as meaning making, reconnection with family, and positive experiences with mental health professionals. Characteristics that render the support program effective are also described.

Introduction

The suicide of a family member is an extremely disturbing event. Children bereaved by suicide are at greater risk for severe psychological problems (e.g., depression, posttraumatic stress disorder [PTSD], and complicated grief) than children bereaved after a nonviolent death (Cerel & Aldrich, 2011; Dyregrov & Dyregrov, 2005; Pfeffer et al., 1997). Young survivors may experience a range of feelings such as sadness, anxiety, depressive symptoms, guilt, etc, which can debilitate or regress their development. They may witness their parent(s) and sibling(s) being overwhelmed by the loss, and may experience great pressure on the family relationships. They are often left with a lot of questions: *"Why did my father do this? Wasn't I worthwhile living for? Is the death of my sister my fault? Will I lose other beloved ones?"* Offering group support is one of the possibilities in helping suicide-bereaved children to face these challenges. As Dyregrov and Dyregrov (2004) concluded, people bereaved through suicide wish for the opportunity to meet others who have similar experiences. They can learn from other bereaved people how to survive the pain. Pfeffer and colleagues (2002) examined suicide-bereaved children who participated in a support group program. The study found fewer reports of anxiety and depressive symptoms in the intervention group compared with the control group.

The Victim Care Unit in Brussels is a community-based frontline service offering psychological, practical, and juridical help to those bereaved by a traumatic death (suicide, homicide, accident). It is based on principles of a proactive, flexible support available shortly after the death and offered over a long period of time (Dyregrov & Dyregrov, 2004; Dyregrov, 2009). In 2004, in collaboration with Werkgroep Verder, the Flemish association for suicide survivors, the unit started support groups for children and adolescents bereaved by suicide. Based on the experiences of working with different group formats and the available literature, the groups are organized according to the following principles:

- The groups are open for families with children and adolescents, aged 4–18 years, who have lost a (step)parent or sibling in a traumatic way (suicide, homicide, accident).
- At least one of the parents must participate in the parent group.
- The groups are led by trained professionals from social and community mental health services.
- The groups combine an open and closed format to reduce potential barriers to participation.

Characteristics of the Support Program

Bringing Traumatically Bereaved Families Together

Whereas the groups are open for families bereaved by suicide, homicide, or car accident, the majority of participating families are bereaved by suicide. The choice to include traumatically bereaved (contrary to only suicide bereaved or all bereaved) is the best compromise between sufficient similarities in the bereavement experience, on the one hand, and the need for enough potential group participants, on the other hand. The former is important since empirical evidence and clinical experience clearly distinguish childhood traumatic grief from other forms of grief (Brown & Goodman, 2005; Cohen & Mannarino, 2004; Dowdney, 2000). The latter is important to ensure the start of a new group on a regular basis and to avoid dropout of potential participants who might otherwise have to wait too long.

Many children bereaved by suicide experience PTSD symptoms (Dyregrov & Dyregrov 2004; Pfeffer et al., 1997), which should also be addressed in the group. Children may be restrained from talking about the loss if they fear that this will trigger upsetting memories. It is vital to offer them a safe environment, where they can talk about these issues in a respectful and nonavoiding manner, without being emotionally overwhelmed. The fact that the sudden, violent nature of death is a common background in the group helps children to talk and help each other to verbally share their experience. In this context, it is of vital importance that the therapists leading the group are skilled in recognizing and working with PTSD symptoms in children.

Vignette 1

A 7-year-old girl whose mother was strangled by her father participated in the group. She was the only participant bereaved by homicide. She told her story, in her own "childish" but honest words. This helped another child, whose father hanged himself, to state: "I experienced something similar. My father was also strangled, but he did it himself."

Due attention is given in the group to the differences in the cause of death, age, gender, time since the loss, and the kinship relationship with the deceased. For example, if there is only one boy in a group, this will be discussed in advance with the boy's family. Such differences do not have to become an obstacle if they are openly acknowledged and addressed, and the group therapist facilitates enough activities that create connections and highlight similarities without ignoring differences.

A Flexible Program

The groups combine an open and closed format. The support program starts with one open introductory meeting where families can experience peer support without further obligations. Bereaved people need thorough information about group participation (Dyregrov, Dyregrov, & Johnsen, 2013). The *experience of experiencing* peer support is much more powerful than attending a presentation *about* peer support, and for most families it is a positive experience. Subsequently, a closed group with a minimum of five monthly sessions is held. Once a year, a new open meeting is held, and many families participate more than once in the program.

The initial manual-based support program consisted of 10 weekly group sessions and three follow-up sessions. However, given that grieving is an individual experience, a more flexible program was needed. In addition, changing the meeting frequency from weekly to monthly sessions better matches the grief process, which requires time. In each group, the therapists address themes important for *these* particular families and the issues they are *now* struggling with. This can include, for example, reminiscing and sharing memories, changes in the daily life of the family, trying to understand why, coping with intense sadness and loss, etc. The therapists remain flexible in determining the content of a group session and can manage unpredictable events in the group process. They also make an effort to promote hope in the group.

Commitment of Parents

Initially parents were involved only in two psychoeducational sessions. However, given the importance of creating bridges within the bereaved family, now siblings have the possibility to participate in the support group, and a parent group runs parallel with the group for children and adolescents. This requires substantial investment of the organization's resources, as well as a commitment of the participating families. However, involving the whole family seems to be the best way of providing peer support for young people bereaved by suicide: The family has to find a way of moving on *together*. The shared experience of participating in the group is invaluable, even if not everything can be expressed verbally. Parents can learn about the grief process of their children within the context of an experiential group instead of at lectures or through psychoeducation. Also, rituals shared by parents and children can be powerful instruments to create connections within and between the families.

Strength of Rituals and Symbols

Sometimes, especially when a young child is involved, words are not enough or cannot express the overwhelming loss of a parent or a sibling. The group therapist must search for a new, common language to express the "unspeakable." The unconscious can be expressed by using images and rituals (Fiddelaers-Jaspers, 2004), and the use of symbolic communication, such as drawings, music, and rituals, can support children and adolescents in expressing their feelings and thoughts, and coping with trauma and loss. Group rituals strengthen togetherness, and as such, can be used to create connection within a family (see **Box 31.1**).

Box 31.1. Rituals and symbols

The Sky of Stars
Every group session starts with "the sky of stars" ritual, where each child lights a candle for the person who has died while saying the name of the deceased. This is a powerful ritual symbolizing both the presence and the death of the deceased family member. It is not always easy for children to participate, because it confronts them with the reality of the loss. However, it can be helpful, as it allows them to see and feel that they are not alone and have a never-ending connection with their loved one.

Feathers and Stones
In this group activity, the stones symbolize what burdens the children right now and the feathers symbolize what makes things more bearable. Every child is invited to choose a stone which best symbolizes their burden and to write a few words on it. For example, an 8-year-old girl, chose a big black stone and wrote the words *"the argument with mummy that morning she died by suicide"* on it. The children are invited and encouraged to talk about the meaning of their stone. At the end of the session, the children write on a little piece of paper attached to a feather about what helps them and what makes them laugh. They are also invited to write on a feather a message of support for each other and exchange the feathers.

The Box of Feelings
The therapist draws a box on a sheet of butcher paper and tells the group about the four basic emotions – that is, fear, anger, joy, and sadness. The children are invited to write on Post-It notes about things related to the death of their family member that make them happy or sad, and to post their notes on the butcher paper. They choose what they want to share and what they want to keep to themselves. Some children choose to fold up their notes, while others want to share with the group. One of the group participants said: *"Sometimes I am very angry at my father. He left me, my little sister and my mother alone."* Another child said, *"It makes me very sad, because I think my father did not love me enough. But it helps to dance, that makes me feel better."*

I Carry You With Me
During the last session every family is invited to write a letter to the deceased person, using a variety of materials, such as paper, pencils, and handicraft material. The family members work together. It can be a very powerful experience, even if not many words are said. The enthusiasm of the younger children, sticking hearts and figures onto the letter, often helps to make the tension bearable, and to invite other family members to participate. The letters are attached to balloons and released into the air to symbolize and stress the continuing bond between the bereaved and their loved one, and between the bereaved families (*"we have all lost a loved one"*).

Beneficial Effects of Group Participation

Breaking the Isolation and Providing Emotional Support

The core of the group and its most important strength are recognition and acknowledgement. Many children and adolescents deeply appreciate learning that *"I am not alone."* The participation in the group gives them much-needed hope, consolation, and support. This is invaluable, especially for young people bereaved by suicide, as the taboo and stigma surrounding suicide and the feelings of guilt and shame often stop them from sharing their story. The experience of sharing their story with other bereaved children and speaking freely and without hesitation makes them feel less desolate. They can talk about how they cope with the traumatic loss and can learn that it is normal to feel a variety of emotions, such as sadness, anger, relief, etc. The young participants can also learn new strategies of coping with anger, loss, etc., from other group participants.

Sharing the Story in the Group Helps to Construct Meaning

Grieving is not only about loss and missing, it is also about constructing meaning and sense making (Neimeyer, 1999). *"Why did this happen to me?"*, *"How can I fit this into the story of my life?"* After a suicide, the question of why is particularly challenging. The group can help to find meaning by giving an opportunity to talk about what happened before the suicide (*"Were there earlier attempts?"*, *"Did you notice any warning signs?"*) or about a suicide note. It also gives the young participants an opportunity to discuss in age-appropriate language and manner what it means to be depressed, to share feelings of guilt, to express the continuing bond with the deceased, and to share comforting memories.

Reconnecting With Family Members

Feelings of shame, guilt, and blame often lead to avoidant communication patterns in the family (Dyregrov & Dyregrov, 2004). Such a climate of silence may complicate the grieving process of children and intensify their loneliness. Without an opportunity to talk, children might not be able to make sense of the loss. It is crucial to facilitate open communication and the natural support within the family – participating in the group *together* as a family offers parents and children a unique opportunity to share their loss experience.

A Positive Experience With Mental Health Professionals

Often follow-up help may be needed after the group program is completed, to address ongoing posttraumatic stress symptoms or to treat complicated grief. Unfortunately, suicide-bereaved families are frequently disappointed with professional help (Pettersen, Omerov, Steineck, Dyregrov, et al., 2015; Pettersen, Omerov, Steineck, Titelman, et al., 2015) (*"It did not prevent my dad from killing himself, so how can it be helpful?"*). Development of trust toward the psychotherapists in a safe environment of a support group and positive testimonies of peers about professional help can encourage family members to seek further help.

Conclusions

Further research is needed to explore which factors related to group support are helpful (or harmful) for traumatically bereaved children and adolescents. However, a one-size-fits-all model of support does not exist, and the help offered must be able to meet the child's needs. Often a combination of group support, individual, and/or family counseling is necessary. The positive experiences of the Victim Care Unit in Brussels may encourage others working in the field of grief and trauma to organize group support for child suicide survivors, as this can offer unique and much-needed help.

Corresponding authors

Liselot Willems
Victim Care Unit
Centre for Social Welfare
Brussels
Belgium
liselot.willems@gmail.com

Leen Hoebrechts
Victim Care Unit
Centre for Social Welfare
Brussels
Belgium
leen_hoebrechts@hotmail.com

References

Brown, E. J., & Goodman, R. F. (2005). Childhood traumatic grief: An exploration of the construct in children bereaved on September 11. *Journal of Clinical Child and Adolescent Psychology, 34*(2), 248–259. http://doi.org/10.1207/s15374424jccp3402_4

Cerel, J., & Aldrich, R. S. (2011). The impact of suicide on children and adolescents. In J. R. Jordan & J. L. McIntosh (Eds.), *Grief after suicide: Understanding the consequences and caring for the survivors* (pp. 81–92). New York, NY: Routledge.

Cohen, J. A., & Mannarino, A. P. (2004). Treatment of childhood traumatic grief. *Journal of Clinical Child and Adolescent Psychology, 33*(4), 820–832. http://doi.org/10.1207/s15374424jccp3304_17

Dowdney, L. (2000). Annotation: childhood bereavement following parental death. *Journal of Child Psychology and Psychiatry, 41*(7), 819–830. http://doi.org/10.1111/1469-7610.00670

Dyregrov, K. (2009). How do the young suicide survivors wish to be met by psychologists? A user study. *Omega: Journal of Death and Dying, 59*(3), 221–238. http://doi.org/10.2190/OM.59.3.c

Dyregrov, K., & Dyregrov, A. (2004). Helping the family following suicide. In B. Monroe & F. Kraus (Eds.), *Brief interventions with bereaved children* (pp. 201–215). Oxford, UK: Oxford University Press.

Dyregrov, K., & Dyregrov, A. (2005). Siblings after suicide: The forgotten bereaved. *Suicide and Life-Threatening Behavior, 35*(6), 714–724. http://doi.org/10.1521/suli.2005.35.6.714

Dyregrov, K., Dyregrov, A., & Johnsen, I. (2013). Participants recommendations for the ideal grief group: A qualitative study. *Omega: Journal of Death and Dying, 67*(4), 363–377. http://doi.org/10.2190/OM.67.4.b

Fiddelaers-Jaspers, R. (2004). *Mijn troostende ik. Kwetsbaarheid én kracht van rouwende jongeren* [My comforting self: Vulnerability and strength of grieving youth]. Utrecht, The Netherlands: Ten Have.

Neimeyer, R. A. (1999). Narrative strategies in grief therapy. *Journal of Constructivist Psychology, 12*(1), 65–85. http://doi.org/10.1080/107205399266226

Pettersen, R., Omerov, P., Steineck, G., Dyregrov, A., Titelman, D., Dyregrov, K., & Nyberg, U. (2015). Suicide-bereaved siblings' perception of health services. *Death Studies, 39*(6), 323–331. http://doi.org/10.1080/07481187.2014.946624

Pettersen, R., Omerov, P., Steineck, G., Titelman, D., Dyregrov, A., Nyberg, T., & Nyberg, U. (2015). Lack of trust in the health-care system after losing a child to suicide. *Crisis, 36*(3), 161–172. http://doi.org/10.1027/0227-5910/a000312

Pfeffer, C. R., Jiang, H., Kakuma, T., Hwang, J., & Metsch, M. (2002). Group intervention for children bereaved by the suicide of a relative. *Journal of the American Academy of Child & Adolescent Psychiatry, 41*(5), 505–513. http://doi.org/10.1097/00004583-200205000-00007

Pfeffer, C. R., Martins, P., Mann, J., Sunkenberg, M., Ice, A., Damore, J. P., ... Jiang, H. (1997). Child survivors of suicide: psychosocial characteristics. *Journal of the American Academy of Child & Adolescent Psychiatry, 36*(1), 65–74. http://doi.org/10.1097/00004583-199701000-00019

Chapter 32

Denmark – Support for the Bereaved by Suicide

Annette Erlangsen[1] and Elene Fleischer[2]

[1]Danish Research Institute for Suicide Prevention, Mental Health Centre Copenhagen, Denmark
[2]NEFOS – Region Syddanmark, Fyn, Denmark

Abstract: The aim of this chapter is to describe the support that is available to those bereaved by suicide in Denmark. Both public health care and volunteer organizations provide support to the bereaved by suicide. The offers range from professional therapy to café meetings and seminars. Still, Danish register-based studies have found that people bereaved by suicide have elevated risks of adverse outcomes, such as suicide.

Introduction

Each year approximately 600 persons die by suicide in Denmark, and in 2014, the national suicide rate was 11.2 per 100,000 inhabitants (Sundhedsdatastyrelsen, 2016). Although the World Health Organization (2014) encourages member countries to implement a national suicide prevention strategy, Denmark does not currently have a national strategy (the most recent national action plan for suicide prevention in Denmark was implemented between 1999 and 2004). It is well established that for each person dying by suicide, a substantial number of people are left behind with unanswered questions and a grief to heal (Berman, 2011). This chapter describes the offers of support that bereaved by suicide may draw upon in Denmark.

Psychotherapy

Denmark has public health care for all persons living in the country (Davis, 2002), and all citizen have free of charge access to general practitioners (GPs) and specialist doctors, as well as general and psychiatric hospitals. Consequently, persons with mental disorders that require treatment receive either inpatient or outpatient psychiatric care, as needed, free of charge. Therapy delivered by psychologists or privately practising psychiatrists needs to be prescribed by a GP or paid for out of one's own pocket. The Danish National Board of Health has outlined specific guidelines for GPs, listing circumstances under which a patient can be referred to subsidized psychotherapy (Danish National Board of Health, 2014). One of the guidelines specifies that a person who has experienced a death of a close relative, including a death by suicide, may be referred to psychotherapy. This implies that those bereaved by suicide may be referred to subsidized psychotherapy, in which case 60 % of the therapist's fee will be covered by the public health insurance, while the remaining 40 % is paid by the patient. The referral is valid for a total of 12 consultations (with some flexibility for patients with a diagnosed mental disorder). One limitation is that referral must be requested within the first 6 months after the bereavement. Danish organizations for the bereaved by suicide would like to see the referral period extended to 12 months, as those bereaved by suicide are not always able to use this type of support within such a short time frame. Apart from this, there is no subsidized public support for the bereaved by suicide in Denmark.

Volunteer Organizations

Two Danish volunteer organizations offer support to those bereaved by suicide: the National Association for the Bereaved by Suicide (in Danish: Landsforeningen Efterladte efter Selvmord), and the Network for the Affected by Suicidal Behaviour (in Danish: Netværk for Selvmordsramte, abbreviated as NEFOS).

National Association for the Bereaved by Suicide

The National Association for the Bereaved by Suicide was established in 2002 by a group of suicide survivors, led by Unni Bille-Brahe (http://www.efterladte.dk). The association hosts café meetings in different cities in the country; on a yearly basis, approximately 30 meetings are held where experiences of being bereaved are shared. In addition, theme-based meetings with lectures, readings, or a film presentation, as well as "walk and talk" events are offered in various locations; approximately 20 events of this type are hosted each year. The meetings are generally arranged as open events aiming to provide a forum for social exchange for persons bereaved by suicide. Yearly, a weekend seminar for adults is offered, facilitated by a family therapist. The seminar offers participants ample opportunity to receive professional feedback and to share experiences. The association also organizes an annual weekend trip for adolescents bereaved by suicide, offering young people an opportunity to meet and socialize with bereaved peers and get access to a psychologist.

Network for the Affected by Suicidal Behaviour (NEFOS)

In 2004, NEFOS was founded by Elene Fleischer in Odense, Denmark (http://www.nefos.dk). This organization works with persons affected by suicidal behavior, including the bereaved by suicide and the next of kin of people who self-harm. NEFOS is a volunteer organization but receives public support, for instance, from local municipalities through schemes of public support for volunteer organizations. NEFOS offers support to the bereaved by suicide free of charge and at any time after the death. In 2014, a total of 354 bereaved by suicide received support through NEFOS. Contact with the organization is based on self-referral. NEFOS has made great efforts to distribute information material to priests, funeral directors, and GPs in the regions where the organization operates in order to increase the awareness of NEFOS. Much of the support is provided by volunteers who have undergone a training program developed by the organization (the volunteers are called *professional counselors* although their work is unpaid). To ensure that the volunteers have a theoretical understanding and approach to the work in NEFOS, only candidates with a degree in health or social sciences with minimum of 3 years of studies are admitted to the program. Each volunteer follows two professional counselors at work, which may be the full duration of a support group, or a full course of individual counseling sessions.

The general rule is that the bereaved by suicide is first offered 5 to 10 individual sessions with a professional counselor, and afterwards they can join a support group. Support groups are organized in many cities, including Odense, Copenhagen, and Aarhus, but always with a set number of members – that is, in a closed format where newcomers will not be added to the group after it has started. The groups are formed according to kinship and age. The group participants share the same type of relationship with the deceased – for example, child, sibling, partner, or parent – and participants belong to the same age segment – for example, adolescents, adults, or older adults. Based on the experiences of the counselors, the grief process varies by the relation to the bereaved and one's stage in life. Approximately 20–30 support groups are conducted on a yearly basis. Typically, the group meets for 2 hr every second week for a total of 8 to 10 sessions. The first hour of the meeting is used to let the participants share thoughts related to their loss which have preoccupied them. The second hour of the meeting is focused on psycho-education; the professional counselors will take up topics that were mentioned during the first part of the meeting. Each group is facilitated by two professional counselors. This arrangement allows for handling situations where, for instance, a participant becomes overwhelmed and needs to step outside for some time; one counselor can then accompany the participant to make sure that the person is all right. One of the rules of the group is that each participant says goodbye to the other members and counselors at the end of the meeting. This provides a means for checking how each participant is coping with the topics tackled in the group.

In addition, NEFOS has trialed specific programs, such as a mentoring project where children bereaved by suicide are teamed up with mentors who themselves had been exposed to a loss by suicide in the past. Mentors, recruited through advertisements, received training similar to the training for professional counselors, but with a specific focus on children. The project, however, was terminated due to lack of funding. Also, it was quite a challenge to recruit children to the program; because parents were protective about their children's well-being they were reluctant to take part in the project.

A collaborative agreement with local suicide prevention clinics, which provide psychosocial therapy for people at risk of suicide (Erlangsen et al., 2015), has been made. If NEFOS counselors become aware of bereaved clients who may be at risk of suicide, they may refer them directly to a suicide prevention clinic. Similarly, clinical staff may refer clients of the suicide preventive care (or their relatives) to NEFOS if there is a need for support related to bereavement by suicide. Over the years, NEFOS has noticed that children bereaved by suicide prior to the age of 10 or 11 are likely to be in need of professional support also later in their lives. As cognitive skills develop, the memories of the loss are likely to reappear and may need to be readdressed. Consequently, children who receive support from NEFOS are encouraged to contact the organization again after 2 or 3 years, and a substantial number make use of this offer.

Other NEFOS projects include a regional family project in Southern Denmark. Families who contact NEFOS for help and where several family members have been exposed to suicide receive an offer of a family intervention. Two or more professional counselors visit the family at home for a 2-hr session, which includes individual conversations with family members. One of the counselors assumes the role of a facilitator who overviews the intervention and distributes tasks among the counselors. A home-based support allows children to participate or to leave the room, as preferred. Generally, 5 to 10 visits are conducted, some in the family home and others at NEFOS locations.

Another project, titled The Invisible Older Adults, offers support to older adults bereaved by suicide, who may be less inclined to seek help and may have difficulties attending appointments outside the home. Support is offered at home if a bereaved older adult is not able to come to NEFOS.

The support provided by NEFOS is expert-driven – that is, based on observations and expertise of the NEFOS staff. In addition, participants of NEFOS programs are usually asked to provide feedback (i.e., a user questionnaire), and they report that the support provided has been useful.

Books

Several books on suicide bereavement have been published. The book *Mourning After Suicide'* (in Danish: *Sorgen ved selvmord*) by Inger Anneberg was one of the first books to address the issues that the bereaved by suicide face in Denmark (Anneberg, 2002). Another book, *The Ones Left Behind* (in Danish: *De der blev tilbage*), which won several awards, presents stories of the bereaved, accompanied by photos that tell a story in their own right (Andersen & Åndahl, 2011). Other books provide personal accounts of losing a brother or a son to suicide (Jahn, 2008; Nordahl, 2013).

Media Reporting

In 2005, the Werther Award was introduced in Denmark to encourage responsible media reporting of suicide (Dare et al., 2011). International studies show that media reports and fictional portrayal of suicide in dramas and television shows may lead to copycat behavior (Hegerl et al., 2013; Schmidtke & Häfner, 1988). Conversely, media reports omitting details of suicide methods and glorification of suicide, may reduce the likelihood of imitation (Niederkrotenthaler et al., 2010). Each year, the Werther Award is given to a media person who, in the course of their work, has presented issues related to suicidal behavior and bereavement in an ethically correct and preventative manner (Centre for Suicide Research, 2016). The award committee includes a representative of the organizations of the bereaved by suicide.

Research on Suicide Bereavement

Much research in Denmark is based on linkage of individual-level register data available for the entire population. Studies have consistently shown elevated risks of suicide among people bereaved by suicide. Having been exposed to a suicide in a first-degree relative – that is, parent, sibling, or child – is linked to a twofold higher risk of suicide (Qin et al., 2003). Young persons aged 10–21 years whose father had died by suicide were also found to have twofold (2.3) higher risk of dying by suicide as compared with those whose father was alive and living in Denmark. However, young persons who had lost a mother to suicide had a fivefold higher risk of dying by suicide themselves (Agerbo et al., 2002). Adult people aged 25–60 years were noted to have a 22-fold (for married) and 31-fold (for cohabiting) higher risk of suicide if their partner had died by suicide within the last 2 years when compared with peers with alive partners (Agerbo, 2005). It is important to underscore that, statistically speaking, from a total population-based perspective, suicide happens very rarely, including among people bereaved by suicide; a 22-fold higher risk with a general suicide rate of 11 per 100,000 means that 24 out of 10,000 bereaved might die by suicide. Nevertheless, the data show that suicide bereavement is a risk factor for suicide. Consequently, support of the bereaved is a suicide prevention strategy, as emphasized by the World Health Organization (2014).

Conclusions

Denmark does have subsidized support for people bereaved by suicide, albeit with some restrictions and limitations. Volunteer organizations provide open forums as well as extended support to bereaved. Still, findings from register-based studies in Denmark underscore the importance of outreach and support for people bereaved by suicide.

Corresponding author
Annette Erlangsen
Danish Research Institute for Suicide Prevention
Mental Health Centre Copenhagen
Denmark
annette.erlangsen@regionh.dk

References

Agerbo, E. (2005). Midlife suicide risk, partner's psychiatric illness, spouse and child bereavement by suicide or other modes of death: A gender specific study. *Journal of Epidemiology and Community Health, 59*(5), 407–412. http://doi.org/10.1136/jech.2004.024950

Agerbo, E., Nordentoft, M., & Mortensen, P. B. (2002). Familial, psychiatric, and socioeconomic risk factors for suicide in young people: Nested case-control study. *BMJ, 325,* 74. http://doi.org/10.1136/bmj.325.7355.74

Andersen, B., & Åndahl, T. (2011). *De der blev tilbage. En portrætbog om efterladte efter selvmord* [Those who were left behind: A portrait book on bereaved by suicide]. Frederiksberg, Denmark: Frydenlund.

Anneberg, I. (2002). *Sorgen ved selvmord* [Mourning after suicide]. Copenhagen, Denmark: Høst & Søn.

Berman, A.L. (2011). Estimating the population of survivors of suicide: Seeking an evidence base. *Suicide and Life-Threatening Behavior, 41*(1), 110–116. http://doi.org/10.1111/j.1943-278X.2010.00009.x

Centre for Suicide Research. (2016). *Wertherprisen* [Werther Award]. Retrieved from http://selvmords-forskning.dk/viden/presse/werther-prisen/

Danish National Board of Health. (2014). *Henvisning til psykolog* [Referral to a psychologist]. Danish National Board of Health. Retrieved from http://sundhedsstyrelsen.dk/da/sundhed/planlaegning-og-be-redskab/praksisomraadet/psykologer/henvisning-til-psykolog

Dare, A., Andriessen, K., Nordentoft, M., Meier, M., Husman, A., & Pirkis, J. (2011). Media awards for responsible reporting of suicide: Experiences from Australia, Belgium and Denmark. *International Journal of Mental Health Systems, 5,* 15. http://doi.org/10.1186/1752-4458-5-15

Davis, K. (2002). The Danish health system through an American lens. *Health Policy, 59*(2), 119–132. http://doi.org/10.1016/S0168-8510(01)00202-0

Erlangsen, A., Lind, B., Stuart, E. A., Qin, P., Stenager, E., Larsen, K. J., … Winsløv, J. H. (2015). Short and long term effects of psychosocial therapy provided to persons after suicide attempt: a register-based, nationwide multicentre study using propensity score matching. *Lancet Psychiatry, 2*(1), 49–58. http://doi.org/10.1016/S2215-0366(14)00083-2

Hegerl, U., Koburger, N., Rummel-Kluge, C., Gravert, C., Walden, M., & Mergl, R. (2013). One followed by many? Long-term effects of a celebrity suicide on the number of suicidal acts on the German railway. *Journal of Affective Disorders, 146*(1), 39–44. http://doi.org/10.1016/j.jad.2012.08.032

Jahn, A. W. (2008). *Himmelsmilet* [The smile of heaven]. Copenhagen, Denmark: People's Press.

Niederkrotenthaler, T., Voracek, M., Herberth, A., Till, B., Strauss, M., Etzersdorfer, E., … Sonneck, G. (2010). Role of media reports in completed and prevented suicide: Werther v. Papageno effects. *British Journal of Psychiatry, 197*(3), 234–243. http://doi.org/10.1192/bjp.bp.109.074633

Nordahl, B. (2013). *Sebastians bog – en søns selvmord, en fars sorgarbejde* [Sebastian's book: A son's suicide, a father's mourning process]. Brønshøj, Denmark: Forlaget Nielsens.

Qin, P., Agerbo, E., & Mortensen, P. B. (2003). Suicide risk in relation to socioeconomic, demographic, psychiatric and familial factors: A national register-based study of all suicides in Denmark, 1981–1997. *American Journal of Psychiatry, 160*(4), 765–772. http://doi.org/10.1176/appi.ajp.160.4.765

Schmidtke, A. & Häfner, H. (1988). The Werther effect after television films: New evidence for an old hypothesis. *Psychological Medicine, 18*(3), 665–676. http://doi.org/10.1017/S0033291700008345

Sundhedsdatastyrelsen. (2016). *Tabel over dødsårsager* [Table of causes of death]. Retrieved from http://www.esundhed.dk/sundhedsregistre/DAR01/Sider/Tabel.aspx

World Health Organization. (2014). *Preventing suicide: A global imperative.* Geneva, Switzerland: Author.

Chapter 33

England – Help for People Bereaved by Suicide

Karen Lascelles[1], Alexandra Pitman[2], Sharon McDonnell[3], Hamish Elvidge[4], Helen Garnham[5], and Keith Hawton[6]

[1]Oxford Health NHS Foundation Trust, Oxford, UK
[2]UCL Division of Psychiatry, University College London, UK
[3]Centre for Mental Health and Safety, University of Manchester, UK
[4]National Suicide Prevention Alliance, London, UK
[5]Mental Health, Public Health England, London, UK
[6]Centre for Suicide Research, University of Oxford, UK

Abstract: England has been relatively late in recognizing and prioritizing bereavement by suicide but has advanced considerably over the last decade, particularly following the launch of the 2012 national suicide prevention strategy. A substantial collaboration between the statutory and third sectors in strategy development, care provision, training, and research, has helped embed national awareness and commitment to postvention. Future plans include implementing a nationwide suicide bereavement support framework to ensure equitable access to support for people bereaved or affected by suicide and rigorous evaluation of interventions for this population.

Introduction

The decriminalization of suicide in England in 1961 was the first step in addressing the burden of stigma for those bereaved by suicide. Prior to this, legal, religious, and social sanctions dating back to the Middle Ages had brought shame on families in which someone had died by suicide (Cvinar, 2005). Attention to suicide prevention in England increased in 1992 with the inclusion of national suicide prevention targets in the government's Health of the Nation strategy (Jenkins, 1994). However, it was not until 2002 that the first suicide prevention strategy for England was developed by the newly established National Suicide Prevention Strategy Advisory Group (Department of Health, 2002). As with the US strategy published around the same time (US Department of Health and Human Services, 2001), the strategy for England mentioned a need to promote the mental health of people bereaved by suicide and to clarify their specific needs. The inclusion of this group in both strategies had come about partly due to input from voluntary sector organizations such as Cruse Bereavement Care, Prevention of Young Suicide (PAPYRUS), and Survivors of Bereavement by Suicide, highlighting the needs of the bereaved.

Until this point, limited support had been available to people bereaved by suicide, and this relied heavily on the voluntary sector. Since the 2002 strategy, the range of support across England has increased, but varies geographically. Whilst some general practitioners (GPs) and

National Health Service (NHS) clinicians are able to provide bereavement support, there is no clear NHS infrastructure for providing support after a suicide. In 2012, a revised suicide prevention strategy for England was published (Department of Health, 2012), identifying provision of better information and support for people bereaved or affected by suicide as one of its six key areas of action. There was little evidence on which to base this area of action, as few studies had evaluated the effectiveness of interventions to support people bereaved by suicide, and none at all from England (McDaid, Trowman, Golder, Hawton, & Sowden, 2008). No specific role for the NHS was mentioned, apart from the need for GPs to be "vigilant to the potential vulnerability of family members when someone takes their own life" (Department of Health, 2012, p. 7).

Recent suicide statistics for England indicate that 4,882 people die annually by suicide (Office of National Statistics, 2016). The estimate that up to 6–10 people are affected by each suicide (World Health Organization, 2008) suggests an incidence of up to 48,820 bereaved or affected by suicide annually. Whilst not all will perceive a need for support, it is important that all are aware of the range of resources available.

Developing Infrastructure, Leadership, and Resources

The emphasis in the 2012 suicide prevention strategy on supporting those bereaved or affected by suicide helped galvanize national acknowledgement of the pivotal role that the voluntary sector has in postvention. In 2013 a Support after Suicide (SAS) Partnership was established by a collective of charitable organizations as a hub for those working across England to support people bereaved. The partnership vision that anyone bereaved or affected by suicide should be offered and receive timely and appropriate support underpins the organization's intention to influence policy and practice across the United Kingdom. The SAS Partnership membership currently comprises approximately 20 organizations, predominantly voluntary although there is representation from health, public health, and academia. The partnership has quickly become widely recognized as a leading body in relation to suicide bereavement. **Box 33.1** includes the online addresses of the resources mentioned in this chapter.

Box 33.1. Available resources

Support after Suicide (SAS) Partnership: http://supportaftersuicide.org.uk/
Help Is at Hand: http://www.supportaftersuicide.org.uk/help-is-at-hand
Healthtalk.org: http://www.healthtalk.org/peoples-experiences/dying-bereavement/bereavement-due-suicide/topics
Making Families Count: https://vimeo.com/hundredfamilies
NHS Choices coping with bereavement page: http://www.nhs.uk/livewell/bereavement/Pages/bereavement.aspx
Public Health England Health Matters Blog: https://publichealthmatters.blog.gov.uk/2016/01/07/preventing-suicide-what-can-local-authorities-do/

Public Health England, an executive agency sponsored by the Department of Health and responsible for protecting and improving the nation's health and well-being and reducing inequalities, has a lead role in community-based suicide prevention and has engaged the SAS Partnership and the related National Suicide Prevention Alliance as primary stakeholders in the development of a number of suicide prevention and postvention resources. This included, in 2015, revising *Help Is at Hand*, a freely available, practical, and supportive guide for people bereaved by suicide, originally developed in 2006 by the University of Oxford Centre for Suicide Research in collaboration with other organizations concerned with suicide bereavement and people bereaved through suicide (Hawton, Simkin, & Rees, 2008). This resource was based partly on an earlier *Bereavement Information Pack* (Hill, Hawton, Malmberg, & Simkin, 1997), also developed at the Centre and published by the Royal College of Psychiatrists. Placing leadership with the SAS Partnership facilitated a greater depth of input from those with personal experience, with the aim of a more equal balance between empathy and professional advice. Previous evaluation of *Help Is at Hand* indicated that, while people were very positive about the content, many had experienced difficulty finding out about the resource, particularly in the early days after bereavement when they felt they needed it most (Hawton et al., 2012). The guide can now be downloaded from the easily accessible SAS Partnership website (http://supportaftersuicide.org.uk/help-is-at-hand), which also signposts to Public Health England for online ordering of hard copies.

During 2014/2015 the SAS Partnership developed guidance for establishing a national suicide bereavement framework and pathway model, informed by experience and evidence from relevant voluntary, health and academic organizations. To facilitate dissemination and implementation of this guidance, Public Health England have funded ongoing development of the work to include a standard evaluation structure to provide those piloting the bereavement framework with a common means for assessment and comparison. This work was led by the National Alliance for Suicide Prevention with close involvement from the SAS Partnership and has resulted in Public Health England guidance to help local authorities establish local services for people bereaved by suicide, which is due to be published late 2016. The ultimate aspiration of the partnership is to build a collaborative business case for the realization of a suicide bereavement liaison service available in every local area across the United Kingdom.

NHS England has also collaborated with the voluntary sector, including PAPYRUS (https://www.papyrus-uk.org), to develop and disseminate Making Families Count training, concerned with improving families' experiences of NHS investigations following unexpected deaths, including the deaths by suicide of people under psychiatric care. This training is delivered by bereaved family members, who share negative and positive experiences of investigations and facilitate dialogue focusing on overcoming perceived barriers to family involvement. The aim of Making Families Count is to make the NHS investigatory process more inclusive, respectful, and compassionate in order not to exacerbate the stress and trauma families have already experienced as a result of their loss.

Suicide Surveillance

Suicides in England are determined through coroner's inquests that can take considerable time to complete (Pitman, 2012), and possible or likely suicides do not always result in verdicts indicative of actual suicide (Gunnell, Hawton, & Kapur, 2011). If intent is unclear, *open* or *accidental death* verdicts are likely to result, and recent years have seen an increase in *narrative verdicts* whereby a written chronicle of the circumstances of the death may be given without suicide being determined (Gunnell et al., 2011). This is problematic due to the potential for underestimation of suicide incidence, which has been estimated to have been approximately 6 % across England in 2009 (Gunnell et al., 2011) and as high as 16 % in 2008–2009 in coroners' jurisdictions with the highest rates of narrative verdicts (Carroll, Hawton, Kapur, Bennewith, & Gunnell, 2011). This increases the risk of bereaved families being left unrecognized and unsupported.

Since 1999, the charity Survivors of Bereavement by Suicide (http://uk-sobs.org.uk/) has worked with local police in a small South West county to develop police guidance and a traumatic bereavement leaflet for police to give to relatives. This work arose in recognition of the need for early support and signposting following suspected suicides, and based on experiences of poorly prepared police officers who lacked confidence in responding to families at the scene. The leaflet provides brief information about what to expect over the next few days and weeks and signposts to support agencies. In recent years, this model has been replicated at various sites across England. It has informed local police training on how to manage scenes of suspected suicide, which is being adopted by several police forces across the country.

In 2010 a similar model, involving coroners and public health agencies, was developed in the North East of England (Burke et al., 2012). This *suicide alert system* was developed to maintain contemporaneous oversight of suspected suicides and ensure bereaved families are signposted to appropriate support. Coroners officers alert local public health personnel to suspected suicides and ask the bereaved if they would like follow-up from a local suicide bereavement charity: If U Care Share Foundation (http://www.ifucareshare.co.uk/).

Building on these approaches and informed by pioneering and ongoing work by Barry Mc-Gale and colleagues in Londonderry, Northern Ireland, between 2014 and 2015, Public Health England and the Association of Chief Police Officers supported three areas to pilot police-based systems to test various approaches to real-time suicide surveillance and signposting to bereavement support. In the North East this included comparing a police-based system against the existing coroner-based system outlined above. The findings from these pilots has informed recent Public Health England guidance on local suicide prevention planning (Public Health England, 2016).

Research Into Practice

Much of the evidence describing the impact of bereavement by suicide has been derived from studies conducted in the United States, Canada, and Northern Europe, with UK practitioners extrapolating the findings to local settings. Existing international evidence has highlighted the risk of suicide in partners and mothers bereaved by suicide, and the high levels of stigma perceived by people bereaved by unnatural causes (Pitman, Osborn, King, & Erlangsen, 2014). More recent research in the United Kingdom has confirmed that the probability of suicide attempt is increased in adults bereaved by suicide, even if they are not blood-related to the deceased (Pitman, Osborn, Rantell, & King, 2016). This work has also found an increased probability of dropping out of a job or a course, highlighting the wider impacts on mental well-being and day-to-day functioning.

Research has been undertaken into parents' experiences of suicide bereavement, of finding their deceased child, and perceptions of GP responses in this context (Foggin et al., 2016). This research has informed the development of an evidence-based, theory-driven training resource to guide professionals in their responses to parents bereaved by suicide. The plan is to develop a social enterprise to deliver the training nationally, with profits being reinvested to conduct further suicide bereavement research.

The Internet has played an increasingly supportive role for people in the United Kingdom who are bereaved by suicide (Chapple & Ziebland, 2011). Healthtalk.org is a web resource that provides free and reliable sharing of real-life health experiences through written, audio, and filmed narrative, derived from rigorous qualitative research methods. Healthtalk.org has a module devoted to bereavement by suicide, which covers issues such as finding out about a suicide, changing emotions, viewing the body, police and media involvement, the inquest, family dynamics, and other people's reactions. The research underpinning healthtalk.org has informed professional understandings via the literature – for example, regarding how people bereaved by suicide perceive both media reporting (Chapple, Ziebland, Simkin, & Hawton, 2013) and coroners' verdicts (Chapple, Ziebland, & Hawton, 2012). It is also being used to inform the development of a training resource for early responders.

To help elicit a broader understanding of the impact of suicide in England and the wider United Kingdom, the support people receive, and the support people would find helpful, a UK-wide suicide bereavement survey is due to commence in November 2016. This research is a collaboration between the SAS Partnership and the University of Manchester led by the third author of this chapter (S. M.). The findings from this large-scale research, which will potentially be the largest postvention study conducted internationally, will be used to inform ongoing development of resources for people bereaved and affected by suicide.

Dissemination

Since 2012, a large annual suicide bereavement conference has been held in Manchester, North West England, attracting national and international speakers. This has brought together a diverse audience of delegates from across society, especially those bereaved by suicide and professionals who come into contact with them. The conference attends to all aspects of postvention, providing a platform whereby people can network, share information, learn from each other, and share good practice in this relatively new and developing field in the United Kingdom.

The SAS Partnership website provides information about support agencies and helpline numbers for people who want to speak to someone immediately. It is also shares relevant news about national developments and events and is developing a database that will map existing services in England, enabling site users to easily identify local resources. In addition, most charities concerned with suicide bereavement have websites that reciprocate signposting to the SAS Partnership, further facilitating dissemination. From a statutory perspective, the Department of Health produces annual reports based on the national suicide prevention strategy, the NHS Choices website (http://www.nhs.uk/livewell/bereavement/Pages/bereavement.aspx) includes suicide loss in its bereavement pages, and Public Health England has a *Health Matters Blog* (https://publichealthmatters.blog.gov.uk/) which broadcasts relevant news and information regarding suicide prevention and postvention.

Conclusions

With new support services being piloted at sites throughout England, there is a clear need to evaluate their effectiveness and to disseminate examples of those for which there is good evidence for positive outcomes. This will be a future priority in England, whilst continuing the collaborative endeavor to ensure the needs of people bereaved or affected by suicide are met nationwide.

Corresponding author

Karen Lascelles
Oxford Health NHS Foundation Trust
Oxford
UK
karen.lascelles@oxfordhealth.nhs.uk

References

Burke, W., Colmer, D., Johnson, N., Leigh, J., Key, B., & Parker, C. (2012). An organisational response to an increase in suicides: A case study. *Journal of Public Mental Health, 11*(3), 98–105. http://doi.org/10.1108/17465721211261905

Carroll, R., Hawton, K., Kapur, N., Bennewith, O., & Gunnell, D. (2011). Impact of the growing use of narrative verdicts by coroners on geographic variations in suicide: Analysis of coroners' inquest data. *Journal of Public Health, 34*(3), 447–453. http://doi.org/10.1093/pubmed/fdr091

Chapple, A., & Ziebland, S. (2011). How the internet is changing the experience of bereavement by suicide: A qualitative study in the UK. *Health, 15*(2), 173–187.

Chapple, A., Ziebland, S., & Hawton, K. (2012). A proper, fitting explanation? Suicide bereavement and perceptions of the coroner's verdict. *Crisis, 33*(4), 230–238. http://doi.org/10.1027/0227-5910/a000139

Chapple, A., Ziebland, S., Simkin, S., & Hawton, K. (2013). How people bereaved by suicide perceive newspaper reporting: Qualitative study. *British Journal of Psychiatry, 203*(3), 228–232. http://doi.org/10.1192/bjp.bp.112.114116

Cvinar, J. G. (2005). Do suicide survivors suffer social stigma: A review of the literature. *Perspectives in Psychiatric Care, 41*(1), 14–21. http://doi.org/10.1111/j.0031-5990.2005.00004.x

Department of Health. (2002). *National suicide prevention strategy for England* (Rep. No. 29158). London, UK: HMSO.

Department of Health. (2012). *Preventing suicide in England: A cross-government outcomes strategy to save lives* (Rep. No. 17680). London, UK: HMSO. Published online September 10, 2012. Retrieved from https://www.gov.uk/government/publications/suicide-prevention-strategy-launched

Foggin, E., McDonnell, S., Cordingley, L., Kapur, N., Shaw, J., & Chew-Graham, C. (2016). GPs' experiences of dealing with parents bereaved by suicide: a qualitative study. *British Journal of General Practice, 66*(651), e737–e746.

Gunnell, D., Hawton, K., & Kapur, N. (2011). Coroners' verdicts and suicide statistics in England and Wales. *British Medical Journal, 343*, d6030. http://doi.org/10.1136/bmj.d6030

Hawton, K., Simkin, S., & Rees, S. (2008). Help is at hand for people bereaved by suicide and other traumatic death. *Psychiatric Bulletin, 32*(8), 309–311. http://doi.org/10.1192/pb.bp.107.018242

Hawton, K., Sutton, L., Simkin, S., Walker, D., Stacey, G., Waters, K., & Rees, S. (2012). Evaluation of a resource for people bereaved by suicide. *Crisis, 33*(5), 254–264. http://doi.org/10.1027/0227-5910/a000145

Hill, K., Hawton, K., Malmberg, A., & Simkin, S. (1997). *Bereavement information pack for those bereaved through suicide or other sudden death*. London, UK: Gaskell.

Jenkins, R. (1994). The health of the nation: Recent government policy and legislation. *Psychiatric Bulletin, 18*(6), 324–327. http://doi.org/10.1192/pb.18.6.324

McDaid, C., Trowman, R., Golder, S., Hawton, K., & Sowden, A. (2008). Interventions for people bereaved through suicide: Systematic review. *British Journal of Psychiatry, 193*(6), 438–443. http://doi.org/10.1192/bjp.bp.107.040824

Office of National Statistics. (2016). *Suicides in the United Kingdom: 2014 registrations*. Newport, UK: Author.

Pitman, A. (2012). Reform of the coroners' service in England and Wales: Policy-making and politics. *The Psychiatrist, 36*(1), 1–5. http://doi.org/10.1192/pb.bp.111.036335

Pitman, A., Osborn, D. P. J., King, M. B., & Erlangsen, A. (2014). Effects of suicide bereavement on mental health and suicide risk. *Lancet Psychiatry, 1*(1), 86–94. http://doi.org/10.1016/S2215-0366(14)70224-X

Pitman, A. L., Osborn, D. P. J., Rantell, K., & King, M. B. (2016). Bereavement by suicide as a risk factor for suicide attempt: A cross-sectional national UK-wide study of 3432 young bereaved adults. *BMJ Open, 6*(1), e009948. http://doi.org/10.1136/bmjopen-2015-009948

Public Health England. (2016). *Local suicide prevention planning: a practice resource* (Report No. 2016392). London, UK: HMSO.

US Department of Health and Human Services. (2001). *National strategy for suicide prevention: Goals and objectives for action*. Rockville, MD: Author.

World Health Organization. (2008). *Preventing suicide: How to start a survivors group*. Geneva, Switzerland: Author.

Chapter 34

France – Suicide Postvention

Jean-Pierre Soubrier[1] and Jean-Jacques Chavagnat[2]

[1]Centre de Ressources en Suicidologie – CRES, Paris, France
[2]Centre Hospitalier Henri-Laborit, Fédération Européenne Vivre Son Deuil, Poitiers, France

Abstract: Suicide bereavement support is one of the priorities of the nationwide comprehensive suicide prevention program in France. Over recent decades, the public authorities have launched suicide prevention policies, including postvention, which have been progressively implemented, involving both the public and the private sector. This chapter describes the three major categories of suicide bereavement support available in France: postvention in the workplace, medical and psychological support, and support through bereavement associations.

In memoriam Michel Hanus, postvention pioneer in France

Introduction

Bereavement is the loss of a significant other person. It causes a psychological and physical absence in the daily life of the survivor, and initiates a grief process which may last for life (Fauré, 2007; Hanus, 2004). As time goes on, the pain of the loss might fade. However, survivors may need psychological support in their grief process (Fédération Française de Psychiatrie, 2010; Soubrier, 2009). As Shneidman prophetically stated: "Postvention can be viewed as prevention for the next decade or for the next generation" (Shneidman, 1973, p. 41).

France is a country with a predominantly Catholic tradition, currently with religious diversity and progressing secularization. In 2012, the most recent year with data available, there were approximately 10,000 suicides per year, or 16.7 per 100,000 inhabitants (Observatoire National du Suicide [National Suicide Monitoring Center], 2016). With an estimated average of 6 to 10 persons affected by each suicide, there are annually between 60,000 and 100,000 people recently bereaved by suicide – that is, the survivors.

Suicide bereavement support in France is a part of a comprehensive, progressively implemented program of suicide prevention networks, which includes creation of survivor associations. In 1998 the French health authorities established a scientific committee, followed by the establishment of the National Strategy for Actions against Suicide 2000–2005, by the Ministry of Health and Social Affairs (Ministère de l'Emploi et de la Solidarité, 2001). In 2013, the Observatoire National du Suicide (National Suicide Monitoring Centre) (http://drees.social-sante.gouv.fr/etudes-et-statistiques/la-drees/l-observatoire-national-du-suicide-ons/) was established to support suicidology research and to improve the collection of mortality data, including suicide in violent deaths. These initiatives were the result of an increasing national awareness of suicide and suicide prevention. Events which stirred the public opinion and debate, such as the publication of the book *Suicide, Mode d'emploi* (*Suicide, A manual*) (Guillon & le Bonniec, 1982; Soubrier, 1984), which led in 1987 to a law against incitement to suicide, and the suicide of Pierre Bérégovoy, a former prime minister in 1993, stressed the need for suicide prevention programs in France.

In 2011, the Ministry of Health and Social Affairs launched further actions in the National Program for Actions against Suicide 2011–2014 including "support for persons and groups bereaved by suicide" as Goal 5 (Ministère des Affaires sociales et de la Santé, 2011). This goal highlights the necessity of training professionals in suicide bereavement support, dissemination of information, and increasing the availability of support resources on how to start a survivors' group (e.g., World Health Organization, 2002). These recommendations are addressed to all health and social services, both public and private organizations. Currently, three major categories of support for suicide survivors in France can be identified: postvention in the workplace, medical and psychological support through the public and private sector, and suicide bereavement support provided by associations (e.g., nongovernmental organizations).

Postvention in the Workplace

The need for postvention in the workplace (see Chapter 15 in this volume) became apparent in France in the early 2000s when a number of suicides occurred in major companies of different industrial sectors, and the deaths were widely commented on in the media. Hence, suicide and attempted suicide at work have been recognized as a potential consequence of psychosocial risk factors, such as burnout or work-related stress. In 2010, the Minister of Labor encouraged French industry to tackle the workplace risk factors and to organize suicide postvention programs. In collaboration with occupational health specialists, specialized psychological units were created to offer programs of suicide prevention and postvention. As such, France adheres to the recommendations of the World Health Organization (2006) regarding suicide prevention in the workplace.

When a suicide or a suicide attempt occurs, psychological support is offered to the bereaved colleagues and/or the suicidal person, by specialized teams of psychologists, physicians, psychiatrists, and social workers, in collaboration with the private and public sector (Groupement d'Etudes et de Prévention du Suicide, 2013). Counseling sessions are offered either individually or collectively, inside or outside of the company. Of note, in some cases, a death by suicide has been recognized by the health insurance and professional legislation as an occupational accident, even if the death occurred at home or on the way to work (judgment of the Court de Cassation, 2015, appeal number 14-22227). In addition, recently a special suicide prevention program (including postvention) for farmers facing a drastic economic crisis has been implemented (http://www.msa.fr/lfr/prevention-du-suicide-des-populations-agricoles).

Medical and Psychological Support

The public sector, through medicopsychological centers, offers free of charge support, including individual psychotherapy, for the bereaved by suicide. The professional staff at these specialized health centers includes psychiatrists, psychologists, psychoanalysts, psychiatric nurses, and social workers. Medicopsychological emergency units, which are a part of public hospitals, provide psychotraumatology consultations and group therapies after a violent death. Forensic institutes also support suicide survivors; the pioneer was the Medicolegal Institute of Lyon which started such services in the early 1980s. Indeed, after a violent death, such as a suicide, a forensic autopsy is indicated, and it is essential that the coronial services provide information and support to the bereaved families (see Chapter 14 in this volume).

Private sector support is available through outpatient individual consultations by psychiatrists. Consultations are usually partially refunded by the public social security system. Private psychologists and psychotherapists may also offer professional support through (individual) consultations; however, these are not refunded, unless the patient has a complementary health insurance. Mental health professionals can detect clinically untreated mental disorders, such as depression, psychosis, or substance abuse, and facilitate compliance with, or continuation of previously interrupted, treatment or alternative treatment options.

Support Through Suicide Bereavement Associations

A number of associations, which initially provided help to persons at risk of suicide, have become involved in helping suicide survivors. These nationwide and regional and local organizations are members of l'Union Nationale pour la Prévention du Suicide (National Union for Suicide Prevention; http://www.unps.fr/). Suicide bereavement associations offer help free of charge, such as support groups for bereaved adults, children, or parents, individual counseling, crisis lines, and educational programs, and postvention support for schools. Typically, they involve volunteers working in collaboration with mental health professionals, the media, and society at large. These organizations have been officially recognized and are supported financially by the government and/or private sponsors.

Major postvention associations in France include the Fédération Européenne Vivre Son Deuil (European Grief Federation) established in 1995 (http://vivresondeuil.asso.fr/), Association Jonathan Pierres Vivantes, established in 1978 (http://www.anjpv.org/), Phare Enfants Parents (Lighthouse Children-Parents), established in 1991 (https://phare.pads.fr/), Association Christophe, established in 2001 (http://www.christophe-lavieavanttout.com/), and the Institut Régional Jean Bergeret, established in 1988 (http://www.irjb.fr/).

Over time, a successful collaboration has been established between the suicide bereavement associations and suicidology researchers, resulting in conferences, workshops, and community actions, related to awareness. The postvention associations are a major partner of the National Suicide Prevention Days (http://www.infosuicide.eu/contacts/unps/jnps.htm), organized by the National Association for Suicide Prevention in the first week of February in various cities across the country, and a partner of the annual World Suicide Prevention Day held on September 10.

Conclusions

On February 2, 2016, the minister of health and social affairs received the second report of the Observatoire National du Suicide (2016): "Suicide: Connaître pour prévenir: dimensions nationales, locales et associatives" (Suicide: Knowing to prevent: at the national, local, and associations level). The report stresses the importance of support groups for persons bereaved by suicide, which can

> relieve their psychic pain and prevent suicide in their social circle of family and friends. Such [an] initiative deserves to be developed with other bereaved populations as well, in particular children and adolescents affected by the suicide of a sibling or a peer. (Observatoire National du Suicide, 2016, p. 40)

It is expected that suicide bereavement support will be further studied and implemented in France with the support of governmental organizations, the public and private sector, and the pivotal involvement of the bereavement associations.

Corresponding author

Jean-Pierre Soubrier
Centre de Ressources en Suicidologie – CRES
Paris
France
http://www.cresuicidologie.fr/
pr.jp.soubrier@gmail.com

References

Cour de Cassation: Chambre Civile 2. (2015). *Audience publique du jeudi 9 juillet 2015, n° de pourvoi: 14-22227, France* [Public hearing on July 9, 2015, number of appeal: 14-22227, France]. Retrieved from https://www.legifrance.gouv.fr/affichJuriJudi.do?idTexte=JURITEXT000030875750

Fauré, C. (2007). *Après le suicide d'un proche: vivre le deuil et se reconstruire* [After the suicide of a loved one: Grief and recovery]. Paris, France: Albin Michel.

Fédération Française de Psychiatrie. (2010). *Effets et conséquences du suicide sur l'entourage: Modalités d'aide et de soutien: Les recommandations. Audition publique* [Effects and consequences of suicide for those affected: Modalities of help and support: Recommendations. Public hearing], Paris, 25–26 November 2009. Paris, France: Author. Retrieved from http://www.psydoc-france.fr/conf&rm/conf/endeuilles/recoEndeuilles.pdf

Groupement d'Etudes et de Prévention du Suicide. (2013). *Prévenir le suicide dans le monde du travail* [Suicide prevention in the work environment]. 45e Journées du GEPS, 22–25 Octobre 2013, Lyon, France. Retrieved from http://www.geps.asso.fr/recup.php?nom=Congrs_GEPS_2013_2me_annonce.pdf and http://www.geps.asso.fr/articles.php?rub=19

Guillon, C., & le Bonniec, Y. (1982). *Suicide, mode d'emploi: Histoire, technique, actualité* [Suicide, a manual: History, technique, current issues]. Paris, France: Éditions Alain Moreau.

Hanus, M. (2004). *Le deuil après suicide* [Grief after suicide]. Paris, France: Maloine.

Ministère de l'Emploi et de la Solidarité, Secrétariat d'Etat à la Santé et aux Handicapés: Direction Générale de la Santé. (2001). *Stratégie nationale d'actions face au suicide 2000/2005* [National strategy for actions against suicide 2000–2005]. Paris, France: Author. Retrieved from http://social-sante.gouv.fr/IMG/pdf/strategie_nat-2.pdf

Ministère des Affaires sociales et de la Santé. (2011). *Programme national d'actions contre le suicide (2011–2014)* [National Program for Actions against Suicide, 2011–2014]. Paris, France: Author. Retrieved from http://social-sante.gouv.fr/IMG/pdf/Programme_national_d_actions_contre_le_suicide_2011-2014.pdf

Observatoire National du Suicide. (2016). *Suicide: Connaître pour prévenir: Dimensions nationales, locales et associatives* [Suicide: Knowing to prevent: At the national, local, and associations level]. Paris, France: Publication de la DREES. Retrieved from http://social-sante.gouv.fr/IMG/pdf/2e_rapport_de_l_observatoire_national_du_suicide.pdf

Shneidman, E. (1973). *Deaths of man*. New York, NY: The New York Times Book Co.

Soubrier, J.P. (1984). La prévention du suicide est-elle encore possible depuis la publication autorisée d'un livre intitulé Suicide Mode d'Emploi – Histoire – Technique – Actualité? [Is suicide prevention still possible after the authorized publication of the book: Suicide – How to do it]. National Academy of Medicine Communication, France, January 10, 1984 (Annual Academy Award 1985). *Crisis, 5*(2), 119–124.

Soubrier, J.P. (2009). L'ultime prévention? [The ultimate prevention?] In Fédération Française de Psychiatrie. (Ed.), *Effets et conséquences du suicide sur l'entourage: Modalités d'aide et de soutien* [Effects and consequences of suicide for those affected: Modalities of help and support] (pp. 65–68). Paris, France: Author. Retrieved from http://psydoc-fr.broca.inserm.fr/conf&rm/conf/endeuilles/textesexperts/cd.pdf

World Health Organization. (2002). *Deuil et suicide: Indications pour la mise en place d'un groupe de soutien à ceux qui restent* [J.P. Soubrier, Trans., from: Preventing suicide: How to start a survivors' group]. Geneva, Switzerland: Author. Retrieved from http://www.who.int/mental_health/resources/preventingsuicide/en/and http://apps.who.int/iris/bitstream/10665/67607/1/WHO_MNH_MBD_00.6_fre.pdf

World Health Organization. (2006). *Preventing suicide: A resource at work*. Geneva, Switzerland: Author. Retrieved from http://apps.who.int/iris/bitstream/10665/43502/1/9241594381_eng.pdf

Chapter 35

Italy – Postvention Initiatives

Paolo Scocco, Elena Toffol, Stefano Totaro, Cristina Castriotta, and Alessandro Ferrari

SOPRoxi Project, Padova, Italy

Abstract: Suicide survivors are often in need of professional support. Attention to the needs of this population has been growing in recent years in Italy. Nongovernmental organizations (NGOs) and other private or mental health professional–driven projects are currently active at the local level (e.g., AFIPRES, Palermo; Suicide Prevention Center, Rome). Other programs (e.g., SOPRoxi project and the De Leo Fund) operate both locally and at the national level. The services provided to suicide survivors include, among others, peer and self-help groups, face-to-face and telephone consultations, helplines, workshops, and seminars. This chapter describes the Italian postvention network and its intervention strategies.

Introduction

In spite of a relatively low suicide rate (6.7/100,000 inhabitants in 2012) compared with other European countries, about 4,000 people die by suicide in Italy every year, with the highest suicide rate in the northeast of Italy (Istat, 2014). According to Shneidman (1969), an average of six people is affected by each suicide death, meaning that there are 24,000 new suicide survivors in Italy every year. Between 10 % and 30 % of the survivors appear to be at risk of developing a severe state of psychological distress (de Groot et al., 2007). In Italy, as in many other countries worldwide, only limited clinical attention is paid to the bereaved after suicide. Nevertheless, a growing number of projects and interventions have become available.

Although only limited evidence is available on their quality and effectiveness (Andriessen, 2009), research on postvention strategies has shown some degree of benefit (McDaid, Trowman, Golder, Hawton, & Sowden, 2008). Research-based evidence of the effectiveness of support strategies for people bereaved through suicide is complicated by the fact that only a minority of suicide survivors seek professional help (if needed), accept it, and comply with the proposed therapeutic approaches (Provini, Everett, & Pfeffer, 2000; Saarinen, Viinamäki, Hintikka, Lehtonen, & Lönnqvist, 1999). Conversely, some bereaved by suicide seek multiple information and support programs, both online and face-to-face (Feigelman, Gorman, & Jordan, 2009). Others may decide to help and support people who have lost someone close, and to promote self-help interventions and other projects to increase awareness – that is, through peer support (Feigelman, Gorman, Chastain-Beal, & Jordan, 2008).

It is still unclear when to appropriately intervene: immediately after the suicide, or after a few weeks or months (Maciejewski, Zhang, Block, & Prigerson, 2007). The lack of methodologically sound evidence along with the complexity of the topic, makes it difficult to provide appropriate support strategies. However, to provide proper care, reduce stigma, and improve the outcomes of any associated psychiatric conditions, it is important to have a comprehensive view of the bereavement process following the suicide of a significant other (Pompili et al.,

2013). Over the past few years, the number of suicide survivor programs organized by suicide survivors and by mental health professionals has increased in Italy. Nonetheless, a national suicide prevention program and central coordination of the various local and national projects for suicide survivors is still lacking.

Local Postvention Initiatives

Suicide Prevention Center

The Suicide Prevention Center is part of the Department of Psychiatry at Sant'Andrea Medical Center in Rome. Among others, the activities of the center include psychological autopsy studies. This research method aims to shed light on the psychological state of the person who died by suicide at the time of death, helping survivors to reconcile the memory of the deceased. The bereaved are given detailed guidance on how to reconstruct the state of mind of their loved one. By engaging in a cathartic process, and with the availability of professionals who might answer their questions, the bereaved may gain insights in their grief experiences. Other interventions for suicide survivors include professionally led support groups, and individual, family, and group psychotherapy.

Self-Help Groups for Suicide Survivors

Self-help groups (gruppi di auto mutuo aiuto [A.M.A.]) are common in Italy. They are usually meant for people experiencing different degrees of psychological distress, and more generally aimed at promoting healthy lifestyles and disease prevention. A number of these self-help groups belong to the same association (Self-Help Groups, A.M.A.; http://www.automutuoaiuto.it/) but most of them are independent and lack coordination.

Self-help groups for suicide survivors operate mostly in the north of Italy (Savona, Genova, Imperia, Milan, Biella, Monza-Brianza, Trento, Pordenone, Treviso, Vicenza) and in central Italy, such as in Rome (Suicide Prevention Center) (data updated to October 2015) and Frosinone (the Ceprano Self-Help NGO, which organizes residential workshops for suicide survivors).

National Postvention Initiatives

SOPRoxi Project

The SOPRoxi Project (http://www.soproxi.it/) started in 2006 and is the only organization in Italy specifically designed for those who have lost someone close by suicide (Scocco, Frasson, Costacurta, & Pavan, 2006). The term *SOPRoxi* comes from *survivors* (*sopravvissuti* in Italian) and *proximity,* to define the closeness of the relationship. The main goal of SOPRoxi is to provide information and support to suicide survivors. Through public events, it also aims to raise awareness of suicide risk and the impact of suicide on those left behind.

Originally, SOPRoxi operated on a local basis, in Padua, a city in the northeast of Italy. A website (http://www.SOPRoxi.it/) was created in 2011, and since then the number of activities and contacts has rapidly increased. Since the launch of the project, about 100 people contacted SOPRoxi and received support between 2006 and 2010. The number of contacts rose from 21 in 2011 to 86 in 2012, 120 in 2013, and 174 in 2014, reaching 85 between January and June 2015. Similarly, the number and type of activities and interventions provided by SOPRoxi have significantly grown during recent years, and include information, support, treatment, awareness building, and education.

The SOPRoxi Project is carried out entirely by volunteers, with the exception of the webmaster, who receives payment related to the work performed. The volunteers are specialists (psychiatrists, psychologists, and psychotherapists), students, and artists, and some are survivors who decide to donate their time. The SOPRoxi project activities are funded by donations received from SOPRoxi NGO, established in 2013 to support the project's activities.

Information

Information about suicide prevention and postvention is delivered primarily via the website and social media, as well as through scientific and popular articles and interviews. The website includes a section specifically focused on suicidal behavior and suicide grief (*Voglio Saperne di Più – I Want to Know More*). It also includes a regularly updated reference list of scientific publications on suicide prevention and postvention, accompanied by the respective abstracts translated into Italian. The topics covered in this section include grief after suicide and other types of death, grief treatment, reactions after the suicidal death of a patient, and suicide research and prevention. Additionally, interviews with national and international experts in the field of suicide and grief are posted in the *Expert Corner* of the website. A blog on the representation of suicide and grief in the arts (cinema, painting, literature, etc.) has recently been created (*Le Arti del Sopravvivere – The Arts of Surviving*).

The website includes a web page for parents, designed to help them talk about the suicide with children and adolescents. In addition, there is an online forum available on a 24/7 basis, a place for sharing, writing, discussing, and listening to emotions, ideas, personal histories, perspectives, and expectations on grief and its relief.

Support and Treatment

SOPRoxi's face-to-face counseling service consists of clinical and psychometric assessments designed to help survivors to better understand whether they are experiencing a "normal" grief reaction or need professional help in a therapeutic setting. Suicide survivors may benefit from interventions focused on information about and normalization of the grief reaction. It is challenging for people bereaved through suicide to cope with emotions related to the loss (e.g., pain, sadness, guilt) as well as those related to the suicidal death (e.g., stigma, shame, rejection), and to understand the potential psychological, affective, and relational aftermath of suicide (Bailley, Kral, & Dunham, 1999; Shear, Frank, Houck, & Reynolds, 2005; Totaro & Scocco, 2015). Suicide survivors may need help to gain insight into and better understand their personal and relational skills and to explore whether their suffering requires professional treatment – for example, psychotherapeutic or pharmacological treatment (Prigerson et al., 2009).

In addition to learning to cope with their intense psychological pain, suicide survivors contact SOPRoxi to meet peers, as many believe that "only survivors can fully understand their particular needs and difficulties" (Feigelman et al., 2008, p. 219). The suicide of a family member is often followed by a significant reduction in social contacts with other family members and the larger social net. Social isolation can be either imposed from the outside or a self-inflicted condition. It is important to properly assess stigma levels experienced by suicide survivors to determine the most appropriate therapeutic strategy (Scocco, Castriotta, Toffol, & Preti, 2012).

SOPRoxi also provides a weekly counseling service via Skype or telephone (*Parla con me – Talk to Me*), as well as individual counseling sessions via chat. While face-to-face counseling is offered primarily to residents in the Veneto region, where SOPRoxi is located, counseling sessions via Skype, phone, or chat are offered to those living in other parts of Italy or even abroad.

The results of the clinical and psychometric assessments, and the individual chat records, are examined and discussed by the SOPRoxi team. They are then reported to the survivor to determine the most appropriate strategy of support. In some cases, a psychotherapeutic intervention may be suggested, alone or in combination with pharmacological treatment. SOPRoxi offers interpersonal psychotherapeutic interventions, which include complicated grief treatment strategies (Shear et al., 2005). These interventions seem to help suicide survivors (unpublished data), but the results are not yet supported by comparison with a control group.

Some suicide survivors prefer to participate in self-help groups, either face-to-face or via chat. SOPRoxi organizes closed, highly structured groups (20 weekly 60-min sessions) led by two volunteers (a psychotherapist and a suicide survivor). The invitation to participate in a self-help group rather than in individual psychotherapy depends on the person's individual characteristics and their level of psychological pain, as well as their desire and motivation to enter a group setting. The group setting allows members to share strategies for coping with psychological pain and suffering, and for building new emotional and relational trajectories. To date, a total of 75 suicide survivors have taken part in SOPRoxi chat groups. The results of an uncontrolled study suggest relatively high efficacy in terms of reduction of depressive symptoms evaluated by the Beck Depression Inventory (BDI; Beck, 1967) (BDI score change: 7.0, $p < .001$), complicated grief levels evaluated by the Inventory of Complicated Grief (ICG; Prigerson et al., 1995) (ICG score change: 8.4, $p < .001$), and moderate to high levels of satisfaction and relatively low dropout rates (Scocco & Toffol, 2015).

Twice a year, SOPRoxi organizes a 2-day mindfulness-based residential workshop called Panta Rhei. During these workshops, mindfulness techniques are used to address acceptance of a suicidal loss. The workshops are for suicide survivors who have already experienced the most dramatic and intense stage of grief (i.e., 6 or more months since the suicide). Previous participation in a self-help group (e.g., SOPRoxi chat groups) or psychotherapeutic intervention is recommended. To date, a total of 63 survivors have attended the workshops. The short-term efficacy of such interventions is under evaluation.

Awareness Building and Education

The SOPRoxi team attends public events such as concerts and other cultural gatherings, to provide information to the public about the SOPRoxi Project and its services, and about what it means to be a suicide survivor.

SOPRoxi also organizes training courses for health professionals, teachers, law enforcement staff, journalists, and anyone interested to know more about suicide prevention and suicide grief. Specific training is also offered to suicide survivors who wish to organize self-help or peer groups. In addition, SOPRoxi offers clinical supervision to individuals or groups, as well as suicide grief counseling and support to schools, private companies, or other private and public organizations.

De Leo Fund

The De Leo Fund is an NGO founded in 2007 by Diego and Cristina De Leo with the aim of providing support to those bereaved by a sudden, traumatic death. The work of the De Leo Fund is presented in Chapter 36.

Conclusions

Despite the lack of national coordination and a national suicide prevention program, a number of postvention projects have been developed in Italy over the past 10 years. Data have yet to be published to support the clinical efficacy of such interventions. Nevertheless, the growing development of projects and interventions for suicide survivors in Italy is a promising attempt to promote awareness about suicide bereavement, and to help suicide survivors become active and positive agents of postvention, beyond stigma and isolation.

Corresponding author

Paolo Scocco
SOPRoxi Project
Padova
Italy
progettosoproxi@gmail.com

References

Andriessen, K. (2009). Can postvention be prevention? *Crisis, 30*(1), 43–47. http://doi.org/10.1027/0227-5910.30.1.43

Bailley, S. E., Kral, M. J., & Dunham, K. (1999). Survivors of suicide do grieve differently: Empirical support for a common sense proposition. *Suicide and Life-Threatening Behavior, 29*(3), 256–271.

Beck, A. T. (1967). *The diagnosis and management of depression.* Philadelphia, PA: University of Pennsylvania Press.

de Groot, M., de Keijser, J., Neeleman, J., Kerkhof, A., Nolen, W., & Burger, H. (2007). Cognitive behaviour therapy to prevent complicated grief among relatives and spouses bereaved by suicide: Cluster randomised controlled trial. *British Medical Journal, 334*(7601), 994–996. http://doi.org/10.1136/bmj.39161.457431.55

Feigelman, W., Gorman, B. S., & Jordan, J. R. (2009). Stigmatization and suicide bereavement. *Death Studies, 33*(7), 591–608. http://doi.org/10.1080/07481180902979973

Feigelman, W., Gorman, B. S., Chastain-Beal, K., & Jordan, J. R. (2008). Internet support groups for suicide survivors: A new mode for gaining bereavement assistance. *Omega: Journal of Death and Dying, 57*(3), 217–243. http://doi.org/10.2190/OM.57.3.a

Istat. (2014). *Annuario statistico italiano 2014* [Italian statistical yearbook 2014]. Retrieved from http://www.istat.it/it/archivio/134686

Maciejewski, P. K., Zhang, B., Block, S. D., & Prigerson, H. G. (2007). An empirical examination of the stage theory of grief. *Journal of the American Medical Association, 297*(7), 716–723. http://doi.org/10.1001/jama.297.7.716

McDaid, C., Trowman, R., Golder, S., Hawton, K., & Sowden, A. (2008). Interventions for people bereaved through suicide: Systematic review. *British Journal of Psychiatry, 193*(6), 438–443. http://doi.org/10.1192/bjp.bp.107.040824

Pompili, M., Shrivastava, A., Serafini, G., Innamorati, M., Milelli, M., Erbuto, D., ... Girardi, P. (2013). Bereavement after the suicide of a significant other. *Indian Journal of Psychiatry, 55*(3), 256–263. http://doi.org/10.4103/0019-5545.117145

Prigerson, H. G., Horowitz, M. J., Jacobs, S. C., Parkes, C. M., Aslan, M., Goodkin, K., ... Maciejewski, P. K. (2009). Prolonged grief disorder: Psychometric validation of criteria proposed for DSM-V and ICD-11. *PLoS Medicine, 6*(8), e1000121. http://doi.org/10.1371/journal.pmed.1000121

Prigerson, H. G., Maciejewski, P. K., Reynolds, C. F., Bierhals, A. J., Newsom, J. T., Fasiczka, A., ... Miller, M. (1995). Inventory of Complicated Grief: A scale to measure maladaptive symptoms of loss. *Psychiatry Research, 59*(1), 65–79. http://doi.org/10.1016/0165-1781(95)02757-2

Provini, C., Everett, J., & Pfeffer, C. (2000). Adults mourning suicide: Self-reported concerns about bereavement, needs for assistance, and help-seeking behavior. *Death Studies, 24*(1), 1–19. http://doi.org/10.1080/074811800200667

Saarinen, P., Viinamäki, H., Hintikka, J., Lehtonen, J., & Lönnqvist, J. (1999). Psychological symptoms of close relatives of suicide victims. *European Journal of Psychiatry, 13*(1), 33–39.

Scocco, P., Castriotta, C., Toffol, E., & Preti, A. (2012). Stigma of Suicide Attempt (STOSA) scale and Stigma of Suicide and Suicide survivors (STOSASS) scale: Two new assessment tools. *Psychiatry Research, 200*(2), 872–878.

Scocco, P., Frasson, A., Costacurta, A., & Pavan, L. (2006). SOPRoxi: A research-intervention project for suicide survivors. *Crisis, 27*(1), 39–41. http://doi.org/10.1027/0227-5910.27.1.39

Scocco, P., & Toffol, E. (2015). *Online support group for people bereaved by suicide: The interpersonal approach.* Paper presented at the 6th international ISIPT conference, June 10–13, 2015, London, UK.

Shear, K., Frank, E., Houck, P. R., & Reynolds, C. F. (2005). Treatment of complicated grief: A randomized controlled trial. *Journal of the American Medical Association, 293*(21), 2601–2608. http://doi.org/10.1001/jama.293.21.2601

Shneidman, E. S. (1969). Prologue. In E. S. Shneidman (Ed.), *On the nature of suicide* (pp. 1–30). San Francisco, CA: Jossey-Bass.

Totaro, S., & Scocco, P. (2015). Perché occuparsi di chi è in lutto per un suicidio? L'esperienza di Progetto SOPRoxi [Why take care of someone bereaved by suicide? The experience of SOPRoxi Project]. *Storie e Geografie Familiari, 13/14,* 139–172.

Chapter 36

Italy – Support After a Traumatic Death

The Work of the De Leo Fund

Katarzyna Anna Ratkowska[1] and Diego De Leo[1, 2]

[1]De Leo Fund, Padova, Italy
[2]Australian Institute for Suicide Research and Prevention, Griffith University,
Brisbane, QLD, Australia

Abstract: The De Leo Fund is an association based in Padua, northern Italy. It provides support to people who have lost a loved one in a sudden and violent manner – for example, suicide, homicide, accident, or a natural disaster. The association was founded in 2007 by friends of Prof. Diego De Leo and his wife, Cristina, following the tragic death of their two children, Nicola and Vittorio, aged 18 and 17 years, respectively, in a car accident. Over the years, the De Leo Fund has initiated free services for survivors of a sudden death, such as individual, couple, and family support; self-help groups; a national helpline; a live chat; an online forum; and creative workshops dedicated specifically to suicide survivors.

Services Offered by the De Leo Fund

Whereas the majority of the processes of mourning after suicide are not of a pathological nature (Cleiren & Diekstra, 1995; Farberow, 2001), in many cases, help to survivors can be offered not only by professionals but also by trained volunteers and peers – that is, people who are experiencing similar grief. The association De Leo Fund seeks to use all of these types of resources to meet the specific needs of each survivor.

The De Leo Fund provides both face-to-face (e.g., individual, couple, family, and group) and remote (through a helpline, a chat line, and a forum) support. Offering all services for free, the association follows the recommendations of the World Health Organization (1998) on the importance of providing services to users independently of their financial situation. The toll-free number (+800-168-678), active since 2011, is often the first contact the bereaved have with the association. The phone service serves multiple functions, including remote telephone support and information on the various types of services available within the region and nationally. It is also a gateway for using face-to-face services provided at the headquarters in Padua.

Psychological Assistance

Psychologists and psychiatrists with expertise in bereavement related to trauma and violence have provided psychological services at the De Leo Fund since 2012. To access the service, a potential user has to call the helpline, where they talk to a trained volunteer. Having assessed that the caller is bereaved from a traumatic loss (due to an external cause of death) and needs face-to-face support, the volunteer conducts two telephone interviews within a period of a maximum of 3 days. The initial interview is rather short, while the second interview is more detailed and deeper. The purpose of the interviews is to collect the most relevant information about the mourning, current psychological and social difficulties of the caller, and the resources available to them. These two calls (and subsequent interviews) also allow a better appraisal of the motivation of the caller. At the end of the second telephone interview, an appointment with a mental health professional is made, usually within a week and provided for free.

The counseling sessions aim to facilitate the process of mourning and to support an individual in difficult times. The theory of reference is the dual process model of coping with bereavement (Stroebe & Schut, 1999), characterized by an oscillation between orientation toward the loss and orientation toward the recovery. The *orientation toward the loss* refers to the attachment to the deceased and the feelings of deep sorrow and despair over the death. The *orientation toward recovery* includes adaptation to the new situation, return to life through the construction of new identities and relationships, and through learning new skills and new roles, including those previously belonging to the deceased (Clark & Goldney, 1995; Stroebe & Schut, 1999). During the counseling sessions, there is space for both expression of pain and the search and reinforcement of positive coping strategies.

After the shocking experience of death, communication within the family can become unproductive and lacking (De Leo et al., 2014), and survivors may need advice on how to deal with these difficulties (Dyregrov, 2002; Wilson & Clark, 2005). Family members may blame each other for the suicide and avoid talking about it, as they fear being overwhelmed by the pain (McMenamy et al., 2008; Stroebe et al., 1993). It is important to provide psychological interventions not only at the individual level, but also for couples and the entire family, and the De Leo Fund offers this type of support, as required.

The association De Leo Fund also offers children and adolescents a space reserved only for them, where professionals specialized in traumatic bereavement of young individuals can offer much-needed help (Dyregrov, 2002; McMenamy et al., 2008; Wertheimer, 2001; Wilson & Clark, 2005). In some cases, there is a need for a more targeted psychological support. This may happen in cases of chronic and debilitating grief, leading to a psychological disorder, such as complicated grief or posttraumatic stress disorder (Wilson & Clark, 2005). The trained psychotherapists at the De Leo Fund provide help to the bereaved of all ages, including those who present with complicated grief and severe psychological problems.

Support Groups

The association De Leo Fund acknowledges the importance of mutual help in a peer group. Social support, in particular mutual help, is considered to be very important in the process of adjustment to a loss (Feigelman & Feigelman, 2008; Lehman et al., 1986; Thoits, 1995; Trolley, 1993). On April 2013, the De Leo Fund organized the first group for adult suicide survivors. It was an open group where participants could enter at any time after the loss and could participate for as long as they felt the need. The group has been operating on the principle of mutual help among people sharing a similar experience of bereavement. The group is open and is facilitated by a psychologist, who promotes a dialogue between participants and provides support in case of emotional difficulties of group members. The facilitator is also available for individual counseling if personal matters arise that cannot be discussed in the group setting.

The support groups include an observer, generally a psychology student. This person is responsible for taking notes, observing the group dynamics, and sharing their observations with the facilitator to improve the functioning of the group. Supervised by the facilitator, the observer prepares two types of reports after each group meeting. One is a summary of the issues raised during the group session and is available to all participants. The other report includes facilitators' observations and comments and is available only to them (De Leo et al., 2014). The number of participants and the composition of the groups vary. As there is no scientific evidence that groups based on the relationship with the deceased are the most effective (Cerel et al., 2009), the groups are open to all survivors of suicide, regardless of the relationship with the deceased. Nonetheless, only one member per family can enter the group, to guarantee free expression of any emotional difficulties, including those related to the family.

To join a group, the participants are asked to make a phone call, undergo the two telephone interviews (described above), and have a number of individual sessions with a mental health professional at the De Leo Fund. These sessions enable a better understanding of the needs and difficulties of a bereaved person struggling with the loss, and help to find the best time to join the group. As mentioned above, there are no rules regarding the time elapsed since the death to join the support group, and the bereaved themselves decide if the group could be a valuable source of support and when they would like to join. Nonetheless, an assessment by a mental health professional can show whether a prospective group member struggles with mental health problems that may interfere with group activities.

The group sessions take place every 2 weeks at the site of the association De Leo Fund and last for about one hour and a half. The most structured part of the meeting involves sharing emotional experiences and events of the previous weeks and reflecting on them. Participants sit in a circle; everyone speaks only if they feel they are ready, otherwise they can remain silent and listen to others. At the end of each meeting, light refreshments are offered, and participants can socialize with each other, the facilitator, and the observer.

Helpline

Because of the high number of phone calls received from all over Italy, in March 2013, the De Leo Fund decided to expand its support services by starting a toll-free national helpline. The helpline aims to help the bereaved cope with the feelings of loneliness and despair in the aftermath of a tragic event, and allows survivors to receive immediate and anonymous support, regardless of where they reside. Given the scarcity of local services in Italy, this is a particularly valuable resource for survivors of suicide.

Active during regular working hours (until 7:00 p.m.), Monday through Friday, the service is offered by professionals and volunteers, usually psychology and social sciences students. All of those who attend to phone calls are trained and supervised to provide support for people experiencing traumatic bereavement and to manage suicide risk. Both professionals and volunteers are selected on the basis of their characteristics, such as empathy and the willingness to listen. The helpline is based on Rogers's empathic approach (Rogers, 1951) combined with a more active crisis intervention approach, and direct questions are asked to identify the type of problem, personal and environmental resources, and to assess suicide risk (Mishara, 2012).

Online Resources: Chats and Forums

Two online support services are offered: a live chat and forums (available at http://www.deleo fundonlus.org/; in Italian and English). The live chat has been operating since June 2014 and provides survivors of a traumatic loss with an anonymous and direct contact with a trained volunteer or a mental health professional. The live chat is available at the same days and hours as the helpline, and is based on the same approach to providing help and support.

The forum, Breaking the Silence: The Suicide of a Loved One, has been in operation since November 2012 and is available only to people who have lost someone to suicide. The forum provides an anonymous virtual space for discussion and sharing of emotions, and although reading threads does not require registration, registration is needed to post a message. The forum is monitored and moderated by a psychologist to ensure the accuracy of information and to avoid any unethical activity, such as incitement to suicide or providing information on lethal means (Wong et al., 2007).

Art Workshop, Events, and Publications

The De Leo Fund provides an opportunity to participate in more informal activities, such as art workshops and events to promote and raise awareness about suicide and bereavement. Online information is available on the website (http://www.deleofundonlus.org/), including a bibliography on bereavement, and books and other publications can be accessed at the headquarters of the association in Padua. On World Suicide Prevention Day (September 10) the De Leo Fund organizes an annual bike ride through the streets of Padua. The De Leo Fund has also published articles and books, also for nonprofessionals, including *Bereavement After Traumatic Death: Helping the Survivors* by Diego De Leo and colleagues (2014).

In July 2014, the art workshop was initiated to offer a space to be together and to be creative. The meetings, which last for approximately two hours, and are facilitated by a volunteer, take place twice a week. The workshops are open to those who have suffered a traumatic loss and to third parties. The main purpose of the meetings is to increase the social support network, which is very important in the adaptation to the loss and reduction of psychological distress (Callahan, 2000; Sherkat & Reed, 1992; Wilson & Clark, 2004). Although generally grief is not a topic of discussion during the workshop, a professional is available to manage any issues which may arise, such as relationship difficulties or arguments. Of interest, the handicrafts produced at the art workshops are available for sale in street markets.

Over 2013–2014, the De Leo Fund participated in the European Regions Enforcing Actions Against Suicide (EUREGENAS) Project, leading two subprojects: the mapping of services for suicide survivors in Italy (Mascalzoni et al., 2014) and creating a training package for general practitioners (Riello & Carbone, 2014).

Conclusions

People bereaved by suicide often feel isolated and "hushed" in sharing their experience, as many people do not feel at ease listening to stories of suffering and despair. Most mourners do not need professional help or interventions outside their social network. However, it is very important for suicide survivors to have an option to choose what is best for them and to make a decision regarding the help and support they need. Some will prefer to cope with their tragedy alone or with the help of family and friends. Others will contact services specifically for bereaved persons, such as those offered by the De Leo Fund.

Corresponding author

Diego De Leo
Australian Institute for Suicide Research and Prevention
Griffith University
Brisbane, QLD
Australia

De Leo Fund
Padova
Italy
d.deleo@griffith.edu.au

References

Callahan, J. (2000). Predictors and correlates of bereavement in suicide support group participants. *Suicide and Life-Threatening Behavior, 30*(2), 104–124.

Cerel, J., Padgett, J. H., Conwell, Y., & Reed, G. A. (2009). A call for research: The need to better understand the impact of support groups for suicide survivors. *Suicide and Life-Threatening Behavior, 39*(3), 269–281. http://doi.org/10.1521/suli.2009.39.6.588

Clark, S. E., & Goldney, R. D. (1995). Grief reactions and recovery in a support group for people bereaved by suicide. *Crisis, 16*(1), 27–33. http://doi.org/10.1027/0227-5910.16.1.27

Cleiren, M., & Diekstra, R. (1995). After the loss: Bereavement after suicide and other types of death. In B. Mishara (Ed.), *The impact of suicide* (pp. 7–39). New York, NY: Springer.

De Leo, D., Cimitan, A., Dyregrov, K., Grad, O., & Andriessen, K. (2014). *Bereavement after traumatic death: Helping the survivors.* Göttingen, Germany: Hogrefe.

Dyregrov, K. (2002). Assistance from local authorities versus survivors' needs for support after suicide. *Death Studies, 26*(8), 647–669. http://doi.org/10.1080/07481180290088356

Farberow, N. (2001). Helping suicide survivors. In D. Lester (Ed.), *Suicide prevention: Resources for the millennium* (pp. 189–212). Philadelphia, PA: Brunner-Routledge.

Feigelman, B., & Feigelman, W. (2008). Surviving after suicide loss: The healing potential of suicide survivor support groups. *Illness, Crisis and Loss, 16*(4), 285–304. http://doi.org/10.2190/IL.16.4.b

Lehman, D. R., Ellard, J. H., & Wortman, C. B. (1986). Social support for the bereaved: Recipients and providers' perspectives on what is helpful. *Journal of Consulting and Clinical Psychology, 54*(4), 438–446. http://doi.org/10.1037/0022-006X.54.4.438

Mascalzoni, E., Carbone, S., & Riello, M. (2014). *Catalogue of resources for survivors for people bereaved by suicide (WP8).* Verona, Italy: Euregenas. Retrieved from http://www.euregenas.eu/publications/

McMenamy, J., Jordan, J., & Mitchell, A. (2008). What do suicide survivors tell us they need? Results of a pilot study. *Suicide and Life-Threatening Behavior, 38*(4), 375–389. http://doi.org/10.1521/suli.2008.38.4.375

Mishara, B. L. (2012). How best to help suicidal persons over the telephone and internet. In D. Lester & J. R. Rogers (Eds.), *Crisis intervention and counseling by telephone and the internet* (3rd ed.; pp. 74–83). Springfield, IL: Charles C. Thomas.

Riello, M., & Carbone, S. (2014). *Establishing and sustaining a support group for people bereaved by suicide: A toolbox for facilitators (WP8).* Verona, Italy: Euregenas. Retrieved from http://www.euregenas.eu/publications/

Rogers, C. R. (1951). *Client-centered therapy: Its current practice, implications, and theory.* Boston, MA: Houghton Mifflin.

Sherkat, D. E., & Reed, M. D. (1992). The effects of religion and social support on self-esteem and depression among the suddenly bereaved. *Social Indicators Research, 26*(3), 259–275. http://doi.org/10.1007/BF00286562

Stroebe, M. S., & Schut, H. (1999). The dual process model of coping with bereavement: Rationale and description. *Death Studies, 23*(3), 197–224. http://doi.org/10.1080/074811899201046

Stroebe, M. S., Stroebe, W., & Hansson, R. O. (1993). *Handbook of bereavement.* New York, NY: Cambridge University Press. http://doi.org/10.1017/CBO9780511664076

Thoits, P.A. (1995). Stress, coping, and social support processes: Where are we? What next? *Journal of Health and Social Behavior, 35*(Extra issue), 53–79. http://doi.org/10.2307/2626957

Trolley, B. (1993). Kaleidoscope of aid for parents whose child died by suicidal and sudden non-suicidal means. *Omega: Journal of Death and Dying, 27*(3), 239–250. http://doi.org/10.2190/HUMQ-KVBQ-A02B-YDYB

Wertheimer, A. (2001). *A special scar*. Philadelphia, PA: Brunner Routledge.

Wilson, A., & Clark, S. (2004). Desperate to tell: Towards improving the care of people bereaved through suicide. A report of work in progress. *RED Snapshots, 2*, 75–85.

Wilson, A., & Clark, S. (2005). *South Australian Suicide Postvention Project report to mental health services*. Adelaide, Australia: Department of Health.

Wong, P.W. C., Chan, W. S. C., & Beh, P. S. L. (2007). What can we do to help and understand survivors of suicide in Hong Kong? *Crisis, 28*(4), 183–189. http://doi.org/10.1027/0227-5910.28.4.183

World Health Organization. (1998). *World report on disability*. Geneva, Switzerland: Author.

Chapter 37

Lithuania – Suicide Bereavement Support Beyond Cultural Trauma

Vaiva Klimaitė, Paulius Skruibis, and Danutė Gailienė

Department of Clinical and Organizational Psychology, University of Vilnius, Lithuania

Abstract: Though Lithuania has one of the highest suicide rates in the world, suicide bereavement support is underdeveloped in the country, at least partly due to the history of the country. A recent qualitative study revealed that in addition to the scarcity of postvention resources, survivors themselves are reluctant to seek help. These findings are discussed with regards to challenges and opportunities for suicide bereavement support in Lithuania.

Introduction

Suicide rates have been registered in Lithuania since 1924. Over the decades, the country has witnessed extreme fluctuations in suicide rates related to major historical transformations. In the interwar independent era (1918–1940), the suicide rate was relatively low: approximately 8.1/100,000 (Gailienė, 2004). After the first Soviet occupation, from June 1940 to June 1941, the country was occupied by Nazi Germany until the second Soviet occupation (1944–1990). During that second Soviet occupation, suicide rates increased from 16/100,000 in 1962 to 36/100,000 in 1984. During the period of emerging independence, the suicide rates decreased by almost one third to 25/100,000 in 1986 (Gailienė, 2005). However, after Lithuania regained independence in 1991 and radical reforms started, suicide rates increased again, and over the last 2 decades, the number of suicides has remained high. In 2012, Lithuania had the highest rate in the European Union and almost three times the average EU suicide rate (31.5/100,000 vs. 12.3/100,000) (Statistics Lithuania, 2014; European Statistics, 2015). Currently around 1,000 people (out of the population of 2.95 million) die by suicide every year, and many are left to grieve.

Although suicidal behavior has been strongly stigmatized in many countries and cultures (Dyregrov, Grad, De Leo, & Cimitan, 2013; Lester & Walker, 2006; World Health Organization, 2014), there are specific reasons for stigmatization of suicide in Lithuania. The suicide rate in Lithuania is one of the highest in the world, and research has found that high prevalence of suicides may be linked to internalized stigma and shame with regard to suicidal tendencies and negative attitudes to help seeking (Reynders, Kerkhof, Molenberghs, & van Audenhove, 2014). Also, mental health issues and suicide were stigmatized during the years of Soviet occupation, and the Lithuanian Catholic Church, quite influential in the society, was cutoff from the Universal Catholic Church for half a century. Consequently, attitudes of the clergy toward suicide seem to be "frozen in time." Although the situation has evolved since Lithuania has regained its independence, the changes have been rather slow.

Suicide Bereavement Support

Two support groups have been organized in Vilnius and Kaunas, two major cities in the country, and individual mental health professionals are specializing in helping the bereaved, mostly in these two major cities. In September 2015, bereaved people established the Association of People Bereaved by Suicide Artimiems ("For the ones close to us"). The association maintains a website (http://www.artimiems.lt/), facilitates a peer support group, and aims to educate society about bereavement after suicide. However, there is a lack of specialized state-funded mental health services for the bereaved throughout the country. Without acknowledgement at a policy level, suicide survivors have to deal with and organize bereavement support themselves.

A biomedical model rather than a bio-psycho-social model still dominates the mental health sector, and the professional support available to the bereaved by suicide is mostly of a medical, and not a psychological nature. The dominance of the biomedical model can be traced back to the Soviet times, when people struggling with mental health problems were treated only with drugs and in most cases, in big psychiatric institutions. Consequently, even today, the bereaved are usually offered medication, not counseling. (It is also important to note that psychiatry was often used as a tool to deal with people who opposed the Soviet regime; see Van Voren, 2013. Subsequently, psychiatry was associated with repression and distrusted in society. Moreover, the Soviet occupation has caused significant cultural trauma; see Sztompka, 2000, which has had serious negative consequences for the Lithuanian society, including negative attitudes toward suicide and mental health.)

Nonetheless, the bereaved by suicide are starting to get organized. There is also an increasing push from society for mental health reforms, reflected by the fact that the topics of mental health and suicide prevention have been increasingly included in political debates. As a result of public pressure to tackle the problem of suicide in Lithuania, in 2015, the State Suicide Prevention Bureau was established. The main aims of the bureau include a systematic analysis of suicide trends in Lithuania and initiating programs on suicide prevention and postvention.

A Qualitative Study of the Experiences and Needs of Those Bereaved by Suicide

A first qualitative study in the country has recently provided important insights into suicide bereavement and postvention in Lithuania (Skruibis, Geležėlytė, & Dadašev, 2015; Grigien et al., 2015). This study was part of the project Psychological Effects and Coping of Extreme Trauma and Social Transformations, funded by the European Social Fund under the Global Grant measure. The aim of the study was to explore the cultural peculiarities of bereavement after suicide and the type of help that is most needed. The study included 23 bereaved family members (20 women, 3 men) of 23 people who died by suicide (9 women, 14 men). Time elapsed since the death ranged from 1 to 2 years, with an average of 17 months. Semistructured in-depth interviews were conducted with study participants, who were asked to share their experience of bereavement and how they have been coping with the loss. The recruitment process of study participants itself showed how much people avoid talking about bereavement after suicide. Only three persons responded to the call for participants, two more were reached using the *snowball* method, and the remaining 18 participants were identified with the help of police officers, who are the first responders at the scene of a suicide.

Thematic analysis (Boyatzis, 1998; Braun & Clarke, 2006) of the interviews showed the duality of the problem of bereavement support in Lithuania: There are not enough services and specialists to provide help, and the bereaved avoid seeking professional help. This double avoidance may reflect the predominantly negative attitudes toward suicide in society (Skruibis, Geležėlytė, & Dadašev, 2015), as well as other reasons (discussed below) for the bereaved not to seek help.

Previous Experiences and Unrealistic Expectations Regarding Help Providers

Some of the study participants did not look for professional help although they thought that it might be needed. Some participants did not have access to information about help available after the suicide of a significant other, and also lack of trust in mental health professionals might have affected their readiness to seek help. Some of the bereaved people avoided seeking psychological help because of the negative experience they had had with psychologists or other specialists. For some, the help provided was not suitable or did not meet their needs: *"I said I was strong and I will cope myself. But he* [the psychologist] *said: 'I see you need help. We have to clean your wound and you will have to tell me everything.' And I was frightened."* Such experiences, together with the negative stereotypes dominant in the society, create a negative image of mental health professionals. However, some participants had unrealistic expectations toward psychologists and the help available: *"Maybe the talking will help to solve problems with the children, such as washing dishes or walking the dog."* Such negative (or unrealistic) experiences of people bereaved by suicide may impede their further attempts to get help.

Experiences of Others With Help Providers

The negative experiences of others may be another reason to avoid seeking help: *"He* [the deceased] *did not get help. He went. I don't know, maybe he didn't know how to talk about his feelings, I do not analyze why, but the fact is – he did not get help."* Such "mistakes" may become an important obstacle standing in the way of seeking psychological help, especially if the person who did not get suitable psychological help died by suicide. A wish to avoid the "mistakes" of others, and the anger or disappointment of the bereaved may contribute to the lack of trust toward professionals and not seeking help (Pettersen et al., 2015; see also Chapter 20 in this volume).

Stereotypes About Mental Health Professionals and Suicide

Study participants expressed their fear of psychologists, psychiatrists, and other mental health professionals. For example, some of them believed that only *"crazy or weak people"* seek professional help, that *"people will see and gossip,"* and a visit to a mental health specialist will be recorded and they will risk losing their job: *"Everybody thinks: ah, the teacher went to a psychotherapist; so what now, if the parents find out, they will forbid their children going to that class."* Some participants mentioned other stereotypes about suicide, such as *"suicide is a sin"* and *"the damnation will follow the family for seven generations,"* which could prevent them from talking about the "shameful" experience of suicide loss.

Tendency Not to Speak About Suicide and Grief

The tendency not to speak about suicide or grief may pose major challenges to the bereaved and mental health professionals with respect to seeking and providing professional help, respectively. The bereaved may be prone to self-isolation (*"I just keep the distance"*), as a result of their wish to hide their "inappropriate," and "unacceptable" feelings, such as anger at the deceased or relief (*"It is very shameful, but now it is much more quiet, there are no quarrels at home"*). Others may experience guilt or fear of being blamed. Some participants distanced themselves from others and did not talk about the suicide of their close family member, because they wanted to protect the deceased from condemnation or other expected negative reactions: *"I don't want to talk much, because I think that nobody will understand me. But it's really like that, nobody understands."* Is this fear of being blamed and condemned well-grounded? A comparison of attitudes toward suicide among Lithuanian, Hungarian, Austrian, Norwegian, and Swedish regional politicians has shown that Lithuanian regional politicians indeed have quite condemnatory attitudes toward people who die by suicide (Skruibis et al., 2010).

Some participants also experienced avoidant reactions of others: *"Some people were afraid of me. They thought that maybe I will burst into tears."* It is hard for others to handle the intense emotions of the bereaved, and to accept that after the loss, their bereaved loved one has changed: *"There are [a] few people who are angry at me for real; they say "you disappeared from life, when it was hard for me you were not there." But it was hard for me too, but for me it lasts for a very long time."* The confused feelings toward the bereaved may trigger inappropriate reactions that may hurt them even more.

The study showed that bereaved people may totally avoid talking about their loss and grief, because of their own feelings and experience with others, including mental health professionals. This avoidance may be reinforced by dismissive and stigmatizing reactions in society. Despite the recruitment efforts, a self-selection bias might hinder the generalizability of the findings. Nevertheless, the study provided valuable insights into the experiences of the bereaved by suicide in Lithuania.

Implications for Postvention Research and Practice

The suicide rate in Lithuania is very high, and many people struggle with loss due to suicide. Still, there is not sufficient bereavement support available. A biomedical model has been prevailing in the mental health system, and medication is often the first treatment option. Moreover, suicidal behavior is strongly stigmatized, which makes seeking support even more difficult. The high prevalence of suicide, negative consequences of mental health professionals' participation in Soviet repression, and the cultural trauma caused by the Soviet occupation, may have additionally strengthened the stigma. A reform of the mental health system is needed to address the distrust toward mental health professionals. Strengthening of psychosocial services and debates on the policy level will help in creating a more positive image of the health care system and to better meet the needs of the bereaved.

The social climate will benefit from a more open discussion about suicide. Mental health professionals and researchers can contribute to this discussion by providing evidence-based data and information on suicidal behavior and bereavement. The bereaved themselves can play a major role in changing the public attitudes. The initiatives of the recently founded Association of People Bereaved by Suicide are an important step in that direction, which should be strongly supported and encouraged.

Stigmatization and misconceptions about suicide and suicide bereavement have challenged research on suicide bereavement in Lithuania. However, this must change as soon as possible, as scientific studies can provide a much-needed better understanding of the challenges and needs of people bereaved by suicide in Lithuania. There may be a reciprocal connection here: The changing attitudes can help research, and research findings can stimulate an open discussion and change of attitudes.

Corresponding author

Vaiva Klimaitė
Department of Clinical and Organizational Psychology
University of Vilnius
Vilnius
Lithuania
vaiva.kl@gmail.com

References

Boyatzis, R. E. (1998). *Transforming qualitative information: Thematic analysis and code development.* London, UK: Sage.

Braun, V., & Clarke, V. (2006). Using thematic analysis in psychology. *Qualitative Research in Psychology, 3*(2), 77–101. http://doi.org/10.1191/1478088706qp063oa

Dyregrov, K., Grad, O., De Leo, D., & Cimitan, A. (2013). Surviving suicide. In D. De Leo, A. Cimitan, K. Dyregrov, O. Grad, & K. Andriessen (Eds.), *Bereavement after traumatic death: Helping the survivors* (pp. 37–48). Göttingen, Germany: Hogrefe.

European Statistics. (2015). *Statistical data.* Retrieved from http://ec.europa.eu/eurostat

Gailienė, D. (2004). Suicide in Lithuania during the years of 1990 to 2002. *Archives of Suicide Research, 8*(4), 389–395. http://doi.org/10.1080/13811110490476806

Gailienė, D. (Ed.). (2005). *The psychology of extreme traumatisation: The aftermath of political repression.* Vilnius, Lithuania: Akreta.

Grigienė, D., Skruibis, P., Dadašev, S., Klimaitė, V., Geleželytė, O., & Bieliauskaitė, R. (2015). In D. Gailienė (Ed.), *Lithuanian faces after transition: Psychological consequences of cultural trauma* (pp. 234–248). Vilnius, Lithuania: Eugrimas.

Lester, D., & Walker, R. L. (2006).The stigma for attempting suicide and the loss to suicide prevention efforts. *Crisis, 27*(3), 147–148. http://doi.org/10.1027/0227-5910.27.3.147

Pettersen, R., Omerov, P., Steineck, G., Titelman, D., Dyregrov, A., Nyberg, T., & Nyberg, U. (2015). Lack of trust in the health-care system after losing a child to suicide: A nationwide population survey. *Crisis, 36*(3), 161–172. http://doi.org/10.1027/0227-5910/a000312

Reynders, A., Kerkhof, A. J. F. M., Molenberghs, G., & van Audenhove, C. (2014). Attitudes and stigma in relation to help-seeking intentions for psychological problems in low and high suicide rate regions. *Social Psychiatry and Psychiatric Epidemiology, 49*(2), 231–239. http://doi.org/10.1007/s00127-013-0745-4

Skruibis, P., Gailienė, D., Hjelmeland, H., Fartacek, R., Fekete, S., Knizek, B. L., … Rohrer, R. (2010). Attitudes towards suicide among regional politicians in Lithuania, Austria, Hungary, Norway and Sweden. *Suicidology Online, 1,* 79–87.

Skruibis, P., Geleželytė, O., & Dadašev, S. (2015). The stigma of suicide behavior. In D. Gailienė (Ed.), *Lithuanian faces after transition: Psychological consequences of cultural trauma* (pp. 217–233). Vilnius, Lithuania: Eugrimas.

Statistics Lithuania. (2014). *Statistical data: Mortality.* Retrieved from http://www.stat.gov.lt

Sztompka, P. (2000). Cultural trauma. The other face of social change. *European Journal of Social Theory, 3*(4), 449–466. http://doi.org/10.1177/136843100003004004

Van Voren, R. (2013). *Psychiatry as a tool for coercion in Post-Soviet countries.* Brussels, Belgium: European Parliament Directorate-General for External Policies of the Union Policy Department.

World Health Organization. (2014). *Preventing suicide: A global imperative.* Geneva, Switzerland: Author.

Chapter 38

Norway – Networking and Participation Among Young Suicide Bereaved

Christoffer Back Vestli

LEVE – The Norwegian Organization for the Suicide Bereaved, Oslo, Norway

Abstract: The Norwegian Organization for the Suicide Bereaved (LEVE), established in 1999, has always envisioned a platform that could meet the needs of the younger bereaved. In 2012, 13 young members called for a new approach to youth work. After introducing informal organizational structures and youth-driven activities, the participation of young people has significantly increased, and a national network for young suicide bereaved (Unge [young] LEVE) was established. This chapter presents the youth division of LEVE and its major challenges, including organizational sustainability and implementation of local activities throughout Norway.

Introduction

Understanding the needs of suicide-bereaved people in the 15–30 age bracket is not only a matter of research. Whereas empirical studies can be a useful point of departure by drawing attention toward – for example, risks of adverse outcomes of the grief process (Brent et al., 1993; Pfeffer et al., 1997) and other relevant issues – the practice of long-term youth work provides a unique possibility to listen to the young bereaved and their needs, and offers them opportunities to share their experience of loss over longer periods of time. In Norway, such elements had never been considered on an institutional-organizational level, and in the search for a suitable platform for the young bereaved, the "learning by doing" model has been a challenging, however, a quite successful method.

The Norwegian Organization for the Suicide Bereaved (LEVE) was founded in 1999. It was the first network of suicide survivors to emerge in the country, and today, LEVE has approximately 1,200 members, including approximately 100 members under the age of 30. In the early stages of the organization, no special attention was given to the young members, who started to feel underrepresented and less involved. In fact, they were "the forgotten bereaved" (McIntosh & Wrobleski, 1988). Consequently, the strategic thinkers of the organization along with other members, started to argue for the establishment of a youth division. This initiative was also inspired by the positive experiences of youth camps and other youth meetings organized by LEVE, as well as by research (Dyregrov, 2008) clearly showing that young people bereaved by suicide may be able to help each other.

Consolidation of a New Platform for the Young Bereaved

The new initiative to organize the younger members of LEVE, and young people bereaved by suicide in general, started in 2012. Thirteen young suicide survivors, invited from all over the country by a former youth LEVE representative, met in Steinkjer in central Norway. At that meeting, a number of important questions were raised: "How do we want to characterize the youth work in this organization?" and "How do we get there?" These were followed by other crucial questions: "What is Unge [youth] LEVE?" and "Do we need Unge LEVE?"

The approach of encouraging young people to define and develop the core values and activities of the youth division represented a significant change for LEVE. The participants at the Steinkjer meeting embraced the value of grass-roots participation and bottom-up thinking, and wanted to develop this further into something bigger, nationwide, and significant. Another gathering was arranged in October 2012, now with more than 20 participants. In 2013, only 12 months after the Steinkjer meeting, the third gathering took place in Geilo, a mountain town in southern Norway, attended by almost 30 participants. Parallel to this increasing youth engagement, LEVE solicited funding through a foundation aiming to ensure further growth and establishment of a sustainable youth network in Norway. Now, the young suicide bereaved could themselves define the direction and activities of the youth division.

The Organization

There are both pros and cons to establishing a new division within an already existing organizational framework, and access to existing communication channels and guidance by experienced professionals were important tools in the consolidation period. However, starting almost from nothing was challenging for both the existing members of LEVE and participants of the new youth division. Critical questions needed answers. Was this new development a call for a separate youth organization in the future, with its own members and structures? Or alternatively, should the youth division continue to be a part of LEVE, and if this is the case, who will be the decision makers and what will be the organizational structure? What would be sustainable?

The young participants soon agreed on a simple structure for the network and successfully gained the support of the mother organization. There was no need for a separate organization, and as part of LEVE, the youth division could utilize the experience and the resources of the mother organization, while maintaining the flexibility of an independent network. Unge LEVE is based on participation and a simple membership structure. In this way, it may resemble a social movement – an informal action group related to a particular political or social issue (Della Porta & Diani, 2006).

Activities and Participation Today

Norway is a vast country with a relatively small population and many remote communities. It is a challenge to reach out to all young suicide bereaved, from the big cities down to the small rural towns. To overcome this challenge, a main thrust has been to establish annual national gatherings. These gatherings have undergone a slight change in profile, from urban hotel-based gatherings, toward a decentralized cabin-style meeting. The first gatherings placed an emphasis on grief groups and sharing one's history. The more recent gatherings have focused more on social activities and alternative methods of expressing grief – for example, through art and hiking in the surrounding forest. Cooperation with professionals has been essential, as both research and practice show that some of the young bereaved find it quite difficult to deal with their emotions (Brent et al., 1993; Rakic, 1992).

By providing an opportunity to meet others who share a similar experience of loss, Unge LEVE works to establish local meeting points and social arenas. Many participants have called for such initiatives and are currently involved in local activities. There has been substantial progress in establishing informal local meeting points in many major cities and in the more populated parts of the country. In some areas, there are monthly meetings, and in other places there is cooperation and integration with the regional activities of LEVE. Experience shows that the best type of help Unge LEVE can offer is the conversation itself, the message "you are not alone." Still, a lack of experience and a shortage of volunteers who can develop these local networks over a longer period of time remains a big challenge.

External Relations

Despite the increasing activity of Unge LEVE at a national and regional levels, the size of the network of young suicide bereaved is still relatively modest, no more than 150 participants. With more than 500 suicides in Norway annually, and approximately six closely related bereaved persons for each suicide (Shneidman, 1972), the network has potential to grow. LEVE has become an authority on matters relating to suicide, and various organizations, including the national media and local health services, have increasingly been seeking Unge LEVE's inputs. Some of the young suicide bereaved have shared their stories at conferences, given interviews, and provided resources for students at nursing schools. Unge LEVE has been very successful in their approach to the media, and has appeared in featured articles in major daily newspapers and on national TV and radio. Unge LEVE has also produced a documentary *Livet går faktsik videre* (*Actually, Life Goes On*) about young suicide survivors. It has been aired on national TV and distributed throughout different suicide prevention networks (NRK, 2014).

Implications for the Future

Successful collaboration with the media and other organizations has been pivotal in increasing the awareness of issues related to suicide bereavement. Still, there remains a challenge of ensuring stability and further growth of the youth network. It is expected that with more coordinated volunteer work (now based on 3 years of experience), employment of a professional youth worker, and a central steering group, Unge LEVE will reach more regions and attract more participants. Three priorities must be emphasized to ensure further development: raising policy awareness, cooperation with professionals, and funding.

Raising awareness at a policy level should be a priority, as it will have a direct positive spillover effect on the succeeding priorities. The inclusion of awareness raising and dissemination of information on suicide bereavement support as an important part of the suicide prevention debate has been an ongoing struggle in Norway. However, the voice of the bereaved can be an essential and reliable resource, and already politicians on occasion have invited members of Unge LEVE to discussions and public meetings at a regional and national level.

Cooperation and consultation with professionals, such as psychologists and other representatives of the health services, will prove mutually beneficial. On the one hand, the increasing number of participants in the youth network increases the need for professional help. There have been cases where professional help was necessary to effectively assist volunteers when dealing with new participants. On the other hand, cooperation is important to integrate Unge LEVE throughout the nationwide professional networks.

Finally, looking for financial resources and persistent solicitation and dialogue with funding organizations, both public and private, is essential for the sustenance and growth of the organization and its activities. To date, funding has been ensured through short-term projects, but more resources will be needed in the future to ensure that Unge LEVE can continue its mission. The nonmembership model is a significant challenge in this case, as membership data is often a requirement for funding in Norway.

Conclusions

The organized youth work for the suicide bereaved in Norway has focused on participation and network expansion, and today there is an increasing interest from the national media, health services, and networks of professionals in the activities of Unge LEVE. Consequently, Unge LEVE has developed a dual approach: suicide bereavement support and contributing to the debate on suicide and grief in general. Due to the establishment of the youth division for those aged 15–30, the young suicide bereaved are no longer an overlooked group in society, and they have a forum to ensure that their voices are heard. It will require long-term coordination and the involvement of volunteers and employed personnel to consolidate a nationwide movement, but as long as stability in its central organization is ensured, a network for the young suicide bereaved will have a solid base.

Unge LEVE has already made important steps, and a more active and diverse network of suicide bereaved is envisaged in the future. The most important aim is to continue listening to the bereaved and their needs. A successful social organization lets its members define its direction, and this may be the most important factor to keep in mind when Unge LEVE reaches new milestones or challenges.

Corresponding author

Christoffer Back Vestli
LEVE – The Norwegian Organization for the Suicide Bereaved
Oslo
Norway
christoffer.vestli@gmail.com

References

Brent, D.A., Perper, J.A., Moritz, G., Liotus, L., Schweers, J., Roth, C., ... Allman, C. (1993). Psychiatric impact of the loss of an adolescent sibling to suicide. *Journal of Affective Disorders, 28*(4), 249–256. http://doi.org/10.1016/0165-0327(93)90060-W

Della Porta, D., & Diani, M. (2006). *Social movements: An introduction*. Oxford, UK: Blackwell.

Dyregrov, K. (2008). Psychosocial stress for young suicide bereaved. Requests for support by assistance services. *Tidsskrift for Norsk Psykologforening, 45*(1), 14–18.

McIntosh, J., & Wrobleski, A. (1988). Grief reactions among suicide survivors: An exploratory comparison of relationships. *Death Studies, 12*(1), 21–39. http://doi.org/10.1080/07481188808252217

NRK. (2014). *Actually, life goes on after suicide*. Retrieved from http://www.nrk.no/nordland/_-livet-gar-videre-etter-selvmord-1.11612310

Pfeffer, C.R., Martins, P., Mann, J., Sunkenberg, R.N., Ice, A., Damore, J.P., ... Jiang, H. (1997). Child survivors of suicide: Psychosocial characteristics. *Journal of American the Academy of Child & Adolescent Psychiatry, 36*(1), 65–74. http://doi.org/10.1097/00004583-199701000-00019

Rakic, A.S. (1992). *Sibling survivors of adolescent suicide* (Doctoral dissertation). The California School of Professional Psychology Berkeley, Alameda, USA.

Shneidman, E. (1972). Foreword. In A.C. Cain (Ed.), *Survivors of suicide* (pp. ix–xi). Springfield, IL: Charles C. Thomas.

Chapter 39

Portugal – First Steps of Postvention Practice and Research

Inês Areal Rothes[1], José Carlos Santos[2], and Sara Santos[3]

[1]Faculty of Psychology and Educational Sciences, University of Porto, Portugal
[2]Nursing School of Coimbra, Portugal
[3]Centre for Research in Education and Psychology, University of Evora, Portugal

Abstract: This chapter discusses the state of the art of postvention in Portugal, organized into three sections: postvention at school, families bereaved by suicide, and impact of a patient suicide. The first section describes postvention activities in schools when a student dies by suicide. The second part summarizes the studies concerning families bereaved through suicide and implications for practice. The third section presents the research findings about the impact of a patient suicide on health professionals, and the help resources used by these professionals. Despite the major developments of the past decade, there remains a clear need to further implement postvention initiatives.

Introduction

Over the years, the national suicide rate in Portugal has been approximately 10 per 100,000 inhabitants (Instituto Nacional de Estatística, 2016; World Health Organization, 2013). Research has revealed that Portugal is among the European Union countries with the highest rates of deaths of undetermined intent (Värnik et al., 2010; World Health Organization, 2013), and there are marked differences in suicide rates between different regions, with currently high rates in Algarve and Alentejo (14 and 15 per 100,000, respectively) (Instituto Nacional de Estatística, 2016; Gusmão & Quintão, 2013). Postvention research and interventions aimed at people bereaved through suicide have taken initial steps in Portugal, and the first National Suicide Prevention Plan recognizes the importance of providing specialized support to the bereaved (Direcção Geral de Saúde, 2013). However, its terminology, supportive principles, and interventions are not well known to the general population and to health professionals, including mental health professionals. There could be several reasons for this lack of knowledge. Although suicidology in Portugal has been developing and growing, it is a recent research area with a small number of specialized researchers. There is also a scarcity of professional training in suicide intervention, including postvention, and the majority of the bereaved by suicide in Portugal do not receive professional or other support. In addition, the heritage of religious and sociocultural stigmatization in a country with a strong Catholic tradition can contribute to the low awareness of suicide prevention and postvention.

This chapter is organized into three sections: postvention in schools, developed as a part of a mental health and suicide prevention program; studies on families bereaved by suicide and the available support; and the experiences and support resources used by Portuguese psychologists, psychiatrists, and general practitioners (GPs) after a patient suicide.

Postvention in Schools

The Núcleo de Estudos do Suicídio (NES Group; Suicide Studies Group; http://www.NES.pt/) is a multidisciplinary team of the Psychiatric Service of Santa Maria Hospital in Lisbon. It includes psychiatrists, child psychiatrists, clinical and social psychologists, pediatricians, family physicians, sociologists, social workers, and teachers. Since the 1980s, the NES Group has been pivotal in adolescent suicide prevention, both in schools and in the community, particularly in the south of Portugal (Cruz, Sampaio, Santos, & Narciso, 2007). The NES Group, and Brás and Santos (2014) have significantly contributed to the discussion about postvention activities in schools. Recently, empirical data and descriptive reports on a school-based suicide prevention program +Contigo (More With You) have also been published (Santos, Erse, Simões, Façanha, & Marques, 2013; Santos, Erse, Façanha, Marques, & Simões, 2014).

The +Contigo program, developed by the Nursing School of Coimbra in different regions of Portugal, was designed to promote mental health and well-being, and to prevent suicidal behavior in young people aged 12 to 18 years. Since 2009, approximately 13,000 students from 100 schools have participated in the program. Any school can apply to run the program in partnership with local health services, the only condition being that a school health team is available to attend a special training before the program starts. Intervention activities in the program include training for health professionals and teachers, awareness sessions for tutors and caregivers, and four socioeducational sessions for students. The student sessions last 45 min each and address stigma and mental health, adolescence, self-concept, coping and well-being, and depressive symptomatology. In schools where a suicide has recently occurred, the program additionally includes a crisis intervention aimed at facilitating bereavement, reducing feelings of guilt and trauma, preventing isolation, and avoiding identification with suicidal behavior (Chapter 3 in this volume discusses suicide bereavement of adolescents). Parents attend an educational session about suicidal behaviors, whereas teachers and assistants attend a 20-hr training course for gatekeepers.

In each participating school, a control group (without any intervention) is designated. Prequestionnaires and postquestionnaires are used, including a 6-month follow-up assessment, to measure the effects of the +Contigo program on students' self-concept, well-being, coping, and depressive symptomatology. Evaluations of the effectiveness of the program have shown a decrease in students' depressive symptomatology, and an improvement in well-being and self-concept, although there were no significant effects regarding students' coping skills (Santos et al., 2013).

There are also empirical data on the effectiveness of the +Contigo program after a suicide of a student (Santos, Erse, Simões, Façanha, & Marques, 2011). Questionnaires were used to measure self-concept, well-being, coping, and depressive symptomatology, before and after a postvention intervention, which aimed at promoting the expression of feelings, and was based on cognitive behavior techniques, to improve students' strategies to deal with bereavement. The results showed an increase in self-concept and coping strategies for problem solving before and after the intervention, and a decrease in symptoms of depression. One year after the suicide, no suicidal behaviors were reported among students (Santos et al., 2011).

In summary, the program has had positive effects on two levels. First, it has developed adolescents' social skills by exploring active and effective strategies to deal with problems and negative events. Second, it has improved the school's psychological atmosphere by promoting affective and emotional bonds between peers, teachers, and family, which are crucial to strengthen the solidarity network and prevent mental disturbances (Santos et al., 2011).

Families Bereaved by Suicide

Studies in Portugal have involved families bereaved by suicide (Santos, 2014), including two studies, which analyzed the grieving process using a qualitative methodology on a small sample of individuals who had lost a relative by suicide (6–10 subjects) (Sampaio, 2013; Batista & Santos, 2014). In line with reports in the international literature, Batista and Santos (2014) concluded that the bereaved experienced isolation, loneliness, distress, a feeling of abandonment, and high levels of complicated grief and depression.

A larger study (Santos, Tavares, & Campos, 2015; Santos, Campos, & Tavares, 2015) using a quantitative methodology examined the impact of suicide on well-being and suicide risk of families bereaved by suicide. Two sample groups participated in the study. The first was a convenience sample of 93 family members bereaved by suicide (individuals who had lived with the deceased prior to the suicide) living in the Alentejo Central region in Portugal. The second sample was a convenience control community sample (102 participants), also residing in the Alentejo Central region, and without a family suicide history. Family members bereaved by suicide reported high levels of distress and suicidal ideation. The study also found that general distress, depression, anxiety, and hostility of family members were related to suicidal ideation, and that the survivor's age and the time passed since the suicide were positively related to suicidal ideation. Results of the study (Santos, Tavares, & Campos, 2015) also suggested that sociodemographic and suicide-related variables, such as advanced age, being the spouse of the deceased, and lack of coping strategies, may help to identify high-risk family members bereaved by suicide, who are in need of professional help and assessment of distress.

Despite the empirical results and conclusions providing indications for clinical intervention with the bereaved family members, the existing support associations for bereaved people in Portugal, including Nossa Âncora (Our Anchor; http://www.anossaancora.org/) and Apelo (Appeal; http://www.apelo.web.pt/), provide no specific support for suicide survivors. This may change in the future, as Eutimia (the Alliance against Depression in Portugal; http://www.eutimia.pt/), a nongovernmental organization started in 2013, aims to offer help, advice, and support to family and friends of people who have died by suicide.

Impact of a Patient Suicide on Health Professionals

A national survey among health professionals in Portugal (242 participants) added further evidence to the existing international data (presented in Chapter 21 in this volume) showing that patient suicide is a frequent and difficult experience in clinical practice (Rothes, 2014a; Rothes, Henriques, & Correia, 2013). The survey results reinforced the conclusion that a patient suicide is a learning experience, leading to a change in professional practice, and they provided knowledge about postvention measures effectively used by health professionals. The study showed that 55 % of Portuguese psychiatrists, 38 % of GPs, and 11 % of psychologists had experienced at least one patient suicide, and that it is more likely for male health professionals to have patients who die by suicide than for female health professionals (Rothes, Henriques, & Correia, 2013). The differences found between genders are in line with other studies (Rothes, Scheerder, Van Audenhove, & Henriques, 2013), and can be related to the more positive attitudes toward suicidal patients in female professionals (e.g., Anderson, Standen, Nazir, & Noon, 2000). Another hypothetical explanation can be related to the different type or number of patients followed by male and female professionals: Do men follow more patients and with more severe mental illness than women?

A questionnaire including both open and closed questions was developed, based on a review of the existing literature and instruments, to assess the impact of patient suicide (Rothes,

Henriques & Correia, 2013). The answers to the open questions were analyzed using content analysis, resulting in eight categories of emotional reactions: (1) emotional suffering; (2) concerns, doubts, and fears; (3) frustration and other negative feelings toward patient or families; (4) surprise and shock; (5) failure and defeat; (6) guilt and self-blame; (7) impotence and powerlessness; and (8) understanding, acceptance, or resignation. It could be concluded that Portuguese professional survivors of a patient suicide experienced emotional reactions similar to those reported in international studies (Grad, Zavasnik, & Groleger, 1997; Rothes et al., 2013; Wurst et al., 2010). However, in contrast with previous studies, no differences between genders were found in the Portuguese sample.

After a patient suicide, a considerable proportion of Portuguese health professionals reported increased attention and accuracy in the assessment and management of suicidal patients, as well as increased insecurity and anxiety in the process. The results of this national study are in line with the general agreement of the international literature that a patient's death by suicide is a disturbing experience for health professionals. The outcomes regarding the recovery time from negative feelings tend to support previous studies, which found that the majority of health professionals have resources to functionally recover from this event (Pieters, De Gucht, Joos, & De Heyn, 2003; Ruskin, Sakinofsky, Bagby, Dickens, & Sousa, 2004). This means that the majority of health professionals are able to deal adaptively with this difficult and even traumatic event. Nevertheless, a significant percentage of Portuguese health professionals (13 %) indicated the need for special help, such as psychotherapy or psychological support. Above all, patient suicide is a very demanding experience, both emotionally and professionally, that requires support measures, such as discussing the case with the team in a supportive context. Almost all participants reported the nonexistence of formal resources of support in their workplaces aimed at professionals experiencing a patient suicide. The results of the Portuguese study highlighted the existence of an underdeveloped postvention culture among health professionals (Rothes, 2014a, 2014b).

Soliciting support of colleagues, contact with the patient's family, seeking help from the professional's family, and carrying out a case review with the team were the postvention activities frequently reported by the Portuguese health professionals (Rothes, Henriques, & Correia, 2013). The study showed that the most-used postvention actions were not always the ones rated as the most useful for coping with the patient suicide event and vice versa – that is, some postsuicide measures, such as supervisor meetings, used by only a few professionals, were perceived by those who used them as very supportive. Other postvention actions, such as seeking help from one's family, were widely used but perceived as less helpful. Beyond the supervisor, the team case review and the support of colleagues were the most useful resources, while the nonspecialized supports (family and friends) were rated as less helpful (Rothes, Henriques, & Correia, 2013).

Conclusions

Postvention in Portugal is a recent research area undergoing development, largely due to the studies summarized above and to the work of the Portuguese Society of Suicidology (SPS; http://www.spsuicidologia.pt/. SPS is a scientific association devoted to the study of suicide and suicidal behaviors and to the dissemination of good practices in the field. Founded in 2000, SPS organizes an annual national symposium and develops training for professionals. SPS has launched a national scientific prize and edited two reference books) (Saraiva, Peixoto, & Sampaio, 2014). Yet, postvention is still little developed and acknowledged by the scientific and clinical community in Portugal. Suicide represents a huge emotional burden for the community, families, and health professionals, and is often associated with serious mental health risks. This chapter has aimed to encourage further national multicenter research in this domain and to help develop and implement adequate postvention initiatives in Portugal.

Corresponding author

Inês Areal Rothes
Faculty of Psychology and Educational Sciences
University of Porto
Porto
Portugal
irothes@gmail.com

References

Anderson, M., Standen, P., Nazir, S., & Noon, J. P. (2000). Nurses' and doctors' attitudes towards suicidal behaviour in young people. *International Journal of Nursing Studies, 37*(1), 1–11. http://doi.org/10.1016/S0020-7489(99)00057-7

Batista, P., & Santos, J. C. (2014). The family in the grieving process of the suicide elderly [in Portuguese]. *Revista Portuguesa de Enfermagem de Saúde Mental, 12*, 17–24.

Brás, M., & Santos, J. (2014). Suicide prevention in school. In C. B. Saraiva, B. Peixoto, & D. Sampaio, (Eds.), *Suicide and self-injurious behavior: From concepts to clinical practice* (pp. 485–492) [in Portuguese]. Lisboa, Portugal: Lidel Edições Técnicas.

Cruz, D., Sampaio, D., Santos, N., & Narciso, I. (2007). Self-destructive behaviors in adolescence: A hospital group's experience of clinical evaluation [in Portuguese]. *Saúde Mental, 9*(4), 10–23.

Direcção Geral de Saúde. (2013). *National Plan of Suicide Prevention. National Programme of Mental Health 2013–2017* [in Portuguese]. Lisboa, Portugal: Author. Retrieved from https://www.dgs.pt/documentos-e-publicacoes/plano-nacional-de-prevencao-do-suicido-20132017-pdf.aspxx

Grad, O. T., Zavasnik, A., & Groleger, U. (1997). Suicide of a patient: Gender differences in bereavement reactions of therapists. *Suicide and Life-Threatening Behavior, 27*(4), 379–386.

Gusmão, R., & Quintão, S. (2013). Suicide and death resulting from events of undetermined intent register in Portugal. Revisiting "The truth about suicide in Portugal, 20 years later" [in Portuguese and in English]. *Portugal Saúde em Números: Revista da Direcção-Geral de Saúde, 1*, 80–95.

Instituto Nacional de Estatística. (2016). *Standardized mortality rate by intentional self-harm (suicide) per 100,000 inhabitants (No.) by place of residence and sex; yearly*. Retrieved from http://www.ine.pt/

Pieters, G., De Gucht, V., Joos, G., & De Heyn, E. (2003). Frequency and impact of patient suicide on psychiatric trainees. *European Psychiatry, 18*(7), 345–349. http://doi.org/10.1016/j.eurpsy.2003.02.003

Rothes, I. (2014a). *Suicidal behaviors: Explanations, current practices and difficulties of health professionals and the impact of a patient suicide* (Unpublished doctoral dissertation). Faculdade de Psicologia e de Ciências da Educação, Universidade do Porto, Portugal.

Rothes, I. (2014b). Patient suicide impact in health professionals. In C. B. Saraiva, B. Peixoto, & D. Sampaio (Eds.), *Suicide and self-injurious behavior: From concepts to clinical practice* [in Portuguese] (pp. 455–470). Lisboa, Portugal: Lidel Edições Técnicas.

Rothes, I., Henriques, M., & Correia, R. (2013). Patient suicide: the experiencie of Portuguese doctors and psychologists [in Portuguese]. *Revista Portuguesa de Saúde Pública, 31*(2), 193–203.

Rothes, I., Scheerder, G., Van Audenhove, C., & Henriques, M. (2013). Patient suicide: The experience of Flemish psychiatrists. *Suicide and Life-Threatening Behavior, 43*(4), 379–394. http://doi.org/10.1111/sltb.12024

Ruskin, R., Sakinofsky, I., Bagby, R. M., Dickens, S., & Sousa, G. (2004). Impact of patient suicide on psychiatrists and psychiatric trainees. *Academic Psychiatry, 28*, 104–110. http://doi.org/10.1176/appi.ap.28.2.104

Sampaio, I. (2013). *Grieving families who lost a loved one by suicide* [in Portuguese] (Unpublished master's thesis). Universidade de Trás-os-Montes e Alto Douro UTAD, Portugal.

Santos, J., Erse, M., Façanha, J., Marques, L., & Simões, R. (2014). + Contigo: Mental health promotion and prevention of suicidal behaviours within the educational community [in Portuguese]. *Monographic Series Health Sciences Education and Research*. Coimbra, Portugal: Health Sciences Research Unit, Nursing, Nursing School of Coimbra.

Santos, J., Erse, M., Simões, R., Façanha, J., & Marques, L. (2011). School-based suicide prevention ... after the final goodbye. *Chinese Mental Health Journal, 25*(9), 242s–243s.

Santos, J., Erse, M., Simões, R., Façanha, J., & Marques, L. (2013). Contigo na promoção da saúde mental e prevenção de comportamentos suicidários em meio escolar [+ Contigo in the mental health promotion and suicidal behaviors prevention in schools]. *Revista de Enfermagem Referência, 10,* 203–207. http://doi.org/10.12707/RIII13121

Santos, S. (2014). *The impact of suicide on family: Psychopathological symptoms and suicidal ideation* [in Portuguese] (Unpublished doctoral dissertation). Universidade de Évora, Portugal.

Santos, S., Campos, R. C., & Tavares, S. (2015). Suicidal ideation and distress in family members bereaved by suicide in Portugal. *Death Studies, 39*(6), 332–341. http://doi.org/10.1080/07481187.2014.946626

Santos, S., Tavares, S., & Campos, R. C. (2015). Distress in Portuguese family members bereaved by suicide: An exploratory study. *Journal of Loss and Trauma, 20*(3), 267–280. http://doi.org/10.1080/15325024.2014.934618

Saraiva, C., Peixoto, B., & Sampaio, D. (2014). *Suicide and self-injurious behavior: From concepts to clinical practice* [in Portuguese]. Lisboa, Portugal: Lidel Edições Técnicas.

Värnik, P., Sisask, M., Värnik, A., Laido, Z., Meise, U., Ibelshauser, A., ... Hegerl, U. (2010). Suicide registration in eight European countries: A qualitative analysis of procedures and practices. *Forensic Science International, 202*(1–3), 86–92. http://doi.org/10.1016/j.forsciint.2010.04.032

World Health Organization. (2013). *Mortality Indicator Database.* Retrieved from http://data.euro.who.int/hfamdb/

Wurst, F. M., Mueller, S., Petitjean, S., Euler, S., Thon, N., Wiesbeck, G., & Wolfersdorf, M. (2010). Patient suicide: A survey of therapists' reactions. *Suicide and Life-Threatening Behavior, 40*(4), 328–336. http://doi.org/10.1521/suli.2010.40.4.328

Chapter 40

Slovenia – Development of Postvention

Onja T. Grad[1], Vita Poštuvan[2], Nada Wolf[3], Polona Ozbič[4], and Anka Zavasnik[4]

[1]University Psychiatric Hospital, Ljubljana, Slovenia
[2]Slovenian Centre for Suicide Research, Andrej Marušič Institute, University of Primorska, Koper, Slovenia
[3]Slovenian Association Hospice, Maribor, Slovenia
[4]Slovenian Association for Suicide Prevention, Ljubljana, Slovenia

Abstract: Slovenia is a central European country with a high suicide rate. Postvention activities emerged at the end of the 1980s, when the first suicide survivor group was organized. Since the start of this pioneering initiative, a number of service providers have offered valuable services and activities to the bereaved by suicide, postvention research has been conducted, and publications and websites have been developed to raise public awareness. Priorities for the future include more concerted postvention efforts and promotion of the available resources for lay people and professionals.

Introduction

Slovenia is a small central European country with a high suicide rate, actually one of the highest in Europe – that is, 30–35 per 100,000 inhabitants over the period 1970–1990 (Grad, 1995). Even though over the years, a lot of work was done regarding the prevention of suicidal behavior, postvention was overlooked in Slovenia. Similar to other European countries at that time, there was no specific help available for the bereaved after suicide. In the 1980s, the United States was the leading country developing new approaches in postvention (see Chapter 9 in this volume). The Los Angeles Suicide Prevention Center, under the leadership of Prof. Norman Farberow organized and conducted clinical work and research with groups of suicide survivors (Farberow, 1992), and the Slovenian psychologist (first author of this chapter) Dr. Onja Grad had the privilege of working with him. In 1989, after returning to Slovenia, Dr. Grad and her colleague, a clinical psychologist, Anka Zavasnik, initiated the first group for suicide survivors. To the best of the authors' knowledge, this was the first professionally organized suicide survivor group in Europe. Subsequently, postvention activities and services developed slowly but steadily in Slovenia, followed by evaluation through research and scientific publications. The chapter presents the growth and expansion of postvention into different fields of professional and public life in the country.

Postvention in Slovenia Over the Decades

The First Suicide Survivors Group

The seminal support group for survivors after suicide was organized at the University Psychiatric Hospital in Ljubljana in 1989. At that time, Slovenia had a well-organized free-of-charge public health system. General practitioners (GPs) and the police, who were the first responders at the scene of a suicide, were informed about the new service and encouraged to refer the bereaved they encountered in their work. The media and the public were also informed. The aim of the group was to support the survivors, to help them acknowledge and process their loss, to understand basic factors related to suicidal behavior, and to learn how to cope with everyday life without the deceased. The group was led by two psychotherapists with ample experience in working with seriously suicidal individuals and their relatives.

The format of the group was inspired by the example of the Los Angeles Suicide Prevention Center. The group was planned in advance and did not accept newcomers after the first session (i.e., a *closed* group format). The number of members was limited (8–10 members), they met once a week for 8 weeks, and the meetings had a structure – for example, an agenda. The group gathered in a supportive and understanding atmosphere, and offered mutual support among the participants and the group leaders. The expression of emotions was facilitated, and different strategies were used to address coping with suicide loss (Grad & Zavasnik, 1997; Tekavčič Grad, 1994). The facilitators were supervised by a senior clinical psychologist or certified supervisor. Since the start until today, these support groups have been available to the suicide bereaved in Slovenia. The experience from the groups has been instrumental in expanding support offered to individuals and families bereaved by suicide (Tekavčič Grad & Zavasnik, 1990). In 1996, an outpatient clinic for the bereaved was established at the University Psychiatric Hospital in Ljubljana, and the clinic has been working ever since.

The Slovenian Hospice

Since 2000, the Slovenian Hospice (a nongovernment organization) has been providing help for bereaved adults and children after any type of death. The help is offered individually and in groups. The group participants meet 8 to 10 times; the open groups meet monthly, whereas the closed groups meet weekly. The group leaders are either professionals or trained lay persons. After the suicide of a student, the Hospice provides support to fellow students, teachers, and school counselors, either within the class or through individual counseling. Once a year, the Hospice organizes the Lionheart Camp, a camp for youngsters who have lost a family member by any type of death. At the same time, the parents can attend a gathering organized at a venue nearby to the children's camp. The camps are run by professional and lay counselors, who receive training and supervision on a regular basis. The Hospice also offers education and support for those who work with the bereaved after sudden or expected death, and all support is offered free of charge (Wolf, 2015).

The Slovenian Centre for Suicide Research

The Slovenian Centre for Suicide Research was founded in 2011 within the Andrej Marušič Institute at University of Primorska. The center is engaged in many national and international research and intervention projects, as well as postvention activities. It provides debriefing, based on the critical incident stress management model (Mitchell & Everly, 1993) designed for individuals and groups (usually first responders, witnesses, or victims) exposed to a critical event, such as suicide. The center also offers workshops for classmates and teachers after the suicide of a student, and occasional consultations have been offered to school counseling personnel in cases of suicidal behavior.

The center has offered training sessions and workshops for gatekeepers, including police officers, police peer supporters (i.e., police personnel trained in offering psychological support to their colleagues), and firefighters, and the content of these activities has been tailored to their specific needs. The center has developed a website Živ? Živ! (Alive? Alive!; http://www.zivziv.si/) to raise public awareness of suicide prevention and suicide bereavement (Poštuvan, 2015). It also offers support through mindfulness-based cognitive therapy groups called Programme NARA (http://www.zivziv.si/NARA/) and individual support to students who have lost someone close, due to suicide.

Further Development of Postvention

Based on knowledge from the literature and clinical experience with people bereaved by suicide, postvention initiatives in Slovenia gradually expanded to reach professionals who come into contact with the bereaved, work with them, or have become suicide survivors themselves. Postvention initiatives have been developed for elementary and high school teachers, students, and their parents (Tekavčič Grad & Zavasnik, 2009; Zavasnik & Grad, 1999b), GPs (Tekavčič Grad, 2012; Zavasnik & Grad, 1999a), police officers, special intervention forces, prison personnel (Grad & Zavasnik, 1995), and mental health workers (Grad, 2012; Grad, Zavasnik & Groleger, 1997). Working with the media has helped to raise public awareness (Roškar, Tančič Grum, & Poštuvan, 2010), and film and drama directors have solicited advice when producing their work (Tekavčič Grad, 1996). All of these activities have been aiming at the destigmatization of suicide bereavement and motivating the survivors to seek and accept available help and support (Grad, 2011).

Postvention Research in Slovenia

The work with groups and individuals bereaved by suicide presented in this chapter has resulted in many research studies. These have included the first longitudinal study in Slovenia to compare the bereavement process after different modes of death – that is, suicide, traffic fatalities, and terminal illness – using randomized samples of bereaved spouses (Grad & Zavasnik, 1999). The same methodology was applied in a comparative study in The Netherlands and Slovenia (Cleiren, Grad, Zavasnik, & Diekstra, 1996). These studies were based on in-depth structured interviews, and used the Eysenck Personality Questionnaire (Lojk, 1979), the Beck Depression Inventory (Beck & Beck, 1972), and the Slovenian Bereavement Scale (Grad & Zavasnik, 1996). The participants were interviewed 2 months and 14 months after the death. The data showed that the process of bereavement was influenced by the mode of death, the time that had passed between the loss and the interview, and the quality of the spousal relationship (Grad & Zavasnik, 1996, 1999). The comparison between Slovenia and The Netherlands found more similarities than differences (Cleiren et al., 1996). The symptomatology of depression was slightly higher in the Slovenian bereaved, but the symptoms patterns were almost identical. In both national samples, the suicide bereaved perceived themselves to be less socially accepted, especially in the Slovenian sample.

A study by Tekavčič Grad and Zavasnik (1998) evaluated the effects of a support group for suicide bereaved. The study questionnaire was sent by mail to the support group participants (N = 108) and answered anonymously by 59 % of participants. Eighty-one percent of respondents reported that the group work was helpful, and the three most helpful elements were *"learning about the experiences of other group members," "increased acceptance of my own reality,"* and *"knowledge about suicide."* Still, the participants reported that "the answer to *why?*" was missing, and that *"more explanations from the group leaders"* and *"more group sessions"* would have improved their experience (Tekavčič Grad & Zavasnik, 1998). The study showed that the suicide survivors were frequently referred to the group by their GPs; however, many GPs lacked basic knowledge about the process of bereavement. Consequently, in 1997, Zavasnik and Grad (1999b) conducted a study to examine the effect of a patient's suicide in this professional group.

In 1994, a questionnaire-based study investigated the effects of a patient's suicide on therapists, including psychiatrists and clinical psychologists, working in public health institutions, such as psychiatric hospitals and outpatient clinics (Grad, Zavasnik, & Groleger, 1997). The response rate was high, as 72 % of the 87 clinicians contacted returned the anonymous questionnaire. After the suicide of a patient, the therapists reported increased caution in the treatment of other patients (94 %) and more consultations with colleagues (91 %) and supervisors (43 %), as well as talking to partners in their private life (63 %). The therapists experienced strong feelings of guilt (66 %), grief, depression, and loss, which are also commonly reported by other survivors of suicide. Of note, female therapists more often than their male colleagues felt shame and guilt, sought consolation, or doubted their professional knowledge. There was no significant difference between vocational groups or the number of years of work experience. The respondents agreed that support was important both on the professional and personal level. The study resulted in the development of the Slovenian guidelines on how to support hospital staff after the suicide of a patient (Grad, 2007).

Suicide survivors have also been included in other national research projects, such as a randomized study of bereaved men and women after different modes of death and with different kinships (Ozbič, 2015). The study aimed to investigate gender differences in the bereavement process at the cognitive, emotional, behavioral, social, and physical levels. It focused on the strategies that the bereaved use to cope with their loss and the different types of help they seek or receive. The study identified more similarities than differences between genders; however, specific characteristics in the bereavement process found in men offered suggestions regarding adaptation of professional help to the male population. In addition, a recent study (Treven et al., 2013) focusing on GPs' reactions to the suicide of a patient, factors influencing these reactions, the effect of suicide on treatment of patients, and identification of GPs' needs for support, was conducted over the period 2012–2013 (see Chapter 21 in this volume).

Conclusions

The experience of over 25 years of working with suicide survivors in Slovenia has confirmed that support and information can be effective in preventing emotional and suicidal crises, can modify negative perceptions of suicide bereavement, and can reduce perceived barriers to seeking peer support and professional help. An important challenge for the future is strengthening the postvention network and supporting collaboration among the various support services and activities throughout the country. This is necessary in order to effectively reach survivors after suicide and their social environment, and to be available to them as soon as they need help.

Corresponding author

Onja T. Grad
University Psychiatric Hospital
Center for Mental Health
Grablovičeva 44a
1000 Ljubljana
Slovenia
onja.grad@guest.arnes.si

References

Beck, A. T. & Beck, R. W. (1972). Screening depressed patients in family practice. *Postgraduate Medicine, 52*(6), 81–85. http://doi.org/10.1080/00325481.1972.11713319

Cleiren, M., Grad, O., Zavasnik, A., & Diekstra, R. F. W. (1996). Psycho-social impact of bereavement after suicide and fatal traffic accident: A comparative two-country study. *Acta Psychiatrica Scandinavica, 94*(1), 37–44. http://doi.org/10.1111/j.1600-0447.1996.tb09822.x

Farberow, N. L. (1992). The Los Angeles survivors-after-suicide program: An evaluation. *Crisis, 13*(1), 23–34.

Grad, O. (2007). *The guidelines for the medical team after the suicide of a patient.* Ljubljana, Slovenia: Psihiatrična klinika in SASP.

Grad, O. T. (1995). Why is the incidence of suicide in Slovenia one of the highest in the world? In O. T. Grad (Ed.), *How to reduce suicide in Slovenia* (pp. 81–88). Ljubljana, Slovenia: WHO Regional Office for Slovenia.

Grad, O. T. (2011). The sequelae of suicide: survivors. In R. C. O'Connor, S. Platt, & J. Gordon (Eds.), *International handbook of suicide prevention: research, policy and practice* (pp. 561–576). Chichester, UK: Wiley-Blackwell.

Grad, O. T. (2012). *Guidelines to assist clinical staff after the suicide of a patient.* Retrieved from https://www.iasp.info/pdf/postvention/guidelines_to_assist_clinical_staff_after_suicide_patient_grad.pdf

Grad, O. & Zavasnik, A. (1995). Proposal for a national program for suicide prevention in Slovenia. In O. T. Grad. (Ed.), *How to reduce suicide in Slovenia* (pp. 3–19). Ljubljana, Slovenia: WHO Regional Office for Slovenia.

Grad, O., & Zavasnik, A. (1996). Similarities and differences in the process of bereavement after suicide and after traffic fatalities in Slovenia. *Omega: Journal of Death and Dying, 33*(3), 243–251. http://doi.org/10.2190/YU2C-ACR8-UG6V-JWCJ

Grad, O., & Zavasnik, A. (1997). Shame: The unbearable legacy of suicide. In D. De Leo, A. Schmidtke, & R. F. W. Diekstra (Eds.), *Suicide prevention: A holistic approach* (pp. 163–166). Boston, MA: Kluwer.

Grad, O. T., & Zavasnik, A. (1999). Phenomenology of bereavement process after suicide, traffic accident and terminal illness (in spouses). *Archives of Suicide Research, 5*(2), 157–172. http://doi.org/10.1023/A:1009657623859

Grad, O., Zavasnik, A., & Groleger, U. (1997). Suicide of a patient: Gender differences in bereavement reactions of therapists. *Suicide and Life-Threatening Behavior, 27*(4), 379–386.

Lojk, L. (1979). *EPQ manual.* Ljubljana, Slovenia: Zavod za produktivnost dela.

Milčinski, L., & Virant Jaklič, M. (1992). *Samomor in samomorilni poskus v Sloveniji v letu 1991* [Suicide and suicide attempts in Slovenia in 1991]. Ljubljana, Slovenia: Univerzitetna psihiatrična klinika Ljubljana.

Mitchell, J. T., & Everly, G. S., Jr. (1993). *Critical Incident Stress Debriefing (CISD): An operations manual for the prevention of traumatic stress among emergency services and disaster workers.* Ellicott City, MD: Chevron.

Ozbič, P. (2015). Medsebojna podpora partnerjev v procesu žalovanja po otrokovi smrti [Mutual partners' support in the process of the bereavement after the death of the child]. *Psihološka obzorja, 24*, 44–56. Retrieved from http://psy.ff.uni-lj.si/psiholoska_obzorja/arhiv_clanki/2015/ozbic.pdf

Poštuvan, V. (2015). *Živ? Živ! Spletna postaja za razumevanje samomora* [Alive? Alive! Platform for understanding suicide] Koper, Slovenia: Slovene Centre for Suicide Research UP IAM.

Roškar, S., Tančič Grum, A., & Poštuvan, V. (2010). *Spregovorimo o samomoru in medijih* [Let's talk about suicide in the media]. Ljubljana, Slovenia: IVZ.

Tekavčič Grad, O. (1994). Countertransference problems inside the group of relatives bereaving suicide. *Horizons of Psychology, 3*(3–4), 151–157.

Tekavčič Grad, O. (1996). *Nevzdržna zapuščina samomora* [The unbearable legacy of suicide]. Ljubljana, Slovenia: Metuljev let, Drama SNG.

Tekavčič Grad, O. (2012). Helping the bereaved. In N. Kopčaver Guček & D. Petek, (Eds.), *Kakovostna obravnava bolnika v družinski medicine* [Quality treatment of a patient in family medicine] (pp. 71–74). Ljubljana, Slovenia: ZZD Medicine.

Tekavčič Grad, O., & Zavasnik, A. (1990). The emotional relations inside the survivors group. In G. Ferrari, M. Bellini & P. Crepet (Eds.), *Suicidal behaviour and risk factors* (pp. 1045–1048). Bologna, Italy: Monduzi Editore.

Tekavčič Grad, O., & Zavasnik, A. (1998). *Evaluation of the suicide survivors programmes: What helps?* Programme and Abstracts of seventh European symposium on suicide and suicidal behaviour (pp. 1–8). Ghent, Belgium: ESSSB.

Tekavčič Grad, O., & Zavasnik, A. (2009). How can we recognize depressed or suicidal child or adolescent in the school environment? In S. Gaber (Ed.), *Za manj negotovosti: aktivno državljanstvo, zdrav življenjski slog, varovanje okolja* [For less uncertainty: Active citizenship, healthy life-style and taking care of the environment] (pp. 165–176). Ljubljana, Slovenia: University of Ljubljana.

Treven, M., Rotar Pavlič, D., & Grad, O. (2013). *General practitioners' reactions to patients' suicides* [Abstract]. Proceedings of the XXVII world congress of the International Association for Suicide Prevention: Suicidologi: Final programme and book of abstracts (pp. 231–232). Oslo, Norway: IASP.

Wolf, N. (2015). Proces žalovanja v praksi paliativne oskrbe [The process of bereavement within palliative care]. In B. Kaučič, D. Plank, D. Presker Planko, & K. Esih (Eds.), *Paliativna oskrba* [Palliative care] (pp. 139–144). Maribor, Slovenia: Association of Palliative Care.

Zavasnik, A., & Grad, O. (1999a). How well did GPs know their patients who committed suicide? *Book of Abstracts, 20th Congress of IASP* (p. 55). Athens, Greece: IASP.

Zavasnik, A., & Grad, O. (1999b). Preprečevanje samomora in samomorilnega vedenja v šolah [Prevention of suicide and suicidal behavior in schools]. In E. Kraševec Ravnik (Ed.), *Varovanje duševnega zdravja otrok in mladostnikov* [Mental health protection of children and adolescents] (pp. 217–222). Ljubljana, Slovenia: WHO Collaborative Centre.

Chapter 41

The Netherlands – Support After Suicide on the Railways

Angela van der Veer[1] and Cobi Nijhuis[2]

[1]Suicide Prevention – ProRail, Utrecht, The Netherlands
[2]Security, Support and Aftercare – National Railways, Utrecht, The Netherlands

Abstract: A substantial number of suicides occur on the railways in The Netherlands affecting not only family and friends, but also the exposed passengers and railway staff. This chapter presents the support offered to passengers and the family of a person who dies by suicide on the Dutch railway network, as well as the support for the train drivers and railway staff. The support is offered by a designated Department of Aftercare, which expresses the shared corporate social responsibility of the Dutch railway companies. The chapter also presents the policy on memorials for railway victims.

Introduction

Suicide on the railways accounts for approximately 12 % of all suicides in The Netherlands (van Houwelingen, Kerkhof, & Beersma, 2010), and there are approximately 200 fatal and 50 nonfatal suicide incidents per year on the Dutch railways (ProRail, 2014a). A violent death can have an immense emotional impact on approximately 10 people, such as family, friends, and colleagues who personally knew the deceased. This means that approximately 2,000 people will be personally affected each year, which may put them at increased risk of suicide, grief complications, and mental health problems such as depression, anxiety, and substance abuse (De Groot & Kollen, 2013; Harwood, Hawton, Hope, & Jacoby, 2002; Jordan, 2001; Qin, Agerbo, & Mortensen, 2002). There are also, on the average, 25 people present at the scene or functionally involved with an incident, including train drivers and conductors from Nederlandse Spoorwegen (NS; Dutch Railways), staff and accident managers of the rail infrastructure manager (ProRail), fire department, police, undertakers, and dedicated cleaning companies. In addition, there are operational costs related to the logistic process: The cost of the average disruption time of 2 hr 15 min has been estimated at approximately €100,000 per incident (Rail Safety and Standards Board, 2014), plus other costs, such as the disruption to the service experienced by passengers and freight transporters.

NS is the largest passenger transport company in The Netherlands, and ProRail is the Dutch rail infrastructure manager. Both companies aim to prevent suicides on the railway property, and to reduce the impact of suicide on people involved, as well as the costly disruption of services. These aims can be achieved by implementing technical and nontechnical prevention measures, which are based on research studies concerning suicide on railways and its environmental characteristics, including the vicinity of a mental health institution (van Houwelingen, 2011).

Both companies have well-established protocols for support after an incident, including a suicide. This chapter presents the support available to passengers and the family of a person who dies by suicide on the railways, and the support for the train drivers and railway staff. The support is offered by the NS Department of Aftercare, which operates jointly on behalf of ProRail, NS, and other railway companies, which expresses their shared corporate social responsibility. The chapter also presents the policy on memorials set up by the bereaved in the vicinity of the tracks.

Support for Passengers

After a collision with a person, the train staff will decide which actions involving the passengers should be taken. The train conductor or the train driver informs the passengers of the incident through the intercom, and the conductor walks through the train to reassure passengers by providing them with information and answering their questions. If a passenger needs care, contact details are written down, and this person will be contacted by Aftercare. Passengers in distress receive information about the NS Customer Service and Slachtofferhulp Nederland (Victim Care; http://www.slachtofferhulpnederland.nl/). When a passenger contacts customer service with questions about the incident or to seek psychological help, customer service contacts the Department of Aftercare, which in turn calls the passenger, and in some cases, when considered appropriate, may also send flowers or a handwritten card with a personal message. If needed, the Department of Aftercare will refer the person to a general practitioner (GP) for treatment; in The Netherlands, most people have a GP who serves as point of contact for health- and mental health–related questions. This procedure also applies to passengers who witness other traumatic events, such as a collision with a vehicle or passenger aggression.

Support for the Bereaved Family

The objective of Aftercare is to let the bereaved know that ProRail and NS empathize with them and to provide a point of contact for any questions. Often family members want to do something for the train driver or conductors involved in the incident – for example, write a letter or send a card to express their feelings. Family members may also feel guilty or ashamed, and writing a card or a letter can give them a sense of relief, which may help in the grief process. However, to protect the employee involved in the incident, personal contact of the bereaved family with train staff is not possible, and the Department of Aftercare acts as an intermediary.

In case of a fatal incident, Aftercare asks the funeral director if the family would like to receive flowers for the funeral on behalf of the NS or ProRail management. The family decides whether they accept this offer or not; some families do not want any contact, while others appreciate a phone call from Aftercare. Sometimes family members ask questions regarding the circumstances of the death, such as the behavior of the victim (e.g., *"Did my son stand on the tracks?"* or *"What did the train driver see in the last minutes of my husband's life?"*), or express sympathy for the train driver (e.g., *"I would like to let the train driver know that I feel sorry for them; what can I do for them?"*). Aftercare can facilitate contact between the bereaved and the staff, and ask questions about the incident through the team manager of the employee involved. In this way, the NS responds to the questions of the bereaved without burdening the staff. Aftercare contacts the bereaved by phone or arranges a meeting at railway headquarters, or, in some cases, at the home of the bereaved. Besides flowers, handwritten letters or postcards can also be sent. If necessary, the Department of Aftercare will refer the person to a GP, or the Landelijk Steunpunt Rouw (National Center for Bereavement Support; http://www.landelijksteunpuntrouw.nl/).

Support for Train Drivers and Other Railway Staff

The NS offers mandatory care after a traumatic event, including a suicide or a suicide attempt. At the scene of the incident, care is offered by the on-call officer, who makes sure that the employee arrives home safely. The team manager contacts the employee the day after the incident and keeps in touch with them, also to assess when the employee is ready to return to work. After a week, the employee can fill out an online self-test assessing well-being and coping, which is provided by the HSK Group, institute for mental health care, specialized in employee health (https://www.hsk.nl), an independent expert organization. The test provides a three-level score, which indicates the level of coping: *green* = "you are coping well"; *orange* = "you have started dealing with the incident, but you need support";, and *red* = "you are at risk; steps are being taken to provide professional support for you." The online self-test is not mandatory; however, it is highly recommended. HSK contacts the employee, even if the result is green. When the score is red, NS offers free-of-charge psychotherapy at the HSK, for instance eye movement desensitization and reprocessing (EMDR) treatment (Shapiro, 2001). The procedure aims to detect posttraumatic stress disorder (PTSD) at an early stage, and to offer treatment as soon as possible.

In most cases, the employee does not call in sick as a consequence of the incident. Still, if they make an appointment with the railway occupational health service, the doctor will liaise with the HSK, and will assess if additional treatment or actions are needed. Besides the formal aftercare, there is Vangrail (literally: the crash barrier), a national peer support network involving 160 volunteer railway staff. The peer volunteers can be recognized by a pin on their lapel to facilitate direct contact, and they can be called or e-mailed individually or through the organization.

Gatekeeper Training

NS and ProRail have developed a 1-day gatekeeper training program Contact With Possible Suicidal Persons on the Railway, for railway staff, including conductors, train drivers, and safety personnel. The training addresses self-confidence, knowledge, and skills of staff, and offers an opportunity to learn about suicide risk factors, how to identify a person who may be at risk of suicide, how to assess the level of risk, and how to manage a crisis situation by applying intervention skills (Restrail, 2013). Participants also learn to refer a person at risk to emergency services and the suicide helpline (http://www.113Online.nl/).

ProRail and NS introduced the training in 2013, and by 2016 approximately 3,000 people working in the railway environment had participated. The development of the course included a qualitative study based on in-depth interviews with railway staff who had experienced contact with a suicidal person during their years on the job. An evaluation study, using a control group, was carried out over 2013–2014: The first 100 training participants received a pretraining questionnaire, and were assessed again 2 and 12 months after the training (Restrail, 2014; ProRail, 2014b; Van der Veer & Bourgonje, 2015). The results showed a significant improvement in the level of staff knowledge, and increased confidence and initiative to recognize and approach people who may be suicidal (Restrail, 2014). The course seems to provide necessary information, meets the needs of the railway staff with regards to suicide, and helps them to cope more effectively after a suicide incident.

Policy Concerning Memorials on the Railways

The Dutch railway companies have a policy to remove memorials set up by the bereaved families in the vicinity of the tracks or on the railway property. Memorials, consisting of – for example, flowers, a cross, candles, or photos – are usually reported to the NS Safety Center by the railway staff. The Safety Center reports back to the ProRail point of contact responsible for inspecting the tracks, and a safety officer is delegated to remove the memorial (in some cases, safety officers find memorials while inspecting the tracks). The safety officer moves the memorial objects out of sight of the train driver, and leaves a letter for the bereaved at the memorial site. The letter explains the actions taken and offers the bereaved an option to contact the Department of Aftercare. After consultation with the family, ProRail either removes the memorial after photographing the site, or relocates it to a safe location, away from the railway tracks. If the memorial is located on municipal premises, but in sight of railway staff, Aftercare or the safety officer contacts the city council for further deliberation.

The current protocol is based on a number of observations. Memorials can prime people who may be at risk of suicide – that is, at risk of copycat behavior – and can remind a train driver (either the one who drove the train when the incident happened or any other train driver) of what has happened at a particular location. This can be traumatizing in itself or can trigger traumatic memories of an incident. Also, memorials are often placed at an unsafe location, unsuitable for mourning or holding a gathering. When the relatives are contacted, they also receive information about the dedicated national monument for railway fatalities (see below), and sometimes they appreciate the presence of a representative of the railways (Aftercare) when they visit the monument.

National Monument for Railway Fatalities

The Landelijk Monument Spoorwegongevallen (National Monument for Railway Fatalities) was erected in 2004 to commemorate victims of all railway accidents (**Figure 41.1**). The memorial is located in Utrecht, a city in the geographical center of The Netherlands, between the offices of NS and ProRail. The monument was designed by Anton Broos and is engraved with a poem written by a Dutch theologian and preacher, Anne van der Meiden:

Figure 41.1. Landelijk Monument Spoorwegongevallen (National Monument for Railway Fatalities), The Netherlands, size: 15 m x 3 m. Photographer: Anton Broos. Reprinted by permission.

Poem on National Monument for Railway Fatalities by Anne van der Meiden:

Herinneringen lopen samen op met hen *die op het spoor de wissel van de dood* *passeerden.* *Met onze voeten meten wij verdriet en* *rouw.* *Een lieve groet van dit verstild station.* *Tot weerziens op de volgende* *bestemming*	*Memories accompany those who passed* *the switch of death.* *Our feet measure pain and sadness.* *A heartfelt note from this silenced* *station.* *Until we meet again at the next stop.*

Conclusions

A suicide on the railway network often has a major impact on the individuals involved. Due to the violent nature of the death, it can seriously affect the psychological well-being of passengers and railway staff. Over the years, ProRail and NS have gained considerable experience in managing the psychological effects of such deaths. Both companies have learned that professional help can be effective in better dealing with the aftermath of a suicide, including minimizing the risk of a copycat behavior. Contact with the bereaved and aftercare have become a part of the corporate social responsibility of NS and ProRail. Suicide on the railways affects many people in many ways; aftercare is important to help them cope with the incident, and is a part of effective suicide prevention on the railways.

Corresponding authors

Angela van der Veer
Suicide Prevention – ProRail
Utrecht
The Netherlands
angela.vanderveer@prorail.nl

Cobi Nijhuis
On behalf of the department of
Security, Support and Aftercare – National Railways
Utrecht
The Netherlands
cobi.nijhuis@ns.nl

References

De Groot, M. H., & Kollen, B. J. (2013). Course of bereavement over 8–10 years in first degree relatives and spouses of people who committed suicide: longitudinal community based cohort study. *British Medical Journal, 347*, f5519. http://doi.org/10.1136/bmj.f5519

Harwood, D., Hawton, K., Hope, T., & Jacoby, R. (2002). The grief experiences and needs of bereaved relatives and friends of older people dying through suicide: A descriptive and case-control study. *Journal of Affective Disorders, 72*(2), 185–194. http://doi.org/10.1016/S0165-0327(01)00462-1

Jordan, J. (2001). Is suicide bereavement different? A reassessment of the literature. *Suicide and Life-Threatening Behavior, 31*(1), 91–102. http://doi.org/10.1521/suli.31.1.91.21310

ProRail. (2014a). *Jaarverslag* [Annual report]. Retrieved from http://www.jaarverslagprorail.nl/verslag/spoorvervoer/veiligheid/

ProRail. (2014b). *Gatekeeper course: 'Contact with a suicidal person.'* Poster at final RESTRAIL meeting, 18 September 2014. Retrieved from http://restrail.eu/spip.php?article16 and http://restrail.eu/IMG/pdf/prorail.pdf

Qin, P., Agerbo, E., Mortensen, P. B. (2002). Suicide risk in relation to family history of completed suicide and psychiatric disorders: a nested case-control study based on longitudinal registers. *Lancet, 360*(9340), 1126–1130. http://doi.org/10.1016/S0140-6736(02)11197-4

Rail Safety and Standards Board. (2014). *Research brief: Improving suicide prevention measures on the rail network in Great Britain.* Retrieved from http://www.rssb.co.uk/Library/research-development-and-innovation/2014–02-research-brief-t845-tackling-suicide-on-the-railways.pdf

Restrail. (2013). *Gatekeeper training for front line staff.* Retrieved from http://restrail.eu/toolbox/spip.php?article142

Restrail. (2014). *Evaluation of measures, recommendations and guidelines for further implementation. Pilot test no. 9, Gatekeeper programme – ProRail.* Retrieved from http://restrail.eu/toolbox/IMG/pdf/gatekeeper_programme_-_prorail_ns_the_netherlands.pdf

Shapiro, F. (2001). *Eye movement desensitization and reprocessing (EMDR).* New York, NY: Guilford Press.

Van der Veer, A. M., & Bourgonje, M. (2015). *ProRail/NS Gatekeeper course: 'Contact with a suicidal person' on railway premises.* Paper presented at World Congress Rail Training 2015, Lisbon, April 15–17, 2015. Retrieved from http://wcrt2015.org/

van Houwelingen, C. A. J. (2011). *Studies into train suicide. The contribution of psychopathology, railway parameters and environmental factors* (Doctoral dissertation). Amsterdam, The Netherlands: Vrije Universiteit.

van Houwelingen, C. A., Kerkhof, A. J., & Beersma, D. G. (2010). Train suicides in the Netherlands. *Journal of Affective Disorders, 127*(1–3), 281–286. http://doi.org/10.1016/j.jad.2010.06.005

Part IV.3
Africa

Chapter 42

South-Africa – Experiences of Suicide Survivor Support

Lourens Schlebusch

Nelson R. Mandela School of Medicine, University of KwaZulu-Natal, Durban, South Africa

Abstract: Suicidal behavior is a significant problem in South Africa. Because of this, interest in postvention has taken on a new impetus. However, although it is provided in some areas, there is a shortage of postvention programs and therapists with specialized postvention skills. Postvention strategies must be appropriate to the sociocultural needs of the diverse populations they serve. Elements of a recommended national suicide prevention program for the country can be utilized as baseline guidelines for furthering postvention programs. This chapter provides an overview of recent advances and major themes in this regard.

Introduction

Several studies show that in South Africa suicidal behavior is a significant health care problem. Figures reflect only a part of the problem and are beset with many difficulties, including underreporting, different cultural and religious perceptions of suicide, disguised causes or precipitators of suicide to avoid stigma or potential legal problems, and the absence of comprehensive surveillance or recording systems. Therefore, data must be interpreted with caution when making cross-cultural and cross-regional comparisons (Schlebusch, 2005a, 2011a) in this country which has a multicultural population of about 54 million and where 11 official languages are spoken (Statistics South Africa, 2014).

Suicide rates in South Africa have ranged from about 11 per 100,000 (or lower in early studies, mostly from predemocratic era, based on pre-1994 limited data), to as high as 25 per 100,000 of the population (based on more recent figures) (Bantjes & Kagee, 2013; Burrows, Schlebusch, Musisi, Kinyanda, & Kizza, 2011; Mars, Burrows, Hjelmeland, & Gunnell, 2014; Schlebusch, 2005a, 2012a, 2012b). About 9.6% to 12% of nonnatural deaths per annum in all age groups and about 9.5% in young people are suicide-related. In suicides, males predominate (about 80% of suicides) with an approximate male to female ratio of 4–5:1. Consistent with global findings, there is a shift from older to younger people (Schlebusch, 2005a, 2012b). Recent figures show the highest prevalence rate (35.9%) is in the 15–29 age range (Bantjes & Kagee, 2013). These statistics confirm that thousands of people's lives annually are affected by suicidal behavior directly or indirectly, underscoring the dire need to provide postvention services in South Africa.

In this context, interest in postvention programs, which have been lacking in many geographical areas in the past, has taken on a new impetus. Rapid sociopolitical, economic, and other changes associated with transformation have occurred in the country since the advent of a democratic system of government in 1994 (i.e., in the post-apartheid era). These changes have impacted on the population at risk for suicidal behavior and suggested requirements regarding policy development, prevention, and postvention (Schlebusch, 2005a, 2012a). By contextualizing related issues, this chapter provides an overview of relevant major themes.

Role of Depression and Other Considerations

The strong influence of culture requires a deep understanding of the cultural context in which to help survivors. Their reactions can vary cross-culturally, and postvention has to be done judiciously. Several South African publications by survivors have (generalized reactions aside), mirrored how personalized their grieving can be (Magubane, 2005; Schlebusch, 2005a; Shand, 2013; Walne, 2014). This ranges from finding the strength to write about their intense grief and self-doubts, to a journey of searching for answers and sharing their experiences of learning to live with their loss and achieving eventual hope and recovery.

Survivors who become severely depressed following the suicide of a loved one often lack the cognitive, psychological, or physical capacity to cope, and frequently turn to their family physician as a first option because of a scarcity of mental health resources and limited access to, and a shortage of, postvention programs. Accordingly, as in the case of the general population (Schlebusch, 2005b), depression is commonly found among survivors in primary health care settings. Still, it remains often underdiagnosed because the survivors tend to fall into a heterogeneous group that lack the clear-cut symptoms of the various depressed subgroups described in official nomenclatures. Survivors can be unaware themselves that they are depressed. It is wise, therefore, to be alert to the possibility of depression (or other mental health problems) in survivors seen in postvention efforts. However, therapists should be aware that cultural aspects can modify the expression and/or presentation of depression in survivors, which can be further obfuscated by traditional beliefs (Schlebusch, 2005a, 2011a).

Further to general bereavement themes for survivors (Dyregrov, Grad, De Leo, & Cimitan, 2014; Dunne & Dunne-Maxim, 2009), cardinal culture-specific reactions require prudent postvention efforts (Schlebusch, 2005a). Examples include the desire to avoid the associated stigma, where secrecy is perpetuated because of negative cultural sanctions, and when the unremitting search for "why" in trying to understand how the suicidal mind works is complicated by perceptions about the role of spirits of the ancestors, and supernatural or evil spirits (Schlebusch, Burrows, & Vawda, 2009). It may also happen that, as part of the blame game, feelings of ambiguity encroach on the survivor's adjustment, because of a sense of abandonment or resentment about being left in the predicament of a survivor. This may also follow discoveries of distressing, previously unknown information about the person who has committed suicide, who had presented a different façade to what was portrayed to the outside world.

In addition, South Africa has a significant HIV/AIDS problem, and a nexus between HIV/AIDS and suicidal behavior has been well-documented (Schlebusch & Govender, 2015). HIV/AIDS carries unique stressors which have to be addressed in a postvention program if the suicidal behavior is HIV/AIDS related, particularly where partner infidelity, complicated family dynamics, and vulnerable children are involved (Schlebusch, 2005a, 2012b). The same applies if other potentially life-threatening diseases played a role in suicidal behavior (Schlebusch, 2011b, 2012c).

Finally, children can be severely affected by a suicide in their family (Schlebusch, 2012b). In a South African exploration of the experiences of adolescent survivors, salient features regarding the emotional legacy involved guilt, self-blame, blaming others, anger, restriction of a sense of self in terms suboptimal coping and behavioral patterns, changes in relationship dynamics, and suicidality (Hoffman, Myburgh, & Poggenpoel, 2010). Although the need to prioritize the prevention, research, capacity building, and resource mobilization for child injury has been emphasized in South Africa (van Niekerk, Suffla, & Seedat, 2012), postvention specifically for children is not widespread.

To deal more effectively with such issues, and to avoid family and other conflict in those who would otherwise be a source of support, the earlier the postvention is instituted, the better. A problem, however, is that postvention has to be designed within a resource-limited context. This can be addressed by relying heavily on community-based trained volunteers and a buddy system drawn from a relevant cultural perspective. Buddy intervention support programs in South Africa have been found to be effective (Naidoo, Gathiram, & Schlebusch, 2014). The *buddies* (survivor-nominated individuals) are trained by clinicians with relevant postvention expertise and empowered to provide postvention counseling, support, and specialized referral where necessary.

Survivor Support Groups

There is no national suicidology association in South Africa that provides guidelines, and no written protocol exists, but after a suicide, the police are usually the first to be contacted, followed by a doctor and priest where applicable. In some areas, crisis teams may be available, and postvention programs have existed for several decades (Schlebusch, 2005a). Nongovernmental organizations such as the South African Depression and Anxiety Group (SADAG), Lifeline, Samaritans/Befrienders Worldwide, and the South African Federation for Mental Health also offer support. There are no specific postvention divisions, but some organizations offer telephone helplines, counseling, referral services to mental health professionals, educational material, and outreach programs that include school visits.

Sometimes, in their struggle to process the traumatic experiences and their need for reciprocal support, the bereaved themselves start support groups. In line with international recommendations (Grad, De Leo, Dyregrov, Andriessen, & Cimitan, 2014), experience has taught that group meetings should be conducted by both an experienced therapist, who is skilled in suicide postvention, and a moderator–survivor. This is a pivotal prerequisite, as in many culture-specific situations, there can be a reluctance to speak openly about being bereaved through suicide. This may be present especially where this status is seen as unacceptable and where it may lead to either social isolation or self-imposed social sanctions. Support groups are then augmented by information to destigmatize suicide and to encourage survivors to mourn for as long as they need to, and as dictated by their relevant cultural traditions.

Some African societies are sensitive to funeral ceremonies, and where a traumatic death such as suicide is involved, it can impact on the community's response (Schlebusch, 2011a) and complicate the course of the bereavement process. Support needs to reach well beyond the family of the deceased, because adverse social reactions can result in secondary traumatization if survivors feel rejected, neglected, or subjected to sociocultural disapproval. In subcultural groups, impediments can arise when survivors initially experience compassion and support from those around them, which may decrease when the survivors attempt to reestablish a sense of meaning and cohesion in their lives. In such situations, postvention practices are not intended to be prescriptive, but aim to psychologically reempower survivors to "survive" and to conceptualize a reconstruction of a future by embracing a renewed appreciation of life. These are highly relevant considerations in a society where suicide-related stigma is often unresolved (Schlebusch, 2005a, 2011a; Vaughan, 2012). As in suicide prevention programs (Schlebusch, 2012a), the aim is to create appropriate and salient local strategies.

Prevention Initiatives as Postvention

It has been suggested that postvention can be a form of suicide prevention among survivors (Andriessen, 2009), because of their risk to develop suicidal behavior themselves. In the light of this, elements of the recommended national suicide prevention program for the country (Schlebusch, 2012a) can be utilized as baseline guidelines for furthering postvention. Since there is no preoperational framework, collaborative action between the various parties requires a comprehensive multisectoral approach that involves health care and non–health care sectors.

Critical key proposed procedures of relevance include suicide awareness raising and wide dissemination of information on suicidal behavior, its risk factors, means restriction regarding access to suicide methods, and the need for postvention. Because of unique circumstances surrounding each suicide, specialized knowledge and skills are required, which create a pressing need to educate clinicians and health professionals in primary health care about postvention and its importance. Informed government strategies should be developed to draw together different government departments and related services, such as the police, the legal profession, the clergy, education and school personnel, and social services. This will help to facilitate improved data collection and collaborative data exchange and research on suicide prevention and postvention. Further, improved networking and interglobal cooperation are necessary, along with facilitating access to the latest information about postvention.

A number of recommendations can be made on an individual level. These include providing access to treatment of comorbid psychiatric/psychological conditions by well-trained health care practitioners with the necessary specialized knowledge and skills, and facilitating follow-up to survivor help immediately after the suicide, as well as in the long term. This should allow for the provision of afterhours, weekend, and workplace support and better information about how to access these services. Moreover, further education and training should be expedited to those who already offer postvention services in order to promote enhanced skills development. Last, but not least, the important role of voluntary agencies and existing networks within a national postvention policy should be emphasized. The World Health Organization has drafted strategy proposals for suicide preventive work and published a series of documents on how to prevent suicide in various settings, including on how to start a postvention group (World Health Organization, 2008). Where possible, these guidelines can be incorporated in the above.

Conclusions

There is an obvious need to prioritize postvention in South Africa. Although postvention is provided in some areas, strong themes continue to emerge that center around facilitating a national effort and improving existing services in a manner that is culturally sensitive and appreciated by the bereaved. Based on the opportunity to gather appropriate information from a mixed forum of personal experiences, research data, bereaved persons, and other sources, recommendations have been formulated for enhanced postvention efforts.

Corresponding author

Lourens Schlebusch
Nelson R. Mandela School of Medicine
University of KwaZulu-Natal
Durban
South Africa
schlebuschl@ukzn.ac.za

References

Andriessen, K. (2009). Can postvention be prevention? *Crisis, 30*(1), 43–47. http://doi.org/10.1027/0227-5910.30.1.43

Bantjes, J., & Kagee, A. (2013). Epidemiology of suicide in South Africa: Setting an agenda for future research. *South African Journal of Psychology, 43*(2), 238–251. http://doi.org/10.1177/0081246313482627

Burrows, S., Schlebusch, L., Musisi, S., Kinyanda, E., & Kizza, R. (2011). Self-directed violence. In O. Kobusingye, B. Bowman, S. Burrows, R. Matzopoulos, & A. Butchart (Eds.), *Violence and health in the WHO African region* (pp. 119–161). Brazzaville, Congo: Regional Office for Africa, World Health Organization.

Dunne, E. J., & Dunne-Maxim, K. (2009). Why suicide loss is different for the survivors. In D. Wasserman & C. Wasserman (Eds.), *Oxford textbook of suicidology and suicide prevention: A global perspective* (pp. 606–608). Oxford, UK: Oxford University Press.

Dyregrov, K., Grad, O., De Leo, D., & Cimitan, A. (2014). Surviving suicide. In D. De Leo, A. Cimitan, K. Dyregrov, O. Grad, & K. Andriessen (Eds), *Bereavement after traumatic death: Helping the survivors* (pp. 37–48). Göttingen, Germany: Hogrefe.

Grad, O., De Leo, D., Dyregrov, K., Andriessen, A., & Cimitan, A. (2014). Postvention: How to organize it. In D. De Leo, A. Cimitan, K. Dyregrov, O. Grad, & K. Andriessen (Eds), *Bereavement after traumatic death: Helping the survivors* (pp. 115–124). Göttingen, Germany: Hogrefe.

Hoffman, W. A., Myburgh, C., & Poggenpoel, M. (2010). The lived experiences of late-adolescent female suicide survivors: "A part of me died." *Health SA Gesondheid, 15*(1), 1–9.

Magubane, F. (2005). *Son, are you standing or hanging?* Pietermaritzburg, South Africa: Shuter & Shooter.

Mars, B., Burrows, S., Hjelmeland, H., & Gunnell, D. (2014). Suicidal behaviour across the African continent: A review of the literature. *BMC Public Health, 14*(14), 606. http://doi.org/10.1186/1471-2458-14-606

Naidoo, S. S., Gathiram, P., & Schlebusch, L. (2014). Effectiveness of a buddy intervention support programme for suicidal behaviour in a primary care setting. *South African Family Practice, 56*(5), 263–270. http://doi.org/10.1080/20786190.2014.980159

Schlebusch, L. (2005a). *Suicidal behaviour in South Africa.* Pietermaritzburg, South Africa: University of Kwa-Zulu Natal Press.

Schlebusch, L. (2005b). Depression and suicidal behaviour. *South African Family Practice, 47*(5), 61–63. http://doi.org/10.1080/20786204.2005.10873234

Schlebusch, L. (2011a). An overview of suicidal behaviour in Africa. In D. M. Ndetei & C. P. Szabo (Eds.), *Contemporary psychiatry in Africa: A review of theory, practice and research* (pp. 375–396). Nairobi, Kenya: Acrodile.

Schlebusch, L. (2011b). Suicide risk and cancer. In L. Berman, & M. Pompili (Eds.), *Medical conditions associated with suicide risk* (pp. 59–74). Washington, DC: American Association of Suicidology.

Schlebusch, L. (2012a). Suicide prevention: A proposed national strategy for South Africa. *African Journal of Psychiatry, 15*(6), 1–3.

Schlebusch, L. (2012b). Suicidal behaviour. In A. van Niekerk, S. Suffla, & M. Seedat (Eds.), *Crime, violence and injury in South Africa: 21st century solutions for child safety* (pp. 178–194). Johannesburg, South Africa: Psychological Society of South Africa (PsySSA).

Schlebusch, L. (2012c). Suicidal behaviour in the chronic medically ill. In A. Shrivastava, M. Kimbrell, & D. Lester (Eds.), *Suicide from a global perspective: Vulnerable populations and controversies* (pp. 65–71). New York, NY: Nova Science.

Schlebusch, L., Burrows, S., & Vawda, N. (2009). Suicide prevention and religious traditions on the African continent. In D. Wasserman & C. Wasserman (Eds), *Oxford textbook of suicidology and suicide prevention: A global perspective* (pp. 63–69). Oxford, UK: Oxford University Press.

Schlebusch, L., & Govender, R. D. (2015). Elevated risk of suicidal ideation in HIV-positive persons. *Depression, Research and Treatment, 2015*, 1–6. http://doi.org/10.1155/2015/609172

Shand, K. (2013). *Boy: The story of my teenage son's suicide.* Johannesburg, South Africa: Joburg, MF Books.

Statistics South Africa. (2014). *Mid-year population estimates 2014. Statistical release, P0302.* Retrieved from http://www.statssa.gov.za/publications/P0302/P03022014.pdf

van Niekerk, Suffla, & Seedat, M. (Eds.) (2012). *Crime, violence and injury in South Africa: 21st century solutions for child safety.* Johannesburg, South Africa: Psychological Society of South Africa (PsySSA).

Vaughan, M. (2012). The discovery of suicide in Eastern and Southern Africa. *African Studies, 71*(2), 234–250. http://doi.org/10.1080/00020184.2012.702967

Walne, H. (2014). *The diving. Life, loss and everything in-between.* Johannesburg, South Africa: Penguin.

World Health Organization. (2008). *Preventing suicide: How to start a survivors' group.* Geneva: Author.

Part IV.4

Asia-Pacific

Chapter 43

Australia – Postvention Australia

National Association for the Bereaved by Suicide

Dagmar Ceramidas[1,2], Alan Staines[3], and Diego De Leo[4,5]

[1]Academic Unit of General Practice, The Australian National University Medical School, Canberra, ACT, Australia
[2]Research School of Population Health, The Australian National University, Canberra, ACT, Australia
[3]Postvention Australia, National Association for the Bereaved by Suicide, Sydney, NSW, Australia
[4]De Leo Fund, Padova, Italy
[5]Australian Institute for Suicide Research and Prevention, Griffith University, Brisbane, QLD, Australia

Abstract: This chapter presents the development of Postvention Australia – National Association for the Bereaved by Suicide, within the context of Australia's remoteness and its high Indigenous population suicide rates. More specifically, the chapter outlines the activities of Postvention Australia, established specifically to lead an organized approach to the provision of services to Australians bereaved by suicide. The reasons for and difficulties with establishing the organization are presented, along with the vision, mission, and objectives. The chapter also describes activities to date, future programs, and the plans for developing quality standards for the provision of postvention services in Australia.

Introduction

Australia is a big country, and the pattern of Australian habitation provides serious challenges to access and equity, and quality of service provision, particularly mental health and primary health care. Australia's land mass covers an area of about 7,692 million km² (Australian Government, 2015) which is only slightly smaller than that of the adjoining 48 US states, and more than 50% greater than the size of the European Union. However, 70% of mainland Australia is considered desert land, and 70% of the population lives in the major cities, predominantly on the east coast (Australian Government, 2015).

The Australian population experiences a daily average of seven deaths by suicide. In 2014, from the most recent data, the suicide rate was 12 per 100,000 inhabitants (Australian Bureau of Statistics, 2016). The suicide rates of Indigenous populations are 2.5 times higher for men and 3.4 times higher for women compared with the non-Indigenous population (Mindframe, 2016), and they reside predominantly in the most difficult-to-access regions of Australia. The Australian Institute of Health and Welfare (2015) reported that the most common external causes of death for Indigenous people were suicide (4.8% of all deaths), and motor vehicle accidents (3.9% of all deaths).

Similar to rural populations elsewhere in the world, men in remote areas of Australia also present a higher-than-average suicide risk, being 2.6 times more likely to commit suicide than their city-dwelling counterparts (Kõlves, Milner, McKay, & De Leo, 2012). Considering the geographical characteristics of Australia and the imbalance of suicide rates in the most difficult-to-service areas, the challenge to postvention is severe. The National Mental Health Commission has stated that "people living in regional, rural and remote areas of Australia make up 30 per cent of the population, but do not receive anywhere near 30 per cent of funding and services for mental health" (National Mental Health Commission, 2014, p. 97). The need for coordinated pathways in postvention, particularly in regional, rural, and remote Australia is most evident.

Why Does Australia Need a National Postvention Organization?

The social, emotional, health, mental health, and economic repercussions of suicide have been estimated to cost Australia around AUS $17.5 billion annually (Mendoza & Visser, 2009). For every suicide, it is estimated that there is an average of seven people greatly affected by the suicide (Berman, 2011). Based on this estimate, over 20,000 people in Australia will be newly bereaved in any given year. People bereaved through suicide are up to 6 times more likely to take their own life than the general population (Commonwealth of Australia, 2010). Information and support have been demonstrated to be important in helping the bereaved survive through the pain of grief (Mendoza & Visser, 2009; Sakinofsky, 2007).

In the midst of a suicide loss, there is a plethora of emotions among those most closely affected, as well as family and friends making every effort to provide help. One never knows what one needs to know until the need arises, and support at the time of a death by suicide requires a clear and timely approach to minimize confusion, and create a sense of stability and control in what is an overwhelmingly difficult situation. Postvention Australia was established specifically for that reason: to develop clear pathways of support and help for those closest to the grief.

Postvention Australia: Genesis, Vision, and Aims

The concept of developing a national organization for those bereaved by suicide arose through the "Future Directions for the Bereaved by Suicide" session at the third Australian Postvention Conference in 2012. Delegates voted unanimously that a national representative association for the bereaved by suicide should be established. After consultation with a number of experts in the field, Postvention Australia – National Association for the Bereaved by Suicide was launched in June 2013 at New South Wales Parliament House in Sydney, as a not-for-profit organization dedicated to preventing suicide through supporting and helping people who are "left behind" after a suicide. The organization contributes to the work of healing with young Indigenous people and their families, and communities. Postvention Australia aims to create clear pathways to help both the bereaved and those who support them through centralizing information and networking services.

The organization's vision is to reduce the impact of suicide by establishing a network that provides best practice postvention information, and guides those affected to quality holistic, physical, emotional and spiritual support, comfort, and understanding. Postvention Australia is working to grow partnerships that will contribute to developing appropriate community and web-based activities that increase the availability of and access to a knowledge base in postvention. A collaborative and community-based approach facilitates outreach to all areas of Australia.

Activities

National Postvention Conference

The first postvention conference was held in 2007 by the group of people who later created Postvention Australia. The fourth biennial conference, titled "Hope and Healing: Pathways to Hope and Healing for Those Affected by Suicide," was held in Sydney in 2014. This conference drew 200+ delegates from all areas of Australia, including 28% from rural areas, and Indigenous Australians from Western Australia, South Australia, and the Northern Territory. Over the years between 37% and 47% of delegates have been bereaved by suicide. Typically the 3-day conference includes preconference workshops, followed by two days of conference-type sessions, concluding with a healing and remembrance service on the last day. Each conference features prominent national and international plenary speakers and workshop facilitators. Plenary sessions opened with a short presentation by a bereaved-through-suicide delegate. These presentations were important, not only for the ongoing healing of presenters but also for delegates to learn how others have managed aspects of their healing process and recovery following bereavement by suicide.

Website and Newsletter

In November 2014, the interactive website (http://www.postventionaustralia.org/) was launched by radio, newspaper, and television, as the organization's key repository of information and the principal means of disseminating that information. The website includes contact details of more than 50 Australian support groups and other agencies that help people who have lost someone to suicide. In addition, the website lists resources including books, DVDs, and other websites that may be helpful to people bereaved by suicide and to those who support them. The website also supports professionals and paraprofessionals who assist the bereaved through suicide by providing access to information, national and international postvention guidelines, and networking.

The website was developed by a website committee including bereaved-by-suicide representatives, under the leadership of Dr. Sheila Clark. Over the last year, the website has had more than 5,000 unique visitors from all over the world. Postvention Australia's newsletter is e-mailed and published on the website. The aim of the newsletter is to inform the bereaved by suicide and service providers of upcoming events, reports on current activities, and additional resources. Readers include individuals, bereaved, and professionals and service providers. Since 2013, there have been more than 2,000 subscribers to the newsletter.

Partnerships

Collaborative partnerships and an integrated approach at a local, state, national, and international level are integral to supporting those affected by a suicide death. Postvention Australia has regular contact with various service providers and organizations across Australia. Many of these organizations play a vital role in supporting Postvention Australia in planning for each biannual national conference as conference committee members. Organizations include suicide prevention, postvention, and community service providers (Anglicare, Farmwide Pty Ltd, Jesuit Social Services, Lifeline, On The Line, Promote Life NT, Salvation Army Hope for Life, SANE Australia, Wesley Life Force), suicide bereavement support (Bereaved by Suicide Centre for Intense Grief Therapy, Compassionate Friends, Minimisation of Suicide Harm (MOSH), Standby/United Synergies, Wings of Hope), and academia (Griffith University, Brisbane).

One-day forums are conducted collaboratively with local and state suicide bereavement organizations. The ongoing goal is to facilitate networking and collaboration with postvention researchers, policy makers, service providers, volunteers, and related organizations.

Development of Quality Standards and Other Initiatives

Through collaboration with the Australian Institute for Suicide Research and Prevention at Griffith University, Postvention Australia is developing "national quality standards for the provision of suicide bereavement services" throughout Australia. This involves a consultative process with support and input of postvention service organizations in Australia, while also drawing on available national (e.g., Lifeline Australia, 2009) and international best practice and evidence from journal articles and the gray literature. Current models exist in the United States, Canada, and Ireland (Console, 2012), and much can be learned from the experiences that these nations can now reflect on.

Other initiatives of Postvention Australia include establishing a web-based quilt or named memorial for families wanting to honor loved ones lost to suicide. Based on positive evaluations of a previous project (Peters, Staines, Cunningham, & Ramjan, 2015), bereaved families and friends will be invited to provide information, a photo, and a tribute so that their loved ones can be honored and presented on the website. The named memorial or quilt will acknowledge the lives lost to suicide, the pain and grief experienced by the bereaved, and raise awareness of the impact of suicide in the community and the need to prevent further suicides.

Postvention Australia intends to assist (when needed) in the establishment of new support groups, and to participate in research and community projects that develop useful materials and knowledge to support those who have been affected by a suicide death, such as producing a bereaved-by-suicide package for families who have lost relatives or friends to suicide.

Conclusions

In a harsh and difficult geographic landscape, in the sixth largest country in the world, Postvention Australia is forging an awareness of the critical nature of postvention as a preventative health strategy. It is highlighting the need for a range of timely and coordinated pathways for those bereaved by suicide, whether in urban or other areas of Australia, to provide a modicum of stability and support as they start out on a postvention journey that can last a lifetime. Postvention is a relatively new concept in Australia that still requires promotion and explanation of its role in suicide prevention. Postvention Australia is at this early stage raising the profile of postvention as a major suicide prevention strategy.

Through the website's resources for professionals and for those affected by suicide, contact information for support groups across Australia, and knowledge of the existence of a broader community of support, Postvention Australia's "stitch in time" is crucial in providing effective postvention that can improve long-term outcomes in a vast array of areas for those left behind after a suicide. A coordinated postvention approach as a public health strategy maximizes productive life and health outcomes, disrupts the cycle of suicide, and contributes to well-being. In creating such coordination, Postvention Australia highlights the critical nature of care and support to those bereaved by suicide and those helping them through the possibly overwhelming stream of emotions, thoughts, and feelings. Developing pathways for support and recovery to those bereaved by a suicide death, regardless of their location in Australia, can make a positive difference in the lives of those left behind.

Corresponding authors

Dagmar Ceramides
Academic Unit of General Practice
The Australian National University Medical School
Canberra, ACT
Australia

Research School of Population Health
The Australian National University
Canberra, ACT
Australia
dagmar.ceramidas@anu.edu.aum

Alan Staines
Postvention Australia
National Association for the Bereaved by Suicide
Sydney, NSW
Australia
alanstaines@optusnet.com.au

Diego De Leo
Australian Institute for Suicide Research and Prevention
Griffith University
Brisbane, QLD
Australia

References

Australian Bureau of Statistics. (2016). *Causes of death, Australia, 2014.* (Catalogue no. 3303.0). Canberra, Australia: Commonwealth of Australia. Retrieved from http://www.abs.gov.au/

Australian Government. (2015). *The Australian Continent.* Retrieved from http://www.australia.gov.au/search/site/habitable%2520land

Australian Institute of Health and Welfare. (2015). *The health and welfare of Australia's Aboriginal and Torres Strait Islander peoples 2015.* (Catalogue no. IHW 147). Canberra, Australia: Author. Retrieved from http://aihw.gov.au/WorkArea/DownloadAsset.aspx?id=60129551281

Berman, A. (2011). Estimating the population of survivors of suicide: seeking an evidence base. *Suicide and Life-Threatening Behavior, 41*(1), 110–116.

Commonwealth of Australia. (2010). *The hidden toll: Suicide in Australia.* Canberra, Australia: Author. Retrieved from http://www.aph.gov.au/senate/committee/clac_ctte/suicide/report/report.pdf

Console National Office for Suicide Prevention and Turas le Chéile. (2012). *National quality standards for the provision of suicide bereavement services. A practical resource.* Celbridge, Ireland: Console.

Retrieved from http://www.hse.ie/eng/services/list/4/Mental_Health_Services/NOSP/Resources/stand-ardsbereavement.pdf

Kõlves, K., Milner, A., McKay, K., & De Leo, D. (2012). *Suicide in rural and remote areas of Australia*. Brisbane, Australia: AISRAP. Retrieved from http://www.griffith.edu.au/__data/assets/pdf_file/0003/487218/Suicide-in-Rural-and-Remote-Areas-of-Australia2.pdf

Lifeline Australia. (2009). *Towards good practice: Standards and guidelines for suicide bereavement support groups*. Canberra, Australia: Australian Government Department of Health and Ageing. Retrieved from https://www.lifeline.org.au/About-Lifeline/Publications-Library/Publications#research_reports

Mendoza, J., & Visser, V. (2009). *Suicide is preventable: Submission to the Senate Community Affairs Committee Inquiry into Suicide in Australia*. Retrieved from http://suicidepreventionaust.org/wp-content/uploads/2012/05/Submission-to-the-Senate-Community-Affairs-Committee-FINAL-221109-all-logos.pdf

Mindframe. (2016). *Facts and stats about suicide in Australia*. Newcastle, Australia: Author. Retrieved from http://www.mindframe-media.info/for-media/reporting-suicide/facts-and-stats

National Mental Health Commission. (2014). *The national review of mental health programmes and services*. Canberra, Australia: Author. Retrieved from http://www.mentalhealthcommission.gov.au/our-reports/review-of-mental-health-programmes-and-services.aspx

Peters, K., Staines, A., Cunningham, C., & Ramjan, L. (2015). The Lifekeeper Memory Quilt: Evaluation of a suicide postvention program. *Death Studies, 39*(6), 353–359. http://doi.org/10.1080/07481187.2014.951499

Sakinofsky, I. (2007). The aftermath of suicide: Managing survivors' bereavement. *Canadian Journal of Psychiatry, 52*(6), 129S–136S.

Chapter 44

Hong-Kong – Support for People Bereaved by Suicide

Evidence-Based Practices

Yik Wa Law, Paul S. F. Yip, Paul W. C. Wong, and Amy Y. M. Chow

Department of Social Work and Social Administration,
Centre for Suicide Research and Prevention, The University of Hong Kong, China

Abstract: Suicide is one of the leading causes of unnatural death in Hong Kong, and thousands of people experience suicide bereavement every year. With an increased awareness of suicide prevention and postvention, various service models of bereavement care for people bereaved by suicide have been initiated in the past decade in Hong Kong. This chapter discusses the historical development, current practice, and challenges of postvention in Hong Kong. It also presents a multidimensional model for postvention.

Introduction

Hong Kong is a special administrative region of China and has a population of 7.3 million. Suicide is one of the leading causes of unnatural death in Hong Kong (Yip, Law, & Law, 2003), and about 900 people die by suicide every year (Centre for Suicide Research and Prevention, 2015; Yip, Law, & Chan, 2013). It is estimated that thousands of families and friends experience suicide bereavement each year. Stigmatization related to suicide is often present in traditional Chinese societies (Chow & Yip, 2011; Wong, Chan, & Beh, 2007), which may further complicate the complex feelings involved in suicide bereavement (Chow, 2006; Chow & Yip, 2011; Jordan & McMenamy, 2004). For example "feeling shameful" or "losing face" by family members of people who died by suicide may hinder disclosure of the death and help-seeking behavior, often resulting in insufficient care and follow-up (Chow & Chan, 2006). Despite the growing number of services available for people bereaved by suicide in Hong Kong in the past decade, there remain many challenges for developing and implementing high-quality services. This chapter presents the development and an overview of the current practice, and a proposed model for improved care for people bereaved by suicide in Hong Kong.

Historical Review of Suicide Bereavement Care in Hong Kong

Before specialized suicide bereavement care emerged in Hong Kong, the bereaved were usually supported by community mental health and social care services. In general, after a suicide, as well as after other traumatic deaths, social workers from the government social welfare offices approached the families within a day or 2 after death, and tangible services or referrals to clinical psychologists were scheduled a few months later. The bereaved by suicide, who required emotional support, sought help from family service centers, where staff members have been trained in family counseling, but not in suicide bereavement.

The first community-based individual, family, and group bereavement counseling in Hong Kong was offered to people bereaved by suicide in 1997 by the Jessie and Thomas Tam Bereavement Counseling Centre. As the number of bereaved by suicide who sought help remained relatively small, therapeutic groups for the bereaved usually consisted of (and still do) bereaved individuals from all types of death. Although this kind of mixed closed group allowed addressing general bereavement needs, the unique features associated with suicide bereavement, such as a sense of abandonment and rejection by the deceased, could not be fully addressed.

Pilot Suicide Bereavement Study at the University of Hong Kong

The Care for Suicide Survivor Project was developed by the Centre for Suicide Research and Prevention (CSRP) of the University of Hong Kong over 2006–2009. The project was a joint research study with the Department of Health Forensic Pathology Unit, and aimed to identify a viable engagement strategy and an evidence-based bereavement care model for people bereaved by suicide (see also Chapter 14 in this volume). According to the standard procedure, the majority of bodies of victims of unnatural deaths were sent to the three public mortuaries operated by the Department of Health. The next day, two family members were interviewed by forensic pathologists, and formal body identification took place. The Care for Suicide Survivor Project initiated three engagement processes for people bereaved by suicide at the mortuaries and compared the acceptance rates for follow-up tailor-made bereavement services.

The three engagement strategies were: (1) on-site engagement with families bereaved by suicide by CSRP's staff at the mortuary; (2) referral by forensic pathologists to CSRP's staff after consent was granted to pass on the contact information of the bereaved; and (3) the usual practice – that is, a pamphlet about the project was given to the bereaved, and they were encouraged to contact CSRP, if needed. Such collaboration with forensic pathologists working for the Department of Health was innovative at the time, and it was believed that quality bereavement care could be provided in a timely way to people bereaved by suicide in a more proactive manner. In addition, it was acknowledged that not all bereaved by suicide required services, and a website (http://www.csrp.hku.hk/sos/) and a self-help booklet about after-death arrangements, funeral services, suicide and mental health, and grief for both adults and children was developed as a part of the project (Centre for Suicide Research and Prevention [CSRP], 2007, 2012a).

For the bereaved by suicide who needed help, a structured professional-led support group model was developed. The groups aimed to assist the bereaved by helping them to understand their grief, and by normalizing the ways that their grief manifested, in a supportive environment. The six-session group model covered a range of topics, including psychoeducation, emotion management, relaxation techniques, closure in the grief process, and moving on in life with new goals and hope. The model had the following objectives: development of a mutual-support platform and network for participants, enhancement of participants' opportunities to discuss their painful feelings in a constructive and safe manner, enhancement of their understanding of suicide and suicide bereavement, and providing the participants with a list of life skills to adapt to changes and successfully overcome future challenges (CSRP, 2012b).

The pilot project showed that active engagement of the bereaved is related to higher acceptance of follow-up services and motivation to seek help, in comparison with referral by pathologists or engagement through service brochures (Wong, 2014). In addition, the structured professional-led support group for the bereaved was associated with lowered levels of depressive moods, thoughts of death, and suicidal ideation at the eighth month, as compared with the second month of the suicide bereavement (CSRP, 2009). There was also positive feedback from those who participated in the pilot *study: "The service offered us very useful suggestions; we were very satisfied," "the researchers provided us [with] information about funeral services and instant support at the mortuary; it was very helpful," and "I've never thought that someone can still give me advice and emotional support after the loss of my wife, my only family. Thank you so much from the bottom of my heart."*

The pilot study did not include a control group and lasted for about 2 years. However, the positive findings and the feedback received showed that people bereaved by suicide could be greatly assisted by, and benefit from, nonintrusive, proactive, and timely support. Most importantly, the study provided information for local frontline services regarding implementation of the proactive approach piloted in the study.

Current Suicide Bereavement Support by Nongovernmental Organizations in Hong Kong

During the last decade, support for people bereaved by suicide has been developed by nongovernment organizations (NGOs). Project Befriending Service for Lighting Up and Empowering Survivors of Suicide (BLESS), offered by Suicide Prevention Services since 2008 (formally known as Befrienders International, an independent registered charity established in 1995 in Hong Kong), was the first specialized suicide bereavement program in Hong Kong (http://ww.sps.org.hk/bless.php?cid=5). The project has been offering individual and structured group counseling, and organizing memorial gatherings specifically for suicide survivors. A unique feature of the program is the establishment of a virtual cemetery for memorializing people who have died by suicide (http://www.sps.org.hk/virtual-memorial/form_function.html.php) (Chow & Yip, 2011). Special events, such as seminars and public awareness programs have been held on International Survivors' Day to increase public awareness of the needs of the bereaved. Suicide Prevention Services have published books on the experiences of people bereaved by suicide, with practical tips for dealing with the loss (https://www.facebook.com/spshongkong/posts/654565167942522), including a book of artwork made by bereaved children and adolescents, and they have produced video clips and television documentaries on suicide bereavement for the general public. Of note, since the forensic pathologists have started to distribute folders for the bereavement care services, the number of the bereaved who have contact the Suicide Prevention Services has increased substantially. These efforts and ongoing collaborations have contributed to the growing public awareness and acceptance of bereavement due to suicide.

In approximately the same time period, the Samaritans (a 24-hr multilingual suicide prevention service) identified the needs of a group of English-speaking people bereaved by suicide and offered open-group and regular monthly meetings to those in need of help (Samaritans, 2013). Suicide bereavement services have also been provided by another local suicide prevention NGO, Samaritan Befrienders Hong Kong (subsequently financially supported by the government), which applies a group-work approach to empower people bereaved by suicide and to advocate for their rights.

Challenges and the Way Ahead

After 10 years of development of services for people bereaved by suicide, Hong Kong is ready to advance to the next stage. There is a need to develop evidence-based and theory-driven intervention models. Based on the literature and clinical experience, Chow (2015) proposed a new intervention model for people bereaved by suicide, which addresses the challenges posed by the diverse needs of this group. The model does not constitute a one-size-fits-all approach; instead, it includes and addresses six dimensions: family communications, traumatization, tangible needs, grief, guilt and self-blame, and stigmatization. According to the individual needs of the bereaved, different interventions can be offered at the individual, couple, family, and/ or group level. This model is currently undergoing pilot testing, and although a randomized controlled trial would be optimal from a research perspective, that methodology would involve randomization of the bereaved into an intervention and a control group, which raises substantial practical and ethical concerns.

Although public awareness of suicide can be raised by sudden suicide incidents, especially those followed by sensational media reports (Au, Yip, Chan, & Law, 2004), receptivity and commitment to suicide prevention are prone to be episodic, and tend to greatly diminish after a short period of time (Yip, Law, & Chan, 2013). Thus, establishing a long-term common goal for researchers, stakeholders, and practitioners in suicide prevention, intervention, and postvention is needed to sustain the efforts to reduce suicide and to address the pain of suicide survivors. Development of innovative community services has increased people's receptivity to sharing their experiences, resulting in a more positive atmosphere for open discussion and long-term sustainability for suicide intervention and postvention. CSRP and key stakeholders will continue to work in partnership to strive for better integration between research and practice, and dissemination and application of knowledge in suicide prevention and postvention.

Corresponding author

Yik Wa Law
Department of Social Work and Social Administration
Centre for Suicide Research and Prevention
University of Hong Kong
Hong Kong
China
flawhk@hku.hk

References

Au, J. S. K., Yip, P. S., Chan, C. L. W., & Law, Y. W. (2004). Newspaper reporting of suicide cases in Hong Kong. *Crisis, 25*(4), 161–168. http://doi.org/10.1027/0227-5910.25.4.161
Centre for Suicide Research and Prevention. (2007). *A guide to help survivors of suicide.* Retrieved from http://csrp.hku.hk/wp-content/uploads/2015/06/GuideToHelpSurvivors.pdf
Centre for Suicide Research and Prevention. (2009). *Care for Suicide Survivor Project preliminary findings* (Unpublished report). Hong Kong, China: Author.
Centre for Suicide Research and Prevention. (2012a). *Behind the grief: A handbook for survivors of suicide.* Hong Kong, China: Author. Retrieved from http://www.mindmap.hk/wordpress/wp-content/uploads/2012/10/CSRP_booklet_EngV_FINALc.pdf
Centre for Suicide Research and Prevention. (2012b). *Training manual on support groups for suicide survivors.* Hong Kong, China: Author.

Centre for Suicide Research and Prevention. (2015). *1981–2014 suicide statistics in Hong Kong*. Hong Kong, China: Author. Retrieved from http://csrp.hku.hk/statistics/

Chow, A. Y. M. (2006). The day after: The suicide bereavement experience of Chinese in Hong Kong. In C. L. W. Chan & A. Y. M. Chow (Eds.), *Death, dying and bereavement: The Hong Kong Chinese experience* (pp. 293–308). Hong Kong; China: Hong Kong University Press.

Chow, A. Y. M. (2015, June). *ADAPTS – A new bereavement care model*. Paper presented at the 2nd Hong Kong University – Tsing Hua University Academic Salon on Social Work and Counseling, Shenzhen, China.

Chow, A. Y. M., & Chan, C. L. W. (2006). Bereavement care in Hong Kong: Past, present and future. In C. L. W. Chan & A. Y. M. Chow (Eds.), *Death, dying and bereavement: The Hong Kong Chinese experience* (pp. 253–260). Hong Kong, China: Hong Kong University Press.

Chow, A. Y. M., & Yip, P. S. F. (2011). Grief after suicide: A Hong Kong Chinese perspective. In J. R. Jordan & J. L. McIntosh (Eds.), *Grief after suicide* (pp. 427–438). New York, NY: Routledge.

Jordan, J., & McMenamy, M. (2004). Interventions for suicide survivors: A review of the literature. *Suicide and Life-Threatening Behavior, 34*(4), 337–349. http://doi.org/10.1521/suli.34.4.337.53742

Samaritans. (2013). *Annual report 2012-2013*. Retrieved from https://issuu.com/samaritanshk/docs/annualreport13_finalpreview

Wong, P. W. C. (2014). Active engagement for people bereaved by suicide. *Lancet Psychiatry, 1*(2), 109. http://doi.org/10.1016/S2215-0366(14)70252-4

Wong, P. W., Chan, W. S., & Beh, P. S. (2007). What can we do to help and understand survivors of suicide in Hong Kong? *Crisis, 28*(4), 183–189. http://doi.org/10.1027/0227-5910.28.4.183

Yip, P. S. F., Law, Y. W., & Chan, M. (2013). Suicide prevention in Hong Kong: Opportunities and challenges. In J. Rogers & D. Lester (Eds.), *Preventing suicide* (Vol. 2; pp. 219–247). Westport, CT: Praeger.

Yip, P. S., Law, C. K., & Law, Y. W. (2003). *Suicide in Hong Kong: Epidemiological profile and burden analysis*, 1981 to 2001. *Hong Kong Medical Journal, 9*(6), 419–426.

Chapter 45

Japan – Research-Informed Support for Suicide Survivors

Daisuke Kawashima[1] and Kenji Kawano[2]

[1]School of Psychology, Chukyo University, Nagoya, Japan
[2]College of Comprehensive Psychology, Ritsumeikan University, Kyoto, Japan

Abstract: This chapter presents the key points concerning support for suicide survivors (i.e., the bereaved by suicide) in Japan. After describing the sociocultural context of postvention in Japan and the lack of research and related efforts, the chapter presents the results of an empirical study regarding mental health and meaning making of the bereaved by suicide. The chapter concludes with several methods of postvention, including guidelines on care for suicide survivors, training programs for professionals, a workbook for survivors, and future directions.

Introduction: Sociocultural Context of Postvention in Japan

Every year, since 1998, approximately 30,000 people die by suicide in Japan (21.4/100,000 inhabitants in 2013). With a moderate estimate of six bereaved per suicide (Shneidman, 1969), at least 180,000 people become bereaved by suicide annually. However, studies and efforts related to suicide prevention have been underdeveloped in Japan (e.g., Cho, 2006; Hirayama, 2004; Nakanishi, Yamauchi, & Takeshima, 2014). The Basic Act for Suicide Prevention was instituted by the Japanese government in June 2006 to address this situation. The purpose of the Act is comprehensive suicide prevention and improvement of support for suicide survivors. Suicide prevention and support for the bereaved are two wheels of a cart. The Act was immediately followed by the launch of General Principles of Suicide Prevention Policy (Cabinet Office, Government of Japan, 2007). The Principles note the demand for postvention, as well as the importance of suicide prevention and intervention. They also call for research to study the experiences of suicide survivors.

The literature on support for suicide survivors in Japan includes reports on survivors' mental health and social contexts. Cho (2006) describes the mental health and grief reactions of the suicide survivors, and Hirayama (2004) reports on grief reactions and the needs of the suicide survivors. These reports have several shortcomings, such as small sample sizes (fewer than 20 participants), use of nonvalidated instruments, and an unclear sampling process. These studies also did not consider theoretical and methodological perspectives.

Mental Health and Social Contexts of Japanese Suicide Survivors: Empirical Findings

Working toward overcoming the aforementioned issues, a study was conducted to investigate the mental health status and the social context of Japanese suicide survivors (Kawashima, Kawano, Koyama, & Ito, 2010). Thirty-two known support groups for suicide survivors were contacted and asked for their assistance and 23 agreed to cooperate. A total of 461 questionnaires were sent to the groups with an invitation to circulate them among their members and contacts. One hundred and eleven suicide survivors returned the questionnaire (24.1%) and these were analyzed in the study. The questionnaire looked at the mental health status, meaning reconstruction, social context, and time since the loss.

To assess the mental health status of the suicide survivors, the six-item Kessler Psychological Distress Scale (K6; Kessler et al., 2003) and the Life-Fulfillment Scale (Kawashima et al., 2010) were used. Total scores on the K6 range from 0 to 24, with scores of 5 or above indicating the possibility of psychological distress (e.g., mood and anxiety disorders) in the Japanese population (Sakurai, Nishi, Kondo, Yanagida, & Kawakami, 2011). The Life-Fulfillment Scale consists of 6 items, and the total score ranges from 0 to 24. Its factor validity, construct validity, and internal consistency were confirmed (Kawashima et al., 2010).

Meaning reconstruction – that is, meaning sense making and benefit finding – was assessed using single-item questions (Currier, Holland, & Neimeyer, 2006; Davis, Wortman, Lehman, & Silver, 2000; Holland, Currier, & Neimeyer, 2006; Lehman, Wortman, & Williams, 1987). *Sense making* is the activity of questioning, finding, and gaining a sense of comprehension about the bereavement. *Benefit finding* is the activity of building new meaning structures and finding positive implications of the loss (Gillies & Neimeyer, 2006, Kawashima, 2008). Participants were asked to answer each question on a Likert scale (from 1= *not at all*, to 4 *strongly felt*). Participants also answered questions about social support and "secondary wounding" – that is, a psychological scar that occurs postsuicide (Hirayama, 2004; Jishi Iji Henshu Iinkai & Ashinaga Ikueikai, 2005). Participants were asked to report their experiences of support and "wounding" from other people, such as a family member, a relative, a friend, etc. The experience of support and wounding ranged from 0=*none*, to 4=*strongly felt*.

Using the score of 5 as a cutoff point on the K6, 78% of the participants were found to have a mood and/or anxiety disorder. Similarly, Cho (2006) reported that 63% of Japanese suicide survivors have depression and 81% of the survivors have posttraumatic stress disorder (PTSD) symptoms (the levels of depression and PTSD before the suicide were not reported by Cho, 2006). Previous international studies have also mentioned that suicide survivors may experience psychological difficulties and may require professional support (Cerel & Campbell, 2008; de Groot, de Keijser, & Neeleman, 2006; Provini, Everett, & Pfeffer, 2000), and professionals should offer specialized help, including psychological and/or psychiatric support (Kawano, 2011; Kawashima et al, 2010).

The experience of suicide bereavement is a critical wound for the survivors, but they can also be wounded by the insensitive comments and behaviors of others after the suicide (Hirayama, 2004; Jishi Iji Henshu Iinkai & Ashinaga Ikueikai, 2005). Participants reported that they were most frequently wounded, and also most frequently supported, by family members, as shown in **Figure 45.1**. In accordance with previous reports (Hirayama, 2004; Jishi Iji Henshu Iinkai & Ashinaga Ikueikai, 2005), almost 60% of the participants reported an experience of secondary wounding by relatives. However, nearly 70% of participants also reported social support by them at the same time. Further, the results of the current study showed a low percentage of experience of secondary wounding by health professionals and police officers. It differs slightly from previous studies showing that suicide survivors are often wounded by those professionals, relatives, health professionals, and police officers (Hirayama, 2004; Jishi Iji Henshu Iinkai & Ashinaga Ikueikai, 2005). In addition, participants in the current study reported that they were wounded, as well as supported, by other suicide bereaved. They also reported less secondary wounding and less social support by local government officers, lawyers, and emergency service workers, suggesting that these professionals were not recognized as significant people by the suicide survivors.

A multiple linear regression analysis was conducted to identify the statistical model that best explained the reported mental health status of the bereaved. In the analysis, mental health variables (i.e., K6 and the life-fulfillment score) were incorporated as dependent variables, and meaning reconstruction (i.e., sense making and benefit finding), social context (i.e., social support and secondary wounding), and information concerning how many months previously the death had occurred were included as independent variables.

The analysis showed that sense making predicted the participants' adaptation to loss – that is, degree of depression and life fulfilment – as shown in **Table 45.1**. Social support and amount of time elapsed since the loss was also significantly related to their mental health status. This could imply that professionals and other people surrounding suicide survivors can be significant sources of social support and make a scaffold for survivors' meaning reconstruction.

In summary, the study revealed a number of important points (Kawashima, Kawano, Koyama, & Ito, 2010). First, it seems that a significant percentage of suicide survivors suffer psychological distress, which underlines the importance of providing mental health support. Second, the suicide survivors in this study were most frequently wounded, and also most frequently supported, by family members. Third, sense making seemed to facilitate the suicide survivors' adaptation to loss; and social support and time elapsed since the loss were also significantly related to mental health status of the bereaved. The study shows that despite the possibility of mental health problems, suicide survivors may use existing support and show resilient adaptation after the traumatic loss. The survivors also tried to confront their situation

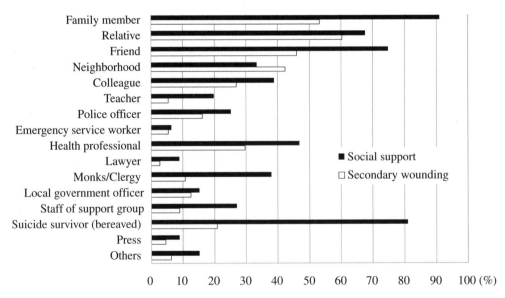

Figure 45.1. Social support and secondary wounding of Japanese suicide survivors.
Source: Based on Kawano, 2011.

proactively, rather than passively allowing the traumatic loss to overwhelm them (Hirayama, 2004; Jishi Iji Henshu Iinkai & Ashinaga Ikueikai, 2005; Zenkoku Jishiizoku Soudan Center, 2008). Thus, professionals should not only consider survivors' mental health; they should also encourage the bereaved to grieve actively.

Table 45.1. Results of regression analysis

	Mental Health	
	K6	Life Fulfillment
Independent variables	β	β
Sense making	−.24*	.26*
Benefit finding	−.21	.19
Social support (Sum)[a]	−.09	.33**
Secondary wounding (Sum)	.20	−.16
Months since the death occurred	−.23	.32**
R^2	.26**	.33***

Notes. Source: Kawashima, Kawano, Koyama, & Ito, 2010, p. 60.
[a] Regarding support and wounding, "Others" was excluded in the regression analysis. Thus, the sum of the support and the sum of wounding ranged from 0 to 60.
*$p < .05$, **$p < .01$, ***$p < .001$.

Postvention in Action: Future Directions

The above findings have served as a basis for a number of postvention initiatives. They have been incorporated into the guidelines for care for suicide survivors in Japan (Ministry of Health, Labour and Welfare, 2009), which was established as a useful tool for those who provide support for survivors. The guidelines contain illustrations of survivors' mental health status, grief reactions, and techniques and recommendations for support. The guideline will be revised in the near future and will include special care for children who have lost a parent by suicide. Training programs were also established for specialists such as clinicians, local government officers, and clinical psychologists. The programs included lectures on suicide prevention and postvention, group work, and exercises. The effectiveness of the training programs was assessed using validated scales such as the Japanese version of the Suicide Intervention Response Inventory (SIRI-J: Kawashima & Kawano, 2012, 2013; Kawashima, Kawano, & Ito, 2010) and the Japanese version of the Attitudes to Suicide Prevention Scale (ASP-J: Kawashima, Kawano, & Shiraga, 2013).

Further, a narrative workbook for suicide survivors has been developed (Kawashima, 2014, 2015). It is based on a narrative approach, and contains activities to facilitate meaning reconstruction, to promote survivors' commitment to their own grief work and their communication with other people. The workbook consists of six chapters, each with two to four exercises (Kawashima, 2014). For example, the "Mapping the Influence of Loss" exercise asks the bereaved to consider the influence of the loss and to write down narratives in several meaning construction domains, such as daily activities, priorities, and my emotion (Kawashima, 2015).

Despite the increasing research evidence from Japan, there is still insufficient knowledge and community awareness to support suicide survivors. In particular, the bereaved frequently report difficulties in their grief work because of social stigma (Hirayama, 2004; Jishi Iji Henshu Iinkai & Ashinaga Ikueikai, 2005; Zenkoku Jishiizoku Soudan Center, 2008). Future studies should investigate the effects of stigma on survivors' ability to adapt and how to destigmatize suicide. Evaluation of the effectiveness of clinical interventions and/or support groups also remains a priority issue. Moreover, Japanese people often have empathic attitudes toward beautification of suicide, as shown in Japanese novels and films (Fuse, 1984), and these attitudes might affect the grief process of Japanese suicide survivors. Cross-cultural research is needed to investigate the differences of attitude toward suicide. Further studies should address these issues along with the continuing postvention efforts.

Corresponding author

Daisuke Kawashima
School of Psychology
Chukyo University
Nagoya
Japan
daisuke1102@hotmail.com

References

Cabinet Office, Government of Japan. (2007). *Jisatsu Sogo Taisaku Taiko* [General principles of suicide prevention policy]. Tokyo, Japan: Author.

Cerel, J. & Campbell, F. (2008). Suicide survivors seeking mental health services: A preliminary examination of the role of an active postvention model. *Suicide and Life-Threatening Behavior, 38*(1), 30–34. http://doi.org/10.1521/suli.2008.38.1.30

Cho, Y. (2006). *Hitowa naze jisatsu surunoka* [Why do people die by suicide?]. Tokyo, Japan: Bensei.

Currier, J. M., Holland, J. M., & Neimeyer, R. A. (2006). Sense-making, grief, and the experience of violent loss: toward a mediational model. *Death Studies, 30*(5), 403–428. http://doi.org/10.1080/07481180600614351

Davis, C. G., Wortman, C. B., Lehman, D. R., & Silver, R. C. (2000). Searching for meaning in loss: Are clinical assumptions correct? *Death Studies, 24*(6), 497–540. http://doi.org/10.1080/07481180050121471

de Groot, M., de Keijser, J., & Neeleman, J. (2006). Grief shortly after suicide and natural death: A comparative study among spouses and first-degree relatives. *Suicide and Life-Threatening Behavior, 36*(4), 418–431. http://doi.org/10.1521/suli.2006.36.4.418

Fuse, T. (1984). *Jisatsu to bunka* [Suicide and culture]. Tokyo, Japan: Shincho Sensho.

Gillies, J., & Neimeyer, R. A. (2006). Loss, grief, and the search for significance: Toward a model of meaning reconstruction in bereavement. *Journal of Constructivist Psychology, 19*(1), 31–65. http://doi.org/10.1080/10720530500311182

Hirayama, M. (2004). *Mizukara itta anata, nokosareta watashi: Kazoku no jishi to mukiau* [You made away with yourself, and I am bereaved]. Tokyo, Japan: Asahi Shinbunsha.

Holland, J. M., Currier, J. M., & Neimeyer, R. A. (2006). Meaning reconstruction in the first two years of bereavement: The role of sense-making and benefit-finding. *Omega: Journal of Death and Dying, 53*(3), 175–191. http://doi.org/10.2190/FKM2-YJTY-F9VV-9XWY

Jishi Iji Henshu Iinkai, & Ashinaga Ikueikai. (2005). *Jisatsu tte ienakatta* [Can't say "Jisatsu" (Suicide)]. Tokyo, Japan: Sunmark.

Kawano, K. (2011). The mental health of persons bereaved by suicide. *Seishin Shinkeigaku Zasshi, 113*(1), 87–93.

Kawashima, D. (2008). Meaning reconstruction theory: Perspectives and future approaches. *Japanese Psychological Review, 51*(4), 485–499.

Kawashima, D. (2014). *Jishi de taisetsu na hito wo ushinatta anataheno naratibu wa-kubukku* [Narrative workbook for suicide survivors]. Tokyo, Japan: Shinyosha.

Kawashima, D. (2015). Mapping the influence of loss. In R. A. Neimeyer (Ed.), *Techniques of grief therapy. Volume 2: Assessment and intervention* (pp. 113–116). New York, NY: Routledge.

Kawashima, D., & Kawano, K. (2012). Development of a short version of the suicide intervention response inventory. *Japanese Journal of Psychology, 83*(4), 330–336. http://doi.org/10.4992/jjpsy.83.330

Kawashima, D., & Kawano, K. (2013). The validity of the Japanese version of the suicide intervention response inventory. *Journal of Mental Health (Seishinhoken Kenkyu), 59*, 67–74.

Kawashima, D., Kawano, K., & Ito, H. (2010). Development of the Japanese version of the suicide intervention response inventory (SIRI). *Seishin Igaku, 52*(6), 543–551.

Kawashima, D., Kawano, K., Koyama, T., & Ito, H. (2010). Exploring the variables related to mental health of suicide survivors. *Journal of Mental Health (Seishinhoken Kenkyu), 56*, 55–63.

Kawashima, D., & Kawano, K., & Shiraga, K. (2013). Validity and reliability of the Japanese version of the attitudes to suicide prevention scale (ASP-J): To evaluate health practitioner's attitudes toward suicide prevention. *Seishin Igaku, 55*(4), 347–354.

Kessler, R. C., Barker, P. R., Colpe, L. J., Epstein, J. F., Gfroerer, J. C., Hiripi, E., ... Zaslavsky, A. M. (2003). Screening for serious mental illness in the general population. *Archives of General Psychiatry, 60*(2), 184–189. http://doi.org/10.1001/archpsyc.60.2.184

Lehman, D. R., Wortman, C. B., & Williams, A. F. (1987). Long-term effects of losing a spouse or child in a motor vehicle crash. *Journal of Personality and Social Psychology, 52*(1), 218–231. http://doi.org/10.1037/0022-3514.52.1.218

Ministry of Health, Labour and Welfare. (2009). *Jishiizoku wo sasaeru tameni: Soudan tantousha no tameno shishin* [Guideline on the support for suicide survivors]. Tokyo, Japan: Author.

Nakanishi, M., Yamauchi, T., & Takeshima, T. (2014). National strategy for suicide prevention in Japan: Impact of a national fund on progress of developing systems for suicide prevention and implementing initiatives among local authorities. *Psychiatry and Clinical Neurosciences, 69*(1), 55–64. http://doi.org/10.1111/pcn.12222

Provini, C., Everett, J. R., & Pfeffer, C. R. (2000). Adults mourning suicide: Self-reported concerns about bereavement, needs for assistance, and help-seeking behavior. *Death Studies, 24*(1), 1–19. http://doi.org/10.1080/074811800200667

Sakurai, K., Nishi, A., Kondo, K., Yanagida, K., & Kawakami, N. (2011). Screening performance of K6/K10 and other screening instruments for mood and anxiety disorders in Japan. *Psychiatry and Clinical Neurosciences, 65*(5), 434–441. http://doi.org/10.1111/j.1440-1819.2011.02236.x

Shneidman, E. (1969). Prologue: Fifty-eight years. In E. Shneidman (Ed.), *On the nature of suicide* (pp. 1–30). San Francisco, CA: Jossey-Bass.

Zenkoku Jishiizoku Soudan Center. (2008). *Jisatsu de kazoku wo nakushite: Watashitachi izoku no monogatari* [Bereaved by suicide: Survivors' narratives]. Tokyo, Japan: Sanseido.

Chapter 46

New Zealand – Development of Postvention Guidelines for Pacific Communities

Jemaima Tiatia-Seath

Pacific Health, School of Population Health, University of Auckland, New Zealand

Abstract: The New Zealand Suicide Prevention Action Plan 2013–2016 aims to support families and communities after a suicide by ensuring accessibility and availability to support services for bereaved families. In 2012, there were 30 Pacific peoples' suicides (an age-standardized rate of 10.2 per 100,000 inhabitants). The term Pacific peoples, refers to a population in New Zealand with a lineage in the major subregions of Oceania – Polynesia, Melanesia, and/or Micronesia. Given the lack of Pacific-focused postvention support, resources, and research, a Pacific-centered study was undertaken. The aim of this research was to engage communities so as to identify the most important, appropriate, and effective elements to include, not only in building a knowledge base, but also toward the development of Pacific suicide postvention guidelines.

Introduction

Objective 2 of The New Zealand Suicide Prevention Action Plan 2013–2016 (Ministry of Health, 2013) aims to support families and communities after a suicide, with a focus around action areas 4 and 5: the former, ensuring a range of accessible support services is available for families and others who are bereaved by suicide; and the latter, supporting communities to respond following suicides, particularly where there is unease around suicide clusters and suicide contagion (also see Chapter 19 in this volume). The Suicide Prevention Action Plan considers that coordinated community responses are imperative when dealing with suicide clusters. For instance, communities impacted by suicide contagion are often experiencing a suicide death for the first time and therefore need guidance to ensure an expeditious and appropriate response.

New Zealand is a multiethnic country in the Pacific Ocean with 4.6 million inhabitants (Statistics New Zealand, 2015a). English is the most widely spoken language, and Christianity the main religion. The indigenous Māori ethnic group make up 15 % of the population, with 74 % of New Zealanders identifying with at least one European ethnicity (Statistics New Zealand, 2015b).

In New Zealand, there were 30 suicides recorded for Pacific peoples (20 males and 10 females) in 2012 (Ministry of Health, 2015). The term *Pacific peoples* refers to a population in New Zealand with a lineage in the major subregions of Oceania – Polynesia, Melanesia, and/or Micronesia. They are the fourth largest major ethnic group following European, Māori and Asian ethnic groups, and make up 7.4 % of the total New Zealand population (Statistics New Zealand, 2013). Pacific communities are highly urbanized (97 %) with 92.9 % or 274,806 people living in the North Island. They are very youthful, with a median age of 21 years, in comparison with 35 years for the total population. The New Zealand–born (NZ-born) cohort, make up 62.3% or 181,791 of the total Pacific population (Statistics New Zealand, 2013). There are more than 40 diverse Pacific ethnic groups in New Zealand (Ministry of Health, 2014). It is predicted that by 2026, the Pacific population will comprise 10% of the New Zealand population (Statistics New Zealand, 2013).

Currently, there is a lack of Pacific-focused postvention research, other than work undertaken by Beautrais (2004) and Henare Ehrhardt Research (2004). It is recognized that most New Zealand District Health Boards have suicide prevention and postvention plans in place, and a recent study titled Suicide Prevention for Tongan Youth in New Zealand, provides an ethnic-specific overview of both suicide prevention and postvention (Tiatia-Seath, 2015). Yet, a knowledge gap remains in addressing Pacific-specific suicide postvention needs that are culturally appropriate, engaging, and sustainable.

Effective suicide postvention ensures that the suicide-bereaved family members, friends, and also those indirectly affected by a suicide, can receive the optimal support and help required (Andriessen & Krysinska, 2012). In addition, training is imperative for all services to increase awareness of the needs of people bereaved by suicide and available support services and resources (Peters, Cunningham, Murphy, & Jackson, 2016). The dilemma, however, is that there is a major deficit of Pacific-focused suicide postvention support training and resources, and thus, there tends to be a reliance on mainstream frameworks which may be inappropriate and irrelevant in diverse Pacific contexts. A Pacific-centered study developed and led by Tiatia-Seath (2016) in response to the concerns outlined, was funded by New Zealand's first national Māori and Pacific suicide prevention program called Waka Hourua (a metaphoric double-hulled canoe). The primary aim of that research was to engage Pacific communities in determining the most important, appropriate, and effective elements for inclusion in the development of Pacific suicide postvention guidelines. It would also contribute new knowledge to the field of suicide postvention. This would result in more culturally appropriate, relevant, and effective support for Pacific individuals, families, and communities bereaved by suicide (Tiatia-Seath, 2016).

The Pacific Postvention Study

The research design was an adaption of the South Australian Suicide Postvention Project involving a mixed methods approach with two phases over an 18-month period (October 2014 to April 2016) (Wilson & Clark, 2005). Phase 1 comprised two online surveys. One survey targeted Pacific communities bereaved by suicide and primarily looked at the types of support they received, barriers to services, and available resources. The other survey, which examined service providers working with suicide-bereaved Pacific communities or who had themselves been impacted by a suicide death, mainly addressed the types of postvention services they offered, the challenges faced when supporting suicide-bereaved families and issues around postvention training. There were 173 Pacific community respondents bereaved by suicide who took part in the online survey, and 70 service provider respondents who work with Pacific communities and/or have also been impacted by a suicide death. In addition, a further 74 Pacific peoples impacted by suicide engaged in focus group discussions in Auckland and Christchurch. Phase 2 comprised *fono* (a commonly used term by some Pacific groups for meetings) in Auckland, Christchurch, Hamilton, and Wellington, with 80 representatives from a mix of families who are bereaved by suicide, and service providers who again, work with Pacific communities and/or have been impacted by a suicide death. Participants were asked to share their views on what suicide postvention guidelines should look like for Pacific communities and what needed to be included. A total of 397 participants responded in the study.

Findings and Recommendations

It was crucial to this research that in any attempt to address Pacific suicide postvention, the voices of Pacific peoples impacted by suicide bereavement were central. There was a respectable number of responses, particularly as the topic of suicide is still very much a *tapu* (forbidden, sacred) discussion among most Pacific communities.

This chapter focuses mainly on their views contributing toward the development of Pacific specific postvention guidelines and what they should look like. The findings affirmed that there is a need for more Pacific-appropriate information. While there is some awareness of current mainstream postvention resources, there is not nearly enough, and what is available has very little impact on Pacific communities. This is primarily due to the lack of culturally relevant and appropriate written information and services. When asked what the guidelines should look like visually, responses included: concise and clear bullet-pointed messages void of clinical language or jargon which can easily be translated into the various Pacific languages and potentially reproduced into a bilingual resource. Suggestions were also made to include poetry, narratives, and proverbial sayings, to incorporate traditional and contemporary concepts, vibrant color, artwork/photos, and showcasing Pacific diversity. All of these elements are important as they resonate with Pacific peoples, and would feel Pacific owned. These factors were believed to do well to increasing the guidelines' appeal and uptake. It is also important that the postvention guidelines are an evolving document that can easily be adapted and amended to serve Pacific diversity, and are underpinned by an empowerment model and strengths-based approach.

Participants when asked what they considered were the most important topics to include in these guidelines, recommended that antistigma messages should be publicized which avoid religious condemnation and address common misconceptions that suicide is a cowardly or selfish act. Also that guidance is given to families in dealing with the coroner, the police, funeral arrangements, and key contacts, all of whom do much to alleviate the anxiety of grieving families. In addition, when working with a Pacific suicide-bereaved family, a communal approach is needed as opposed to the more mainstream individualistic approach. Not only would this prove effective, but demonstrate a good level of cultural competence. Furthermore, it was shared that Pacific communities need to feel they are in a safe environment to talk openly about their grief. Furthermore, as is the challenge of including each Pacific group's cultural protocols and processes, there are some values that apply to most and should be incorporated in Pacific-centered postvention training. These may include, for example, knowing the Pacific ethnicity or ethnicities of the family before arriving, removing footwear when entering a home, not wearing inappropriate attire (i.e., anything revealing too much skin: short skirts, tight shorts, etc), not standing directly over the person lying in state, but rather taking a seat beside them and allowing loved ones enough time with the suicide decedent at the scene to say their farewells before the investigation takes place.

With regard to the types of training and cultural models that could work in conjunction with the guidelines, it was suggested by participants that a cultural response first, before a clinical one, is a must; cultural competence training is needed particularly for those involved in the initial interaction with the grieving family – that is, the police, ambulance staff, the Victim Support organization, the coroner's office, and non-Pacific peoples in supporting roles. Face-to-face engagement, building rapport, and listening are vital. Training is needed for Pacific communities in suicide postvention who then can provide immediate and culturally safe support for families. This would also build Pacific workforce capacities in the area. It is also vitally important that the support person is well connected or has access to translators, legal advisors, financial advisors, police, mental health services, and child and youth services. The support person(s) should identify the key person(s) or champion(s) to liaise with the family and to link them into services and resources that will benefit the family. As the Pacific population is commonly seen as a homogenous group, there is value placed on Pacific ethnic-specific postvention initiatives. Moreover, there is also a growing recognition of Pacific diversity, be it multiethnic heritage, various gender identities, sexual orientation, and a decrease in religious affiliations. It was shared that there should be separate support groups offered for adults, older adults, and youths. Additionally, it was mentioned that students usually do not have the capabilities to provide support for a peer. They need information and improved access to resources to provide support for friends affected by suicide. The school is regarded as playing a key role in supporting suicide-bereaved youths. It is also fundamental that cultural reference points like respect, reciprocity, family, nurturing relationships, and identity are used, as they remind Pacific peoples of their historical resilience, values, beliefs, traditions, and strong identity.

As gatekeepers and knowledge holders, Pacific *matua* (elders) need to be included in the dialogue around suicide postvention training and support. Also community leaders and church ministers who know how to support families in initial and ongoing stages of bereavement should be trained in postvention activities. Promoting Pacific resilience is a strength, and addressing root issues rather than medicalizing the situation is essential.

The strength of this research is that suicide postvention solutions are based on the views of Pacific communities themselves and their needs. It is recognized that partnership and cooperation are crucial to this project, and that existing activities contributing to suicide postvention should be further developed (Yip, 2011). This research aimed to provide information to enhance health outcomes for Pacific communities and help inform future service delivery with the goal of supporting Pacific communities bereaved by suicide.

Conclusions

The impact this study brings is the altering of current understandings, or lack thereof, around Pacific suicide postvention. This research has enabled Pacific communities themselves to identify issues impacting those bereaved by suicide and determining the best possible means of support based on their unique experiences and a resilience that endures.

Corresponding author

Jemaima Tiatia-Seath
Pacific Health
School of Population Health
University of Auckland
Auckland
New Zealand
j.tiatia-seath@auckland.ac.nz

References

Andriessen, K., & Krysinska, K. (2012). Essential questions on suicide bereavement and postvention. *International Journal of Environmental Research and Public Health, 9*(1), 24–32. http://doi.org/10.3390/ijerph9010024

Beautrais, A. L. (2004). *Suicide postvention support for families, whānau and significant others after a suicide: A literature review and synthesis of evidence.* Wellington, New Zealand: Ministry of Youth Development.

Henare Ehrhardt Research. (2004). *Support for Māori whānau and Pacific and Asian families and significant others who have been affected by suicide attempts: An analysis of the published and grey literature.* Wellington, New Zealand: Ministry of Youth Development.

Ministry of Health. (2013). *New Zealand suicide prevention action plan 2013–2016* Wellington, New Zealand: Author.

Ministry of Health. (2014). *Tagata Pasifika in New Zealand.* Wellington, New Zealand: Author. Retrieved from http://www.health.govt.nz/our-work/populations/pacific-health/tagata-pasifika-new-zealand

Ministry of Health. (2015). *Suicide facts: Deaths and intentional self-harm hospitalisations 2012.* Wellington, New Zealand: Author.

Peters, K., Cunningham, C., Murphy, G., & Jackson, D. (2016). Helpful and unhelpful responses after suicide: Experiences of bereaved family members. *International Journal of Mental Health Nursing.* Advance online publication.

Statistics New Zealand. (2013). *2013 Census QuickStats about culture and identity.* Retrieved from http://www.stats.govt.nz/Census/2013-census/profile-and-summary-reports/quickstats-culture-identity/pacific-peoples.aspx

Statistics New Zealand. (2015a). *National population estimates: At 30 June 2015 – Media Release.* Retrieved from http://www.stats.govt.nz/browse_for_stats/population/estimates_and_projections/NationalPopulationEstimates_MRAt30Jun15.aspx

Statistics New Zealand. (2015b). *Census 2013.* Retrieved from http://www.stats.govt.nz/Census.aspx

Tiatia-Seath, J. (2015). *Suicide prevention for Tongan youth in New Zealand: Report to the Health Research Council of New Zealand and Ministry of Health for the Pacific Partnership Programme.* Auckland, New Zealand: Uniservices, The University of Auckland.

Tiatia-Seath, J. (2016). *Suicide postvention: Support for Pacific communities. A report for Waka Hourua – National suicide prevention programme for Maori and Pasifika communities.* Auckland, New Zealand: Hibiscus Research.

Wilson, A., & Clark, S. (2005). *South Australian suicide postvention project report to Mental Health Services Department of Health.* Adelaide, Australia: University of Adelaide.

Yip, P. S. F. (2011). Towards evidence-based suicide prevention programs. *Crisis, 32*(3), 117–120. http://doi.org/10.1027/0227-5910/a000100

Chapter 47

Thailand – Suicide Bereavement Support

Prakarn Thomyangkoon

College of Medicine, Rangsit University, Pathumthani, Thailand

Abstract: With an annual suicide rate of 6 per 100,000 inhabitants in Thailand, there are at least 24,000 new survivors of suicide loss annually. However, because suicide bereavement support was not available, the PRAKARN model of group psychotherapy for survivors of suicide loss was initiated approximately 5 years ago and implemented to diminish stigma among the survivors. Thai psychiatrists are also affected by suicide loss. Thus, awareness raising of suicide bereavement support should be focused on family members as well as mental health professionals.

Introduction

When someone dies by suicide, approximately six people are bereaved by the death, such as parents, siblings, cousins, and friends (Thomyangkoon, Leenaars, & Wasserman, 2005; World Health Organization, 2002). In Thailand, at least 4,000 people die by suicide every year, with hanging as the most common method, and there are at least 24,000 newly bereaved people annually. The family is often the initial target group for intervention and treatment after a suicide loss (Greenberg & Shefler, 2014). However, clinicians and care providers, such as psychiatrists, may also be affected by a suicide loss. International studies have reported that a patient's suicide may be a very distressing experience for health professionals and may have an impact on their personal and professional functioning, as presented in Chapter 21 in this volume (Bongar & Greaney, 1994; Greenberg & Shefler, 2014; Leenaars et al., 2002; Wurst, Kunz, & Skipper, 2013). Thomyangkoon and Leenaars (2008) found that more than half of Thai psychiatrists (56%) had lost a patient by suicide and experienced that event as very stressful. Therefore, it is necessary to provide postvention support to families, as well as mental health professionals such as psychiatrists, social workers, and general practitioners.

Families

When a suicide occurs in the family, the first reaction is often to deny that a suicide has happened. Family members frequently experience guilt and shame, and they may struggle with depression and stigma. Survivors of suicide loss often withdraw socially – for example, stop performing their jobs, avoid socializing, or move out of town. Some try to decrease their sadness by not looking at loved ones' mementos, such as photos. The impact of the loss not only happens in real life, but may also occur in a dream. Some of the bereaved may have suicidal thoughts or plans, or may attempt suicide. Religious practice is an important part of the daily life of the Thai people and in the northeastern part of Thailand the bereaved families often take a photo, clothes, or other personal belongings of the deceased to a Buddhist temple as a donation to the poor and in this way accrue merit for the deceased (*merit* is a concept in Buddhism and Hinduism that refers to that which accumulates as a result of good deeds, acts, or thoughts. Merit carries over throughout the life or the subsequent incarnations, and contributes to a person's growth toward spiritual liberation). In the case of hanging, the rope is normally donated to the temple (there is also a superstitious belief linking the rope to black magic rites, which may lead the bereaved relatives to feel resentment).

Psychiatrists

Both families and psychiatrists can experience stigma after a suicide loss. In 2008, in Thailand, 40% of psychiatrist reported having had one patient die by suicide, 53% had experienced this kind of loss between two and eight times, and 7.5% between 10 and 50 times (Thomyangkoon & Leenaars, 2008). More than half of Thai psychiatrists who had had a patient who died by suicide reported experiencing sadness, depression, hopelessness, and guilt. Similar results were reported in other studies (Greenberg & Shefler, 2014; Litman, 1965; Wurst et al., 2013). Regarding help seeking and support, 90% of Thai psychiatrists reported that working through the loss with colleagues was very helpful. Also, family and friends helped. A majority of psychiatrists (72%) prayed or acquired merit through almsgiving to monks, and 89% of them found that helpful. This practice is seen as benevolence intended for the deceased patient who eventually, based on their belief, wished them all blessings from heaven. The study found that 50% of Thai psychiatrists attended the patient's funeral, and half of them found it helpful (Thomyangkoon & Leenaars, 2008). As a result of the recognition of the impact of patient suicide on psychiatrists, the Royal College of Psychiatrists in Thailand has included a core lecture on suicide prevention and suicide bereavement in the training of all psychiatrist residents.

In addition, on World Suicide Prevention Day, September 10, 2015, the Royal College of Psychiatry, the Thai Psychiatric Association, the Department of Mental Health of the Ministry of Public Health, the Samaritans of Thailand, Rajavithi Hospital, and the Suicide Prevention Society of Thailand organized a conference on the impact of suicide on survivors. The meeting received media coverage from newspapers, local TV channels, and social media, raising public awareness of suicide on a scale previously unseen in Thailand.

The PRAKARN Model of Group Psychotherapy

In the past, the health care worker would pay a support visit to the bereaved family on a case-by-case basis; however, there was no group psychotherapy available in the country to help the survivors of suicide loss. The PRAKARN model of group psychotherapy was developed to aid the survivors of suicide loss in Thailand and was initiated in 2008 (Thomyangkoon, 2010). The PRAKARN model was the first group psychotherapy of this kind in Southeast Asia, and has been adopted in many parts of Thailand. This model of group psychotherapy can help the participants deal with depression, stigma, and suicide ideation, and help them function effectively in their community (Mekloi, Sarakan, & Pumratchayakul, 2015). As some of the activities included in the model are related to spiritual practices, individuals who are not religious may find these less helpful. The group psychotherapy comprises six sessions of 60–90 min, once a week or every 2 weeks. The group work involves creative techniques and symbolic communication – for example, through the artwork of the participants. What is different from a standard supportive group therapy is that the PRAKARN model includes dynamic techniques to help participants cope with feelings and cognitions related to stigma (Mekloi, Sarakan, & Pumratchayakul, 2015).

The goal of the first session is to provide insight into the fact that suicide results from many factors, including bio-psycho-social aspects, and not only from the relationships in the family. The participants are asked to write about their loss on a picture of balloons that leave their hands, and are encouraged to talk about their loss. Afterwards, they are asked to explore what remains in their life after the suicide, and to write it down on the picture of balloons remaining in their hands, and to discuss it with the group. Before the end of each session, group participants form a circle by holding each other's hands, and pray for the deceased. This is of great importance, as it helps them feel that they have done a good deed for the loved one who died by suicide.

The second session begins with the lighting of a candle which represents the light of life and guidance to the group members and all survivors of suicide loss in search of a way out of the darkness. Afterwards, the participants are asked to talk about the merits regarding religious benevolence, such as chanting, doing good deeds, and attending ceremonies to help the deceased, which they have performed for the deceased. This activity aims to encourage participants' appreciation for the feeling of self-value, eventually leading to increased self-esteem. In Freud's view (Freud, 1913), dreams are forms of wish fulfillment, an unconscious attempt to resolve a conflict of some sort, whether recent or coming from the recesses of the past. At this point in the group therapy, it is good to let the members share the dreams they might have had about the deceased to help them relieve the stress. If a participant has not dreamed about the person who has died or cannot remember such a dream, they can still participate in this activity by listening to the dreams of others and providing support. The dreams reported in the early stages of the therapy are often related to a story that triggers sadness. After the course of group psychotherapy, dreams of the deceased often gradually become less painful. For instance, a group participant kept accusing herself of causing the death of her sister. After many years of painful dreams, she had a very comforting dream about her deceased sister. In the dream, after 10 years of repeated attempts and failures, her late father who was in heaven, had managed to extend his hand to help the sister who was in hell. In some cases, after having been through the group therapy, the comforting dream about the deceased can bring not only a feeling of happiness, but also a state of utmost contentment. In this way, the therapy may help the bereaved by diminishing their self-blame and self-accusation.

In the third session the participants are encouraged to share with the others the good deeds undertaken and feelings of benevolence for the deceased person, both privately in the family and publicly. The aim is to support each individual's self-esteem, self-value, and feeling of being socially reliable and responsible. Afterwards, the group participants engage in an activity aiming at strengthening the interpersonal bonds within the group in the light of sharing and connecting with other members.

The fourth session aims at stigma relief by letting each member share their experience of stigma. As the Thai community is agriculture-oriented, stigma is presented metaphorically as "bad soil" beneath a rock. Associating the stigma with the soil can lead to more vivid visualizations and associations for group members. Metaphorically speaking, the experience of stigma is like the bad soil under a big stone. The psychotherapy helps to move the stone and rejuvenate the soil for agricultural benefits. Each group member should have the courage to face the stigma and deal with it fearlessly. To make the group relate with the concept and become aware of the roots of their symptoms, an effective comparison and association, and clear examples are needed. The group members are encouraged to cultivate the soil beneath and to replace bad soil with humus-rich soil for new crops to grow.

The fifth session is oriented toward discovering the meaning of life by giving each group member orchid blossoms which are a reminder of the transient beauty of meaningful life. This activity encourages participants to reflect on the truth that the flower bud might fall off before it blossoms, and some people may die young. The final, sixth session aims to establish a plan to create a network of group participants, as well as their families and friends, for helping each other in the future. An activity to recall the good times and fun times the bereaved had with the deceased is included in this session. The group members are encouraged to recognize the value of their lives and to be able to help others who have encountered a similar loss.

In total, the six sessions aim not only to help the group participants to deal with stigma, but also to help them flourish, to enable them to go back to work, and to engage in everyday activities. A group participant from Mae Sai District, Chiang Rai Thailand commented: *"the PRAKARN model of group psychotherapy helped us and restored our normal lives. It released us from the stigma"* (Sukkesempong, 2011). Mekloi et al. (2015) reported that participation in the group psychotherapy reduced scores of depression and stigma. After these promising results had been published, the PRAKARN model (after some modifications) was widely adopted in Thailand.

Conclusions

The impact of death by suicide on family and mental health workers varies from culture to culture. The PRAKARN model of group psychotherapy enables group participants to rediscover a sense of normality in daily life and to free themselves from the stigma. Participation in the group therapy can lead to a new revitalized life and can benefit and influence the families of the bereaved and other people, especially other bereaved who might not have the opportunity to participate in the intervention. The therapy can help the bereaved by suicide in Thailand and can help to establish a network of the bereaved in Thai society.

Corresponding author

Prakarn Thomyangkoon
College of Medicine
Rangsit University
Pathumthani
Thailand
karn249@hotmail.com

References

Bongar, B., & Greaney, S. (1994). Essential clinical and legal issues when working with suicidal patients. In A. Leenaars, J. Maltsberger, & R. Neimeyer (Eds.), *Treatment of suicidal people*, (pp. 179–194). Washington, DC: Taylor & Francis.

Freud, S. (1913). *The interpretation of dreams*. New York, NY: Macmillan. http://doi.org/10.1037/10561-000

Greenberg, D., & Shefler, G. (2014). Patient suicide. *Israeli Journal of Psychiatry, 51*(3), 193–198.

Leenaars, A., Cantor, C., Connolly, J., EchoHawk, M., Gailiene, D., He, Z. X., ... Schlebusch, L. (2002). Ethical & legal issues in suicidology: International perspectives. *Archives of Suicide Research, 6*(2), 185–197. http://doi.org/10.1080/13811110208951175

Litman, R. (1965). When patients commit suicide. *American Journal of Psychotherapy, 19*(4), 570–584.

Mekloi, C., Sarakan, K., & Pumratchayakul, U. (2015). Group psychotherapy for depression and stigma of family members bereaved by suicide. *Journal of Mental Health of Thailand, 23*(2), 125–134.

Sukkesempong, P. (2011). Survivor story. *IASP Postvention Taskforce Newsletter, 5*(2), 3.

Thomyangkoon, P. (2010). *PRAKARN group psychotherapy treatment: Handout for the bereaved* [in Thai]. Bangkok, Thailand: Family Network Foundation, Thai Health Promotion Foundation.

Thomyangkoon, P., & Leenaars, A. A. (2008). Impact of death by suicide of patients on Thai psychiatrists. *Suicide and Life-Threatening Behavior, 38*(6), 728–740. http://doi.org/10.1521/suli.2008.38.6.728

Thomyangkoon, P., Leenaars, A. A., & Wasserman, D. (2005). *Suicide in Thailand*, 1977–2002. *Archives of Suicide Research, 9*(4), 361–368.

World Health Organization. (2002). *World report on violence and health.* Geneva, Switzerland: Author.

Wurst, F. M., Kunz, I., & Skipper, G. (2013). How therapists react to patient's suicide: Findings and consequences for health care professionals' wellbeing. *General Hospital Psychiatry, 35*(5), 565–570. http://doi.org/10.1016/j.genhosppsych.2013.05.003

Contributors

Karl Andriessen
School of Psychiatry
University of New South Wales
Sydney, NSW
Australia

Ella Arensman
National Suicide Research Foundation
Department of Epidemiology and Public
Health
University College Cork
Cork
Ireland

Iris Bolton
Link Counseling Center
Atlanta, GA
USA

Frank Campbell
Campbell and Associates Consulting, LLC
Baton Rouge, LA
USA

Dolores Angela Castelli Dransart
School of Social Work Fribourg
University of Applied Sciences and Arts
Western Switzerland
Givisiez
Switzerland

Cristina Castriotta
SOPRoxi Project
Padova
Italy

Dagmar Ceramides
Australian National University Medical
School
Research School of Population Health
Australian National University
Canberra, ACT
Australia

Jean-Jacques Chavagnat
Centre Hospitalier Henri-Laborit
Fédération Européenne Vivre Son Deuil
Poitiers
France

Amy Y.M. Chow
Department of Social Work and Social
Administration
The University of Hong Kong
Hong Kong
China

Sheila Clark
Unihealth Highbury
Adelaide Unicare network
University of Adelaide
Adelaide, SA
Australia

Erminia Colucci
Centre for Psychiatry
Queen Mary University of London
London
UK

Edward A. Connors
Onkwatenro'shon'a Health Planners
Orillia, ON
Canada

Jean-Claude Daoust
Suicide Action Montréal
Montréal, QC
Canada

Diego De Leo
Australian Institute for Suicide Research and
Prevention
Griffith University
Brisbane, QLD
Australia

Brian Draper
School of Psychiatry
University of New South Wales
Sydney, NSW
Australia

Michael Dudley
School of Psychiatry
University of New South Wales
Sydney, NSW
Australia

Mic Eales
Little Warrior Studios
Sydney, NSW
Australia

Louanne Ebert
Bedford Medical Clinic
Adelaide, SA
Australia

Hamish Elvidge
National Suicide Prevention Alliance
London
UK

Annette Erlangsen
Danish Research Institute for Suicide
Prevention
Mental Health Centre Copenhagen
Copenhagen
Denmark

Beverly Feigelman
School of Social Work
Adelphi University
Garden City, NY
USA

William Feigelman
Sociology Department
Nassau Community College
Garden City, NY
USA

Alessandro Ferrari
SOPRoxi Project
Padova
Italy

Colleen Fitzpatrick
NSW Department of Forensic Medicine
Health Pathology
Sydney, NSW
Australia

Elene Fleischer
NEFOS – Region Syddanmark
Fyn
Denmark

Danutė Gailienė
Department of Clinical and Organizational
Psychology
University of Vilnius
Vilnius
Lithuania

Helen Garnham
Mental Health
Public Health England
London
UK

Robert Gebbia
American Foundation for Suicide Prevention
(AFSP)
New York, NY
USA

Christine Genest
CRISE – Centre for Research and Intervention on Suicide and Euthanasia
Université de Montréal
Montréal, QC
Canada

Robert D. Goldney
Discipline of Psychiatry
Faculty of Health Sciences
University of Adelaide
Adelaide, SA
Australia

Onja T. Grad
University Psychiatric Hospital
Center for Mental Health
Ljubljana
Slovenia

Keith Hawton
Centre for Suicide Research
University of Oxford
Oxford
UK

Leen Hoebrechts
Victim Care Unit
Centre for Social Welfare
Brussels
Belgium

Danielle R. Jahn
Department of Psychiatry
University of Maryland
Baltimore, MD
USA

John R. Jordan
Private Practice
Pawtucket, RI
USA

Kenji Kawano
College of Comprehensive Psychology
Ritsumeikan University
Kyoto
Japan

Daisuke Kawashima
School of Psychology
Chukyo University
Nagoya
Japan

Vaiva Klimaitė
Department of Clinical and Organizational
Psychology
University of Vilnius
Vilnius
Lithuania

Karolina Krysinska
School of Psychiatry
University of New South Wales
Sydney, NSW
Australia

Karen Lascelles
Oxford Health NHS Foundation Trust
Oxford
UK

Yik Wa Law
Department of Social Work and Social
Administration
Centre for Suicide Research and Prevention
The University of Hong Kong
Hong Kong
China

Antoon A. Leenaars
Private Practice
Windsor, ON
Canada

Sean McCarthy
Suicide Prevention
HSE South St Patrick's Hospital
Waterford
Ireland

Sharon McDonnell
Centre for Mental Health and Safety
University of Manchester
Manchester
UK

John L. McIntosh
Academic Affairs
Indiana University South Bend
South Bend, IN
USA

Jill McMahon
EMPACT – Suicide Prevention Center
Tempe, AZ
USA

Sandra McNally
EMPACT – Suicide Prevention Center
Tempe, AZ
USA

Philip B. Mitchell
School of Psychiatry
University of New South Wales
Sydney, NSW
Australia

Melinda Moore
Department of Psychology
Eastern Kentucky University
Richmond, KY
USA

Christine Moutier
American Foundation for Suicide Prevention
(AFSP)
New York, NY
USA

Jane Mowll
The University of Notre Dame
Sydney, NSW
Australia

Robert A. Neimeyer
Department of Psychology
University of Memphis
Memphis, TN
USA

Clinton M. Nowicke
Department of Psychology
Eastern Kentucky University
Richmond, KY
USA

Cobi Nijhuis
Security, Support and Aftercare –
National Railways
Utrecht
The Netherlands

Olga Oulanova
Private Practice
Toronto, ON
Canada

Polona Ozbič
Slovenian Association for Suicide Prevention
Ljubljana
Slovenia

Silvia Peláez
Último Recurso
Montevideo
Uruguay

Rossana Pettersén
Department of Clinical Neuroscience
Karolinska Institute
Stockholm
Sweden

Vita Poštuvan
Slovenian Centre for Suicide Research
Andrej Marušič Institute
University of Primorska
Koper
Slovenia

Alexandra Pitman
UCL Division of Psychiatry
University College London
London
UK

Katarzyna Anna Ratkowska
De Leo Fund
Padova
Italy

Jerry Reed
Suicide Prevention Resource Center
Education Development Center
Washington DC
USA

John Rice
Canadian Mental Health Association
First Nations Métis Inuit Healer
Barrie, ON
Canada

Inês Areal Rothes
Faculty of Psychology and Educational
Sciences
University of Porto
Porto
Portugal

Diana Sands
Bereaved by Suicide Centre for Intense Grief
Sydney, NSW
Australia

José Carlos Santos
Nursing School of Coimbra
Coimbra
Portugal

Sara Santos
Centre for Research in Education and
Psychology
University of Evora
Evora
Portugal

Karen Scavacini
Instituto Vita Alere de Prevenção e
Posvenção do Suicídio
São Paulo
Brasil

Lourens Schlebusch
Nelson R. Mandela School of Medicine
University of KwaZulu-Natal
Durban
South Africa

Paolo Scocco
SOPRoxi Project
Padova
Italy

Monique Séguin
Department of Psychology and
Psychoeducation
Université du Québec en Outaouais
Gatineau, QC
Canada

Regina Seibl
Pro Mente Tirol
Innsbruck
Austria

Keisuke Shiraga
Graduate School of Education
Joetsu University of Education
Joetsu, Niigata
Japan

Paulius Skruibis
Department of Clinical and Organizational
Psychology
University of Vilnius
Vilnius
Lithuania

Holly Smith
NSW Department of Forensic Medicine
Health Pathology
Sydney, NSW
Australia

Jean-Pierre Soubrier
Centre de Ressources en
Suicidologie – CRES
Paris
France

Sally Spencer-Thomas
Carson J Spencer Foundation
Denver, CO
USA

Alan Staines
Postvention Australia
National Association for the Bereaved by
Suicide
Sydney, NSW
Australia

Jess Stohlmann-Rainey
Carson J Spencer Foundation
Denver, CO
USA

Denis Thirion
EMPACT – Suicide Prevention Center
Tempe, AZ
USA

Prakarn Thomyangkoon
College of Medicine
Rangsit University
Pathumthani
Thailand

Jemaima Tiatia-Seath
Pacific Health
School of Population Health
University of Auckland
Auckland
New Zealand

Elena Toffol
SOPRoxi Project
Padova
Italy

Stefano Totaro
SOPRoxi Project
Padova
Italy

Marta Treven
Slovenian Association for Suicide Prevention
Ljubljana
Slovenia

Isaias Valencia
Último Recurso
Montevideo
Uruguay

Angela van der Veer
Suicide Prevention – ProRail
Utrecht
The Netherlands

Christoffer Back Vestli
LEVE – The Norwegian Organization for
the Suicide Bereaved
Oslo
Norway

Patricia Wels
Último Recurso
Montevideo
Uruguay

Liselot Willems
Victim Care Unit
Centre for Social Welfare
Brussels
Belgium

Nada Wolf
Slovenian Association Hospice
Maribor
Slovenia

Paul W. C. Wong
Department of Social Work and Social
Administration
Centre for Suicide Research and Prevention
The University of Hong Kong
Hong Kong
China

Paul S. F. Yip
Department of Social Work and Social
Administration
Centre for Suicide Research and Prevention
The University of Hong Kong
Hong Kong
China

Anka Zavasnik
Slovenian Association for Suicide Prevention
Ljubljana
Slovenia

Subject Index

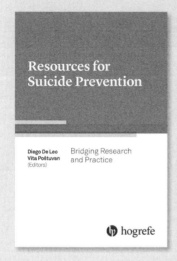

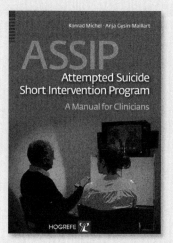